THE ULTIMATE BOOK
OF POP TRIVIA

THE ULTIMATE BOOK OF POP TRIVIA

BY PHIL SWERN & TOBY ROWAN

Robson Books

First published in Great Britain in 2001 by Robson Books, 64 Brewery Road,
London N7 9NY

A member of the Chrysalis Group

British Library Cataloguing in Publication Data
A catalogue reocrd for this title is available from the British Library

ISBN 1861054343

Typeset by SX Composing DTP, Rayleigh, Essex
Printed and bound in Great Britain by
Creative Print & Design (Wales), Ebbw Vale

INTRODUCTION

'START IT UP'

Where to begin? The book you are at this very moment holding in your hands was born out of a love of all things pop and rock, be they good or bad, creative or sedative.

Of course, the idea of a trivia book is nothing new – such books come and go. However, we hope, with this *The Ultimate Book of Pop Trivia*, to have created something a little different.

You'll still find the old favourites, such as the real names of the stars (always good for a laugh) or accounts of pop's criminal collective at their worst. In addition though, we delve into the very depths of popular music, as we examine some of pop's finest moments, from the beginnings of the charts to the present day.

Anyway, enough from us, the world of pop awaits you, so in the eternal words of Mick, Keith and the boys, 'start it up!'

NAMES AND PROFESSIONS

'THERE'S A GUY WORKS DOWN THE CHIP SHOP SWEARS HE'S ELVIS'
Pop Stars' Former Professions

Well, while he's more than likely not Elvis, he could well be the next Mick Jagger, Jon Bon Jovi or Rod Stewart. For as the following list testifies, many of today's stars had less than golden beginnings.

Paula Abdul – waitress

Damon Albarn – runner for a recording studio

Ian Anderson (Jethro Tull) – cleaner at the ABC cinema, Luton

Tom Bailey (Thompson Twins) – teacher

Pat Benatar – bank cashier

Chuck Berry – hairdresser

Ritchie Blackmore – aircraft radio mechanic

Marc Bolan – model

Jon Bon Jovi – Burger King employee; recording studio assistant

David Bowie – commercial artist for ad agency

Captain Sensible – toilet cleaner (Fairfield Hall, Croydon)

Belinda Carlisle – petrol station attendant

Chubby Checker – chicken plucker

Gary Clail – scaffolder

Dave Clark – stuntman

Joe Cocker – plumber/gas fitter

Phil Collins – child actor (*Oliver!*)

Paul Cook (Sex Pistols) – apprentice electrician

Gaz Coombes (Supergrass) – waiter at a Harvester restaurant

Elvis Costello – computer technician

Roger Daltrey – sheet-metal worker

Terence Trent D'Arby – army corporal

Jonathan Davis (KoRn) – coroner's assistant

Carol Decker – lifeguard, Shrewsbury baths

Dave Dee – policeman

Craig Douglas – milkman

Keith Duffy – lost-ball finder at a golf course

Ian Dury – art teacher, Luton College of Technology

Keith Emerson – bank clerk

John Entwistle – tax clerk

Adam Faith – film editing department at the Rank studios

Bryan Ferry – teacher of ceramics at a girls school

Peter Gabriel – travel agent

Stephen Gately – barman; sales assistant

Bob Geldof – journalist for NME; pea-sheller; Soho hot-dog vendor

Daryl Hall – apple picker

Geri Halliwell – gameshow hostess on Turkish TV

Steve Harley – journalist for a local newspaper in Colchester

Deborah Harry – Playboy Bunny

Faith Hill – music publisher's secretary

Peter Hooton – social worker

Chrissie Hynde – journalist with NME

Ice-T – jewel thief

Chris Isaak – tour guide at a film studio in Japan

Mick Jagger – ice-cream seller

Elton John – teaboy at a London music publishers

Brian Jones – salesman at Whiteley's department store in London

Howard Jones – stock control, Perfawrap clingfilm factory, High Wycombe

R Kelly – busker

Cyndi Lauper – racehorse walker

Lemmy – roadie for Jimi Hendrix and Pink Floyd

Annie Lennox – fish filleter/waitress

Courtney Love – stripper

Keavy Lynch (B*Witched) – trainee car-mechanic

Shane Lynch (Boyzone) – petrol pump attendant

Madonna – employee in a Times Square doughnut shop

Shane MacGowan – barman (some would say he had a passion for his work)

Freddie Mercury – one-time Kensington Market clothing tycoon along with pal Roger Taylor

George Michael – cinema usher

Matt Monro – bus driver

Keith Moon – plaster salesman

Van Morrison – window cleaner

Vince Neil (Mötley Crüe) – electrician

Stevie Nicks – hostess at Bob's Big Boy restaurant

Phil Oakey – hospital porter

Des O'Connor – Butlin's Redcoat

Ozzy Osbourne – slaughterhouse worker

John Otway – dustman

Les Pattinson (Echo & The Bunnymen) – apprentice boat builder

Elvis Presley – truck driver

PJ Proby – farm labourer

Otis Redding – chauffeur to Johnny Jenkins and The Pinetoppers

Lou Reed – assistant accountant

Cliff Richard – credit control clerk, Ferguson's TV and Radio

Keith Richards – tennis ball-boy

Henry Rollins – ice-cream shop manager

Tom Scholtz – computer designer

Peter Sellers – lifeguard

Gene Simmons – teacher

Percy Sledge – hospital orderly

Rod Stewart – gravedigger; apprentice footballer – Brentford FC

Sting – teacher

Neil Tennant – assistant editor with *Smash Hits*

Richard Thompson (Fairport Convention) – designer of stained glass

Donnie Wahlberg (New Kids On The Block) – shoe salesman

Rick Wakeman – organist in residence, Top Rank Ballroom, Watford

Mary Wilson (The Supremes) – record shop assistant

Malcolm Young (AC/DC) – maintenance man for sewing machines in a bra factory

Paul Young – apprentice at Vauxhall car factory

TAKE A WALK DOWN
'ALPHABET STREET'
100 Band Names Made Easy

1. A
2. A+
3. A1
4. ABC
5. AC/DC
6. A.K.A.
7. ATB
8. A.T.F.C. presents ONEPHATDEEVA
9. A.T.G.O.C.
10. A Vs B

11. B15
12. B-52s (RLI)
13. B B and Q Band
14. B.B.E.
15. BBG
16. BBM
17. BBMAK
18. B.E.F.
19. B.M.R. feat Felicia
20. B.M.U.
21. BT
22. B.V.S.M.P.

23. C.C.S.
24. C.L.S.
25. C.O.D.

26. D.B.M. and T
27. D.J.H. featuring STEFY
28. DMX
29. DNA
30. D.O.P.

31. E-17

32. E.B.T.G
33. EMF
34. ETA
35. E.V.E.
36. E.Y.C.

37. F.A.B.
38. FKW
39. F.P.I. PROJECT

40. G.B.H.
41. G.Q.
42. G.S.P.
43. G.T.O.

44. H2O
45. H.H.C.
46. H.W.A. featuring SONIC THE HEDGEHOG

47. INXS

48. J.A.L.N. BAND
49. JX

50. K7
51. KLF
52. KRS ONE
53. K.W.S.

54. L7
55. LCD
56. LFO
57. LSG
58. L.V.

59. M
60. M2M
61. M.A.N.I.C.
62. M/A/R/R/S
63. M.A.S.H.
64. MAW
65. MC5
66. MFSB

67. NKOTB
68. N.W.A.
69. N.Y.C.C.

70. OMC
71. O.M.D.
72. O.R.G.A.N.
73. OTT

74. P.I.L.
75. PJB featuring HANNAH AND HER SISTERS
76. P.H.D.

77. R.A.F.
78. R.E.M.

79. S2S
80. S.F.X.
81. S-J
82. SL2
83. S*M*A*S*H
84. S.O.A.P.

85. 2K
86. T.A.F.K.A.P.
87. TLC
88. TQ

89. U2
90. U96
91. UB40
92. U.F.O.
93. U.H.F.
94. US3
95. U.T.F.O.

96. V.I.P.'s

97. W.A.S.P.

98. XTC
99. Y & T

100. ZZ Top

'ROCK 'N' ROLL CHILDREN'
Names of Pops Stars' Children

Sick of Stephen? Bored of Bart? Fed up with Faye? If so, then take a leaf out of the *Complete Book of Rock' 'n' Roll Names for Children* and steer away from the norm, when choosing a name for your child. Something with a religious ring like 'Lourdes' (Madonna's daughter) perhaps, or maybe something a little more adventurous like 'Moon Unit' (Frank Zappa's daughter). Whatever your fancy, you'll see from the following selection that a good helping of imagination (and maybe something else) can go a long way:

Ahmet Emuuka Rodin – Frank Zappa

Aisha Zakiya – Stevie Wonder

Brooklyn (1) – Donna Summer

Brooklyn (2) – Victoria Beckham aka Posh Spice (guess Donna must have been to Brooklyn before Posh and Becks)

Chastity – Sonny and Cher

Cherish – Johnny Lee and Charlene Tilton

China – Grace Slick

Chynna – John and Michelle Phillips

Dakota Star Blanket Wolfchild – Buffy Sainte-Marie

Dandelion – Keith Richard

Dhani – George Harrison

Django – Dave Stewart

Dweezil – Frank Zappa

Elijah Blue – Greg Allman and Cher

Elijah Bob Patricius Guggi Q Hewson – Paul 'Bono' Hewson and Alison Stewart

Fifi Trixibelle – Bob Geldof and Paula Yates

Heavenly Hiraani Tiger Lily – Paula Yates and Michael Hutchence

Jada – Anita Pointer

Jade – Mick and Bianca Jagger

Kecalf – Aretha Franklin

Kita Swan Di – Stevie Wonder

Lennon – Liam Gallagher and Patsy Kensit

Lourdes Maria Ciccone Leon – Madonna

Memphis Eve – Bono and Alison Stewart

Mirage – Eric Burdon

Moon Unit – Frank Zappa

Oriole – Donovan

Peaches – Bob Geldof and Paula Yates

Phoenix Chi – Mel B aka Scary Spice

Pixie – Bob Geldof and Paula Yates

Planet – Billy Swan

Rocco – Guy Richie and Madonna

Rolan – Marc Bolan

Sam Hurricane – Dave Stewart

Stella – Paul and Linda McCartney

Tamla – Smokey and Claudette Robinson

Zak – Ringo Starr

Zeke – Neil Young

Zoe – John 'Bonzo' Bonham

Zowie – David Bowie

'WHAT'S YOUR NAME?'
The Origins of Band Names

So, you're thinking of forming a band. Well, one of the first things you'll have to do is think of a catchy name, something with staying power, panache, a name that encapsulates the very essence of rock 'n' roll. In short, something your prospective fans won't forget in a hurry. Problem is, though, there are already hundreds of groups out there, some with great names, others with not so great names: consider boy-bands, you've got Backstreet Boys, Bad Boys Inc., Very Bad Boys Inc. (only joking!), Boyz II Men, Boyzone etc. Whatever next? Boyz II Girls. Let's hope not but if you need a little inspiration why not take a look at the following?

Beastie Boys – but why Beastie? 'Boys Entering Anarchistic States Towards Internal Excellence' of course.

Bee Gees – not a play on the Brothers Gibb as so many believe. It is in fact due to a meeting with racetrack promoter Bill Good, whilst performing as the Rattlesnakes, at Brisbane's Speedway Circus in 1960. Good subsequently introduced the brothers to a local radio DJ by the name of Bill Gates who began to play their material on his show. With their rising popularity, Good felt a name change to be in order and used his and Gates's initials as the brothers' new moniker, hence the B.G.s.

Boomtown Rats – singer Bob Geldof took the name from a passage in Woody Guthrie's autobiography, *Bound For Glory*, wherein Guthrie describes the discovery of oil in his Oklahoman hometown and the resultant influx of workers and their families. The oil-workers' children, finding themselves ostracised by local kids, formed their own gang, going by the name of the Boomtown Rats.

Bush – the lads hail from Shepherds Bush, west London – say no more, squire.

The Communards – Jimmy Somerville's post Bronski Beat outing took their name from the group of French revolutionaries, who held Paris between 18 March and 28 May 1871.

Crowded House – inspired by the band's non-too-spacious living conditions while renting an apartment on Los Angeles' Sunset Boulevard during their early years.

Cypress Hill – named after a neighbourhood of the Southgate area of Los Angeles, where band member Sen Dog had moved to with his parents, following their emigration from Cuba.

Deacon Blue – formed by vocalist Ricky Ross in 1985, the band took their name from a song of the same name featured on the Steely Dan album *Aja*.

Deep Purple – apparently the pioneering guitar-driven rockers named themselves after Ritchie Blackmore's grandmother's favourite song, 'Deep Purple'; recorded by Nino Temple and April Stevens, it reached number one in 1963.

Depeche Mode – formed in 1980, by Dave Gahan, Vince Clarke, Martin Gore and Andy Fletcher. Gahan, at the time a student of fashion at Southend Technical College, took the band's moniker from a French fashion magazine, *Dépêche Mode* (meaning 'fast fashion'), to which his studies had led him.

Dire Straits – the band adopted their name at the suggestion of a friend, who felt it best described their financial situation.

Duran Duran – Founding member and bassist John Taylor took the band's name from the character played by Milo O'Shea, in director Roger Vadim's sexy sci-fi spoof, *Barbarella* (1967), which of course starred Vadim's then wife, Jane Fonda. Incidentally, many of the band's first gigs were at Barbarella's club in Birmingham.

Everything But The Girl – comprised Tracey Thorn and Ben Watt; the duo, who met while at Hull University, took their name from a nearby second-hand furniture store, where one could buy everything but . . .

The Farm – the band took their name from their local rehearsal hall, Maghull Farm.

Fine Young Cannibals – ex-English Beat members David Steele and Andy Cox formed the band in 1984, the addition of singer Roland Gift completing the line-up. The name was taken from the film *All The Fine Young Cannibals* (1960), which starred Natalie Wood and Robert Wagner.

Fleetwood Mac – named after the band's founding members, drummer Mick Fleetwood and bass-player John McVie.

Frankie Goes To Hollywood – the inspiration for the band's name was found in a newspaper headline reporting the attempts of Frankie Vaughan to make it big in Hollywood.

Half Man Half Biscuit – the Birkenhead boys took their name from a comment made by fellow Liverpool act, punk group Instant Agony. They had made the comment 'half man half biscuit' when describing Prince Charles.

Hawkwind – according to one-time vocalist Lemmy (since of Motörhead) the band's name came about as a result of his then bandmate Nick Turner's unusually large nose and recurring flatulence problem.

The Hollies – were quite literally Buddy Holly mad.

Jethro Tull – a booker at Chrysalis, having previously studied history, suggested the name. It refers to the 18th century agriculturalist responsible for the invention of the seed drill.

Joy Division – to fully appreciate the irony of this name, one must refer to the sadomasochistic book *House of Dolls*, wherein the 'Joy Division' refers to the barracks of a Nazi concentration camp, housing prisoners solely for the pleasure of the guards.

Led Zeppelin – according to an interview given by Led Zeppelin's tour manager, Richard Cole, the name came about as a result of a conversation between Keith Moon, John Entwistle and himself, during which Moon and Entwistle chatted over the possibility of forming a new group. When the conversation drifted towards a possible name for the band, Keith Moon supposedly suggested that they should call it Lead Zeppelin, since 'it will go down like a lead balloon'. Having adopted the name for his band, Jimmy Page proceeded to drop the 'a' from Lead so as to avoid any confusion amongst Americans.

L.L. Cool J – apparently the 'Ladies Love Cool James'. So there!

Lynyrd Skynyrd – took their name from their school gym teacher, one Leonard Skinner, a man legendary among the band and their peers for his hostility towards long-haired students.

Madness – the originators of the 'nutty sound' took their name from the title of a 1963 ska hit by the Jamaican musician Prince Buster, the man who originally coined, what was to become a Madness anthem, 'One Step Beyond'.

Marillion – originally called Silmarillion, after the novel of the same name by J.R.R. Tolkien, the band subsequently shortened their name to Marillion.

M People – short for Mike's People, after band member (and former Happy Mondays producer) Mike Pickering.

Mungo Jerry – took their name from a cat featured in a poem by T.S. Eliot.

Pearl Jam – named after an hallucinogenic preserve, of infamous repute, made by singer Eddie Veder's great-grandmother Pearl.

The Pet Shop Boys – the name takes its inspiration from a couple of friends of Neil Tennant and Chris Lowe, who perchance owned a pet shop in Ealing, west London.

Pink Floyd – founding member Syd Barrett took the first names of Georgia bluesmen, Pink Anderson and Floyd Council, and arrived at the Pink Floyd Sound, later dropping 'Sound' from the band's tag.

The Pogues – a derivative of their original name, Pogue Mo Chone, which is the Gaelic for 'Kiss My Arse'.

The Police – drummer Stewart Copeland, chose the band's moniker as a tongue-in-cheek reference to his father, who had led the CIA's Political Action Staff, or dirty tricks department as it also known, during the fifties.

The Propellerheads – took their name from the Californian slang for computer geeks.

The Righteous Brothers – non-brothers Bill Medley and Bobby Hatfield gained their name following the reaction of black marines who saw them perform in southern California, 'That's righteous brother.'

Right Said Fred – the particularly camp Fairbrass brothers, Richard and Fred, took the name of their band from a 1962 novelty record by funnyman Bernard Cribbins.

Savage Garden – took their name from a novel by horror writer Ann Rice.

Scritti Politti – fronted by Green Gartside, the punky-popsters took their name from the Italian phrase meaning 'political writings'.

Simply Red – apparently then the nightclub DJ Mick Hucknall, after a spontaneous decision to try his hand at singing, was asked by the compere by what title he would like to be introduced. 'Just "Red",' replied Hucknall, a nickname given to him on account of his distinctive red hair. The compere not quite hearing Hucknall's response, asked again. 'Simply "Red",' he answered.

Sixpence None The Richer – took their name from C.S. Lewis's book *Mere Christianity*.

Steely Dan – named after a giant steam-powered dildo featured in William Burroughs' novel *The Naked Lunch*.

Talking Heads – TV-speak for a head-and-shoulders shot of a presenter.

The Teardrop Explodes – the name is taken from the Marvel comic, *Daredevil*.

Tears For Fears – the duo of Curt Smith and Roland Orzabal were inspired by the writings of psychologist Arthur Janov, an advocate of 'Primal Scream' (hmmn!) therapy, in particular his book *Prisoners of Pain*, in which Janov encouraged the subject to confront hidden fears and to release suppressed emotions.

TLC – this highly successful, all-girl, R&B trio, comprising Tionne 'T-Boz' Watkins, Lisa 'Left-Eye' Lopes and Rozonda 'Chilli' Thomas, got their name by taking the first letter of each of their nicknames and joining them together. It is, of course, also an acronym for 'tender, loving care'.

The Waterboys – taken from a line in the Lou Reed song, 'The Kids'.

Wet Wet Wet – the Glaswegian band's name is taken from a line in the song 'Getting Having and Holding', by Scritti Politti.

'THE NAME GAME'
Nicknames of Pop Stars

As we all know from experience, it doesn't take long before friends and enemies alike begin to refer to us, not by our names, but by something more immediate, a nickname.

Such names usually pick upon the characteristics or habits of the person concerned, and as such can be flattering or derogatory, humorous or cruel. Consider Grateful Dead guitarist, Jerry Garcia, who was known as 'Captain Trips', on account of his predilection for all things hallucinatory, particularly the drug LSD.

So, without further ado, here's a collection of pop's more memorable nicknames:

The Artist / T.A.F.K.A.P / Symbol – Prince

The Big 'O' – Roy Orbison

Boom Boom – Freddy Cannon (a consequence of the cannon-like bass drum sound on his recordings)

The Boss – Bruce Springsteen

Bubba – Tommy Facenda

Burly Chassis – Shirley Bassey

Cannonball – Julian Adderley (adapted from the word 'cannibal': given in honour of his fondness for anything edible)

Captain Trips – Jerry Garcia (The Grateful Dead)

The Cherokee Cowboy – Ray Price

The Divine One – Sarah Vaughan

Electric Fingers – Richard Carpenter (given to him by Carpenter's hair stylist and one-time beau, Maria Luisa Galeazzi)

The Fab Four – The Beatles

The Fat Man – Fats Domino

Fieldy – Reginald Arvizu or 'Fieldy' as he is known plays bass for US rock band KoRn. Why 'Fieldy' you might ask? Well, as a child he had cheeks like a chipmunk. Consequently the other kids began to call him 'Gopher', this in turn became 'Garr[field]', which in turn became 'Fieldy'.

The First Lady of Country Music – Tammy Wynette

The Frozen Noses – Crosby, Stills and Nash – a consequence of their quite exceptional ability to snort in harmony (quite literally)

The Glimmer Twins – Mick Jagger and Keith Richards

The Gloved One – Michael Jackson

God – Eric Clapton

The Godfather of Grunge – Neil Young

The Godfather of Punk – Lou Reed

The Godfather of Soul – James Brown

The Killer – Jerry Lee Lewis

The King – Elvis Presley

The King of Pop – Michael Jackson

Little Miss Sharecropper – LaVern Baker

Lizard King – Jim Morrison

Material Girl – Madonna

Miss Lonely – Joan Baez, as referred to in Bob Dylan's 'Miss Lonely' – she was a one-time romantic interest

The Man – Van Morrison

Pearl – Janis Joplin

The Polish Prince – Bobby Vinton

The Queen of Disco – Donna Summer

The Red Rocker – Sammy Hagar

The Rockville Rocket – Gene Pitney

Slowhand – Eric Clapton

The Soul Philosopher – Johnnie Taylor

The Southern Gentleman – Sonny James

The Tan Canary – Johnny Adams

The Thin White Duke – David Bowie

The Toxic Twins – Joe Perry and Steve Tyler

The Twisting Vocalist from Pontypridd – Tom Jones

Wacko Jacko – Michael Jackson

Whispering Bill – Bill Anderson

'I CALL YOUR NAME'
Original Band Names

When choosing a band name, the best names don't always come along immediately; sometimes you can struggle along for months, even years, with a less than catchy moniker.

For instance, would Abba have enjoyed the success they did, had they continued to pursue their music career as the Engaged Couples. Doesn't exactly roll off the tongue, does it?

The following names were all adopted by now-famous bands, prior to choosing the name with which they would go on to find success:

Arabacus Pulp – Pulp
Architectural Abdabs – Pink Floyd
Atomic Mass – Def Leppard
Backyard – Lynyrd Skynyrd
Bastard – Motörhead
The Beefeaters – The Byrds
Café Racers – Dire Straits
Cap'n Swing – The Cars
Carl and the Passions – The Beach Boys
Cranberry Saw Us – The Cranberries
Dead Elvis – Death In Vegas
The Deltas – The Hollies
The Dust Brothers – Chemical Brothers
Earth – Black Sabbath
Easy Cure – The Cure
The Empty Vessels – Wishbone Ash
The Engaged Couples – Abba
The Excitements – The Farm
Ed, Ted and Fred – Nirvana
The Executive – Wham!
The Fanatics – Ocean Colour Scene
Fecal Matter – Nirvana again, ooh those boys were so outrageous!
Feedback – U2
The Four Aims – The Four Tops
Future Primitive – Bush
Good Earth – Mungo Jerry
The Heartbeats – Herman's Hermits

The High Numbers – The Who
Hocus Pocus – UFO
The Id – Orchestral Manoeuvres In The Dark
The Invaders – Madness
The Jennifers – Supergrass
Johnny and the Moondogs – The Beatles
Judge Happiness – The Mock Turtles
The Largest Living Things – Crowded House
The Mann Hugg Blues Brothers – Manfred Mann
Mookie Blaylock – Pearl Jam
Morris & The Minors – Madness
Naked – Reef
The N'Betweens – Slade
The Nightlife Thugs – The Boomtown Rats
Nine Foot Worm Makes Own Food – The Butthole Surfers
On A Friday – Radiohead
The Patrol – The Stone Roses
Polka Tulk – Black Sabbath
Pud – The Doobie Brothers
Rain – Oasis
Rat Salade – Van Halen
Roundabout – Deep Purple
The Salty Peppers – Earth, Wind and Fire
The Saxons – Bay City Rollers
Seventeen – Alarm
Seymour – Blur
Sex Gang Children – Culture Club
Smile – Queen
Southern Death Cult – The Cult
The Spoilt Bratz – Terrorvision
Stiff Kittens – Joy Division
Teen Kings and the Emergencies – The Eagles
Tom and Jerry – Simon and Garfunkel
Tony Flow and the Miraculous Majestic Masters of Mayhem – Red
Hot Chili Peppers
Touch – Spice Girls
Tragic Love Company – Stereophonics
Two Tons Of Fun – The Weather Girls
Vague Dots – Talking Heads
VCL XI – Orchestral Manoeuvres In The Dark
Warlocks – The Grateful Dead
Wee Johnnie Hayes & The Bluecats – The Bee Gees

'YOU CAN CALL ME AL'
10 Pop Pseudonyms

Often stars wish to remain anonymous, be it a question of modesty, privacy or potential embarrassment. The following pseudonyms have all been used by some of pop's biggest stars during their recording careers:

1. **Caesar And Cleo** – Sonny And Cher.

2. **Barbara Campbell** – the name used by Lou Adler, Herb Alpert and Sam Cooke as writing credit for Cooke's hit 'Wonderful World'. Barbara Campbell was in fact the name of Cooke's high school sweetheart and later wife.

3. **Kris Carson** – luckily no relation to Frank but instead the name used by Kris Kristofferson whilst recording in Britain prior to his American debut.

4. **Joey Coco** – one of Prince's writing pseudonyms.

5. **Elmo Glick** – used by two of the greatest songwriters in the history of popular music, Jerry Leiber and Mike Stoller, responsible for such hits as 'Stand By Me' (Ben E. King), 'Love Potion No. 9' (The Clovers) and 'On Broadway' (The Drifters), to name but a very few.

6. **Larry Lurex** – Freddie Mercury (as used for a single titled 'I Can Hear Music').

7. **Bonnie Jo Mason** – used by pop diva Cher for the Beatles tribute record, 'I Love You Ringo', which she recorded for Phil Spector.

8. **L'Angelo Misterioso** – George Harrison's credit on Cream's album *Goodbye* for his guitar work on 'Badge'.

9. **A. Nugetre** – in reality one Ahmet Ertegun, writer, producer and founder of Atlantic Records. The pseudonym is a reversal of his real name, and can be found on the recordings of Ray Charles ('Mess Around'), the Drifters ('Whatcha Gonna Do'), the Clovers ('Ting-a-Ling') *et al.*

10. **Rubber Bucket** – Gary Glitter in his Paul Gadd days, when he recorded a song entitled 'We All Live In One Place'

'MY NAME IS JACK'
Pop Stars' Real Names

The parents of pop stars don't always have the future careers of their offspring at heart when they name them. Were this the case Lynda Denise Crapper would have been spared the trouble of changing her name to something a little more alluring: should you wish to know just who she became then read on.

A

Adamski – Adam Tinley

Tori Amos – Myra-Ellen Amos

Adam Ant – Stuart Leslie Goddard

Marc Anthony – Marco Antonio Muniz

Apache Indian – Steve Kapur

ATB – Andreas Tanneberger

B

Babybird – Stephen Jones

Babyface – Kenneth Edmonds

Cheryl Baker – Rita Crudgington

John Barry – John Barry Prendergast

Lou Bega – David Loubega

Pat Benatar – Pat Andrejewski

Tony Bennett – Anthony Dominick Bendetto

Irving Berlin – Israel Baline

Dave Berry – David Grundy

Jello Biafra (Dead Kennedys) – Eric Boucher

The Big Bopper – Jiles Perry Richardson

Acker Bilk – Bernard Bilk

Cilla Black – Priscilla Maria Veronica White

Black Francis (Pixies) – Charles Michael Kitteridge Thompson IV

Fatty Buster Bloodvessel (Bad Manners) – Douglas Trendle

Marc Bolan – Mark Feld

Jon Bon Jovi – John Bongiovi

Betty Boo – Alison Moira Clarkson

Bono – Paul Hewson

David Bowie – David Robert Hayward-Jones

Boy George – George Alan O'Dowd

Elkie Brooks – Elaine Bookbinder

Foxy Brown – Inga Marchand

C

Marti Caine – Lynda Denise Crapper

Captain Beefheart – Don Van Vliet

Captain Sensible – Ray Burns

Cher – Cherilyn Sarkisian La Pierre

Chubby Checker – Ernest Evans

Tony Christie – Anthony Fitzgerald

Chuck D – Carlton Douglas Ridenhour

Eric Clapton – Eric Patrick Clapp

Patsy Cline – Virginia Patterson-Hensley

Russ Conway – Trevor Herbert Stanford

Coolio – Artis Ivey

Alice Cooper – Vincent Furnier

Julian Cope – Kevin Stapleton

Elvis Costello – Declan Patrick McManus

Christopher Cross – Christopher Geppert

D

Dana – Rosemarie Brown

Bobby Darin – Walden Robert Cassoto

Doris Day – Doris Kappelhoff

Chris De Burgh – Christopher John Davidson

Kiki Dee – Pauline Matthews

John Denver – John Henry Deutschendorf

Rick Derringer – Rick Zehringer

Jackie De Shannon – Sharon Myers

Neil Diamond – Noah Kaminsky

Bo Diddley – Otha Ellis Bates McDaniel

Ronnie James Dio – Ronald Padavona

Dr. Alban – Alban Nwapa

Dr. Dre – Andre Young

Donovan – Donovan Philip Leitch

Craig Douglas – Terry Perkins

Bob Dylan – Robert Alan Zimmerman

E

Linda Eastman / McCartney – Linda Epstein

Sheena Easton – Sheena Shirley Orr

Eazy-E – Eric Wright

The Edge – David Evans

Eminem – Marshall Mathers

Brian Eno – Brian Peter George St Baptiste De La Salle Eno

Enya – Eithne Ni Bhraonain

David Essex – David Albert Cook

F

Adam Faith – Terence Nelhams

Georgie Fame – Clive Powell

Don Fardon – Donald Maughan

Chris Farlowe – John Henry Deighton

Fish – Derek Dick

Flavor Flav – William Drayton

Flea – Michael Balzary

Wayne Fontana – Glyn Geoffrey Ellis

Connie Francis – Concetta Rosa Maria Franconera

Billy Fury – Ronald Wycherly

G

Kenny G – Kenneth Gorelick

Gabrielle – Louise Gabrielle Bobb

Bobbie Gentry – Roberta Streeter

Ginuwine – Elgin Lumpkin

Glamma Kid – Iyael Constable

Goldie – Clifford Price

Macy Gray – Natalie McIntyre

Peter Green – Peter Greenbaum

H

Daryl Hall – Daryl Hohl

Hammer (previously M.C. Hammer) – Stanley Kirk Burrell

Steve Harley – Steven Nice

Jet Harris – Terence Hawkins

Faith Hill – Audrey Faith Perry

Buddy Holly – Charles Hardin Holley

Howlin' Wolf – Chester Burnett

Engelbert Humperdinck – Arnold George Dorsey

I

Janis Ian – Janis Eddy Fink

Ice Cube – O'Shea Jackson

Ice-T – Tracy Marrow

Billy Idol – William Broad

J

Jay-Z – Shawn Carter

Jazzie B – Beresford Romeo

Jellybean – John Benitez

Elton John – Reginald Kenneth Dwight

Paul Jones – Paul Pond

John Paul Jones – John Baldwin

Tom Jones – Thomas James Woodward

Judge Jules – Julius O'Rearden

K

Chaka Khan – Yvette Marie Stevens

Kid Creole – August Darnell

Kid Rock – Bob Ritchie

Ben E. King – Benjamin Nelson

Freddie King – Freddie Christian

Jonathan King – Kenneth King

Beverley Knight – Beverley Ann Smith

Billy J. Kramer – William Howard Ashton

L

Patti LaBelle – Patricia Louise Holt

k.d. lang – Kathy Dawn if you've ever wondered

D.C. Lee – Diane Sealey

Peggy Lee – Norma Jean Egstrom

Cleo Laine – Clementina Dinah Campbell

Lemmy – Ian Fraser Kilmister

Huey Lewis – Hugh Cregg III

L.L. Cool J – James Todd Smith

Lobo – Roland Kent Lavoie

Monie Love – Simone Johnson

Lene Lovich – Marlene Premilovich

Lulu – Marie McDonald McLaughlin Laurie

M

Madonna – Madonna Louise Veronica Ciccone

The Mad Professor – Neil Fraser

Mama Cass – Ellen Naomi Cohen

Barry Manilow – Barry Alan Pinkus

Manfred Mann – Michael Lubowitz

Marilyn Manson – Brian Warner

Phil Manzanera – Philip Target-Adams

Teena Marie – Mary Christine Brockert

Marilyn – Peter Robinson

Martika – Marta Marrero Martinez

Ricky Martin – Enrique Martin Morales

Hank Marvin – Brian Rankin

Meat Loaf – Marvin Lee Aday

Freddie Mercury – Frederick Bulsara

George Michael – Georgious Panayatiou

Little Milton – James Milton Campbell

Joni Mitchell – Roberta Joan Anderson

Moby – Richard Melville Hall

Zoot Money – George Bruno Money

Matt Monro – Terrence Parsons

Van Morrison – George Ivan Morrison

Morrissey – Stephen Patrick Morrissey

N

Jimmy Nail – James Bradford

Nico – Christa Paffgen

Notorious B.I.G. – Christopher Wallace

Gary Numan – Gary Anthony James Webb

O

Billy Ocean – Leslie Charles

William Orbit – William Wainwright

Roland Orzabal – Roland Orzabal de la Quintana

Ozzy Osbourne – John Osbourne

P

Elaine Page – Elaine Bikerstaff

Gram Parsons – Cecil Connor III

John Peel – John Ravenscroft

Marti Pellow – Mark McLoughlin

Esther Phillips – Esther Mae Jones

Iggy Pop – James Jewel Osterberg

Posdmus (De La Soul) – Kelvin Mercer

Cozy Powell – Colin Flooks

Reg Presley – Reginald Maurice Ball

Maxi Priest – Max Alfred Elliott

Prince – Prince Rogers Nelson

P.J. Proby – James Marcus Smith

Puff Daddy – Sean Combs

Bobby Purify – Robert Lee Dickey

Q

Q-Tip – Jonathan Davis

Suzi Quatro – Susan K. Quatrocchio

Queen Latifah – Dana Owens

R

Shabba Ranks – Rexton Rawlston Gordon

Lou Reed – Louis Firbank

Jimmy Reid – James Mathis

Nick Rhodes – Nicholas James Bates

Busta Rhymes – Trevor Smith Jnr

Roy Rogers – Leonard Slye

Henry Rollins – Henry Garfield

Sonny Rollins – Theodore Walter Rollins

Axl Rose – William Bailey

Jennifer Rush – Heidi Stern

S

Sade – Helen Folasade Adu

Salt-N-Pepa – Cheryl James and Sandy Denton

Sasha – Alexander Coe

Rat Scabies – Christopher Miller

Bon Scott (AC/DC) – Ronald Belford

Seal – Sealhenry Samuel

Shaggy – Orville Richard Burrell

Tupac Shakur – Lesane Crooks

Del Shannon – Charles Weedon Westover

Sandie Shaw – Sandra Goodrich

Michelle Shocked – Karen Johnson

Gene Simmons – Chaim Witz

Nina Simone – Eunice Kathleen Waymon

Siouxsie Sioux – Susan Dallion

Sisqo – Mark Andrews

Nikki Sixx (Mötley Crüe) – Frank Carlton Serafino Ferranno

Roni Size – Ryan Williams

Skin (Skunk Anansie) – Deborah Anne Dyer

Slash – Saul Hudson

Grace Slick – Grace Wing

Memphis Slim – Peter Chaman

Dee Snider (Twisted Sister) – Clarene Eugene Snow

Snoop Doggy Dogg – Calvin Broadus

David Soul – David Richard Solberg

Dusty Springfield – Mary Isobel Catherine O'Brien

Alvin Stardust – Bernard William Jewry

Edwin Starr – Charles Hatcher

Ringo Starr – Richard Starkey

Cat Stevens – Stephen Demetri Georgiou (later Yusuf Islam)

Shakin' Stevens – Michael Barrett

Sting – Gordon Sumner

Joe Strummer – John Mellor

Suggs – Graham McPherson

Donna Summer – Adrian Donna Gaines

Andy Summers – Andy Somers

David Sylvian – David Batt

T

Tricky – Adrian Thaws

Tina Turner – Anna Mae Bullock

Shania Twain – Eilleen Regina Edwards

Conway Twitty – Harold Lloyd Jenkins

Bonnie Tyler – Gaynor Hopkins

Steve Tyler – Steven Tallarico

V

Frankie Valli – Francis Castelluccio

Vangelis – Evangelos Papathanassiou

Dave Vanian – David Letts

Vanilla Ice – Robert Van Winkle

Eddie Vedder – Edward Louis Severson III

Sid Vicious – John Simon Ritchie

Gene Vincent – Vincent Eugene Craddock

W

Gary Walker – Gary Leeds

Dinah Washington – Ruth Lee Jones

Muddy Waters – McKinley Morganfield

Paul Weller – John William Weller

Whigfield – Sannie Charlotte Carlson

Kim Wilde – Kim Smith

Jah Wobble – John Wordle

Stevie Wonder – Steveland Morris

Roy Wood – Ulysses Adrian Wood

Bill Wyman – William Perks

Tammy Wynette – Virginia Wynette Pugh

Z

Rob Zombie – Robert Straker

FAMILIES AND RELATIONSHIPS

'LIKE SISTER AND BROTHER'
Bands with Members of the Same Family

The following acts have all included, or consisted entirely of, members of the same family:

702 – sisters Irish and Lemisha Grinstead

AC/DC – brothers Malcolm and Angus Young

Ace of Base – sisters Jenny and Linn Berggren, along with their brother Jonas 'Joker' Berggren

Alisha's Attic – Shellie and Karen Poole

The Allman Brothers Band – Gregg and Duane Allman

All Saints – sisters Natalie and Nicole Appleton

The Ames Brothers – Ed, Gene, Joe and Vic

The Angels – sisters Phyllis and Barbara Allbut

Another Bad Creation – brothers Marliss and Demetrius Pugh

Atlantic Starr – brothers David, Wayne and Jonathan Lewis

Bachman-Turner Overdrive – brothers Randy and Robbie Bachman

Bangles – sisters Vicki and Debbi Peterson

Bay City Rollers – brothers Alan and Derek Longmuir

The Beach Boys – brothers Brian and Carl Wilson, as well as their cousin Mike Love

Bee Gees – brothers Barry, Maurice and Robin Gibb (the latter two are twins)

The Black Crowes – brothers Chris and Rich Robinson

The Bobbettes – sisters Emma and Jannie Pought

The Boys – brothers Khiry, Hakee, Tajh and Bilal Samad

The Braxtons – Tamar, Towanda and Trina (sisters of the oh-so-famous Toni)

Bros – Matt and Luke Goss

The Brothers Johnson – George and Louis Johnson

The Browns – sisters Maxine and Bonnie, and their brother Jim

B*Witched – twin sisters Edele and Keavy Lynch (sisters of Boyzone's Shane Lynch)

Calloway – brothers Reggie and Vincent Calloway

Carpenters – brother and sister Richard and Karen Carpenter

Christians – brothers Garry, Russell and Roger

Cleopatra – sisters Cleopatra, Zainam and Yonah Higgins

Cornelius Brothers and Sister Rose – Edward, Carter and Rose Cornelius

The Corrs – sisters Andrea, Caroline and Sharon, plus brother Jim

The Cowsills – brothers Bill, Bob, Paul, Barry and John, along with sister Susan and mother Barbara. Whatever happened to dear old Pop Cowsill

The Cranberries – brothers Noel and Mike Hogan

Crash Test Dummies – brothers Dan and Brad Roberts

The Crew-Cuts – brothers John and Ray Perkins

Delfonics – brothers William and Wilbert Hart

Destiny's Child – Beyoncé Knowles and her cousin Kelly Rowland

Dire Straits – brothers Mark and David Knopfler

Earth, Wind & Fire – Maurice and Verdine White

Emotions – sisters Wanda, Sheila and Jeanette Hutchinson

Eternal – sisters Easther and Vernie Bennett

Everly Brothers – brothers Don and Phil

Faithless – Rollo and his sister Dido

Five Star – siblings Deniece, Stedman, Doris, Lorraine and Delroy Pearson

Hanson – brothers Isaac, Taylor and Zac Hanson

Heart – sisters Ann and Nancy Wilson

Heatwave – brothers Johnnie and Keith Wilder

H-Town – brothers Shazam and John Connor

INXS – brothers Andy and Jon Farriss

Isley Brothers – brothers O'Kelly, Ronald and Rudolph Isley. Later joined by younger brothers Ernie and Marvin, as well as their brother-in-law Chris Jasper.

Jackson Five – brothers Michael, Jermaine, Marlon, Randy, Tito and later Jackie Jackson

Jodeci – brothers Joel 'JoJo' and Cedric 'K-Ci' Hailey, also Dalvin and Donald 'DeVante Swing' DeGrate

K-Ci and JoJo – brothers Joel 'JoJo' and Cedric 'K-Ci' Hailey

The Kinks – brothers Ray and Dave Davies

Gladys Knight & The Pips – Gladys and her brother Merald 'Bubba' Knight, along with their cousins, William Guest and Edward Patten. Managed by another cousin, James 'Pip' Woods (from whom they took the name, the Pips).

Kool & The Gang – Robert 'Kool' Bell and his brother Ronald

Len – Marc and Sharon Costanzo (brother and sister)

Ziggy Marley And The Melody Makers – David 'Ziggy' Marley and his siblings Stephen, Sharon and Cedella. All four are the children of legendary reggae singer Bob Marley.

McGuire Sisters – Phyllis, Christine and Dorothy

Mel & Kim – the Appleby sisters

Musical Youth – Kelvin and Michael Grant, and Patrick and Junior Waite

98ß – brothers Nick and Drew Lachey

Nelson – brothers Gunnar and Matthew Nelson

Neville Brothers – brothers Art, Aaron, Charles and Cyril Neville

New Kids On The Block – Jon and Jordan Knight

Oasis – brothers Noel and Liam Gallagher

Orbital – brothers Paul and Phil Hartnoll

The Osmonds – brothers Alan, Wayne, Merrill, Jay and Donny

The Partridge Family – David Cassidy and his stepmother Shirley Jones

Patience and Prudence – Patience and Prudence McIntyre

P.M. Dawn – Attrell 'Prince Be' Cordes and his brother Jarrett

Pointer Sisters – sisters Ruth, Anita, June and Bonnie Pointer

The Proclaimers – identical twins, Craig and Charlie Reid

Redbone – brothers Lolly and Pat Vegas

Right Said Fred – brothers Richard and Fred Fairbrass

Santo and Johnny – brothers Santo and Johnny Farina

Sister Sledge – Debra, Joni, Kim and Kathy Sledge

Sly & The Family Stone – Sylvester 'Sly' Stone, brother Freddie, sister Rosie and cousin Larry Graham

Soul For Real – brothers Chris, Andre, Brian and Jason Dalyrimple

Spandau Ballet – Martin and Gary Kemp

3 T – brothers Taryll, T.J. and Taj Jackson; all the sons of Jacksons member Tito Jackson

The Springfields – the legendary Dusty Springfield and brother Tom

The Staple Singers – Roebuck 'Pop' Staples and his daughters, Mavis, Cleotha and Yvonne

Styx – twins Chuck and John Panozzo

The Sylvers – siblings Olympia-Ann, Leon, Charmaine, James, Edmund, Ricky, Angelia, Pat, John and Foster Sylvers

Tavares – brothers Ralph, Antone, Feliciano, Arthur and Perry Tavares

The Tokens – brothers Phil and Mitch Margo

Tony! Toni! Toné – brothers Raphael Saadiq and Dwayne Wiggins, along with their cousin Tim Riley

Toto – brothers Steve, Jeff and Mike Porcaro

UB40 – brothers Ali and Robin Campbell

Van Halen – Eddie Van Halen and his brother Alex

The Whispers – twin brothers Walter and Wallace Scott

Wilson Phillips – Carnie Wilson and her sister Wendy

Xscape – sisters LaTocha and Tamika Scott

The following acts, on the other hand, have never included members of the same family:

Allisons – supposedly brothers John and Bob Allison, though in reality the unrelated Colin Day and Brian Alford

Blues Brothers – Dan Akroyd and John Belushi

Brother Beyond – Nathan Moore, David White, Carl Fysh and Steve Alexander

Brothers Four – Dick Foley, Bob Flick, John Paine and Mike Kirkland

Buchanan Brothers – Dennis 'Terry Cashman' Minogue, Eugene Pistilli and Thomas 'Tommy West' Picardo

Chemical Brothers – non-brothers Tom Rowlands and Ed Simons

Cochran Brothers – Hank Cochran, along with future rock'n'roll star Eddie Cochran

Doobie Brothers – Pat Simmons, Tom Johnston, Jeff 'Skunk' Baxter, Tiran Porter, John Hartmann, Keith Knudsen and Michael McDonald

Righteous Brothers – vocal duo of Bill Medley and Bobby Hatfield

Shakespear's Sister – Siobhan Fahey (ex-Bananarama) and Marcella Detroit

Sister Hazel – Ken Black, Ryan Newell, Andrew Copeland, Jeff Beres and Mark Trojanowski

Swing Out Sister – Corinne Drewery, Andy Connell and Martin Jackson

Thompson Twins – Tom Bailey, Alannah Currie and Joe Leeway

Walker Brothers – Scott Engel, Gary Leeds and John Maus

'FAMILY AFFAIR'
Bands with Husbands and Wives

The following pop acts have all consisted of, or included, husbands and wives:

Abba – Benny Andersson and Anni-Frid Lyngstad; Björn Ulvaeus and Agnetha Faltskog

Ashford and Simpson – Nick Ashford and Valerie Simpson

Jack Blanchard and Misty Morgan

Boy Meets Girl – Shannon Rubicam and George Merrill

Captain & Tennille – Toni Tennille and Daryl Dragon

Delaney and Bonnie & Friends – Delaney and Bonnie Lynn Bramlett

Enigma – Michael Cretu and his wife Sandra

5th Dimension – Marilyn McCoo and Billy Davis Jr.

Fleetwood Mac – John and Christine McVie (née Perfect)

Friend and Lover – Jim Houston and Cathy Post

The Mamas and the Papas – John and Michelle Phillips

Paul McCartney & Wings – Paul and Linda McCartney (née Eastman)

Miami Sound Machine – Gloria and Emilio Estefan

The Miracles – Smokey Robinson and Claudette Rogers

Nu Shooz – John Smith and Valerie Day

Les Paul and Mary Ford

Plastic Ono Band – John Lennon and Yoko Ono

The Poppy Family – Susan and Terry Jacks

Prelude – Brian and Irene Hume

Louis Prima and Keely Smith

Quarterflash – Marv and Rindy Ross

Raindrops – Ellie Greenwich and Jeff Barry

Carly Simon and James Taylor

Siouxsie And The Banshees – Siouxsie Sioux and husband Budgie

Sonic Youth – Kim Gordon and Thurston Moore

Sonny and Cher – Sonny Bono and Cher

Starland Vocal Band – Bill Danoff and his wife Taffy with John Carroll and future wife Margot Chapman

Talking Heads – Chris Frantz and Tina Weymouth

Timbuk 3 – Patrick and Barbara MacDonald

Art and Dotty Todd

Tom Tom Club – Chris Frantz and Tina Weymouth

The Tune Weavers – Margo and John Sylvia

Ike and Tina Turner

Womack and Womack – Cecil and Linda Womack (daughter of Sam Cooke)

'GIRLS, GIRLS, GIRLS'
Girls and Groupies of the Rich and Famous

When it comes to the dating game, rock stars are in a league of their own as models and actresses alike rush to be by their side.
The following ladies have all been romantically linked with rock stars, and on occasion with the same one:

Pamela Anderson – Bret Michaels (Poison), Vince Neil (Mötley Crüe), Tommy Lee (Mötley Crüe)

Nicole Appleton – Robbie Williams, Gavin Rossdale (Bush), Liam Gallagher

Barbara Bach – Ringo Starr

Tyra Banks – Seal

Halle Berry – Danny Wood (New Kids On The Block), Eric Benét

Valerie Bertinelli – Eddie Van Halen

Christine Boris – Robert Plant, Jimmy Page, Paul Rodgers, Dean Kilpatrick (Lynyrd Skynyrd)

Angie Bowie – David Bowie, Billy Murcia (New York Dolls), Marianne Faithfull

Patti Boyd – Eric Clapton, George Harrison, Ron Wood

Christie Brinkley – Billy Joel

Bobbie Brown – Matthew Nelson (Nelson), Tommy Lee, Mark McGrath (Sugar Ray), Jay Gordon

Carla Bruni – Eric Clapton, Mick Jagger

Bebe Buell – Rod Stewart, Elvis Costello, Steven Tyler, Todd Rundgren, Jimmy Page, Ritchie Blackmore, David Bowie, Iggy Pop

The mother of actress Liv Tyler, whom she raised with Todd Rundgren following her split from Aerosmith's Steven Tyler.

Naomi Campbell – Eric Clapton, Adam Clayton, Lenny Kravitz

Mariah Carey – Q-Tip, Sean 'Puffy' Combs, Tommy Motola (head of Sony Music)

Kelly Carter – Alex Van Halen

Cher – Greg Allman, Sonny Bono, David Geffen (Geffen Records / SKG Dreamworks), Gene Simmons (Kiss), Richie Sambora (Bon Jovi), Alan Gorrie (Average White Band),

Helena Christensen – Michael Hutchence, Chris Isaak, Liam Gallagher, Billy Corgan (Smashing Pumpkins), Morten Harket (A-Ha),

Sheryl Crow – Eric Clapton

Amanda De Cadenet – John Taylor

Pamela Des Barres – Jimmy Page, Mick Jagger, Keith Moon, Jim Morrison, Chris Hillman (The Byrds), Noel Redding (Jimi Hendrix), Nick St Nicholas (Steppenwolf), Terence Trent D'Arby, Dave Navarro

One of the greatest groupies of all time, Pamela was a member of Frank Zappa's all-groupie band, the G.T.O.s

Britt Ekland – Rod Stewart, Slim Jim Phantom (Stray Cats)

Carmen Electra – Prince, B-Real (Cypress Hill), Mark McGrath (Sugar Ray), Tommy Lee, Kid Rock, Fred Durst (Limp Bizkit), Dave Navarro

Kelly Emberg – Rod Stewart

Faith Evans – Notorious B.I.G., Tupac Shakur

Erin Everly – Axl Rose, Anthony Kiedis, Matthew Nelson, Donovan Leitch Jr
Erin is the daughter of Don Everly of Everly Brothers fame, and was the inspiration behind Guns 'n' Roses hit single, 'Sweet Child Of Mine'.

Marianne Faithfull – Mick Jagger, Brian Jones, Keith Richards, Anita Pallenberg, David Bowie, Jimi Hendrix, Allan Clarke (The Hollies), Gene Pitney, Angie Bowie, Chris Blackwell (Island Records)

Justine Frischmann – Damon Albarn (Blur), Brett Anderson (Suede), Bobbie Gillespie (Primal Scream)

Jill Goodacre – Harry Connick Jr

Jerry Hall – Bryan Ferry, Mick Jagger

Alana Hamilton – Rod Stewart

Patti Hansen – Keith Richards

Eva Herzigova – Tico Torres

Whitney Houston – Bobby Brown

Jo Howard – Ron Wood

Kate Hudson – Lenny Kravitz, Chris Robinson (Black Crowes)
Kate is the daughter of Goldie Hawn and Bill Hudson; although she was raised by Goldie and her longtime beau Kurt Russell. She can be seen in the movie *Almost Famous* (2001) as groupie Penny Lane.

Nancy Hunter – John Oates

Rachel Hunter – Rod Stewart, Kip Winger (Winger), Mark Wahlberg

Iman – David Bowie

Natalie Imbruglia – Brett Anderson, Robbie Williams, Lenny Kravitz

Elaine Irwin – John Mellencamp

Bianca Jagger – Mick Jagger, David Bowie

Patsy Kensit – Dan Donovan (Big Audio Dynamite), Jim Kerr (Simple Minds), Liam Gallagher

Heather Locklear – Tommy Lee, Richie Sambora

Courtney Love – Billy Corgan (Smashing Pumpkins), Eric Erlandson (Hole), Evan Dando (The Lemonheads), Gavin Rossdale (Bush), Trent Reznor (Nine Inch Nails), Twiggy Ramirez (Marilyn Manson), Bill Gould (Faith No More), Scott Weiland (Stone Temple Pilots), Liam Gallagher (Oasis), Fred Durst (Limp Bizkit)

Madonna – Vanilla Ice, Bobby Brown, Tony Ward, Prince, Sean Penn, Guy Ritchie

Linda McCartney – Mick Jagger, Jim Morrison, Jimi Hendrix, Tim Buckley, Steve Winwood, Eric Burdon, Neil Young, Warren Beatty, John Lennon, Paul McCartney

Kylie Minogue – Michael Hutchence, Lenny Kravitz, Robbie Williams

Joni Mitchell – Chuck Mitchell, Leonard Cohen, David Crosby, Graham Nash, James Taylor, Jackson Browne

Kate Moss – Antony Langdon (Spacehog), Lenny Kravitz, Liam Gallagher, Twiggy Ramirez (Marilyn Manson), Evan Dando (Lemonheads), Goldie, Nelle Hooper, Robert Del Naja (Massive Attack), Jeremy Healey (DJ), Johnny Depp

Stevie Nicks – Lindsey Buckingham (Fleetwood Mac), Mick Fleetwood (Fleetwood Mac), Don Henley, Jimmy Irvine, Tom Petty

Nico – Jackson Browne, Jimi Hendrix, Brian Jones (Rolling Stones), Jim Morrison, Lou Reed, Leonard Cohen, Iggy Pop

Anita Pallenberg – Brian Jones (Rolling Stones), Keith Richards (Rolling Stones), Mick Jagger (Rolling Stones)

Vanessa Paradis – Lenny Kravitz, Johnny Depp

Yasmin Parvaneh – Simon Le Bon

Julianne Phillips – Bruce Springsteen

Paulina Porizkova – Ric Ocasek

Victoria Principal – Andy Gibb

Lisa-Marie Presley – Michael Jackson

Winona Ryder – Dave Pirner (Soul Asylum), Tre Cool (Green Day), Evan Dando (Lemonheads), Jay Kay (Jamiroquai), Dave Grohl (Nirvana), Stephan Jenkins (Third Eye Blind), Beck

Savannah (porn star) – Gregg Allman, Mark Wahlberg, Slash, Axl Rose, Billy Sheehan (Dave Lee Roth Band, Mr Big), David Lee Roth, Billy Idol Danny Boy (House of Pain), Vince Neil (Mötley Crüe)

Edie Sedgwick – Bob Dylan

Stephanie Seymour – Axl Rose

Chrissie Shrimpton – Mick Jagger, Steve Marriott

Ione Skye (the daughter of sixties popster Donovan) – Anthony Kiedis (Red Hot Chilli Peppers), Adam Horovitz (Beastie Boys)

Talia Soto – Nick Kamen

Nancy Spungen – Sid Vicious, Keith Richards, Jerry Nolan (New York Dolls)

Charlize Theron – Stephan Jenkins (Third Eye Blind)

Paula Yates – Terence Trent D'Arby, Michael Flatley, Bob Geldof, Michael Hutchence

'THE KIDS ARE ALRIGHT'
Pop Stars with Famous Parents

There's an old saying, 'it's not what you know: it's who you know,' and having the right connections can certainly help when it comes to making a career in music. And when it comes to connections, you can't do much better than having a famous pop star for a parent.

The following are all sons or daughters of famous musicians:

Jason Bonham – son of Led Zeppelin's hard-drinking drummer John

Debby Boone – Pat Boone

Sam Brown – daughter of Joe Brown

Jeff Buckley – Tim Buckley

Rocky Burnette – Johnny Burnette

David Cassidy – Jack Cassidy

Shaun Cassidy – Jack Cassidy and Shirley Jones

Eagle-Eye Cherry – Don Cherry

Neneh Cherry – Don Cherry

Natalie Cole – Nat' King' Cole

Daryl Dragon (aka the Captain of Captain & Tennille) – Carmen Dragon (conductor)

Jakob Dylan (The Wallflowers) – Bob Dylan

Sheila E. – Pete Escovedo (of Azteca)

Andrew Gold – Ernest Gold (film composer) and Marni Nixon

Kennedy Gordy (aka Rockwell) – son of Motown chairman Berry Gordy

Chesney Hawkes – Len 'Chip' Hawkes

Whitney Houston – Cissy Houston

Enrique Iglesias – Julio Iglesias

Jack Jones – John Jones

Julian Lennon – John Lennon

Sean Lennon – John Lennon

Gerald and Sean Levert (both of Levert) – Eddie Levert (of the O'Jays)

Gary Lewis – Jerry Lewis (comic)

Terry Melcher (of The Rip Chords) – Bruce Johnston (of The Beach Boys) and Doris Day

Gunnar and Matthew Nelson (of Nelson) – Ricky Nelson

Ricky Nelson – Ozzie Nelson

Chynna Phillips (of Wilson Phillips) – John and Michelle Phillips (of The Mamas and the Papas)

Bonnie Raitt – John Raitt

L.A. Reid (of The Deele) – Herb Rooney and Brenda Reid (of The Exciters)

Bob Rosenberg –(of Will to Power) – Gloria Mann

Dr. J. Rosenberg (Will To Power) – Gloria Mann

Dara Sedaka – Neil Sedaka

Nancy Sinatra – Ol' Blue Eyes himself

Zak Starkey – Ringo Starr

Brenda K. Starr – Harvey Kaplan (of The Spiral Starecase)

Carla Thomas – Rufus Thomas

David Townsend (of Surface) – Ed Townsend

Kim Wilde – Marty Wilde

Carnie and Wendy Wilson (both of Wilson Phillips) – Brian Wilson (of The Beach Boys)

Linda Womack (of Womack and Womack) – Sam Cooke

Dweezil Zappa – Frank Zappa

BIRTHDAYS

'HAPPY BIRTHDAY'
Pop Stars' Birthdays

If you're anything like us, even remembering your own mother's birthday can prove something of a problem. Heaven forbid you'd forget the birthday of your favourite star. However, worry no longer, for below you'll find the birth-dates of anyone worth remembering:

January 1
Grandmaster Flash (1958)

January 2
George Martin (1926)
Roger Miller (1936)

January 3
Stephen Stills (1945)

January 4
Martin McAloon (Prefab Sprout) (1962)
Michael Stipe (REM) (1960)
Bernard Sumner (New Order) (1956)
Tim Wheeler (Ash) (1977)

January 5
George Brown (Kool and the Gang) (1949)

Marilyn Manson (1969)
Sam Phillips (founder Sun Records) (1923)
Chris Stein (Blondie) (1950)

January 6
Syd Barrett (Pink Floyd) (1946)
Sandy Denny (Fairport Convention) (1948)

January 7
Dave Cousins (Strawbs) (1945)
Kenny Loggins (1948)
Paul Revere (Paul Revere and the Raiders) (1942)

January 8
David Bowie (1947)
R. Kelly (1969)
Stove King (Mansun) (1975)
Robbie Krieger (Doors) (1946)
Elvis Presley (1935)
Terry Sylvester (Hollies) (1945)

January 9
Joan Baez (1941)
Scott Engel (Walker Brothers) (1944)
A.J. McLean (Backstreet Boys) (1978)
Jimmy Page (Led Zeppelin) (1944)

January 10
Pat Benatar (1953)
Shawn Colvin (1958)
Jim Croce (1943)
Donald Fagen (Steely Dan) (1948)
Rod Stewart (1945)
Jerry Wexler (1917)

January 11
Mary J. Blige (1971)
Vicki Peterson (Bangles) (1960)
Tom Rowlands (Chemical Brothers) (1971)

January 12
Mel C (1974)
Long John Baldry (1941)

January 13
Suggs (Madness) (1961)

January 14
LL Cool J (1968)
Allen Toussaint (1938)

January 15
Captain Beefheart (1941)
Ronnie Van Zandt (Lynyrd Skynyrd) (1948)

January 16
Aaliyah (1979)
Maxine Jones (En Vogue) (1966)
Sade (1959)

January 17
Chris Montez (1943)
Shabba Ranks (1966)
Mick Taylor (Rolling Stones) (1948)
Paul Young (1956)

January 18
Crispian Mills (Kula Shaker) (1963)
David Ruffin (Temptations) (1941)

January 19
Phil Everly (1939)
Janis Joplin (1943)
Robert Palmer (1949)

January 20
Gary Barlow (1971)
Heather Small (M People) (1965)
Eric Stewart (Mindbenders / 10CC) (1945)
Wayne Williams (Another Level) (1977)
Nicky Wire (Manic Street Preachers) (1969)

January 21
Emma Bunton (1976)
Richie Havens (1941)
Billy Ocean (1950)
Edwin Starr (1942)

January 22
Sam Cooke (1935)
Michael Hutchence (INXS) (1960)
Malcolm McLaren (1946)
Steve Perry (Journey) (1953)

January 23
Earl Falconer (UB40) (1959)
Anita Pointer (Pointer Sisters) (1948)
Pat Simmons (Doobie Brothers) (1950)

January 24
Tatyana Ali (1979)
Neil Diamond (1941)
Warren Zevon (1947)

January 25
Andy Cox (Beat / Fine Young Cannibals)
Richard Finch (KC and the Sunshine Band) (1954)

January 26
Jazzie B (Soul II Soul) (1963)
Eddie Van Halen (1957)

January 27
Nick Mason (Pink Floyd) (1945)
Mark Owen (Take That) (1972)

January 28
Nicholas Carter (Backstreet Boys) (1980)
Lee Latchford Evans (Steps) (1975)
Joey Fatone (N Sync) (1977)

January 29
Roddy Frame (Aztec Camera) (1964)
Rob Manzoli (Right Said Fred) (1954)
Tommy Ramone (Ramones) (1949)

January 30
Steve Marriott (1947)
Jody Watley (1959)

January 31
Henry Wayne Casey (KC and the Sunshine Band) (1951)
Terry Cath (Chicago) (1946)
Lloyd Cole (1961)
Phil Collins (1951)
John Lydon (1956)
Phil Manzanera (Roxy Music) (1951)
Justin Timberlake (N Sync) (1981)

February 1
Don Everly (1937)
Rick James (1952)

February 2
Robert DeLeo (Stone Temple Pilots) (1966)
Graham Nash (1942)

February 3
Dave Davies (Kinks) (1947)
Val Doonican (1928)
Dennis Edwards (Temptations) (1943)
Eric Haydock (Hollies) (1943)
Johnny 'Guitar' Watson (1935)

February 4
Tim Booth (James) (1960)
Alice Cooper (1948)
Natalie Imbruglia (1975)

February 5
Christopher Barron (Spin Doctors) (1968)
Bobby Brown (1969)
Al Kooper (Blood, Sweat and Tears) (1944)

February 6
Rick Astley (1966)
Mike Batt (Wombles) (1950)
Natalie Cole (1950)
Bob Marley (1945)
Axl Rose (Guns 'N' Roses) (1962)

February 7
Steve Bronski (Bronski Beat) (1960)
David Bryan (Bon Jovi) (1962)
Alan Lancaster (Status Quo) (1949)
Brian Travers (UB40) (1959)

February 8
Vince Neil (Mötley Crüe) (1961)
Tom Rush (1941)

February 9
Carole King (1942)

February 10
Peter Allen (1944)
Roberta Flack (1939)

February 11
Brandy (1979)
Sheryl Crow (1962)
Gerry Goffin (1939)
Kelendria Rowland (Destiny's Child) (1981)
Gene Vincent (1935)

February 12
Steve Hackett (Genesis) (1950)
Ray Manzarek (Doors) (1935)
Chynna Phillips (Wilson Phillips) (1968)

February 13
Tony Butler (Big Country) (1947)
Mark Fox (Haircut 100)(1958)
P J Harvey (1962)
Peter Hook (New Order) (1956)
Sonia (1971)

Peter Tork (Monkees) (1944)
Robbie Williams (1974)

February 14
Tim Buckley (1947)

February 15
Mick Avery (Kinks) (1944)
Ali Campbell (UB40) (1959)
Mickey Craig (Culture Club) (1960)
Melissa Manchester (1951)

February 16
Sonny Bono (Sonny and Cher) (1935)
Ice-T (1958)
Andy Taylor (Duran Duran) (1961)

February 17
Gene Pitney (1941)

February 18
Robbie Bachman (Bachman-Turner Overdrive) (1953)
Dr. Dre (1965)
Yoko Ono (1933)
John Travolta (1954)

February 19
Lou Christie (1943)
Falco (1957)
Tony Iommi (1948)
Smokey Robinson (1940)
Seal (1963)

February 20
Walter Becker (Steely Dan) (1950)
Ian Brown (Stone Roses) (1963)
Kurt Cobain (1967)
J. Geils (J. Geils Band) (1946)
Brian Littrell (Backstreet Boys) (1975)

February 21
James Dean Bradfield (Manic Street Preachers) (1969)

Mary-Chapin Carpenter (1958)
Jerry Harrison (Talking Heads) (1949)
Ranking Roger (General Public / Beat) (1961)

February 22
Michael Wilton (Queensrÿche) (1962)

February 23
Elkie Brooks (1945)
Howard Jones (1955)
Brad Whitford (Aerosmith) (1952)
Johnny Winter (1944)

February 24
Paul Jones (Manfred Mann) (1942)

February 25
George Harrison (1943)
Stuart 'Woody' Wood (Bay City Rollers) (1957)

February 26
Michael Bolton (1953)
Johnny Cash (1932)
Fats Domino (1928)
Bob 'The Bear' Hite (Canned Heat) (1945)
Sandie Shaw (1947)

February 27
Peter Andre (1973)
Paul Humphreys (Orchestral Manoeuvres in the Dark) (1960)

February 28
Brian Jones (Rolling Stones) (1942)
Joe South (1940)
Cindy Wilson (B-52's) (1957)

February 29
Gretchen Christopher (Fleetwoods) (1940)

March 1
Harry Belafonte (1927)
Mike D'Abo (Manfred Mann) (1944)

Roger Daltrey (Who) (1944)

March 2
Jon Bon Jovi (Bon Jovi) (1962)
Lou Reed (1943)

March 3
Ronan Keating (1977)
Mike Pender (Searchers) (1942)

March 4
Evan Dando (Lemonheads) (1967)
Emilio Estefan (Miami Sound Machine) (1953)
Patsy Kensit (1968)
Chris Rea (1951)
Shakin' Stevens (1948)
Michael 'Mick' Wilson (Dave Dee, Dozy, Beaky Mick & Tich (1944)
Bobby Womack (1944)

March 5
Andy Gibb (1958)
Eddy Grant (1948)

March 6
Kiki Dee (1947)
Dave Gilmour (Pink Floyd) (1944)
Shaquille O'Neal (1972)
Mary Wilson (Supremes) (1944)

March 7
Paul Cattermole (S Club 7) (1977)
Matthew Fisher (Procol Harum) (1946)
Peggy March (1948)
Chris White (Zombies) (1943)

March 8
Cheryl Baker (Bucks Fizz) (1954)
Mickey Dolenz (Monkees) (1945)
Peter Gill (Frankie Goes To Hollywood) (1964)
Cheryl 'Salt' James (Salt 'n' Pepa) (1964)
Gary Numan (1958)

March 9
Jeffrey Osborne (1948)
Lloyd Price (1933)
Robin Trower (Procul Harum) (1945)

March 10
Tom Scholz (Boston) (1947)

March 11
Letoya Luckett (Destiny's Child) (1981)
Bobby McFerrin (1950)
Bruce Watson (Big Country) (1961)

March 12
Steve Harris (Iron Maiden) (1957)
Graham Coxon (Blur) (1969)
James Taylor (1948)

March 13
Adam Clayton (U2) (1960)
Neil Sedaka (1939)

March 14
David Byrne (Talking Heads) (1952)
Taylor Hanson (Hanson) (1983)
Quincy Jones (1933)

March 15
Mike Love (Beach Boys) (1941)
Bret Michaels (Poison) (1963)
Sly Stone (Sly and the Family Stone) (1944)
Terence Trent D'Arby (1962)

March 16
Jimmy Nail (1954)
Jerry Jeff Walker (1942)
Nancy Wilson (Heart) (1954)

March 17
Billy Corgan (Smashing Pumpkins) (1967)
Stephen Gately (Boyzone) (1976)
John Sebastian (Lovin' Spoonful) (1944)

March 18
Irene Cara (1959)
Wilson Pickett (1941)
Vanessa Williams (1963)

March 19
Ricky Wilson (1953)

March 20
Carl Palmer (Emerson, Lake and Palmer) (1947)

March 21
Jonas 'Joker' Berggren (Ace Of Base) (1967)
Mark Hamilton (Ash) (1977)
Roger Hodgson (Supertramp) (1950)
Russell Thompkins Jnr (Stylistics) (1951)

March 22
George Benson (1943)
Stephanie Mills (1957)

March 23
Damon Albarn (Blur) (1968)
Chaka Khan (1953)
Ric Ocasek (Cars) (1949)
Marti Pellow (1966)

March 24
Nick Lowe (1949)
Mase (De La Soul) (1970)

March 25
Melanie Blatt (All Saints) (1976)
Aretha Franklin (1942)
Elton John (1947)

March 26
Teddy Pendergrass (Harold Melvin & The Blue Notes) (1950)
Diana Ross (1944)
Steven Tyler (Aerosmith) (1948)

March 27
Mariah Carey (1970)
Clark Datchler (Johnny Hates Jazz) (1961)
Billy MacKenzie (Associates) (1957)

March 28
Johnny Burnette (1934)

March 29
Vangelis (1943)

March 30
Eric Clapton (1945)
Celine Dion (1968)
Graeme Edge (Moody Blues) (1944)
MC Hammer (1962)
Randy Vanwarmer (1955)

March 31
Herb Alpert (1935)
Angus Young (AC/DC) (1959)

April 1
Alan Blakley (Tremeloes) (1942)
Billy Currie (Ultravox) (1952)
Rudolph Isley (Isley Brothers) (1939)
Hannah Spearritt (S Club 7) (1981)

April 2
Marvin Gaye (1939)
Leon Russell (1941)
Keren Woodward (Bananarama) (1961)

April 3
Tony Orlando (Dawn) (1944)

April 4
Dave Hill (Slade) (1952)
Major Lance (1941)
Muddy Waters (1915)

April 5
Agnetha Fältskog (Abba) (1950)
Ronnie White (Miracles) (1939)

April 6
Tony Connor (Hot Chocolate) (1947)
Michelle Phillips (Mamas & The Papas) (1944)

April 7
Mick Abrahams (Jethro Tull) (1943)

April 8
Steve Howe (Yes / Asia) (1947)
Julian Lennon (1963)

April 9
Mark Kelly (Marillion) (1961)
Carl Perkins (1932)
Rachel Stevens (S Club 7) (1978)

April 10
Babyface (1959)
Mandy Moore (1984)
Brian Setzer (Stray Cats) (1960)
Bunny Wailer (Wailers) (1947)

April 11
Stuart Adamson (Big Country) (1958)
Cerys Matthews (Catatonia) (1969)
Delroy Pearson (Five Star) (1970)
Nigel Pulsford (Bush) (1965)
Lisa Stansfield (1966)

April 12
David Cassidy (1950)
Herbie Hancock (1940)
John Kay (Steppenwolf) (1944)
Bryan McFadden (Westlife) (1980)

April 13
Lou Bega (1975)
Al Green (1946)

April 14
Ritchie Blackmore (Deep Purple / Rainbow) (1945)

April 15
Graeme Clark (Wet, Wet, Wet) (1966)
Allan Clarke (Hollies) (1942)
Dave Edmunds (1944)
Oscar Harrison (Ocean Colour Scene) (1965)

April 16
Gabrielle (1970)
Gerry Rafferty (1947)
Dusty Springfield (1939)
Bobby Vinton (1935)

April 17
Victoria Beckham (Spice Girls) (1975)
John Oates (Hall and Oates) (1949)
Pete Shelley (Buzzcocks) (1955)

April 18
Mike Vickers (Manfred Mann) (1941)

April 19
Alan Price (1942)
Mark Volman (Turtles) (1947)

April 20
Luther Vandross (1951)
Jimmy Winston (Small Faces / Winston's Fumbs) (1945)

April 21
Johnny McElhone (Texas) (1963)
Iggy Pop (1947)
Robert Smith (Cure) (1959)

April 22
Glen Campbell (1938)
Peter Frampton (1950)

April 23
Roy Orbison (1936)

April 24
Barbra Streisand (1942)

April 25
Andy Bell (Erasure) (1964)
Tony Christie (1944)
Albert King (1923)
Derek Dick (aka Fish) (Marillion) (1958)
Simon Fowler (Ocean Colour Scene) (1965)
Björn Ulvaeus (Abba) (1945)

April 26
Célena Cherry (Honeyz) (1977)
Jon Lee (S Club 7) (1982)
Jo O'Meara (1979)
Bobby Rydell (1942)
Roger Taylor (Duran Duran) (1960)

April 27
Sheena Easton (1959)
Pete Ham (Badfinger) (1947)
Yonah Higgins (Cleopatra) (1984)
Kate Pierson (B-52's) (1948)
Marco Pirroni (Adam & The Ants) (1959)

April 28
Howard Donald (Take That) (1968)
Duane Eddy (1938)

April 29
Kian Egan (Westlife) (1980)
Tommy James (1947)
Francis Rossi (Status Quo) (1949)
Klaus Voorman (Manfred Mann) (1942)
Carnie Wilson (Wilson Phillips) (1968)

April 30
Madonna Higgins (Cleopatra) (1982)
Johnny Horton (1927)
Willie Nelson (1933)
Bobby Vee (1943)

May 1
Bernard Butler (Suede) (1970)
Judy Collins (1939)
Rita Coolidge (1944)
Ray Parker Jr (1954)

May 2
Lesley Gore (1946)
Lou Gramm (Foreigner) (1950)

May 3
James Brown (1928)
Christopher Cross (1951)
Mary Hopkin (1950)
Pete Seeger (1919)
Frankie Valli (1937)

May 4
Nicholas Ashford (Ashford and Simpson) (1943)
Jay Aston (Bucks Fizz) (1961)
James Lance Bass (N Sync) (1979)
Ronnie Bond (Troggs) (1943)
Eric Burdon (Animals) (1941)

May 5
Ian McCulloch (Echo and the Bunnymen) (1959)
Johnny Taylor (1938)

May 6
Bob Seger (1945)

May 7
Eagle-Eye Cherry (1969)
Jimmy Ruffin (1939)

May 8
John Fred (John Fred and his Playboy Band) (1941)
Gary Glitter (1940)
Ricky Nelson (1940)
Dave Rountree (Blur) (1964)
Paul Samwell-Smith (Yardbirds) (1943)
Toni Tennille (Captain and Tennille) (1943)

Alex Van Halen (1955)
Ian Watkins (Steps) (1976)

May 9
Paul Heaton (Beautiful South) (1962)
Paul 'Guigsy' McGuigan (Oasis) (1971)
Tommy Roe (1943)
Billy Joel (1949)

May 10
Bono (aka Paul Hewson) (1960)
Donovan (1946)
Dave Mason (Traffic) (1947)
Danny Rapp (Danny and the Juniors) (1941)

May 11
Apache Indian (1967)
Les Chadwick (Gerry and the Pacemakers) (1943)

May 12
Ian Dury (1942)
Steve Winwood (1948)

May 13
Peter Gabriel (1950)
Lorraine McIntosh (Deacon Blue) (1964)
Ritchie Valens (1941)
Mary Wells (1943)
Stevie Wonder (1950)

May 14
Natalie Appleton (All Saints) (1973)
Jack Bruce (Cream) (1943)
Bobby Darin (1936)
Martine McCutcheon (1976)
Sinead O'Carroll (1978)
Danny Wood (New Kids On The Block) (1969)

May 15
Ian 'Tich' Amey (Dave Dee, Dozy, Beaky, Mick & Tich (1944)
Brian Eno (Roxy Music / U2 Producer) (1948)
Mike Oldfield (1953)

May 16
Glenn Gregory (Heaven 17) (1958)
Janet Jackson (1966)
Jimmy Osmond (1963)

May 17
Bill Bruford (Yes) (1948)
Enya (1961)
Jordan Knight (New Kids On The Block) (1970)
Trent Reznor (Nine Inch Nails) (1965)

May 18
Rick Wakeman (1949)

May 19
Jenny Berggren (Ace Of Base) (1972)
Paul Brady (1947)
Dusty Hill (ZZ Top) (1949)
Grace Jones (1952)
Joey Ramone (Ramones) (1952)
Pete Townshend (1945)
Martyn Ware (Heaven 17) (1956)

May 20
Cher (1946)
Joe Cocker (1944)
Nick Heywood (Haircut 100) (1961)
Brian Nash (Frankie Goes To Hollywood) (1963)
Busta Rhymes (1972)

May 21
Mike Barson (Madness) (1958)
Ronald Isley (Isley Brothers) (1941)
Notorious B.I.G. (1972)
Leo Sayer (1948)

May 22
Morrissey (1959)
Bernie Taupin (Elton John's songwriting partner) (1950)

May 23
Terese Bazaar (Dollar) (1957)
Jewel (1974)
Humphrey Lyttelton (1921)
Junior Waite (Musical Youth) (1967)

May 24
Bob Dylan (1941)
Heavy D (1967)
Patti LaBelle (1944)

May 25
Lauryn Hill (1975)
Paul Weller (1958)

May 26
Stevie Nicks (Fleetwood Mac) (1948)
Lenny Kravitz (1964)

May 27
Cilla Black (1943)
Neil Finn (Split Enz / Crowded House) (1958)
Siouxsie Sioux (Siouxsie and the Banshees) (1957)

May 28
John Fogerty (Creedence Clearwater Revival) (1945)
Roland Gift (Fine Young Cannibals) (1962)
Gladys Knight (1944)
Kylie Minogue (1968)

May 29
Mel B (Spice Girls) (1975)
Gary Brooker (Procol Harum) (1945)
Melissa Etheridge (1961)
Noel Gallagher (Oasis) (1967)

May 30
Tim Burgess (Charlatans) (1968)
Lenny Davidson (Dave Clark Five) (1954)
Nicky Headon (Clash) (1955)

May 31
John Bonham (Led Zeppelin) (1948)
Wendy Smith (Prefab Sprout) (1963)
Peter Yarrow (Peter, Paul and Mary) (1938)

June 1
Pat Boone (1934)
Jason Donovan (1968)
Damon Minchella (Ocean Colour Scene) (1969)
Alanis Morissette (1974)
Ron Wood (Rolling Stones / Jeff Beck Group / Faces)

June 2
B-Real (Cypress Hill) (1970)
Tony Hadley (Spandau Ballet) (1959)
Charlie Watts (Rolling Stones) (1941)

June 3
David Cole (C+C Music Factory) (1962)
Curtis Mayfield (1942)
Suzi Quatro (1950)
Deniece Williams (1951)

June 4
El DeBarge (1961)
Steve Grimes (Farm) (1962)
Michelle Phillips (Mamas and the Papas) (1945)
Gordon Waller (Peter and Gordon) (1945)

June 5
Laurie Anderson (1947)
Dominic Chad (Mansun) (1974)

June 6
Tom Araya (Slayer) (1961)
Gary 'US' Bonds (1939)
Chris Isaak (1956)
Levi Stubbs (Four Tops) (1936)

June 7
Tom Jones (1940)
Paddy McAloon (Prefab Sprout) (1957)
Prince (1958)

June 8
Mick Hucknall (Simply Red) (1960)
Neil Mitchell (Wet Wet Wet) (1967)
Boz Scaggs (1944)
Nancy Sinatra (1940)

June 9
Jon Lord (1941)
Les Paul (1915)
Ed Simons (Chemical Brothers) (1970)
Jackie Wilson (1934)

June 10
Shirley Owens (Shirelles) (1941)
Mark Shaw (Then Jericho) (1961)
Howlin' Wolf (1910)

June 11
Joey Dee (1940)
Lynsey De Paul (1951)

June 12
Len Barry (1942)
Reg Presley (Troggs) (1943)

June 13
Jason 'J' Brown (Five) (1976)
Dennis Locorriere (Dr Hook) (1949)
Deniece Pearson (Five Star) (1968)

June 14
Rod Argent (Zombies / Argent) (1945)
Boy George (1961)
Jimmy Lea (Slade) (1952)
Billie Myers (1971)
Muff Winwood (Spencer Davis Group) (1943)

June 15
Ice Cube (1969)
Johnny Halliday (1943)
Noddy Holder (Slade) (1946)
Harry Nilsson (1941)
Demis Roussos (1947)

June 16
2 Pac (1971)
Lamont Dozier (one third of the songwriting team, Holland-Dozier-Holland) (1941)

June 17
Barry Manilow (1946)
Chris Spedding (1944)

June 18
Tom Bailey (1957)
Paul McCartney (1942)
Nathan 'Alex-Vanderpool' Morris (Boyz II Men) (1971)
Alison Moyet (1961)

June 19
Paula Abdul (1963)
Tommy DeVito (Four Seasons) (1936)
Ann Wilson (Heart) (1954)

June 20
Chet Atkins (1924)
Cyndi Lauper (1953)
Anne Murray (1946)
Lionel Richie (1949)
John Taylor (1960)
Brian Wilson (Beach Boys) (1942)

June 21
Ray Davies (Kinks) (1944)
Marcella Detroit (Shakespear's Sister) (1959)
Joey Kramer (Aerosmith) (1950)
Nils Lofgren (E Street Band) (1951)

June 22
Peter Asher (Peter and Gordon / record producer) (1944)
Tom Cunningham (Wet Wet Wet) (1965)
Green Gartside (Scritti Politti) (1956)
Bobby Gillespie (Primal Scream) (1964)
Howard Kaylan (Turtles) (1945)
Todd Rundgren (1948)
Jimmy Somerville (Bronski Beat / Communards) (1961)

June 23
Paul 'Bonehead' Arthurs (Oasis) (1965)
Richard Coles (Communards) (1962)
Adam Faith (1940)
Leee John (Imagination) (1957)

June 24
Jeff Beck (1944)
Colin Blunstone (Zombies) (1945)
Arthur Brown (1944)
Alan McClusky (OMD) (1959)
Curt Smith (Tears For Fears) (1961)

June 25
Eddie Floyd (1935)
Harold Melvin (Harold Melvin & The Blue Notes) (1954)
George Michael (1963)
Carly Simon (1945)

June 26
Georgie Fame (1943)
Mick Jones (Clash / Big Audio Dynamite) (1954)
Colonel Tom Parker (Elvis's manager) (1910)

June 27
Bruce Johnston (Beach Boys) (1944)
Jerome 'Doc' Pomus (one half of the Pomus–Shuman songwriting partnership) (1925)

June 28
Andy Couson (All About Eve) (1963)
Bobby Harrison (Procol Harum) (1943)
David Knight (1945)

June 29
Little Eva (1945)
Dervin and Lincoln Gordon (Equals) (1945)
Colin Hay (Men At Work) (1953)

June 30
Florence Ballard (Supremes) (1943)
Tony Hatch (1939)
Julianne Regan (All About Eve) (1962)
Andy Scott (Sweet) (1951)

July 1
Delaney Bramlett (Delaney and Bonnie) (1939)
Willie Dixon (1915)
Deborah Harry (Blondie) (1945)
Fred Schneider (B-52's) (1951)

July 2
Marvin Rainwater (1925)
Dave Parsons (Bush) (1966)
Tom Springfield (Springfields) (1936)
Paul Williams (Temptations) (1939)

July 3
Fontella Bass (1940)
Laura Branigan (1957)
Vince Clarke (Depeche Mode / Yazoo / Erasure) (1961)

July 4
Louis Armstrong (1900)
John Waite (Babys) (1954)
Al 'Blind Owl' Wilson (Canned Heat) (1943)
Bill Withers (1938)

July 5
Shane Filan (Westlife) (1979)
Huey Lewis (1950)
Robbie Robertson (The Band) (1944)

July 6
Gene Chandler (1937)
Nanci Griffith (1953)
Bill Haley (1925)
Jet Harris (1939)

July 7
Vonda Shepherd (singer from *Ally McBeal*) (1963)
Ringo Starr (1940)

July 8
Russell Christian (Christians) (1956)
Billy Eckstine (1914)

July 9
Marc Almond (1959)
Jim Kerr (Simple Minds) (1959)
Bon Scott (AC/DC) (1946)

July 10
John 'Beaky' Dymond (Dave Dee, Dozy, Beaky, Mick & Tich) (1944)
Arlo Guthrie (1947)
Jason Orange (1970)
Jessica Simpson (1980)
Neil Tennant (Pet Shop Boys) (1954)

July 11
Mel Appleby (Mel and Kim) (1966)
Rick McMurray (Ash) (1975)
Ruth Pointer (Pointer Sisters) (1951)
Richie Sambora (Bon Jovi) (1959
Suzanne Vega (1959)

July 12
Christine McVie (Fleetwood Mac) (1943)

July 13
Roger McGuinn (Byrds) (1942)

July 14
Chris Cross (Ultravox) (1952)
Woody Guthrie (1912)

July 15
Trevor Horn (producer) (1949)
Millie Jackson (1944)
Linda Ronstadt (1946)

July 16
Stewart Copeland (Police) (1952)
Desmond Dekker (1941)
Tony Jackson (Searchers) (1940)

July 17
Spencer Davis (1942)
Zoot Money (1942)
Phoebe Snow (1952)

July 18
Dion Dimucci (Dion and the Belmonts) (1939)
Screamin' Jay Hawkins (1929)
Martha Reeves (Martha and the Vandellas) (1941)

July 19
Alan Gorrie (Average White Band) (1946)
Bernie Leadon (Eagles) (1947)
Brian May (1947)

July 20
Kim Carnes (1946)
Paul Cook (Sex Pistols) (1956)
John Lodge (1945)
Carlos Santana (1947)

July 21
Terry Coldwell (East 17) (1974)
Henry Priestman (Christians) (1958)
Cat Stevens (1947)

July 22
Richard Davies (Supertramp) (1944)
Don Henley (Eagles) (1947)

July 23
David Essex (1947)

Martin Gore (Depeche Mode) (1961)
Andy Mackay (Roxy Music) (1946)

July 24
Jennifer Lopez (1970)
Alan Whitehead (Marmalade) (1946)

July 25
Jim McCarty (1943)
Verdine White (Earth Wind & Fire) (1951)

July 26
Andy Connell (Swing Out Sister) (1961)
Mick Jagger (Rolling Stones) (1943)
Roger Taylor (Queen) (1949)

July 27
Bobbie Gentry (1944)

July 28
Andy Fraser (Free) (1948)

July 29
Geddy Lee (Rush) (1953)
Wanya 'Squirt' Morris (Boyz II Men) (1973)

July 30
Paul Anka (1941)
Kate Bush (1958)
David Joseph (Hi-Tension) (1957)
Sean Moore (Manic Street Preachers) (1970)
Rat Scabies (Damned) (1957)

July 31
Norman Cook (aka Fatboy Slim) (1963)
Lobo (1943)

August 1
Coolio (1963)
Robert Cray (1953)
Chuck D (Public Enemy) (1960)
Adam Duritz (Counting Crows) (1964)

Joe Elliot (Def Leppard) (1959)
Jerry Garcia (Grateful Dead) (1942)

August 2
Pete De Freitas (Echo & The Bunnymen) (1961)
Andy Fairweather-Low (1950)
Andrew Gold (1951)

August 3
Tony Bennett (1926)
James Hetfield (Metallica) (1963)

August 4
Marie Brennan (Clannad) (1952)
Ian Broudie (Lightning Seeds) (1958)

August 5
Philip Bailey (1951)
Pete Burns (Dear Or Alive) (1959)
Rick Derringer (1947)

August 6
Geri Halliwell (1972)
Joyce Sims (1959)

August 7
Rodney Crowell (1950)
Bruce Dickinson (Iron Maiden) (1958)
Andy Fraser (Free) (1952)

August 8
The Edge (U2) (1961)
David Grant (1956)
Brian Harvey (East 17) (1974)
Bradley McIntosh (S Club 7) (1981)
Joe Tex (1933)

August 9
Kurtis Blow (1959)
Whitney Houston (1963)

August 10
Ian Anderson (Jethro Tull) (1947)
Patti Austin (1948)
Jon Farriss (1961)
Eddie Fisher (1928)
Bobby Hatfield (Righteous Brothers) (1940)
Ronnie Spector (Ronettes) (1945)

August 11
Eric Carmen (1949)
Mike Hugg (Manfred Mann) (1942)
Joe Jackson (1954)
Richie Ramone (Ramones) (1957)

August 12
Kid Creole (1950)
Mark Knopfler (Dire Straits) (1949)
Ron Mael (Sparks) (1948)
Tanita Tikaram (1969)

August 13
Craig Douglas (1941)
Feargal Sharkey (1958)
George Shearing (1919)

August 14
Sarah Brightman (1961)
David Crosby (Byrds / Crosby, Stills & Nash) (1941)
Larry Graham (Sly & the Family Stone / Graham Central Station) (1946)

August 15
Matt Johnston (The The) (1961)
MCA (Beastie Boys) (1967)
Oscar Peterson (1925)
Jim Webb (1946)
Pete York (Spencer Davis Group) (1942)

August 16
Kevin Ayers (Soft Machine) (1944)
LL Cool J (1968)
Madonna (1958)
James 'J.T.' Taylor (Kool & The Gang) (1953)

August 17
Belinda Carlisle (1958)
Maria McKee (1964)
Posdnuos (De La Soul) (1969)
Claire Richards (Steps) (1977)
Kevin Rowland (Dexy's Midnight Runners) (1953)
Donnie Wahlberg (New Kids On The Block) (1969)

August 18
Johnny Preston (1939)
Carl Wayne (The Move) (1944)

August 19
Ginger Baker (Cream) (1939)
Roger Cook (1940)
John Deacon (Queen) (1941)
Don Fardon (1943)
Ian Gillan (Deep Purple) (1945)
Billy J. Kramer (1943)
Johnny Nash (1940)

August 20
Isaac Hayes (1938)
Phil Lynott (Thin Lizzy) (1951)
Robert Plant (Led Zeppelin) (1948)

August 21
Jackie De Shannon (1944)
Kenny Rogers (1938)
Joe Strummer (Clash) (1952)

August 22
Tori Amos (1963)
Steve Cradock (Ocean Colour Scene) (1969)
Howie D (Backstreet Boys) (1973)
John Lee Hooker (1917)
Roland Orzabal (Tears For Fears) (1961)
Debbie Peterson (Bangles) (1961)

August 23
Edwyn Collins (1959)
Bobby G (Bucks Fizz) (1957)

Roger Greenaway (1942)
Keith Moon (Rolling Stones) (1947)

August 24
Jim Capaldi (Traffic) (1944)
Arthur 'Big Boy' Crudup (1905)
Jean-Michel Jarre (1948)
Mason Williams (1938)

August 25
Elvis Costello (1954)
Gene Simmons (Kiss) (1949)

August 26
Chris Curtis (Searchers) (1941)
Valerie Simpson (Ashford & Simpson) (1948)

August 27
Willie De Ville (Mink De Ville) (1950)
Glenn Matlock (Sex Pistols / Rich Kids) (1956)

August 28
Kim Appleby (1961)
Hugh Cornwell (Stranglers) (1949)
LeAnn Rimes (1982)
David Soul (1943)
Shania Twain (1965)

August 29
Michael Jackson (1958)
Eddi Reader (1959)
Dinah Washington (1924)

August 30
John Phillips (Mamas and the Papas) (1935)
Dana (1951)
John McNally (Searchers) (1941)
Robert Clivillés (C+C Music Factory) (1964)

August 31
Debbie Gibson (1970)
Van Morrison (1945)
Glenn Tilbrook (Squeeze) (1957)

September 1
Gloria Estefan (1957)
Bruce Foxton (Jam) (1955)
Barry Gibb (1947)
Conway Twitty (1933)

September 2
Russ Conway (1925)
Bobby Purify (1939)
Joe Simon (1943)

September 3
Al Jardine (Beach Boys) (1942)
Freddie King (1934)
Gary Leeds (Walker Brothers) (1944)
Memphis Slim (1915)

September 4
Martin Chambers (Pretenders) (1951)
Beyoncé Knowles (Destiny's Child) (1981)

September 5
Terry Ellis (En Vogue) (1966)
Dean Ford (Marmalade) (1946)
Freddie Mercury (1946)
Buddy Miles (1946)
Sal Solo (Classix Nouveaux) (1958)
Loudon Wainwright III (1946)
Dweezil Zappa (1969)

September 6
Buster Bloodvessel (Bad Manners) (1958)
Dolores O'Riordan (Cranberries) (1971)
Jimmy Reid (1925)
Sylvester (1947)
Pal Waaktaar (A-Ha) (1961)
Roger Waters (Pink Floyd) (1944)

September 7
Gloria Gaynor (1949)
Buddy Holly (1936)
Chrissie Hynde (1951)

Little Milton (1934)
Sonny Rollins (1929)
Jermaine Stewart (1962)

September 8
Patsy Cline (1932)
Pink (1979)
Andie Rathbourne (Mansun) (1972)
David Steel (Fine Young Cannibals / Beat) (1960)

September 9
Inez Foxx (1942)
Peter Noone (Herman's Hermits) (1947)
Billy Preston (1946)
Otis Redding (1941)
Dave Stewart (Eurythmics) (1952)

September 10
Roy Ayers (1940)
Roy Brown (1925)
Carol Decker (T'Pau) (1957)
Siobhan Fahey (1960)
José Feliciano (1945)
Robin Goodridge (Bush) (1966)
Don Powell (Slade) (1950)

September 11
Richard Ashcroft (1971)
Moby (1965)
Jon Moss (Culture Club) (1957)
Mick Talbot (Style Council) (1958)

September 12
Maria Muldur (1943)
Barry White (1944)

September 13
Peter Cetera (Chicago) (1944)
David Clayton-Thomas (Blood, Sweat & Tears) (1941)
Dave Mustaine (Megadeth) (1961)
Zak Starkey (1965)

September 14
Morten Harket (A-Ha) (1959)
Paul Kossoff (Free) (1950)
Nas (1973)

September 15
Jimmy Gilmer (Fireballs) (1940)

September 16
Marc Anthony (1969)
Tina Barrett (S Club 7) (1976)
David Bellamy (Bellamy Brothers) (1950)
Eric Haydock (Hollies) (1944)
Kenny Jones (Faces) (1948)
B.B. King (1925)
Richard Marx (1963)

September 17
Anastacia (1973)
Bill Black (1926)
Hank Williams (1923)

September 18
Frankie Avalon (1939)
Ricky Bell (New Edition / Bell Biv DeVoe) (1967)

September 19
Mama Cass (Mamas and the Papas) (1941)
Jarvis Cocker (Pulp) (1963)
Bill Medley (Righteous Brothers) (1940)
Freda Payne (1945)
Nile Rodgers (Chic) (1952)

September 20
Alannah Currie (Thompson Twins) (1959)
David Hemmingway (Housemartins / Beautiful South) (1960)

September 21
Leonard Cohen (1934)
Trugoy The Dove (De La Soul) (1968)
Liam Gallagher (Oasis) (1972)
Faith Hill (1967)

Henry Priestman (Christians) (1955)
Jimmy Young (1923)

September 22
Steve Boone (Lovin' Spoonful) (1943)
Andy Cairns (Therapy?) (1965)
Nick Cave (1957)
David Coverdale (1949)
Paul Draper (Mansun) (1972)
Joan Jett (1960)
Richard Peter John Fairbrass (Right Said Fred) (1953)
Billie Piper (1982)

September 23
Ray Charles (1930)
Julio Iglesias (1943)
Ben E. King (1938)
Bruce Springsteen (1949)

September 24
Gerry Marsden (Gerry and the Pacemakers) (1942)
Linda McCartney (1942)
Anthony Newley (1931)

September 25
Onnie McIntyre (Average White Band) (1944)
Will Smith (1968)

September 26
Lynn Anderson (1947)
Bryan Ferry (1945)
Cindy Herron (En Vogue) (1965)
Olivia Newton-John (1948)
Tracey Thorn (Everything But The Girl) (1962)

September 27
Brett Anderson (Suede) (1967)
Randy Bachman (Bachman-Turner Overdrive) (1943)
Meat Loaf (1951)
Alvin Stardust (1942)

September 28
Jim Diamond (1953)
Peter Hooton (Farm) 1962)
Helen Shapiro (1946)

September 29
Matt Goss (Bros) (1968)
Luke Goss (Bros) (1968) (20 minutes after brother Matt)
Jerry Lee Lewis (1935)
Jennifer Rush (1960)
Mari Wilson (1957)

September 30
Marc Bolan (1947)
Gus Dudgeon (1942)
Frankie Lymon (1942)
Johnny Mathis (1935)

October 1
Richard Harris (1930)
Donny Hathaway (1945)
Scott McKenzie (1944)

October 2
Lene Grawford Nystrom (Aqua) (1973)
Don McLean (1945)
Robbie Nevil (1960)
Phil Oakey (Human League) (1955)
Mike Rutherford (Genesis) 1950)
Sting (1951)
Tiffany (1971)

October 3
Lindsey Buckingham (Fleetwood Mac) (1947)
Chubby Checker (1941)
Eddie Cochran (1938)
Albert Collins (1932)
James Darren (1936)
Kevin Scott Richardson (Backstreet Boys) (1972)
Gwen Stefani (No Doubt) (1969)
Stevie Ray Vaughan (1944)

October 4
Chris Lowe (Pet Shop Boys (1959)
Patti LaBelle (1944)
Jon Secada (1963)

October 5
Brian Connolly (Sweet) (1945)
Bob Geldof (1944)
Brian Johnson (AC/DC) (1947)
Steve Miller (1943)

October 6
Richard Jobson (Skids) (1960)
Millie Small (1947)

October 7
Nicole Appleton (All Saints) (1974)
Toni Braxton (1968)
Sam Brown (1964)
Kevin Godley (Godley & Crème) (1945)
John Mellencamp (1951)
Thom Yorke (Radiohead) (1968)

October 8
Robert 'Kool' Bell (Kool & The Gang) (1950)
Hamish Stewart (Average White Band) (1949)
Tony Wilson (Hot Chocolate) (1947)

October 9
Jackson Browne (1948)
Nicky Byrne (Westlife) (1978)
John Entwistle (Who) (1944)
John Lennon (1940)
Sean Taro Ono Lennon (1974)
Mat Osman (Suede) (1967)
Peter Tosh (1944)

October 10
Martin Kemp (Spandau Ballet) (1961)
Keith Reid (Procol Harum) (1946)
David Lee Roth (Van Halen) (1955)
Midge Ure (Ultravox) (1953)

October 11
Daryl Hall (1948)
Ennio Morricone (1928)

October 12
Sam Moore (Sam & Dave) (1935)
Rick Parfitt (Status Quo) (1948)
Dionne Warwick (1940)

October 13
Chris Farlowe (1940)
Sammy Hagar (Van Halen) (1947)
Marie Osmond (1959)
Paul Simon (1941)

October 14
Thomas Dolby (1958)
Justin Hayward (Moody Blues) (1946)
Shaznay Tricia Lewis (All Saints) (1975)
Cliff Richard (1940)
Karyn White (1965)

October 15
Richard Carpenter (Carpenters) (1946)
Chris De Burgh (1948)
Marv Johnson (1938)
Barry McGuire (1936)

October 16
Max Bygraves (1922)
Gary Kemp (Spandau Ballet (1960)
Nico (Velvet Underground) (1938)
Wendy Wilson (Wilson Phillips) (1969)

October 17
René Dif (Aqua) (1971)
Eminem (1974)
Alan Howard (Tremeloes) (1941)
Wyclef Jean (1971)
Ziggy Marley (1968)
Gary Puckett (Union Gap) (1942)
David St Hubbins (Spinal Tap) (1947)

October 18
Chuck Berry (1926)
Cynthia Weil (1937)

October 19
Jennifer Holliday (1960)
George McCrae (1944)
Jeannie C. Riley (1945)

October 20
Mark King (Level 42) (1958)
Tom Petty (1953)
Snoop Doggy Dogg (1972)

October 21
Julian Cope (Teardrop Explodes) (1957)
Steve Cropper (1941)
Eric Faulkner (Bay City Rollers) (1955)
Manfred Mann (1940)
Tony Mortimer (East 17)

October 22
Eddie Brigati (Young Rascals) (1946)
Bobby Fuller (1943)
Zac Hanson (Hanson) (1985)
Shaggy (1968)

October 23
Ellie Greenwich (1940)
Freddie Marsden (Gerry & The Pacemakers) (1940)

October 24
Edgar Broughton (1946)
Monica (1980)
Paul & Barry Ryan (1948)
Bill Wyman (Rolling Stones) (1936)

October 25
Chris Norman (Smokie) (1950)
Jon Anderson (Yes) (1944)
Helen Reddy (1941)

October 26
Mahalia Jackson (1911)
Keith Strickland (B-52's) (1953)

October 27
Floyd Cramer (1933)
Hazell Dean (1956)
Simon Le Bon (Duran Duran (1958)
Scott Weiland (Stone Temple Pilots) (1967)

October 28
Wayne Fontana (1945)
Cleo Laine (1927)
Curtis Lee (1941)
Hank B Marvin (1941)
Stephen Morris (New Order) (1957)

October 29
Denny Laine (Moody Blues/Wings) (1944)
Peter Green (Fleetwood Mac) (1946)
David Paton (Pilot) (1951)
Stephen Luscombe (Blancmange) (1954)

October 30
Eddie Holland (Holland-Dozier-Holland) (1939)
Gavin Rossdale (Bush) (1967)
Timothy B Schmit (Eagles/Poco) (1947)
Grace Slick (Starship) (1939)
Otis Williams (Temptations) (1941)

October 31
King Ad-Rock (Beastie Boys) (1966)
Russ Ballard (Argent) (1947)
Linn Berggren (Ace Of Base) (1970)
Bernard Edwards (Chic) (1952)
Vanilla Ice (1968)
Johnny Marr (Smiths) (1963)
Ally McErlaine (Texas) (1968)
Larry Mullen (U2) (1961)

November 1
Tina Arena (1967)
Mags Furuholmen (A-Ha) (1962)

Anthony Kiedis (Red Hot Chili Peppers) (1962)
Lyle Lovett (1957)
Latavia Roberson (Destiny's Child) (1981)

November 2
Christopher Abbott Bernard Fairbrass (Right Said Fred) (1956)
Keith Emerson (Emerson, Lake & Palmer) (1944)
Maxine Nightingale (1952)
Brian Poole (1941)
Bruce Welch (Shadows) (1941)

November 3
Adam Ant (1954)
Lulu (1948)
Marilyn (1962)
Ian McNabb (Icicle Works) (1962)
James Prime (Deacon Blue) (1960)

November 4
Chris Difford (Squeeze) (1954)
Louise (1974)
Kool Rock (Fat Boys) (1966)

November 5
Bryan Adams (1959)
David Bryson (Counting Crows) (1961)
Art Garfunkel (1941)
Peter Noone (Herman's Hermits) (1947)
Gram Parsons (Byrds) (1946)
Lisa Scott-Lee (Steps) (1975)
Ike Turner (1931)

November 6
Glenn Frey (Eagles) (1948)
Frankie Miller (1950)
P.J.Proby (1938)
Doug Sahm) (Sir Douglas Quintet) (1941)

November 7
Nick Gilder (1951)
Jellybean (1957)
Joni Mitchell (1943)

Liam O'Maonlai (Hothouse Flowers) (1964)
Sharleen Spiteri (Texas) (1967)
Mary Travers (Peter, Paul & Mary) (1937)

November 8
Ken Dodd (1927)
Rickie Lee Jones (1954)
Bonnie Raitt (1949)
Roy Wood (1946)

November 9
Sandra 'Pepper' Denton (Salt 'N' Pepper) (1969
Tom Fogerty (Creedence Clearwater Revival) (1941)
Roger McGough (Scaffold) (1937)

November 10
Heavenli Abdi (Honeyz (1974)
Warren G (1970)
Junior Giscombe (1961)
Greg Lake (1948)

November 11
LaVern Baker (1929)
Len 'Chip' Hawkes (Tremeloes) (1946)
Ian Craig Marsh (Human League/Heaven 17)
Andy Partridge (XTC) (1953)

November 12
Errol Brown (Hot Chocolate) (1948)
Bob Crewe (1937)
Brian Hyland (1943)
Booker T Jones (Booker T & The MG's) (1944)
John Maus (Walker Brothers) (1943)
Les McKeown (Bay City Rollers) (1955)
Neil Young (1945)

November 13
Terry Reid (1949)
Timmy Thomas (1944)

November 14
Freddy Garritty (Freddy & The Dreamers) (1940)

Alexander O'Neal (1953)
Joseph 'Run' Simmons (Run DMC) (1964)
Faye Tozer (Steps) (1975)

November 15
Petula Clark (1932)
Joe Leeway (Thompson Twins) (1957)
Anni-Frida Lyngstad (Abba) (1945)
C. W. McCall (1928)

November 16
Chi Coltrane (1948)
W. C. Handy (1873)

November 17
Bell Biv De Voe (1967)
Bob Gaudio (Four Seasons) (1942)
Isaac Hanson (Hanson) (1980)
Gordon Lightfoot (1938)

November 18
Graham Parker (1950)
John Parr (1954)
Kim Wilde (1960)

November 19
Tommy Dorsey (1905)
Hank Medress (Tokens) (1938)

November 20
Duane Allman (Allman Brothers Band) (1946)
Mike D (Beastie Boys) (1965)
Sen Dog (Cypress Hill) (1965)
Norman Greenbaum (1942)
Paul King (King) (1961)
Joe Walsh (Eagles) (1947)

November 21
Bjork (1965)
Dave Alex James (Blur) (1968)
Dr John (1941)
Fiachna O'Braonain (Hothouse Flowers (1965)

November 22
Sharon Bailey (Amazulu) (1957)
James Morrison (Carter USM) (1960)
Little Steven (E Street Band) (1950)
Tina Weymouth (Talking Heads) (1950)

November 23
Bruce Hornsby (1954)
Betty Everett (1939)

November 24
Pete Best (1941)
Carmel (1958)
Scott Joplin (1868)

November 25
Bev Bevan (Electric Light Orchestra) (1945)
Amy Grant (1960)
Stacy Lattisaw (1966)
Bob Lind (1944)
Percy Sledge (1940)

November 26
John McVie (Fleetwood Mac) (1945)
Jean Terrell (Supremes) (1944)
Tina Turner (1939)

November 27
Trevor 'Dozy'Davies (Dave Dee, Dozy, Beaky, Mick & Tich) (1944)
Jimi Hendrix (1942)
Eddie Rabbitt (1942)

November 28
Bruce Channel (1940)
Berry Gordy Jnr (founder of Motown records) (1929)
David Jaymes (Modern Romance) (1954)
Randy Newman (1943)
Dawn Robinson (En Vogue) (1968)
David Van Day (Dollar) (1957)

November 29
Felix Cavaliere (Young Rascals) (1944)
Denny Doherty (Mamas & The Papas) (1941)
Jon Knight (New Kids On The Block) (1969)
John Mayall (1933)

November 30
John Ashton (Psychedelic Furs) (1957)
Des'Ree (1968)
Roger Glover (Deep Purple/Rainbow) (1945)
Billy Idol (1955)
Frank Ifield (1936)
David McClymont (Orange Juice) (1958)
Paul Stookey (Peter, Paul & Mary (1937)

December 1
Bette Midler (1945)
Sandy Nelson (1938)
Gilbert O'Sullivan (1946)
Billy Paul (1934)
Lou Rawls (1935)

December 2
Nelly Furtado (1978)
Tom McGuinness (Manfred Mann (1941)
Rick Savage (Def Leppard) (1960)
Britney Spears (1981)
Sydney Youngblood (1960)

December 3
Adamski (1967)
Ralph McTell (1944)
Ozzy Osbourne (1948)
Andy Williams (1928)

December 4
Naima Belkhiati (Honeyz) (1973)
Barry Blue (1950)
Freddy Cannon (1940)
Chris Hillman (Byrds) (1942)
Johnny Lyon (Southside Johnny & The Jukes) (1948)

December 5
Sonny Boy Williamson (1899)
J.J. Cale (1938)
Zainam Higgins (Cleopatra) (1980)
Andy Kim (1946)
Jim Messina (Buffalo Springfield/Poco / Loggins & Messina) (1947)
Little Richard (1932)

December 6
Dave Brubeck (1920)
Rick Buckler (Jam) (1955)
Ulf 'Buddha' Ekberg (Ace Of Base) (1970)
Jonathan King (1944)
Edward Tudor-Pole (Tenpole Tudor) (1955)
Ben Watt (Everything But The Girl) (1962)

December 7
Nicole Marie Appleton (All Saints) (1975)
Claudia Brucken (Propaganda) (1963)
Harry Chapin (1942)
Lindy Layton (1970)
Mike Nolan (Bucks Fizz) (1954)
Tom Waits (1949)

December 8
Gregg Allman (Allman Brothers Band) (1947)
Jerry Butler (1939)
Bobby Elliott (Hollies) (1942)
Paul Rutherford (Frankie Goes To Hollywood) (1959)
Suzanne Vega (1959)

December 9
Joan Armatrading (1950)
Rick Danko (Band) (1943)
Neil Innes (Bonzo Dog Doo Dah Band) (1944)
Donny Osmond (1957)

December 10
Pepsi Demacque (Pepsi & Shirley) (1958)
Paul Hardcastle (1957)
Brian Molko (Placebo) (1972)
Peter Sarstedt (1942)

December 11
Justin Currie (Del Amitri) (1964)
David Gates (Bread) (1940)
Jermaine Jackson (1954)
Brenda Lee (1944)

December 12
Leslie Carter (Carter USM) (1958)
Sheila E (1959)
Connie Francis (1938)
Mike Smith (Dave Clark Five) (1943)
Mike Pinder (Moody Blues) (1942)
Sinead O'Connor (1966)
Paul Rodgers (Free) (1949)
Dionne Warwick (1940)

December 13
Tom DeLonge (Blink) (1975)
Marti Webb (1944)

December 14
Frank Allen (Searchers) (1943)
Charlie Rich (1932)
Mike Scott (Waterboys) (1951)

December 15
Nick Beggs (Kajagoogoo) (1961)
Cindy Birdsong (Supremes) (1939)
Dave Clark (Dave Clark Five) (1942)
Don Johnson (1949)
Edele & Keacy Lynch (B*Witched) (1979)

December 16
Benny Andersson (Abba) (1946)
Tony Hicks (Hollies) (1943)

December 17
Sarah Dallin (Bananarama) (1961)
Dave Dee (Dave Dee, Dozy, Beaky, Mick & Tich) (1943)
Karl Denver (1934)
Edie Kendricks (Temptations) (1939)
Tommy Steele (1936)

December 18
Christina Aguilera (1980)
Chas Chandler (Animals) (1938)
Martha Johnson (Martha & The Muffins) (1950)
Buck Ram (Platters) (1908)
Keith Richards (Rolling Stones) (1943)

December 19
Alvin Lee (Ten Years After) (1944)
Limahl (Kajagoogoo) (1958)
Professor Longhair (1918)
Edith Piaf (1915)
Zal Yanovsky (Lovin' Spoonful) (1944)
Maurice White (Earth, Wind & Fire) (1944)

December 20
Anita Baker (1957)
Billy Bragg (1957)

December 21
Ray Hildebrand (Paul & Paula) (1940)
Gwen McCrae (1943)
Carla Thomas (1942)
Betty Wright (1953)

December 22
Richey Edwards (Manic Street Preachers) (1967)
Robin & Maurice Gibb (Bee Gees) (1949)
Ricky Ross (Deacon Blue) (1957)

December 23
Tim Hardin (1941)
Johnny Kidd (1939)
Esther Phillips (1935)

December 24
Jan Akkerman (Focus) (1946)
Ian Burden (Human League) (1957)
Lemmy (Motorhead) (1945)
Ricky Martin (1971)

December 25
Noel Redding (Jimi Hendrix Experience) (1945)
Robin Campbell (UB40) (1954)
John Edwards (Detroit Spinners) (1944)
Bob James (1939)
O'Kelly Isley (Isley Brothers) (1937)
Annie Lennox (1954)
Shane MacGowan (Pogues) (1962)
Henry Vestine (Canned Heat) (1944)

December 26
Abdul 'Duke' Fakir (Four Tops) (1935)
Phil Spector (1940)

December 27
Mick Jones (Foreigner) (1944)
David Knopfler (Dire Straits) (1952)
Les Maguire (Gerry & The Pacemakers) (1941)

December 28
Charles Hodges (Chas & Dave) (1943)
Edgar Winter (1946)

December 29
Yvonne Elliman (1951)
Marianne Faithfull (1946
Bryan 'Dexter' Holland (Offspring) (1965)
Ray Thomas (Moody Blues) (1942)

December 30
Bo Diddley (1928)
Davy Jones (Monkees) (1945)
Jeff Lynne (Electric Light Orchestra) (1947)
Mike Nesmith (Monkees) (1942)
Tracey Ullman (1959)

December 31
John Denver (1943)
Joe McIntyre (New Kids On The Block) (1972)
Pete Quaife (Kinks) (1943)
Patti Smith (1946)
Donna Summer (1948)
Andy Summers (Police) (1942)

CONTROVERSIAL POP

'BAN[NE]D ON THE RUN'
Rude Boy Rock: 10 Banned Records

Musicians have never been ones to show restraint when it comes to courting controversy, be it the subjects they choose to write about, or a record cover's artwork. For the sake of liberty and other high-sounding ideals, we've trawled the vaults, to make a selection of the worst and best musical offerings to come up against the censor's fury.

1. **'Give Ireland Back To The Irish'** – Paul McCartney's tuneful ditty was banned by the BBC for its comments on affairs of the crown, i.e. criticism bordering on condemnation of the British Government's chosen stance. Released in 1972, the song still got to No. 16 in the UK singles charts, where it remained for 8 weeks.

2. **'God Save The Queen'** – released in 1977, to coincide with celebrations for Queen Elizabeth II's Silver Jubilee, The Sex Pistols' anti-tribute, with its tales of a 'fascist regime' none too surprisingly failed to secure the approval of Her Majesty or the establishment. Even the Pistols' record label (A&M) reacted to this and the band's consistently unsavoury behaviour: they dropped the band, forcing the single to be withdrawn in the process. Undeterred by controversy Richard Branson's then-fledgling label, Virgin, picked up the band, securing a place in music history in the process.

'God Save The Queen' reached No. 2 in the charts, capturing, some would say, the spirit of the times.

3. **'I Can't Control Myself'** – love was evidently all around for Troggs' singer Reg Presley: the single was banned on account of the all-too-convincing way he brought the tune to an aural climax. Released in 1966, the single proved to be The Troggs' second-highest selling single: it made No. 2, spending 14 weeks in the charts.

4. **'Je T'Aime . . . Moi Non Plus'** – Jane Birkin and lover Serge Gainsbourg's overtly sexual record hit the charts twice during 1969, reaching No. 2 on its first outing. After 11 weeks in the charts, however, this ode to the ups and downs of Gallic passion was deleted by record company Fontana, before being re-released by Major Minor, this time round peaking at the No. 1 spot.

5. **'Let's Spend The Night Together'** – Rolling Stones. Released in 1967, this Stones single extolled the values of a hippy life, in particular free love. Consequently, the Beeb sought to distance themselves from it, by denying it airplay. In spite of this, it reached No. 3 in the UK singles chart.

6. **'Love To Love You Baby'** – Donna Summer's 1976 disco smash was banned for containing sounds of a sexual nature, i.e. soft sighs and grinding groans. Miss Summer certainly gave her all though: it went to No. 3 in the charts.

7. **'Relax'** – Frankie Goes To Hollywood made No. 1 with this, their debut single. At the time of its release, Frankie Goes To Hollywood found themselves facing zero airplay from the BBC, on account of the song's none-too-subtle references to the joys of carnal knowledge, in particular the delights of unrestrained orgasm; 'Relax, don't do it . . . when you wanna come'. 'Relax', appropriately enough, ends with the sounds of such an orgasm: apparently achieved by dropping a sponge into a bucket of water.

8. **'Star Star'** – those oh-so-naughty Rolling Stones again. However, this time the reason's more obvious, the song's chorus includes the word 'starf*cker'. Commercial viability obviously took a backseat to artistic integrity this time round, though they did change the title from the original 'Starf*cker'.

9. **'We Call It Acieed'** – responsible for millions of clubbers the world over chanting 'Acieed' in annoying harmony, D-Mob's 1988 hit was banned

by *Top Of The Pops* for its promotion of unnatural highs. It reached No. 3 in the charts, where it spent a respectable 12 weeks, though its influence continued for some years thereafter, as has that of its subject matter.

10. **'The Winker's Song (Misprint)'** – this 1978 release by Ivor Biggun and the Red-Nosed Burglars, a memorable paean of self-love, inevitably provoked controversy. Once again a ban ensued. The song still went on to reach No. 22, remaining in the charts for 12 weeks. Presumably, proving popular in bedrooms across the land.

'A CHANGE WOULD DO YOU GOOD'
5 Records that had to Be Changed

1. **'Brown Eyed Girl'** – the inclusion of the line, 'Making love in the green grass, behind the stadium', meant that Van Morrison's classic track had to be censored before some American radio stations would play it. The aforementioned words, with their imagery of pure filth (*shock, horror, gasp*), were changed to the more palatable, 'laughin' and a-runnin', behind the stadium'. No doubt the idea of physical exercise will seem equally offensive to many rock fans.

2. **'Don't Marry Her'** – the Beautiful South's 1996 hit had to be cleaned up before it could be played on the radio. The line (and incidentally the full title) 'Don't marry her, f*ck me' was replaced with, 'Don't marry her, have me'.

3. **'It Would Be So Nice'** – this Pink Floyd track fell foul of the Beeb, since it made mention of London's *Evening Standard* newspaper, thereby breaking the ban on advertising. As a result the Floydsters were forced to substitute the offending words with *Daily Standard* (an imaginary paper). In spite of all this, the record still bombed in the charts.

4. **'Lola'** – this 1970 Kinks hit was initially denied radio airplay. The reason? It made mention of 'Coca-Cola', and that constituted brand promotion or advertising. Consequently, it was changed to 'Cherry-Cola' and went on to give the band their third No. 2 single.

5. **'Money'** – those Pink Floyd boys again, this time with a number from their phenomenally successful *Dark Side Of The Moon* album (more than 300 weeks in the UK charts since its initial release in 1973). The track had to be changed before being aired on radio in the States. The reason: the inclusion of the line, 'don't give me that goody-good bullshit'. 'Money' was edited for radio and the offending word removed.

'DIRTY LOOKS'
Naughty Record Sleeves: 5 of the Best

1. ***Mom's Apple Pie*** – Grand Funk Railroad's album sleeve featured a painted image of a lady's private parts, most cunningly disguised as a rather tasty-looking apple pie, a comparison most recently hit upon by the makers of the box-office smash, *American Pie*. Grand Funk Railroad were made to redesign said picture so as not to offend, all of which just goes to show that you can't have your pie and eat it!

2. ***A Nod's As Good As A Wink . . . To A Blind Horse*** – this album by seventies rockers The Faces, included a rather sincere photo-journal of life on the road, i.e. the usual sort of thing – sex, drugs and good old rock'n'roll.

3. **'Sanctuary'** – Brit Heavy Metal band Iron Maiden's second single, released in 1980, while not popular musically (it peaked at No. 29 in the British charts), sought to address the concerns of the nation's voters artistically: it showed the band's mascot 'Eddie', knifing the then prime minister, Margaret Thatcher.

4. ***Two Virgins*** – John Lennon and Yoko Ono. Just who did John and Yoko think they were fooling? The cover showed the not-so-prudish pair absolutely starkers, dangly bits and all: hardly the behaviour of virgins, displaying your bits for all the world to see. The cover's front had the pair in a full frontal, while the rear of the sleeve, appropriately chose a rear view. Upon its arrival in the USA 30,000 copies of the album were duly confiscated by authorities at New York's Newark airport. When the record finally reached American shops, it could only be purchased wrapped in brown paper bags.

5. ***Yesterday . . . And Today*** – released in the US only, this 1966 Beatles album showed the Fab Four dressed in blood-stained butcher's smocks, amid a carnage of raw meat and dolls' body-parts. The Beatles had selected this cover in reaction to their US record company, Capitol Records, who had made it a policy to omit selected UK tracks from albums released stateside, only to release said tracks later collectively as a US-only album. Following complaints from record shop owners the album was recalled: however, a small quantity did make it into the hands of fans. *Yesterday . . . And Today* has since become one of the most sought after and valuable of Beatles recordings.

SONGS AND SONGWRITERS

'BAD'
100 Hits from Hell

If the devil had a record collection, it would indubitably be a dark and sordid accumulation, an unrivalled musical perversity. Songs such as 'Agadoo' and 'Teletubbies Say Eh-Oh' would be certainties on 'Old Nick's Nickelodeon'.

However, so as to offer you a little hope against the forces of darkness, we've braved vinyl's very own inferno, to bring you a listing of some of the more sinister songs contained therein.

Before you feast your eyes upon the aforementioned 'hits', allow us a final word. Should you come across a 'friend' who numbers any of the following among his or her favourites, then proceed with caution – never drop your guard and always but always carry ear-plugs. Don't say we didn't warn you!

1. **'Shaddap You Face'** (1981) – Joe Dolce
2. **'The Birdie Song'** (1981) – Tweets
3. **'Agadoo'** (1984) – Black Lace
4. **'Disco Duck'** (1976) – Rick Dees and his Cast of Idiots
5. **'Lily The Pink'** (1968) – The Scaffold
6. **'Orville's Song'** (1982) – Keith Harris and Orville
7. **'There's No-One Quite Like Grandma'** (1980) – St. Winnifred's School Choir
8. **'Grandad'** (1970) – Clive Dunn

9. **'Combine Harvester (Brand New Key)'** (1976) – Wurzels
10. **'Mr. Blobby'** (1993) – Mr. Blobby
11. **'Pump Up The Bitter'** (1988) – Starturn On 45 Pints
12. **'Kinky Boots'** (1990) – Patrick McNee and Honor Blackman
13. **'Cinderella Rockefella'** (1968) – Esther and Abi Ofarim
14. **'The Smurf Song'** (1978) – Father Abraham and the Smurfs
15. **'Mother Of Mine'** (1972) – Neil Reid
16. **'Them Girls Them Girls'** (1994) – Zig and Zag
17. **'Teletubbies Say Eh-Oh'** (1997) – Teletubbies
18. **'Swing The Mood'** (1989) – Jive Bunny and the Mastermixers
19. **'Donald Where's Your Troosers'** (1987) – Andy Stewart
20. **'Lambada'** (1989) – Kaoma
21. **'Stutter Rap (No Sleep 'Til Bedtime)'** (1987) – Morris Minor and the Majors
22. **'Skye Boat Song'** (1986) – Roger Whittaker and Des O'Connor
23. **'Chicken Song'** (1986) – Spitting Image
24. **'Nellie The Elephant'** (1984) – Toy Dolls
25. **'N-N-Nineteen Not Out'** (1985) – The Commentators
26. **'We All Stand Together'** (1984) – Paul McCartney and the Frog Chorus
27. **'Chalk Dust (The Umpire Strikes Back)'** (1982) – Brat
28. **'Wikka Wrap'** (1981) – Evasions
29. **'Walk Like A Man'** (1985) – Divine
30. **'Happy Talk'** (1985) – Captain Sensible
31. **'To Be Or Not To Be (The Hitler Rap)'** (1984) – Mel Brooks
32. **'Vindaloo'** (1998) – Fat Les
33. **'Can We Fix It'** (2000) – Bob the Builder
34. **'Save Your Love'** (1982) – Rénee and Renata
35. **'No. 1'** (2000) – Tweenies
36. **'Singalong-A-Santa'** (1982) – Santa Claus and The Christmas Trees
37. **'I've Got You Under My Skin'** (1983) – Frank Sinatra with Bono
38. **'Arthur Daley (E's Alright)'** (1982) – The Firm
39. **'Rabbit'** (1980) – Chas and Dave
40. **'Snooker Loopy'** (1986) – Chas and Dave
41. **'Ossie's Dream (Spurs Are On Their Way To Wembley)'** (1981) – Tottenham Hotspur FA Cup Final Squad
42. **'We Have A Dream'** (1982) – Scotland World Cup Squad
43. **'We're Gonna Do It Again'** (1995) – Manchester United 1995 Football Squad
44. **'Pass and Move (It's The Liverpool Groove)'** (1996) – Liverpool FC and The Boot Room Boyz

45. **'Blue Day'** (1997) – Suggs & Co featuring Chelsea Football Team
46. **'All Together Now'** (1995) – Everton Football Club
47. **'Purple Heather'** (1996) – Rod Stewart and the Scottish Euro 96 Squad
48. **'Hokey Cokey'** (1981) – Snowmen
49. **'Everything I Own'** (1974) – Ken Boothe
50. **'Da Da Da'** (1982) – Trio
51. **'I Have A Dream'** (1999) – Westlife
52. **'Captain Beaky'** (1980) – Keith Michell
53. **'Day Trip To Bangor'** (1979) – Fiddler's Dram
54. **'Blue Peter'** (1979) – Mike Oldfield
55. **'The Sparrow'** (1979) – Ramblers (from the Abbey Hey Junior School)
56. **'Luton Airport'** (1979) – Cats UK
57. **'OK Fred'** (1979) Erroll Dunkley
58. **'Rat Rapping'** (1983) – Roland Rat Superstar
59. **'One Day At A Time'** (1979) – Lena Martell
60. **'Barcelona'** (1987) – Freddie Mercury and Montserrat Caballe
61. **'Wonderwall'** (1995) – Mike Flowers Pops
62. **'Hooray Hooray It's A Holi-Holiday'** (1979) – Boney M
63. **'Pop Muzik'** (1979) – M
64. **'Wow'** (1979) – Kate Bush
65. **'Who Killed Bambi'** (1979) – Ten Pole Tudor
66. **'My Way'** (1978) – Sex Pistols
67. **'Matchstalk Men and Matchstalk Cats and Dogs'** (1978) – Brian and Michael
68. **'Car 67'** (1978) – Driver 67
69. **'Hurry Up Harry'** (1978) – Sham 69
70. **'Seven Tears'** (1982) – Goombay Dance Band
71. **'Jilted John'** (1978) – Jilted John
72. **''Ullo John Got A New Motor?'** (1984) – Alexei Sayle
73. **'Ally's Tartan Army'** (1978) – Andy Cameron
74. **'Floral Dance'** (1977) – Brighouse and Rastrick Brass Band / Terry Wogan
75. **'I Remember Elvis Presley (the King is Dead)'** (1977) – Danny Mirror
76. **'Gimme Dat Banana'** (1977) – Black Gorilla
77. **'Turtle Power'** (1990) – Partners In Kryme
78. **'Halfway Down The Stairs'** (1977) – The Muppets featuring Robin
79. **'Mississippi'** (1976) – Pussycat
80. **'Y Viva Espana'** (1974) – Sylvia
81. **'Convoy GB'** (1976) – Laurie Lingo and the Dipsticks

82. **'The Ugly Duckling'** (1975) – Mike Reid
83. **'Amazing Grace'** (1972) – The Pipes and Drums and Military Band of The Royal Scots Dragoon Guards
84. **'Christmas In Dreadland'** (1975) – Judge Dread
85. **'King Of The Cops'** (1975) – Billy Howard
86. **'The Trail Of The Lonesome Pine'** (1975) – Laurel and Hardy
87. **'Let's Twist Again'** (1975) – John Asher
88. **'Funky Moped'** (1975) – Jasper Carrott
89. **'Wombling Merry Christmas'** (1974) – Wombles
90. **'Fattie Bum Bum'** (1975) – Carl Malcolm
91. **'Rochdale Cowboy'** (1975) – Mike Harding
92. **'Whispering Grass'** (1975) – Windsor Davies and Don Estelle
93. **'The Funky Gibbon'** (1975) – The Goodies
94. **'Especially For You'** (1998) – Denise and Johnny
95. **'Long Haired Lover From Liverpool'** (1972) – Little Jimmy Osmond
96. **'My Ding-A-Ling'** (1972) – Chuck Berry
97. **'It's Four In The Morning'** (1972) – Faron Young
98. **'Fog On The Tyne (Revisited)'** (1990) – Gazza and Lindisfarne
99. **'Wand'rin' Star'** (1970) – Lee Marvin
100. **'That Noise'** (1962) – Anthony Newley

'FOR ONCE IN MY LIFE'
The One-Hit Wonders

'Is there any such thing as a sure thing?' A good question indeed. Well, if the question concerns the pop-music charts, then the answer has to be a resounding 'No!' The following songs are all what we lovingly refer to as one-hit wonders, that is to say they are by acts who, with their very first single, stormed to the top of the charts, only to subsequently disappear and never be heard of again. In some cases, however, we'd be best advised to thank God for the brevity of their success.

2000	**'Black Legend'** – You See The Trouble With Me
1999	**'Baz Luhrmann'** – Everybody's Free (To Wear Sunscreen)
1999	**'Mr Oizo'** – Flat Beat
1999	**'Chef'** – Chocolate Salty Balls (PS I Love You)
1997	**'Teletubbies'** – Teletubbies Say Eh-Oh
1996	**'Dunblane'** – Knockin' On Heaven's Door / Throw These Guns Away
1994	**'Doop'** – Doop
1991	**'Hale & Pace and the Stonkers'** – The Stonk
1990	**'Partners In Kryme'** – Turtle Power
1988	**'Robin Beck'** – First Time
1987	**'M/A/R/R/S'** – Pump Up The Volume
1985	**'Phyllis Nelson'** – Move Closer
1982	**'Charlene'** – I've Never Been To Me
1981	**'Joe Dolce Music Theatre'** – Shaddup You Face
1980	**'St Winifred's School Choir'** – There's No One Quite Like Grandma
1980	**'MASH'** – Theme From M*A*S*H
1980	**'Fern Kinney'** – Together We Are Beautiful
1979	**'Lena Martell'** – One Day At A Time
1979	**'Anita Ward'** – Ring My Bell
1978	**'Brian and Michael'** – Matchstalk Men And Matchstalk Cats And Dogs
1978	**'Althia And Donna'** – Up Town Top Ranking
1977	**'Floaters'** – Float On
1976	**'J.J. Barrie'** – No Charge
1975	**'Typically Topical'** – Barbados
1973	**'Simon Park Orchestra'** – Eye Level
1971	**'Clive Dunn'** – Grandad

1970 **'Matthews' Southern Comfort'** – Woodstock
1970 **'Norman Greenbaum'** – Spirit In The Sky
1970 **'Lee Marvin'** – Wand'rin' Star
1969 **'Archies'** – Sugar Sugar
1969 **'Jane Birkin and Serge Gainsbourg'** – Je T'Aime . . . Moi Non Plus
1969 **'Zager And Evans'** – In The Year 2525
1968 **'Crazy World Of Arthur Brown'** – Fire
1966 **'Overlanders'** – Michelle
1962 **'B. Bumble And The Stingers'** – Nut Cracker
1960 **'Ricky Valance'** – Tell Laura I Love Her
1959 **'Jerry Keller'** – Here Comes Summer
1958 **'Kalin Twins'** – When
1956 **'Dreamweavers'** – It's Almost Tomorrow
1954 **'Kitty Kallen'** – Little Things Mean A Lot

'ANSWER ME'
The Question and Answer Songs

Pop music in the fifties and sixties, experienced perhaps more than any other period a proliferation of 'Question and Answer songs'. For example, in 1961 country singer Patsy Cline charted with 'I Fall To Pieces' (ironically titled considering she was to die in a plane crash but two years later): Gerrie Lynn subsequently responded with 'I'll Pick Up The Pieces'.

Below is a list of the more interesting Q&A songs to have been released:

Q: 'Don't Let The Stars Get In Your Eyes' – Perry Como
A: 'I Let The Stars Get In My Eyes' – Goldie Hill

Q: 'I Fall To Pieces' – Patsy Cline
A: 'I'll Pick Up The Pieces' – Gerrie Lynn

Q: 'King Of The Road' – Roger Miller
A: 'Queen Of The House' – Jody Miller (no relation)

Q: 'Save The Last Dance For Me' – The Drifters
A: 'I'll Save The Last Dance For You' – Damita Jo

Q: 'My Boyfriend's Back' – The Angels
A: 'Your Boyfriend's Back' – Bobby Comstock and The Counts

Q: 'Oh Carol' – Neil Sedaka
A: 'Oh Neil' – Carole King

Q: 'Tell Laura I Love Her' – Ricky Valance
A: 'Tell Tommy I Miss Him' – Marilyn Michaels

Q: 'Will You Love Me Tomorrow' – Shirelles
A: 'Not Just Tomorrow But Always' – Bertell Dache (pseudonym for Tony Orlando of Dawn fame)

Q: 'Fraulein' – Bobby Helms
A: 'I'll Always Be Your Fraulein' – Kitty Wells

Q: **'Burning Bridges'** – Jack Scott
A: **'You Burned The Bridges'** – Bobbie Jean

Q: **'Bobby's Girl'** – Susan Maughan
A: **'Stay Away From Bobby'** – The Sherry Sisters

Q: **'Work With Me Annie'** – Midnighters
A: **'Roll With Me Henry'** – Etta James

Q: **'Diana'** – Paul Anka
A: **'Remember Diana'** – Paul Anka

Q: **'Roses Are Red'** – Ronnie Carroll
A: **'As Long As The Rose Is Red'** – Florraine Darlin

Q: **'Take Good Care Of My Baby'** – Bobby Vee
A: **'You Should Know I'm Still Your Baby'** – Sammi Lynn
also
A: **'I'll Take Good Care Of Your Baby'** – Ralph Emery

Q: **'He'll Have To Go'** – Jim Reeves
A: **'He'll Have To Stay'** – Jeanne Black

Q: **'Then He Kissed Me'** – The Crystals
A: **'Then I Kissed Her'** – Beach Boys

Q: **'Are You Lonesome Tonight?'** – Elvis Presley
A: **'Yes, I Am Lonesome Tonight'** – Dodie Stevens

Q: **'Ruby Don't Take Your Love To Town'** – Kenny Rogers and The
First Edition
A: **'Billy I've Got To Go To Town'** – Geraldine Stevens (believed to be
the same person as Dodie Stevens (see 'Are You Lonesome Tonight?'))

Q: **'This Diamond Ring'** – Gary Lewis and the Playboys
A: **'(Gary, Please Don't Sell), My Diamond Ring'** – Wendy Hill

Q: **'Who's Sorry Now?'** – Connie Francis
A: **'I'm Sorry Now'** – The Shields

Q: **'Wooden Heart'** – Joe Dowell
A: **'I Know Your Heart's Not Made Of Wood'** – Marie Ann

Q: 'Please Don't Ask About Barbara' – Bobby Vee
A: 'Is It True What They Say About Barbara?' – Mike Regal and The Quotations

Q: 'Honey' – Bobby Goldsboro
A: 'Honey (I Miss You Too)' – Margaret Lewis

Q: 'Roxanne, Roxanne' – UTFO
A: 'Roxanne's Revenge' – Roxanne Shanté

Q: 'Fool' – Brenda Lee
A: 'No You're Not The Fool' – Marc Stewart

Q: 'Who Put The Bomp' – The Viscounts
A: 'I Put The Bomp' – Frankie Lymon and The Teenagers
also
A: 'We Are The Guys' – Bob and Jerry and Friends

Q: 'My Guy' – Mary Wells
A: 'My Girl' – Temptations

Q: 'Wolverton Mountain' – Claude King
A: 'I'm The Girl From Wolverton Mountain' – Jo Ann Campbell

Q: 'Walk On By' – Leroy Van Dyke
A: 'I'll Just Walk On By' – Margie Singleton

Q: 'Please Help Me I'm Falling' – Hank Locklin
A: '(I Can't Help It) I'm Falling Too' – Skeeter Davis

Q: 'Breaking Up Is Hard To Do' – Neil Sedaka
A: 'Making Up Is Fun Too' – Tina Powers

Q: 'My Guy' – Mary Wells
A: 'Your Guy' – Bobby Wells (no relation)

Q: 'Duke Of Earl' – Gene Chandler
A: 'I Stopped The Duke Of Earl' – Up-Fronts

Q: 'There Goes My Baby' – The Drifters
A: 'I Found My Baby' – The Fabulous Fabulairs

Q: **'Southern Man'** – Neil Young
A: **'Sweet Home Alabama'** – Lynyrd Skynyrd

Q: **'The Monster Mash'** – Bobby 'Boris' Pickett and The Crypt-Kickers
A: **'The Vampire Ball'** – Mann Drake

Q: **'Sixteen Tons'** – 'Tennessee' Ernie Ford
A: **'Sixteen Pounds'** – Gloria Becker

Q: **'Short Shorts'** – The Royal Teens
A: **'Who Wears Hotpants'** – Cook E. Jarr

Q: **'A Boy Named Sue'** – Johnny Cash
A: **'A Girl Named Harry'** – Joni Credit

Q: **'My Generation'** – The Who
A: **'My Ken-L Ration'** – The Flying Saucers
and later
A: **'Your Generation'** – Generation X

Q: **'Tom Dooley'** – Lonnie Donegan
A: **'Tom Get's The Last Laugh'** – The Balladeers

Q: **'Speedy Gonzalez'** – Pat Boone
A: **'Juana Ball'** – Mel Blanc

Q: **'Charlie Brown'** – Coasters
A: **'Betty Brown'** – Jayhawks

Q: **'Down Home Girl'** – Alvin Robinson
A: **'I'm Just A Down Home Girl'** – Ad Libs

Q: **'My Boomerang Won't Come Back'** – Charlie Drake
A: **'Our Spaceman Came Back'** – Jeff Hughes

Q: **'Surf City'** – Jan and Dean
A: **'Leavin''** – Dave and The Saints

Q: **'I'll Bring It On Home To Me'** – Sam Cooke
A: **'I'll Bring It On Home To You'** – Carla Thomas

Q: **'Deck Of Cards'** – Wink Martindale
A: **'High School Year Book'** – Ray Stevens

Q: **'They're Coming To Take Me Away Ha-Ha'** – Napoleon XIV
A: **'Don't Take Me Back Oh No'** – Henry IX
also
A: **'I'm Normal'** – The Emperor

Q: **'Hello Muddah Hello Faddah'** – Allan Sherman
A: **'Hello Melvin (This Is Momma)'** – Sandra Gould

Q: **'Stagger Lee'** – Lloyd Price
A: **'The Trial Of Stagger Lee'** – Stella Johnson

Q: **'Runaround Sue'** – Dion and The Belmonts
A: **'I'm No Runaround'** – Ginger and The Snaps
also
A: **'Runaround Sue's Getting Married'** – Danny Jordan

Q: **'Mack The Knife'** – Bobby Darin
A: **'Mackie Got Married'** – Barry Frank

Q: **'Little Sister'** – Elvis Presley
A: **'Hey Memphis'** – LaVern Baker

Q: **'Rag Doll'** – The Four Seasons
A: **'Society Girl'** – The Rag Dolls

Q: **'Tiptoe Thru' The Tulips With Me'** – Tiny Tim
A: **'Get Off My Tulips'** – The Caretakers
and let's not forget
A: **'Tiptoe To The Gas Pumps'** – Tiny Tim

Q: **'He's A Rebel'** – The Crystals
A: **'I'm Your Rebel'** – Paul Thorton

Q: **'Mama Said Knock You Out'** – LL Cool J
A: **'Death Blow'** – Kool Moe Dee

Q: **'Calendar Girl'** – Neil Sedaka
A: **'Calendar Boy'** – Stacey Ames

Q: **'Itsy Bitsy Teenie Weenie Yellow Polka Dot Bikini'** – Brian Hyland
A: **'Four Shy Girls'** – The Girlfriends

Q: **'California Girls'** – The Beach Boys
A: **'Ocean City Girls'** – Kagle and Klender

Q: **'Shop Around'** – Smokey Robinson and The Miracles
A: **'Don't Let Him Shop Around'** – Debbie Dean

Q: **'Get A Job'** – The Silhouettes
A: **'Got A Job'** – Smokey Robinson and The Miracles
also
A: **'I Found A Job'** – The Heartbeats

Q: **'Mrs Brown You've Got A Lovely Daughter'** – Herman's Hermits
A: **'Mrs James I'm Mrs Brown's Daughter'** – Connie Holiday

Q: **'Battle Of New Orleans'** – Lonnie Donegan
A: **'The Battle Of Trip-O-Lee'** – Jerry Wilson

Q: **'Sherry'** – The Four Seasons
A: **'Jerry, I'm Your Sherry'** – Tracey Dey

Q: **'Thriller'** – Michael Jackson
A: **'Dear Michael'** – Kim Fields

Q: **'Mother-in-Law'** – Ernie K Doe
A: **'Brother-in-Law (He's A Moocher)'** – Paul Peek
also
A: **'My Mother-in-Law (Is In My Hair Again)'** – Ernie K Doe
and finally
A: **'Husband-in-Law'** – Jim Nesbitt

Q: **'Eve Of Destruction'** – Barry McGuire
A: **'The Dawn Of Correction'** – The Spokesmen

Q: **'Alley Oop'** – Hollywood Argyles
A: **'Alley Oop Was A Two-Dab Man'** – Gary Paxton (lead singer with the Hollywood Argyles)

Q: **'It's Only Rock 'n' Roll'** – The Rolling Stones
A: **'I Love Rock 'n' Roll'** – Joan Jett and The Blackhearts

Q: **'Maybellene'** – Chuck Berry
A: **'Come Back, Maybellene'** – Big John Greer

Q: **'Dreamin''** – Johnny Burnette
A: **'I'm Still Dreamin''** – Johnny Burnette

Q: **'Can't Do Sixty No More'** – The Du-Droppers
A: **'Sixty Minute Man'** – Dominoes

Q: **'Shaft'** – Isaac Hayes
A: **'Son Of Shaft'** – The Bar-Kays

Q: **'Relax'** – Frankie Goes To Hollywood
A: **'Relapse'** – Freddie Goes To Cricklewood

Q: **''Ullo John Got A New Motor?'** – Alexei Sayle
A: **'Hello Alexei'** – John

Q: **'I Wonder If I Take You Home'** – Lisa Lisa and Cult Jam with Full Force
A: **'Let Me Take You Home – Lisa Lisa'** – Mac, Mac with The Jammalott Kingdom

Q: **'Pass The Kouchie'** – The Mighty Diamonds
A: **'Pass The Dutchie'** – Musical Youth

Q: **'At The Hop'** – Danny and the Juniors
A: **'Back To The Hop'** – Danny and the Juniors

Q: **'Harper Valley P.T.A'** – Jeannie C. Riley
A: **'Continuing Story Of Harper Valley P.T.A'** – Dee Mullins
also
A: **'Harper Valley P.T.A (Later That Same Day)'** – Ben Colder

Q: **'Don't Play That Song'** – Aretha Franklin
A: **'Aretha, Sing One For Me'** – George Jackson

Q: **'Ballad Of The Green Berets'** – Staff Sergeant Barry Sadler
A: **'Ballad Of The Yellow Berets'** – Bob Seger

'A DIFFERENT BEAT'
Songs with the Same Title

The following fifty songs have one thing, and one thing only, in common –
they each share their title with that of a song recorded by a decidedly different
artist. Should you have any doubts about this then take a listen to two songs,
both of which happen to have the title 'Don't Cry'. The first was recorded in
1988 by Boy George, the second in 1991 by Guns N' Roses. As you might
expect, they are most definitely not the same song.

1. **'All My Love'** – Cliff Richard (1967)
   – Queen Pen (1998)
2. **'All Or Nothing'** – Small Faces (1966)
   – Cher (1999)
3. **'All Over The World'** – Françoise Hardy (1965)
   – ELO (1980)
4. **'Alone'** – Petula Clark (1957)
   – Big Country (1993)
5. **'Angel'** – Rod Stewart (1957)
   – Massive Attack (1998)
6. **'Around The World'** – Big Crosby (1957)
   – East 17 (1994)
7. **'Atmosphere'** – Russ Abbot (1984)
   – Joy Davision (1998)
8. **'Bad Boys'** – Marty Wilde (1959)
   – Gloria Estefan (1986)
9. **'Blue Eyes'** – Don Partridge (1968)
   – The Wedding Present (1992)
10. **'Blue Monday'** – Fats Domino (1957)
    – New Order (1983)
11. **'Body Language'** – The Dooleys (1980)
    – Queen (1982)
12. **'Brave New World'** – David Essex (1978)
    – New Model Army (1985)
13. **'Breakaway'** – Tracey Ullman (1983)
    – ZZ Top (1994)
14. **'Breathe'** – Prodigy (1996)
    – Kylie Minogue (1998)
15. **'Breathless'** – Jerry Lee Lewis (1958)
    – Corrs (2000)

16. **'Burn Baby Burn'** – Hudson-Ford (1974)
    – ASH (2001)
17. **'Butterfly'** – Andy Williams (1957)
    – Crazy Town (2001)
18. **'Carrie'** – Cliff Richard (1980)
    – Europe (1987)
19. **'Casanova'** – Petula Clark (1963)
    – Ultimate Kaos (1997)
20. **'Cherry Pie'** – Jess Conrad (1960)
    – Warrant (1990)
21. **'China Doll'** – Slim Whitman (1955)
    – Julian Cope (1989)
22. **'Cold As Ice'** – Foreigner (1978)
    – M.O.P. (2001)
23. **'Crazy'** – Patsy Cline (1990)
    Mark Morrison (1995)
24. **'Dance With Me'** – Drifters (1960)
    – Debelah Morgan (2001)
25. **'Daydreamer'** – David Cassidy (1973)
    – Menswear (1995)
26. **'Doctor Doctor'** – UFO (1979)
    – Thompson Twins
27. **'Don't Cry'** – Boy George (1988)
    – Guns N' Roses (1991)
28. **'Don't Give Up'** – Peter Gabriel & Kate Bush (1986)
    – Chicane featuring Bryan Adams (2001)
29. **'Don't Stop'** – Fleetwood Mac (1977)
    – ATB (1999)
30. **'Downtown'** – Petula Clark (1964)
    – SWV (1994)
31. **'Fever'** – Peggy Lee (1958)
    – Starsailor (2001)
32. **'I Need You'** – BVSMP (1988)
    – LeAnn Rimes (2001)
33. **'Money'** – Flying Lizards (1979)
    – Jamelia (2000)
34. **'Music'** – John Miles (1976)
    – Madonna (2000)
35. **'My Love'** – Petual Clark (1966)
    – Kele Le Roc (1999)
36. **'Never Had A Dream Come True** – Steve Wonder (1970)
    – S Club 7 (2000)

37. **'On The Beach'** – Cliff Richard (1964)
          – York (2000)
38. **'Rise'** – Herb Alpert (1979)
          – Gabrielle (2000)
39. **'Seven Days'** – Anne Shelton (1956)
          – Craig David (2000)
40. **'Stay'** – Hollies (1963)
          – Stephen Gately (2001)
41. **'Straight Up'** – Paula Abdul (1989)
          – Chantée Moore (2001)
42. **'Too Much'** – Elvis Presley (1957)
          – Bros (1989)
43. **'Top Of The World** – The Carpenters (1973)
          – Van Halen (1991)
44. **'Tower Of Strength'** – Frankie Vaughan (1961)
          – Mission (1988)
45. **'Walk Away'** – Matt Monro (1964)
          – Sisters Of Mercy (1984)
46. **'We're In This Together'** – Simply Red (1996)
          – Nine Inch Nails (1999)
47. **'Who's That Girl?'** – Flying Pickets (1984)
          – Madonna (1987)
48. **'Why?'** – Anthony Newley (1960)
          – Mis-teeq (2001)
49. **'You Don't Know Me'** – Ray Charles (1962)
          – Armand Van Helden (1999)
50. **'You're The One'** – Petula Clark (1965)
          – SWV (1996)

'BEG, STEAL OR BORROW'
Songs Containing 'Samples'

Where would today's music be without the benefit of the ubiquitous 'sample'? The sample, i.e. a catchy hook, melody, beat or vocal line lifted from the work of another artist, emerged during the eighties with the records of hip-hop and rap artists such as Grandmaster Flash, the Sugarhill Gang and Afrika Bambaataa to name but three.

Today the sample has become a mainstay in the arsenal of the contemporary musician. It finds a place in the work of artists as diverse as Robbie Williams and Armand Van Helden.

Below we present a list of artists and their hits (shown in bold print), all of which owe more than a passing nod to the work of others:

A+ 'Enjoy Yourself'
Walter Murphy And The Big Apple Band 'A Fifth Of Beethoven'

A.T.F.C. presents Onephatdeeva 'In And Out Of My Life'
Adeva 'In And Out Of My Life'
Fatboy Slim 'Right Here Right Now'

Addis Black Widow 'Innocent'
Brothers Johnson 'Running For Your Love'

All Seeing I 'Beat Goes On'
Buddy Rich (with his 12 year old daughter) 'Beat Goes On'

Allure featuring Nas 'Head Over Heels'
MC Shan 'The Bridge'

Peter André 'All Night All Right'
A Taste Of Honey 'Boogie Oogie Oogie'

Ant and Dec 'Shout'
Lou Reed 'Walk On The Wild Side'

Apollo Four Forty 'Ain't Talkin' 'Bout Dub'
Van Halen 'Ain't Talkin' 'Bout Love'

Rob Base and D.J. EZ Rock 'It Takes Two'
Lyn Collins 'Think (About It)'

Basement Jaxx 'Red Alert'
Locksmith 'Far Beyond'

BBG 'Snappiness'
Soul II Soul 'Happiness'

Beastie Boys 'Alive'
Boogie Down Productions 'I'm Still '

Beck 'Loser'
Dr. John 'Walking On Guilded Splinters'

Beck 'Where It's At'
Mantronix 'Get Up And Dance'

Beck 'Devil's Haircut'
Them 'Out Of Sight'

Bedlam 'Da-Force'
Real Thing 'Can You Feel The Force'

Bellini 'Samba De Janeiro'
Airto 'Celebration Suite'

Black Box 'I Got The Vibration / A Positive Vibration'
Diana Ross 'Love Hangover'

Blackstreet 'Fix'
Grandmaster Flash 'The Message'

Blackstreet featuring Dr. Dre 'No Diggity'
Bill Withers 'Grandma's Hand's'

Memphis Bleek featuring Jay-Z 'What You Think Of That'
Keith Mansfield 'High Velocity'

Mary J. Blige 'You Don't Have To Worry'
James Brown 'Papa Don't Take No Mess'

Mary J. Blige 'Be Happy'
Curtis Mayfield 'You're Too Good To Me'

Mary J. Blige 'Love Is All We Need'
Rick James 'Moonchild'

Mary J. Blige 'Deep Inside'
Elton John 'Bennie And The Jets'

Blueboy 'Sandman'
Undisputed Truth 'You + Me = Love'

Blueboy 'Remember Me'
Marlena Shaw 'Woman Of The Ghetto'

Bone Thugs-N-Harmony 'Tha Crossroads'
Isley Brothers 'Make Me Say It Again'

Betty Boo 'Doin' The Do'
Reparata And The Delrons 'Captain Of Your Ship'

Betty Boo 'Let Me Take You There'
Four Tops 'It's All In The Game'

Boyz II Men 'Thank You'
Doug E. Fresh 'La-Di-Da-Di'

Brock Landars 'S.M.D.U.'
Blur 'Song 2'; Prodigy 'Smack My Bitch Up'

Foxy Brown 'I'll Be'
Rene And Angela 'I'll Be Good'
Blondie 'Rapture'

James Brown 'Funk On Ah Roll'
James Brown 'Hot Pants'

Kenny 'Dope' presents The Bucketheads 'The Bomb (These Sounds Fall Into My Head)'
Chicago 'Streetplayer'

Kenny 'Dope' presents The Bucketheads 'Got Myself Together'
Brass Construction 'Movin' '

Bus Stop 'Kung Fu Fighting'
Carl Douglas 'Kung Fu Fighting'

Capriccio 'Everybody Get Up'
Jazzy Dee 'Get On Up'

Mariah Carey 'Fantasy'
Tom Tom Club 'Genius Of Love'

Mariah Carey 'Honey'
Treacherous 'The Body Rock'

Mariah Carey featuring Jay-Z 'Heartbreaker'
Stacy Lattisaw 'Attack Of The Name Game'

Junior Cartier 'Women Beat Their Men'
Dominatrix 'The Dominatrix Sleeps Tonight'

Cassius 'Cassius 99'
Donna Summer 'Love Is Just A Breath Away'

Cassius 'Feeling For You'
Gwen McCrae 'All The Love That I'm Giving'

Neneh Cherry 'Buddy X'
Juicy 'Sugar Free'

Coolio 'I Remember'
Floaters 'Float On'

Coolio featuring L.V. 'Gangsta's Paradise'
Stevie Wonder 'Pastime Paradise'

Coolio '1,2,3,4 (Sumpin' New)'
Evasions 'Wikka Wrap'

Coolio 'Ooh La La'
Grace Jones 'Pull Up To The Bumper'

Deborah Cox 'It's Over Now'
Harold Melvin and The Blue Notes 'Bad Luck'

Credit To The Nation 'Tacky Love Song'
Radiohead 'High And Dry'

Cypress Hill 'Interlude'
Sly Johnson 'Is It Because I'm Black'

Dimples D 'Sucker DJ'
TV Theme 'I Dream Of Jeannie'

D-Influence 'Good Lover'
Eleanore Mills 'Mr.Right'

D.J.H. featuring Stefy 'Think About . . .' ALSO 'Move Your Love'
Aretha Franklin 'Rock-A-Lott' (both tracks sample this)

Da Click 'We Are Da Click'
Tom Browne 'Funkin' For Jamaica'

Da Fool 'No Good'
SIL 'Blue Oyster'

Daddy's Favourite 'I Feel Good Things For You'
Patrice Rushen 'Haven't You Heard?'

Dario G 'Sunchyme'
Dream Academy 'Life In A Northern Town'

Dee-Lite 'Groove Is In The Heart'
Herbie Hancock 'Bring Down The Birds'

De Funk featuring F45 'Pleasure Love'
Earth, Wind And Fire 'September'

De La Soul 'Eye Know'
Otis Redding '(Sittin' On) The Dock Of The Bay'

De La Soul 'Breakadawn'
Michael Jackson 'I Can't Help It'

De La Soul '3 Is The Magic Number'
Bob Dorough 'The Magic Number'

De La Soul 'Say No Go'
Hall & Oates 'I Can't Go For That'

Definition Of Sound 'Boom Boom'
Moody Blues 'Go Now'

Disco Anthem 'Scream'
Farley Jackmaster Funk 'Love Can't Turn Around'

D.J. Eric presents 'We Are Love'
Alexander Hope 'Brothers & Sisters'

D.J. Kool 'Let Me Clear My Throat'
Kool And The Gang 'Hollywood Swingin''

D.J. Manta 'Holding On'
Orchestral Manoeuvres In The Dark 'Maid Of Orleans (The Waltz Of Joan Of Arc)'

D.J. Sakin And Friends 'Protect Your Mind (For The Love Of A Princess)'
James Horner 'For The Love Of A Princess' (from the film *Braveheart*)

D.J. Sakin And Friends 'Nomansland (David's Song)'
TV Theme 'The Adventures Of David Belfour'

D.J. Supreme 'Tha Wildstyle'
Hijack 'The Badman Is Robbin''

DMX 'Slippin''
Grover Washington Jr 'Moonstream'

DNA 'Rebel Woman'
David Bowie 'Rebel Rebel'

Dream Warriors 'My Definition Of A Boombastic Jazz Style'
Quincy Jones 'Soul Bossa Nova' (Original Mix)

Dust Junkys 'Nothin' Personal'
Fleetwood Mac 'Oh Well'

Elate 'Somebody Like You'
Clannad 'Theme From Harry's Game'

Eminem 'My Name Is' (2)
Labi Siffre 'I Got The'

Eminem 'Stan'
Dido 'Thank You'

Escrima 'Train Of Thought'
King Bee 'Back By Dope Demand'

49ers 'Touch Me'
Alisha Warren 'Touch Me'

Faith Evans featuring Puff Daddy 'All Night Long'
Unlimited Touch 'I Hear Music In The Street'

Everlast 'Ends'
Wu Tang Clan 'C.R.E.A.M.'

Eyes Cream 'Fly Away (Bye Bye)'
Sylvester 'You Make Me Feel Mighty Real'

Fatboy Slim 'The Rockafeller Skank'
Just Brothers 'Sliced Tomatoes'

Fatboy Slim 'Praise You'
Camille Yarborough 'Take Yo Praise'

Cevin Fisher '(You Got Me) Burning Up'
Loleatta Holloway 'Love Sensation'

Five 'Everybody Get Up'
Joan Jett And The Blackhearts 'I Love Rock And Roll'

Five 'If Ya Gettin' Down'
Indeep 'Last Night A DJ Saved My Life'

Fluke 'Electric Guitar'
Jimi Hendrix 'Crosstown Traffic'

Frigid Vinegar 'Dogmonaut 2000 (Is There Anybody Out There?)'
Les Reed (brass arrangement of) 'It's Not Unusual'

Fugees 'Fu-Gee-La'
Teena Marie 'Ooh La La La'

Fugees 'Ready Or Not'
Enya 'Song For Bodecia'

Fugees featuring A Tribe Called Quest, Busta Rhymes And Forte 'Rumble In The Jungle'
Abba 'The Name Of The Game'

Fun Lovin' Criminals 'Big Night Out'
Tom Petty 'American Girl'
Marshall Tucker Band 'Can't You See'

Future Sound Of London 'My Kingdom'
Vangelis 'Rachel's Song'

Warren G 'Do You See'
Junior 'Mama Used To Say'

Gang Starr 'Love Sick'
Young Holt Unlimited 'Ain't There Something Money Can't Buy'

Garbage 'Stupid Girl'
The Clash 'Train In Vain'

Garbage 'Special'
The Pretenders 'The Talk Of The Town'

Michelle Gayle 'Happy Just To Be With You'
Chic 'Good Times'

Gems For Jem 'Lifting Me Higher'
Evelyn Thomas 'High Energy'

Ghostface Killah 'All That I Got Is You'
Jackson Five 'Maybe Tomorrow'

Ginuwine 'What's So Different?'
The Monkees 'Valleri'

Glamma Kid 'Bills 2 Pay'
Blondie 'Rapture'
Visage 'Fade To Grey'

Goldie 'Believe'
Loose Ends 'Hanging On A String'

Alex Gopher 'The Child'
Billie Holiday 'God Bless The Child'

Grandmaster Flash 'Adventures Of Flash On The Wheels Of Steel'
Chic 'Good Times'

Groove Armada 'If Everybody Looked The Same'
Chi-Lites 'We Are Neighbours'
A Tribe Called Quest 'Ince Again (The Twister Mix)'

Groove Armada 'At The River'
Patti Page 'Old Cape Cod'

Scott Grooves 'Mothership Reconnection'
Parliament 'Mothership Connection' (Live Version)

Gusto 'Disco's Revenge'
Harvey Mason 'Groovin' You'

Handbaggers 'U Found Out
Depeche Mode 'Just Can't Get Enough'

Harmonix 'Landslide'
U2 'Where The Streets Have No Name'

Heavy D And The Boyz 'This Is Your Night'
Kool And The Gang 'Ladies Night'
George Benson 'Give Me The Night'

Hed Boys 'Girls + Boys'
Jessie Veles 'Girls Out On The Floor'

Pete Heller 'Big Love'
Stargard 'Wear It Out'

Hinda Hicks 'If You Want Me'
Kool And The Gang 'Too Hot'

Lauryn Hill 'Ex-Factor'
Wu Tang Clan 'Can It All Be So Simple'

Honky 'What's Goin' Down'
Ian Dury 'Sex & Drugs & Rock & Roll'

House Of Pain 'Jump Around'
Bob & Earl 'Harlem Shuffle'

House Of Pain 'Who's The Man'
David Bowie 'Fame'

House Of Pain 'On Point'
Cannonball Adderly 'Inside Straight'

House Of Pain 'It Ain't A Crime'
Red Hot Chili Peppers 'Under The Bridge'

Huff 'Help Me Make It'
Gladys Knight 'Help Me Make It Through The Night' (live version)

Hyperlogic 'Only Me'
U2 'New Year's Day'
Alyson Williams 'Sleep Talk'

Hysteric Ego 'Time To Get Back'
N-Joi 'Adrenalin'

Ice Cube 'Bop Gun (One Nation)'
Funkadelic 'One Nation Under A Groove'

Ice-T 'Gotta Lotta Love'
Mike Oldfield 'Tubular Bells'

Ice-T 'I Must Stand'
Portishead 'Numb'

Ice-T 'The Lane'
Jean Jaques Perrey 'Eva'

Imajin 'No Doubt'
The Spinners 'It's A Natural Affair'

Jay-Z featuring Mary J. Blige 'Can't Knock The Hustle'
Marcus Miller 'Much Too Much'

Jay-Z 'Hard Knock Life (Ghetto Anthem)'
Original Broadway Cast of *Annie* 'It's A Hard Knock Life'

Jazzy Jeff And The Fresh Prince 'Can't Wait To Be With You'
Luther Vandross 'Never Too Much'

Jazzy Jeff And The Fresh Prince 'Lovely Daze'
Bill Withers 'Lovely Day'

Wyclef Jean 'We Trying To Stay Alive'
Bee Gees 'Stayin' Alive'

Jonestown 'Sweet Thang'
Sister Sledge 'He's The Greatest Dancer'

Montell Jordan 'Somethin' 4 Da Honeyz'
Kook And The Gang 'Summer Madness'

Jungle Brothers 'V.I.P.'
TV Theme 'I Dream Of Jeannie'

Jungle Brothers 'Get Down'
Kool And The Gang 'Get Down On It'

Kaleef 'Trials Of Life'
The Pretenders 'Brass In Pocket'

Kaleef 'Sands Of Time'
Clannad 'Theme From Harry's Game'

R. Kelly 'Summer Bunnies'
The Gap Band 'Outstanding'

R. Kelly featuring NAS 'Did You Ever Think'
Curtis Mayfield 'Right On For The Darkness'

Kiss AMC 'A Bit Of . . .'
U2 'Pride (In The Name Of Love)'

KLF 'What Time Is Love? (Live At Trancentral)'
MC5 'Kick Out The Jams'

Klubbheads 'Discohopping'
Patrick Hernandez 'Born To Be Alive'

Beverley Knight 'Made It Back 99'
Chic 'Good Times'

Kon Kan 'I Beg Your Pardon'
Lynn Anderson 'Rose Garden'
GQ 'Disco Nights (Rock Freak)'

Kris Kross 'Alright'
Slave 'Just A Touch Of Love'

Len 'Steal My Sunshine' (8)
Andrea True Connection 'More More More'

Lighter Shade Of Brown 'Hey D.J.'
World Famous Supreme Team 'Hey D.J.'

Lil' Kim 'Crush On You'
Jeff Lorber 'Rain Dance'

Lil' Kim featuring Puff Daddy 'No Time'
Lyn Collins 'Just Take Me As I Am'

Lisa Marie Experience 'Keep On Jumping'
Musique 'Keep On Jumpin'

LL Cool J 'How I'm Comin''
Bobby Byrd 'Hot Pants – I'm Coming – I'm Coming – I'm Coming'

LL Cool J 'Doin' It'
Grace Jones 'My Jamaican Guy'

LL Cool J 'Phenomenon'
Bill Withers 'Who Is He And What Is He To You?'

LL Cool J 'Father'
George Michael 'Father Figure'

Tone Loc 'Wild Thing'
Van Halen 'Jamie's Cryin''

Tone Loc 'I Got It Goin' On'
Tom Browne 'Funkin' For Jamaica'

Loop Da Loop 'Hazel'
Stetasonic 'Sally'

Monie Love 'I Can Do This'
The Whispers 'And The Beat Goes On'

Luniz 'I Got 5 On It'
Timex Social Club 'Rumours'

Luniz 'Playa Hata'
Bobby Caldwell 'What You Won't Do For Love'

Madonna 'Erotica'
Kook And The Gang 'Jungle Boogie'

Madonna 'Bedtime Story'
Main Source 'What You Need'

Mankey 'Believe In Me'
Yazoo 'Situation'

Mantronix 'Strictly Business'
Eric Clapton 'I Shot The Sheriff'

Marc Et Claude 'I Need Your Lovin''
The Korgis 'Everybody's Gotta Learn Sometime'

Ma$e 'Feels So Good'
Kool And The Gang 'Hollywood Swinging'

Ma$e featuring Blackstreet 'Get Ready'
Shalamar 'A Night To Remember'

Massive Attack 'Be Thankful'
William De Vaughn 'Be Thankful For What You've Got'

Massive Attack 'Risingson'
Velvet Underground 'I Found A Reason'

Massive Attack 'Safe From Harm'
Billy Cobham 'Stratus'

MC Hammer 'Can't Touch This'
Rick James 'Superfreak'

MC Lyte 'Cold Rock A Party (Bad Boy Remix)'
Diana Ross 'Upside Down'

MC Lyte featuring Xscape 'Keep On, Keepin' On'
Michael Jackson 'Liberian Girl'

M.C. Skat Kat And The Stray Mob 'Skat Strut'
Earth, Wind And Fire 'Let's Groove'

George Michael 'Fast Love'
Patrice Rushen 'Forget Me Nots'

Mirrorball 'Given Up'
Three Degrees 'Givin' Up Givin' In'

Moby 'Honey'
Bessie Jones 'Sometimes'

Moby 'Bodyrock'
Spoony G And The Treacherous 'Love Rap'

Moby 'Natural Blues'
Vera Hall 'Troubled So Hard'

Modjo 'Lady'
Chic 'Soup For One'

Monica 'Don't Take It Personal (Just One Of Dem Days)'
LL Cool J 'Back Seat (Of My Jeep)'

Monica 'Like This And Like That'
Sugarhill Gang 'Spoonin' Rap'

Monica 'The First Night'
Diana Ross 'Love Hangover'

Monifah 'Touch It'
Laid Back 'White Horse'

Hollis P. Monroe 'I'm Lonely'
Terence Trent D'Arby 'And I Need To Be With Someone Tonight'

David Morales presents The Face 'Needin' U'
Rare Pleasure 'Let Me Down Easy'

Mrs Wood 'Joanna' (Sash Remix) (34)
Alison Price 'Feel My Love'

Mr. Roy 'Something About U (Can't Be Beat)' (Strike Remix)
Nikita Warren 'I Need You'

Keith Murray featuring LL Cool J 'Incredible'
James Brown 'Sportin' Life'

Nas 'It Ain't Hard To Tell'
Michael Jackson 'Human Nature'
Kool And The Gang 'N.T.'

Nas 'Street Dreams'
Eurythmics 'Sweet Dreams'

Naughty By Nature 'O.P.P.'
Jackson Five 'ABC'

Naughty By Nature featuring Zhane 'Jamboree'
Benny Golson 'I'm Always Dancin' To The Music'

New Edition 'Hit Me Off'
Black Moon 'I Gotcha Opin'

New Edition 'Something About You'
Edie Brickell And The New Bohemians 'What I Am'

No Authority 'Don't Stop'
Teddy Riley 'Don't Stop'

Notorious B.I.G. 'Big Poppa'
Isley Brothers 'Between The Sheets'

Notorious B.I.G. featuring Puff Daddy and Ma$e 'Mo Money Mo Problems'
Diana Ross 'I'm Coming Out'

Nuttin' Nyce 'Down 4 Whateva'
Soul II Soul 'Back To Life'

187 Lockdown 'Gunman' (16)
Ennio Morricone 'Sixty Seconds To What'

Offspring 'Pretty Fly (For A White Guy)'
Def Leppard 'Rock Of Ages'

Old Skool Orchestra 'B-Boy Hump'
Engelbert Humperdinck 'Can't Take My Eyes Off You'

Shaquille O'Neal 'I'm Outstanding'
The Gap Band 'Outstanding'
Yarbrough & Peoples 'Don't Stop The Music'
Tom Browne 'Funkin' For Jamaica'

Orbital 'Style'
Suzi Quatro 'Devil Gate Drive'
Dollar 'Mirror Mirror'

Ozomatli 'Cut Chemist Suite' (58)
Jurassic 5 'Unified Rebelution'

Pacifica 'Lost In The Translation (Heart Of Glass)'
Blondie 'Heart Of Glass'

Perfect Phase 'Horny Horns'
49ers featuring Anne Marie Smith 'Move Your Feet'

Perpetual Motion 'Keep On Dancin' (Let's Go)'
D.O.P. 'Here I Go'

Pharcyde 'Passin' Me By'
Quincy Jones 'Summer In The City'

Pharcyde 'Runnin' '
Bob Marley 'Running Away'

Phats and Small 'Turn Around'
Toney Lee 'Reach Up'

Phats and Small 'Tonite' (11)
Delegations 'Heartache No.9'

Phoebe One 'Get On It'
Rod Stewart 'Baby Jane'

PJ 'Happy Days' (Remix)
Northend featuring Michelle Wallace 'Tee's Happy'

PM Dawn 'Set Adrift On Memory Bliss'
Spandau Ballet 'True'

PM Dawn 'Looking Through Patient Eyes'
George Michael 'Father Figure'

PM Dawn 'Downtown Venus'
Deep Purple 'Hush'

PM Dawn 'Gotta Be . . . Movin' On Up'
Imagination 'Just An Illusion'

Portishead 'Glory Box'
Isaac Hayes 'Ike's Rap II'

Powerhouse 'Rhythm Of The Night'
DeBarge 'Rhythm Of The Night'

Maxi Priest featuring Shaggy 'That Girl'
Booker T And The M.G.'s 'Green Onions'

Prince '7'
Lowell Fulsom 'Tramp'

Prodigy 'Firestarter'
Art Of Noise 'Close To The Edit'

Prodigy 'Out Of Space'
Max Romeo and The Upsetters 'Chase The Devil'

Progress presents The Boy Wunda 'Everybody'
Madonna 'Papa Don't Preach'

Public Enemy 'Fight The Power'
James Brown 'Funky Drummer'

Public Enemy 'He Got Game'
Buffalo Springfield 'For What It's Worth'

Puff Daddy featuring Ma$e 'Can't Nobody Hold Me Down'
Grandmaster Flash And The Furious Five 'The Message'

Puff Daddy and Faith Evans featuring 112 'I'll Be Missing You'
The Police 'Every Breath You Take'

Puff Daddy and The Family featuring The Notorious B.I.G. and Ma$e 'Been Around The World'
David Bowie 'Let's Dance'
Lisa Stansfield 'All Around The World'

Puff Daddy featuring Hurricane G 'P.E. 2000'
Public Enemy 'Public Enemy No. 1'

Puff Daddy featuring Mario Winans 'Best Friend'
Christopher Cross 'Sailing'

Queen Latifah 'U.N.I.T.Y.'
The Crusaders 'Message From The Inner City'

Queen Pen featuring Eric Williams Of Blackstreet 'All My Love'
Luther Vandross 'Never Too Much'

Queen Pen 'It's True'
Spandau Ballet 'True'

R.I.P. Productions 'The Chant (We R)'
Lennie De-Ice 'We Are I E'

Rae And Christian featuring Veba 'All I Ask'
Brian and Brenda Russell 'World Called Love'

Rakim 'Stay A While'
Loose End 'Stay A Little While Child'

Rappin' 4-Tay 'I'll Be Around'
The Detroit Spinners 'I'll Be Around'

Redman 'Made It Back '99'
Chic 'Good Times'

Redman 'Da Goodness'
Duke Ellington 'Caravan'

Nicole Renee 'Strawberry'
Grover Washington Jr 'Paradise'

Rest Assured 'Treat Infamy'
Verve 'Bitter Sweet Symphony'

Ruffneck featuring Yavahn
Yello 'Bostich'

Raphael Saadiq and Q-Tip 'Get Involved'
The Intruders 'I'll Always Love My Mama'

Sabres Of Paradise 'Wilmot'
Wilmot Houdini And The Night Owls – calypso record from 1929

Salt 'n' Pepa 'The Brick Track Versus Gitty Up'
Pink Floyd 'Another Brick In The Wall'

Scarface featuring Dr. Dre, Ice Cube and Too Short
Indeep 'Last Night A DJ Saved My Life

S Express 'Theme From S Express'
Rose Royce 'Is It Love You're After?'

Shaft 'Mucho Mambo'
Rosemary Clooney 'Sway'

Shaggy featuring Grand Puba 'Why You Treat Me So Bad'
Bob Marley 'Mr. Brown'

Shaggy featuring Marsha 'Piece Of My Heart'
Erma Franklin 'Piece Of My Heart'

Shaggy 'Boombastic'
King Floyd 'Baby Let Me Kiss You'

Shut Up And Dance 'Raving I'm Raving'
Marc Cohn 'Walking In Memphis'

Shut Up And Dance 'Save It 'Til The Morning After'
Duran Duran 'Save A Prayer'

Shut Up And Dance featuring Richie Davis and Professor T 'I Love U'
Perez Prado 'Guaglione'

Size 9 'I'm Ready'
B-Beat Girls 'For The Same Man'
Raw Silk 'Do It To The Music'

Slacker 'Your Face'
Roberta Flack 'First Time I Ever Saw Your Face'

Will Smith 'Men In Black'
Patrice Rushen 'Forget Me Nots'

Will Smith 'Just Cruisin' '
Al Johnson 'I'm Back For More'

Will Smith 'Getting' Jiggy Wit It'
Sister Sledge 'He's The Greatest Dancer'

Will Smith 'Miami'
The Whispers 'And The Beat Goes On'

Will Smith featuring Dru Hill 'Wild Wild West'
Stevie Wonder 'I Wish'

Snap 'The Power'
Loleatta Holloway 'Love's Gonna Get You'

Snoop Doggy Dogg 'Gin And Juice'
Slave 'Watching You'

Soho 'Hippychick'
The Smiths 'How Soon Is Now'

Solo 'Heaven'
Isley Brothers 'Between The Sheets'

Soulsearcher 'Can't Get Enough'
Gary's Gang 'Let Love Dance Tonight'

Sounds Of Blackness 'Everything's Gonna Be Alright'
Isaac Hayes 'Walk On By'

Spacedust 'Let's Get Down'
Chic 'I Want Your Love'

Spiller 'Groove Jet'
Carol Williams 'Love Is You'

Sporty Thievz 'No Pigeons'
TLC 'No Scrubs'
Sporty Thievz 'Cheapskate'

Stardust 'Music Sounds Better With You'
Chaka Khan 'Fate'

Stereo MC's 'Connected'
Jimmy 'Bo' Horne 'Let Me (Let Me Be Your Lover)'

Stetsasonic 'Talkin' All That Jazz'
Lonnie Liston Smith 'Expansions'

Stretch And Vern present 'Maddog' 'I'm Alive'
Earth, Wind and Fire with The Emotions 'Boogie Wonderland'

Stretch And Vern present 'Maddog' 'Get Up! Go Insane!'
House Of Pain 'Jump Around'

Sub Sub 'Respect'
Fatback Band 'Double Dutch'

Suggs featuring Louchie Lou and Michie One 'No More Alcohol'
The Champs 'Tequila'

SWV 'Right Here'
Michael Jackson 'Human Nature'

2 Eivissa 'Oh La La La'
Crystal Waters 'Gypsy Woman'

2 In A Tent 'When I'm Cleaning Windows (Turned Out Nice Again)'
George Formby 'When I'm Cleaning Windows'

2K '*k The Millennium'**
KLF 'Kick Out The Jams'
Isaac Hayes 'Theme From Shaft'

2Pac 'California Love'
Roger 'So Ruff So Tuff'
Joe Cocker 'Woman To Woman'

2Pac featuring KC And JoJo 'How Do You Want It?'
Quincy Jones 'Body Heat

2Pac featuring Eric Williams of Blackstreet 'Do For Love'
Bobby Caldwell 'What You Can't Do For Love'

2Pac 'Changes'
Bruce Hornsby And The Range 'The Way It Is'

T-Empo 'The Look Of Love'
New Order 'Blue Monday'

Tag Team 'Whoomp! (There It Is)'
Kano 'I'm Ready'

Tamperer featuring Maya 'Feel It'
The Jacksons 'Can You Feel It'

Tamperer featuring Maya 'If You Buy This Record Your Life Will Be Better'
Madonna 'Material Girl'

Tenor Fly 'Bright Side Of Life'
Nina Simone 'My Baby Just Cares For Me'

Third Bass 'Pop Goes The Weasel'
Peter Gabriel 'Sledgehammer'
Stevie Wonder 'You Haven't Done Nothin' '

Third Storee 'If Ever'
Unlimited Touch 'I Hear Music In The Street'

Tinman 'Eighteen Strings'
Monkees '(I'm Not Your) Steppin' Stone'

Tinman 'Gudvibe'
Yello 'The Race'

TLC 'Aint 2 Proud 2 Beg'
James Brown 'Escapeism'
Kool And The Gang 'Jungle Boogie'
Average White Band 'School Boy Crush'
Silver Convention 'Fly Robin Fly'

TLC 'Creep'
Slick Rick 'Hey Young World'

A Tribe Called Quest 'Bonita Applebum'
Carly Simon 'Why'

A Tribe Called Quest 'Can I Kick It?'
Lou Reed 'Walk On The Wild Side'

A Tribe Called Quest 'Find A Way'
Towa Tei 'Dubnova (Parts 1&2)'

Tricky 'Tricky Kid'
The Commodores 'The Zoo (The Human Zoo)'

Tricky 'Makes Me Wanna Die'
Eric B And Rakim 'To The Listeners'

Triple X 'Feel The Same'
Delegations 'You & I'

Trubble 'Dancing Baby (Ooga – Chaka)'
Blue Swede 'Hooked On A Feeling'

UK Apachi with Shy FX 'Original Nuttah'
Cypress Hill 'I Ain't Going Out Like That'

Umboza 'Cry India'
Lionel Ritchie 'All Night Long'

Umboza 'Sunshine'
Gipsy Kings 'Bomboleo'

Usher 'Think Of You'
Ronnie Laws 'Tidal Wave'

US3 featuring Rahsaan 'Cantaloop (Flip Fantasia)'
Herbie Hancock 'Cantaloupe Island'

Utah Saints 'What Can You Do For Me'
Eurythmics 'There Must Be An Angel (Playing With My Heart)'
Gwen Guthrie 'Ain't Nothing Goin' On But The Rent'

Utah Saints 'Something Good'
Kate Bush 'Cloudbusting'

Utah Saints 'Believe In Me'
Crown Heights Affair 'You Gave Me Love'
Human League 'Love Action (I Believe In Love)'

Utah Saints 'I Want You'
Slayer 'War Ensemble'

Utah Saints 'Ohio'
Jocelyn Brown 'Somebody Else's Guy'

Vanilla Ice 'Ice Ice Baby'
Queen and David Bowie 'Under Pressure'

Verve 'Bitter Sweet Symphony'
Rolling Stones 'The Last Time' (arr. Andrew Long Oldham)

A Very Good Friend Of Mine featuring Joy 'Just Round'
Stevie Wonder 'Uptight'

Viper 'The Twister'
Nina Simone 'Feeling Good'

Vybe 'Warm Summer Daze'
William Bell and Judy Clay 'Private Number'

Way Out West featuring Miss Joanna Law 'The Gift'
Joanna Law 'First Time Ever'

Wildchild 'Jump To My Beat'
Mark Ryder 'Get Down'
Aretha Franklin 'Jump To It'
Lisa Lisa 'Let The Beat Hit 'Em'

Freedom Williams 'Voice Of Freedom'
George Michael 'Freedom'

Robbie Williams 'Millennium'
Theme from 'You Only Live Twice'

Robbie Williams 'Rock DJ'
Barry White 'It's Ecstasy When You Lay Down Next To Me'

Wiseguys 'Start The Commotion'
The Ventures 'Wild Child'

Wreckx-N-Effect 'Rump Shaker'
N2Deep 'Back To The Hotel'

Yomanda 'Synth & Strings'
Liquid Gold 'Dance Yourself Dizzy'

Young MC 'I Come Off'
Aaron Neville 'Hercules'

Zhane 'Hey Mr. DJ'
Michael Wycoff 'Looking Up To You'

'SEVEN DAYS'
60 Songs about the Days of the Week

The Beatles would have you believe that there are 'eight days a week'. However, we can assure you that there are indeed only seven: to prove it we've searched high and low (in the charts that is) to compile this list of songs written about all 'seven' days of the week:

Monday
'I Don't Like Mondays' – **Boomtown Rats**
'Monday, Monday' – **Mamas and the Papas**
'Blue Monday' – **Fats Domino / New Order**
'Manic Monday' – **Bangles**
'Rainy Days and Mondays' – **Carpenters**
'New Moon On Monday' – **Duran Duran**
'Stormy Monday Blues' – **Bobby Bland**
'Come Monday' – **Jimmy Buffett**

Tuesday
'Everything's Tuesday' – **Chairmen Of The Board**
'Ruby Tuesday' – **Melanie / Rolling Stones / Rod Stewart**
'Love You Till Tuesday' – **David Bowie**
'Tuesday Morning' – **Pogues**

Wednesday
'Wednesday Morning 3 AM' – **Simon and Garfunkel**
'Wednesday Week' – **Undertones**
'Wednesday Evenin' Blues' – **John Lee Hooker**

Thursday
'Thursday's Child' – **David Bowie**
'Thursday' – **Jim Croce**
'Thursday Afternoon' – **Brian Eno**

Friday
'Friday On My Mind' – **Easybeats / Gary Moore**
'Party People . . . Friday Night' – **911**
'She Left Me On Friday' – **Shed Seven**

'Living It Up (Friday Night)' – **Bell and James**
'Friday Night' – **Kids From Fame**
'Thank God It's Friday' – **R. Kelly**
'Friday I'm In Love' – **Cure**
'Black Friday' – **Steely Dan**
'Friday's Angels' – **Generation X**
'Friday Street' – **Paul Weller**
'Friday's Child' – **Them**

Saturday
'Saturday Night At The Movies' – **Drifters / Robson and Jerome**
'Saturday Love' – **Cherelle with Alexander O'Neal**
'Saturday Night' – **Whigfield**
'Saturday Night's Alright For Fighting' – **Elton John**
'Saturday Night Party (Read My Lips)' – **Alex Party**
'Saturday Night Sunday Morning' – **T-Empo**
'Saturday Nite' – **Earth, Wind and Fire**
'Dancing On A Saturday Night' – **Barry Blue**
'Get Down Saturday Night' – **Oliver Cheatham**
'Another Saturday Night' – **Sam Cooke / Cat Stevens**
'A Roller Skating Jam Named "Saturdays" ' – **De La Soul**
'I Love Saturday' – **Erasure**
'Saturday Night Special' – **Lynyrd Skynyrd**
'Saturday Gigs' – **Mott The Hoople**
'Come Saturday Morning' – **Sandpipers**
'Drive In Saturday' – **David Bowie**
'Saturday Night' – **Bay City Rollers**
'Saturday Night At The World' – **Mason Williams**
'Saturday Night Fish Fry' – **Louis Jordan**

Sunday
'Sunday Girl' – **Blondie**
'Never On A Sunday' – **Chordettes / Lyn Cornell**
'Beautiful Sunday' – **Daniel Boone**
'That Sunday That Summer' – **Nat 'King' Cole**
'Pleasant Valley Sunday' – **Monkees**
'Everyday Is Like Sunday' – **Morrissey**
'Sunday Shining' – **Finlay Quaye**
'I Met Him On A Sunday' – **Shirelles**
'Lazy Sunday' – **Small Faces**

'Sunday Will Never Be The Same' – **Spanky and Our Gang**
'Tell Me On A Sunday' – **Marti Webb**
'Sunday Sunday' – **Blur**
'Sunday Morning Call' – **Oasis**

And as you can see from the above, 'Saturday' is everybody's favourite.

'SOMETHIN' STUPID'
Songs with Stupid Titles

Chart success can't have been at the fore of Bobby Bare's mind when he penned the 'hit' record, 'Drop Kick Me Jesus Through The Goalposts Of Life' but one thing's for sure, he most definitely had a great sense of humour.

He is not alone though, for there are many such songs, all with absolutely silly titles; songs which, more often than not, were brought to life by the stars of country and western.

Below, for your amusement, is a selection of the silliest song titles:

'Drop Kick Me Jesus Through The Goalposts Of Life' – Bobby Bare

'You Can't Roller Skate In A Buffalo Herd' – Roger Miller

'Ain't Going Down (Till The Sun Comes Up)' – Garth Brooks

'Fax Me A Beer' – Hank Williams Jr

'Airmail To Heaven' – Carl Smith

'May The Bird Of Paradise Fly Up Your Nose' – Little Jimmy Dickens

'All My Ex's Live In Texas' – George Strait

'All My Rowdy Friends Are Coming Over Tonight' – Hank Williams Jr

'All My Rowdy Friends (Have Settled Down)' – Hank Williams Jr

'Angel Flying Too Close To The Ground' – Willie Nelson

'(Hey Won't You Play) Another Somebody Done Somebody Wrong Song' – BJ Thomas

'Anything But Yes Is Still A No' – Stephanie Winslow

'Okie From Muskogie' – Willie Nelson

'Between Lust and Watching TV' – Cal Smith

'**Animal Crackers (In Cellophane Boxes)**' – Gene Pitney

'**Blues Plus Booze (Means I Lose)**' – Stonewall Jackson

'**Jeremiah Peabody's Polyunsaturated Quick Dissolving Fast Acting Pleasant Tasting Green And Purple Pills**' – Ray Stevens

'**Cry The Dying Duck In A Thunderstorm**' – Cactus Pryor

'**Boobs A Lot**' – Holy Modal Rounders

'**Days That End In "Y"**' – Sammi Davis

'**Don't Let That Door Knob Hit You**' – Norma Jean

'**Don't Telephone – Don't Telegraph (Tell A Woman)**' – Tex Williams

'**Don't The Girls All Get Prettier At Closing Time**' – Mickey Gilley

'**Don't Toss Us Away**' – Patty Loveless

'**Don't You Think This Outlaw Bit's Don Got Out Of Hand**' – Waylon Jennings

'**Drag 'Em Off The Interstate Sock It To 'Em JP Blues**' – Dick Curless

'**Everytime You Go Outside I Hope It Rains**' – The Burch Sisters

'**5.01 AM (The Pros And Cons Of Hitch Hiking)**' – Roger Waters

'**Frankfurter Sandwiches**' – Streamliners with Joanne

'**Freckles and Polliwog Days**' – Ferlin Husky

'**Freda Comes Freda Goes**' – Bobby G Rice

'**From Levi's To Calvin Klein Jeans**' – Brenda Lee

'**Great Goo-Ga-Moo-Ga**' – Tom & Jerrio

'**Got The All Overs For You All Over Me**' – Freddie Hart

'Have You Seen The Saucers' – Jefferson Airplane

'Hello I'm A Jukebox' – George Kent

'Honeymoon On A Rocketship' – Roy Clark

'(Holy Moses!) Everything's Coming Up Roses' – Jack Wild

'Hootchy Kootchy Henry From Hawaii' – Mitchell Torok

'How Come Your Dog Don't Bite Nobody But Me' – Webb Pierce and Mel Tillis

'I Come Home A-Drinkin' To A Worn Out Wife Like You' – Jay Lee Webb

'I Do My Swinging At Home' – David Houston

'I'd Like To See Jesus (On The Midnight Special)' – Tammy Wynette

'I'm A Truck' – Red Simpson

'I'm Biting My Fingernails And Thinking Of You' – The Andrews Sisters and Ernest Tubb

' 'Round The World With The Rubber Duck' – CW McCall

'I'm Going To Hire A Wino To Decorate Our Home' – David Frizzell

'I'm Just An Old Chunk Of Coal' – John Anderson

'I'm The One Momma Warned You About' – Mickey Gilley

'Sarah Cynthia Sylvia Stout (Would Not Take The Garbage Out)' – Shel Silverstein

'It Took A Lot Of Drinking To Get That Woman Over Me' – Moe Bandy

'It Was Always So Easy To Find An Unhappy Woman' – Moe Bandy

'Where Did Robinson Crusoe Go With Friday On Saturday Night' – Ian Whitcomb

'I WRITE THE SONGS'
Songwriters' Versions of Their Own Songs

Here is a list of one hundred hit songs that have been recorded for commercial release either prior or after their success by the songwriters.

Title	Composer(s)	Hit Version(s)
1. **'I Can't Stand The Rain'**	Ann Peebles	**Eruption**
2. **'I'm Your Puppet'**	Dan Penn	**James & Bobby Purify**
3. **'Blue Turns To Grey'**	Keith Richard / Mick Jagger (Rolling Stones)	**Cliff Richard**
4. **'Out Of Time'**	Keith Richard / Mick Jagger (Rolling Stones)	**Chris Farlowe**
5. **'Claudette'**	Roy Orbison	**Everly Brothers**
6. **'No Matter What'**	Paul McCartney	**Badfinger**
7. **'Don't Turn Around'**	Albert Hammond	**Aswad / Ace Of Base**
8. **'My Toot Toot'**	Rockin' Sydney	**Denise La Salle**
9. **'My Ding-A-Ling'**	Dave Bartholomew	**Chuck Berry**
10. **'Islands In The Stream'**	Bee Gees	**Kenny Rogers & Dolly Parton**
11. **'Crazy'**	Willie Nelson	**Patsy Cline / LeAnn Rimes**
12. **'Living Doll'**	Lionel Bart	**Cliff Richard**
13. **'Georgie Girl'**	Jim Dale	**The Seekers**
14. **'The Air That I Breathe'**	Albert Hammond	**The Hollies**
15. **'The Twist'**	Hank Ballard	**Chubby Checker**
16. **'Bus Stop'**	Graham Gouldman	**The Hollies**
17. **'No Milk Today'**	Graham Gouldman	**Herman's Hermits**
18. **'For Your Love'**	Graham Gouldman	**The Yardbirds**
19. **'Father And Son'**	Cat Stevens	**Boyzone**
20. **'Giving It All Away'**	Leo Sayer	**Roger Daltrey**
21. **'For The Good Times'**	Kris Kristofferson	**Perry Como**
22. **'This Golden Ring'**	Roger Cook / Roger Greenaway	**The Fortunes**
23. **'You've Got Your Troubles'**	Roger Cook / Roger Greenaway	**The Fortunes**
24. **'I Love Rock 'n' Roll'**	Alan Merrill / Jake Hooker (The Arrows)	**Joan Jett & the Blackhearts**

25.	'Since You've Been Gone'	Russ Ballard	**Rainbow**
26.	'I Will Always Love You'	Dolly Parton	**Whitney Houston**
27.	'Candy Man'	Roy Orbison	**Brian Poole & The Tremeloes**
28.	'All Shook Up'	Otis Blackwell	**Elvis Presley**
29.	'Return To Sender'	Otis Blackwell	**Elvis Presley**
30.	'Great Balls Of Fire'	Otis Blackwell	**Jerry Lee Lewis**
31.	'Handy Man'	Otis Blackwell	**Jimmy Jones**
32.	'In The Ghetto'	Mac Davis	**Elvis Presley**
33.	'Something's Burning'	Mac Davis	**Kenny Rogers & First Edition**
34.	'The Wanderer'	Ernie Maresca	**Dion**
35.	'Patches'	General Johnson	**Clarence Carter**
36.	'When You Say Nothing At All'	Paul Overstreet	**Ronan Keating**
37.	'Downtown Train'	Tom Waits	**Rod Stewart**
38.	'Funny Familiar Forgotten Feelings'	Mickey Newbury	**Tom Jones**
39.	'It's The Same Old Song'	Lamont Dozier	**Four Tops**
40.	'One Moment In Time'	Albert Hammond	**Whitney Houston**
41.	'Pink Cadillac'	Bruce Springsteen	**Natalie Cole**
42.	'I'll Never Get Over You'	Gordon Mills	**Johnny Kidd & The Pirates**
43.	'I Shot The Sheriff'	Bob Marley	**Eric Clapton**
44.	'It Doesn't Matter Anymore'	Paul Anka	**Buddy Holly**
45.	'My Way'	Paul Anka	**Frank Sinatra**
46.	'The First Time'	Chris Andrews	**Adam Faith**
47.	'Long Live Love'	Chris Andrews	**Sandie Shaw**
48.	'Ooh I Do'	Barry Blue	**Lynsey De Paul**
49.	'Burning Love'	Dennis Linde	**Elvis Presley**
50.	'An American Trilogy'	Mickey Newbury	**Elvis Presley**
51.	'I Can't Stop Loving You'	Don Gibson	**Ray Charles**
52.	'Rose Garden'	Joe South	**Lynn Anderson**
53.	'Tobacco Road'	John D. Loudermilk	**Nashville Teens**
54.	'Hello Mary Lou'	Gene Pitney	**Ricky Nelson**
55.	'He's A Rebel'	Gene Pitney	**The Crystals**
56.	'Young, Gifted And Black'	Nina Simone	**Bob and Marcia**
57.	'Storm In A Teacup'	Lynsey De Paul	**The Fortunes**
58.	'Solitaire'	Neil Sedaka	**The Carpenters / Andy Williams**
59.	'Stupid Cupid'	Neil Sedaka	**Connie Francis**

60.	'Love Will Keep Us Together'	Neil Sedaka	The Captain & Tennille
61.	'Under The Boardwalk'	Mort Shuman	The Drifters / Bruce Willis
62.	'A Hard Rain's Gonna Fall'	Bob Dylan	Bryan Ferry
63.	'The Mighty Quinn'	Bob Dylan	Manfred Mann
64.	'Mr Tambourine Man'	Bob Dylan	The Byrds
65.	'Gentle On My Mind'	John Hartford	Dean Martin
66.	'Dinner With Gershwin'	Brenda Russell	Donna Summer
67.	'So Emotional'	Billy Steinberg & Tom Kelly	Whitney Houston
68.	'Best Thing That Ever Happened To Me'	Jim Weatherly	Gladys Knight & The Pips
69.	'Chirpy Chirpy Cheep Cheep'	Lally Stott	Middle Of The Road
70.	'It's Late'	Dorsey Burnette	Ricky Nelson / Shakin' Stevens
71.	'Automatic'	Brock Walsh & Mark Goldenberg	The Pointer Sisters
72.	'Crazy For You'	Jon Lind	Madonna
73.	'They Don't Know About Us'	Kirsty MacColl	Tracey Ullman
74.	'Nightshift'	Dennis Lambert & Franne Gould	The Commodores
75.	'Oh No Not My Baby'	Carole King	Manfred Mann
76.	'Up On The Roof'	Carole King	The Drifters / Kenny Lynch / Julie Grant
77.	'You've Got A Friend'	Carole King	James Taylor
78.	'Crying in The Rain'	Carole King	The Everly Brothers/A-HA
79.	'I Wanna Dance With Somebody (Who Loves Me)'	George Merrell & Shannon Rubicam	Whitney Houston
80.	'Everybody's Talkin' '	Fred Neil	Nilsson / The Beautiful South
81.	'Come And Stay With Me'	Jackie De Shannon	Marianne Faithfull
82.	'When You Walk In The Room'	Jackie De Shannon	The Searchers

83. **'Put A Little Love In Your Heart'**   Jackie De Shannon   **Dave Clark Five**
84. **'If I Were A Carpenter'**   Tim Hardin   **Bobby Darin / The Four Tops**
85. **'Many Rivers To Cross'**   Jimmy Cliff   **UB40**
86. **'Wild Thing'**   Chip Taylor   **The Troggs**
87. **'The Boat That I Row'**   Neil Diamond   **Lulu**
88. **'I'm A Believer'**   Neil Diamond   **The Monkees**
89. **'Red Red Wine'**   Neil Diamond   **UB40**
90. **You've Lost That Lovin' Feelin''**   Barry Mann   **The Righteous Brothers / Cilla Black**
91. **'Come On Home'**   Jackie Edwards   **Wayne Fontana**
92. **'I Can Hear Music'**   Ellie Greenwich   **The Beach Boys**
93. **'Maybe I Know'**   Ellie Greenwich   **Lesley Gore**
94. **'Be My Baby'**   Ellie Greenwich   **The Ronettes**
95. **'As'**   Stevie Wonder   **George Michael & Mary J Blige**
96. **'I Ain't Gonna Stand For It'**   Stevie Wonder   **Eric Clapton**
97. **'Isn't She Lovely'**   Stevie Wonder   **David Parton**
98. **'Cherry Oh Baby'**   Eric Donaldson   **UB40**
99. **'I Honestly Love You'**   Peter Allen   **Olivia Newton-John**
100. **'Nothing Compares 2U'**   Prince   **Sinead O'Connor**

'I'M JUST A SINGER (IN A ROCK 'N' ROLL BAND)'
Singers Who've Gone Solo

The following were all members of groups, before choosing to seek success alone:

Kelli Ali (Sneaker Pimps)
Marc Almond (Soft Cell)
Richard Ashcroft (Verve)
Phil Bailey (Earth, Wind & Fire)
Gary Barlow (Take That)
Sophie Bextor-Ellis (Theaudience)
Colin Blunstone (Zombies)
Boy George (Bow Wow Wow/Culture Club)
Bobby Brown (New Edition)
Ian Brown (Stone Roses)
Junior Campbell (Marmalade)
Captain Sensible (The Damned)
Belinda Carlisle (Go Go's)
Eric Clapton (Yardbirds)
Edwyn Collins (Orange Juice)
Phil Collins (Genesis)
Chris Cornell (Soundgarden)
Sarah Cracknell (Saint Etienne)
N'Dea Davenport (Brand New Heavies)
Marcella Detroit (Shakespear's Sister)
Eazy-E (NWA)
Everlast (House Of Pain)
Bryan Ferry (Roxy Music)
Roddy Frame (Aztec Camera)
Peter Frampton (Herd / Humble Pie)
Peter Gabriel (Genesis)
Stephen Gately (Boyzone)
David Gates (Bread)
Mikey Graham (Boyzone)
Brian Harvey (East 17)
Nick Heyward (Haircut 100)
Lauryn Hill (Fugees)

Susanna Hoffs (Bangles)
Ian Hunter (Mott The Hoople)
Ice Cube (NWA)
Billy Idol (Generation X)
Wyclef Jean (Fugees)
Holly Johnson (Frankie Goes To Hollywood)
Paul Jones (Manfred Mann)
David Joseph (Hi-Tension)
Ronan Keating (Boyzone)
Annie Lennox (Tourists / Eurythmics)
Louise (Eternal)
Phil Lynott (Thin Lizzy)
Maxee (Brownstone)
Michael McDonald (Doobie Brothers)
George Michael (Wham!)
Pras Michel (Fugees)
Van Morrison (Them)
Alison Moyet (Yazoo)
Peter Noone (Herman's Hermits)
Mark Owen (Take That)
Q-Tip (A Tribe Called Quest)
Eddi Reader (Fairground Attraction)
Lionel Richie (Commodores)
Diana Ross (Supremes)
David Ruffin (Temptations)
Shaun Ryder (Happy Mondays / Black Grape)
Feargal Sharkey (Undertones)
Sisqo (Dru Hill)
Heather Small (M People)
Mark E. Smith (Fall)
Will Smith (DJ Jazzy Jeff and the Fresh Prince)
Jimmy Somerville (Bronski Beat / Communards)
Sonique (S'Express)
Rod Stewart (Faces)
Suggs (Madness)
David Sylvian (Japan)
Midge Ure (Rich Kids / Slik / Thin Lizzy / Ultravox)
Frankie Valli (Four Seasons)
John Waite (Babys)
Jody Watley (Shalamar)
Paul Weller (Jam / Style Council)
Robbie Williams (Take That)

Steve Winwood (Spencer Davis Group/Traffic)
Jah Wobble (PIL)
Roy Wood (Move/ELO/Wizzard)
Geri Halliwell (Spice Girls)

'CUM ON FEEL THE NOIZE'
50 Pop Songs with Sound FX

In this the age of the cd, it has become all too easy to believe that the band you're listening to are really playing in your own front room. You know this is true when you try and answer the telephone, only to discover that the ring you thought you heard was in fact the beginning of Blondie's 'Call Me'.

'Outside'　　　　　　　　　　　George Michael
Helicopter with voices and siren

'In Our Lifetime'　　　　　　　　Texas
Needle on a vinyl record

'Autobahn'　　　　　　　　　　　Kraftwerk
Car engine starting up, then driving off with horn blasting

'Welcome To The Pleasuredome'　Frankie Goes To Hollywood
Jungle noises

'One For Sorrow'　　　　　　　　Steps
Pouring rain

'Wannabe'　　　　　　　　　　　Spice Girls
Footsteps followed by the healthy sounds of laughter

'Lazy Sunday'　　　　　　　　　Small Faces
The sound of the sea and gulls, also church bells

'19'　　　　　　　　　　　　　　Paul Hardcastle
A chanting crowd and the sound of gunfire

'I'm Mandy, Fly Me'　　　　　　10CC
Doorbell

'Don't Wanna Let You Go'　　　　Five

Loud explosion

'(Sittin' On) The Dock Of The Bay'   Otis Redding
Sound of the rolling tide

'Summer In The City'   The Lovin' Spoonful
Traffic noise

'Surfin' U.S.A.'   Aaron Carter
More sea and seagulls

'Girls On Film'   Duran Duran
Clicking of camera shutters

'5-7-0-5'   City Boy
Telephone ringing tone

'Hanging On The Telephone'   Blondie
There it is again, that telephone ringing tone

'Beautiful Noise'   Neil Diamond
More sounds from the outside traffic

'Mystical Machine Gun'   Kula Shaker
Buzzing of a blowfly and then crowds screaming

'Oxygene Part IV'   Jean Michel Jarre
Heavy wind

'In The Summertime'   Mungo Jerry
You can't get away from that traffic noise

'My Prerogative'   Bobby Brown
Screeching of car tyres

'The Sensual World'   Kate Bush
You'll hear those church bells ringing

'Earth Song'   Michael Jackson
Chirping crickets and birds in the jungle

'Indiana Wants Me'   R. Dean Taylor
Police sirens

'Stand Up For Our Love Rights' Yazz
They haven't given up, there are more of those police sirens

'I'm The Leader Of The Gang (I Am)' Gary Glitter
Revving up of a motorbike engine

'Riding On A Train' The Pasadenas
The whistle of a train

'Zabadak' Dave Dee, Dozy, Beaky, Mick &
Jungle noises and crickets chirping Tich

'Legend Of Xanadu' Dave Dee, Dozy, Beaky, Mick &
Cracking of a whip Tich

'Bicycle Race' Queen
(Surprise, surprise) – The sound of the ringing of several bicycle bells

'Uncle John From Jamaica' Vengaboys
The clock starts ticking then off goes the alarm

'Hole In The Ground' Bernard Cribbins
Workman's drill

'When I Grow Up' Garbage
Scratchy old 78 rpm record

'Apeman' The Kinks
Car engine revving up above the noise of traffic

'Pool Hall Richard' The Faces
You'll love the sound of breaking glass

'School Love' Barry Blue
Children chatting in a school playground

'Ghost Town' The Specials
Eerie sound of the wind blowing

'Kiss And Tell' Bryan Ferry
A secretary busy at her old fashioned typewriter

'Dancing With The Captain'   Paul Nicholas
A raging sea with the sound of seagulls

'Living Doll'   Cliff Richard & The Young
Loud crash   Ones

'Leader Of The Pack'   The Shangri-Las
That motor bike engine is still revving up

'My Oh My'   Aqua
Horse galloping off and making the sound that horses make

'Rhythm Of The Rain'   The Cascades/Jason Donovan
*Who would have guessed it, yes it's the sound of a thunderstorm with the
pouring rain*

'Shotgun Wedding'   Roy C
*Not that obvious, but, yes, you've guessed it, the sound of a shotgun being
fired*

'Ballad Of Bonnie And Clyde'   Georgie Fame
Those bullets are flying as our two heroes are gunned to the ground

'Blockbuster'   The Sweet
Police sirens

'The Way I Am'   Eminem
Needle on a vinyl record and those bells

'Baby Sittin' Boogie'   Buzz Clifford
Well it sounds as if it's a really happy baby

'Star People '97'   George Michael
Another engine being started up then some heavy revving

'Blame It On The Weatherman'   B*Witched
*It must have been a very stormy forecast because there is the thunder and
rain*

'SWEET INSPIRATION'
The Stories behind 10 of Pop's Greatest Songs

'Fame' by David Bowie

According to Bowie the track came about quite by accident. His band had been jamming to a Flares track called 'Foot Stompin'', as a result of which Bowie's guitarist, Carlos Alomar, had come up with a more than slightly infectious riff. One day, John Lennon was in the studio with Bowie and his band, when they began to play him the riff. As he listened, Lennon began to search for lyrics, '. . . aim! . . . aim!, Fame!' At this point the song was born, and a day later it was complete, lyrics and all. Incidentally, John Lennon performs backing vocals on the finished cut.

'Great Balls Of Fire' by Jerry Lee Lewis

Lewis's rollicking, piano thumping hit, was in fact written by Otis Blackwell, a one time New York cinema floor-sweeper turned songwriter to the stars.

Blackwell's big break came when, shortly after beginning work as a songwriter for Shalimar Publishing, record label RCA and their rising star, one Elvis Aaron Presley, expressed a keen interest in the Blackwell composition, 'Don't Be Cruel'. Not ones to miss an opportunity, Blackwell and Shalimar took RCA up on their offer. Now having forged a relationship with Elvis and consequently Sam Phillips' Sun Records, subsequent requests for material began to roll in, among them something of hit potential for a brash young pianist named Jerry Lee Lewis who was already carving a niche for himself on account of his inimitable rockabilly style and wild stage show. In answer to this request Blackwell, as with his earlier hit, 'All Shook Up', looked to the motif of a man who finds himself spellbound by a beautiful woman. However, this time Blackwell chose to use the old saying, 'Goodness gracious, great balls of fire' as the song's hook. Incidentally, it is reported that Blackwell came up with the line 'All Shook Up', after accidentally dropping a bottle of coke.

Over the course of his career Blackwell wrote quite literally hundreds of songs, many of which achieved great success, such as 'Fever', 'Return To Sender', 'Breathless', 'Hey Little Girl' and 'Nine Times Out Of Ten' (a number three hit for our very own Cliff Richard in September 1960).

'Maggie May' by Rod Stewart

This great track would never have reached the record-buying public at large had it not been for a Cleveland DJ who decided to go against the grain and play the B side ('Maggie May') of Rod's then current release, 'Reason To Believe'. During its tenancy as the official A side 'Reason To Believe' was only able to climb as high as number 19 in the British charts. Two weeks after its release 'Maggie May' became the A side, and the single went all the way to the top, remaining in the charts for a total of 21 weeks.

'Peggy Sue' by Buddy Holly

The girl referred to in the title of Buddy Holly's 1957 hit was in fact Peggy Sue Gerron, a pupil at Lubbock High School. At the time she was the girlfriend of Crickets (Buddy's backing band) drummer, Jerry Allison. This perhaps explains Allison's enthusiastic drumming on the track.

'Stand By Your Man' by Tammy Wynette

That Tammy Wynette had a tough childhood is an understatement: she never knew her father, since he had died while she was still a baby and she was subsequently passed back and forth between her impoverished relatives. As an escape from all this Tammy threw herself into music, gaining a modicum of acclaim in her local area of Itawamba County, as both a singer and performer. However this was all to end, for by the time she was seventeen, Tammy had married a local construction worker named Euple Byrd, by whom she was to have three children. No doubt so as to enrich Tammy's life, since as we all know creativity stems from pain, Euple decided to abandon Tammy and her children shortly before the birth of their third child.

Things changed for the better though, when in 1966, single parent Tammy, once again attempting to pursue a career in music, decided to pay an unscheduled visit on CBS Records in Nashville. She subsequently persuaded top CBS producer Billy Sherrill to sign her to the Epic Records label. Sherrill was to provide the creative impetus for what was to be one of Tammy's greatest hits of all time, 'Stand By Your Man'. While recording an album in August 1968, Tammy and her producer Sherrill found themselves in need of a final song. Sherrill, desperate to finish, decided to share with Tammy the title of an as-yet-unwritten song. In less than half an hour Tammy and Sherrill had written both the words and music to 'Stand By Your Man'. In the light of Tammy's life thus far, the song was not without a fair degree of irony, a point that was lost on America's feminist lobby, who claimed the song promoted a submissive ideal of married life. Tammy herself never intended to engage the women's libbers, as she herself remarked, 'Sherrill and I didn't have women's lib in mind. All we wanted to do was to write a pretty love song.'

'Time' by Pink Floyd

Clocks, clocks and more clocks – that's the sound that first greets any listener to the classic Pink Floyd track 'Time' (as featured on the best-selling album *Dark Side Of The Moon*), but where on earth did they find so many clocks?

Well, the answer has a lot to do with then sound engineer Alan Parsons. On the day in question, Parsons had been out and about recording all manner of things for the studio's sound effects library. Upon finishing his work, he hurried back to the studio and enthusiastically approached the band. The reason? Parsons had been recording in a clock shop and knew that Pink Floyd were in the process of recording a track called 'Time'. He suggested that they have a listen to his recordings. The band duly listened, liked what they heard and the rest, as they say, is history.

Parsons subsequently won a 'Grammy' for his engineering work on *Dark Side Of The Moon*.

'While My Guitar Gently Weeps' by the Beatles

At the time of writing, Harrison had been exploring the spiritual insights offered by eastern mysticism, in particular the *I Ching* or *The Book Of Changes* as it is also known, which teaches that all things in the universe are relative to one another. With this in mind, Harrison, while on a visit to his parents, picked up a book, opened it, and decided to write a song based on the first words that he saw; which were 'gently weeps'. For the rest of the day Harrison's guitar wept music's mellow tears.

'You Ain't Seen Nothin' Yet' by Bachman-Turner Overdrive

Singer/songwriter Randy Bachman claims the song came about more as a joke than any attempt at musical genius. Having recorded the music and with the weekend drawing near, Bachman threw down some vocals, so as to give him a base upon which to build the solo over the next couple of days. Since the vocals weren't intended to be final, Bachman didn't give them much thought, treating them as a bit of a joke, even stuttering some of the words, in particular, 'b-b-baby'. However, this is not a reference to the Who's earlier hit, 'My Generation' but probably a reference to Randy's brother, Gary Bachman, who was himself afflicted with a st-st-stutter. When the band returned to the studio to finish recording the track it was decided to leave the vocals as they were.

'When You Say Nothing At All' by Ronan Keating

Prior to becoming the love theme to 1999's runaway box office success *Notting Hill*, (and in the process young Irish crooner Ronan Keating's first solo number one), 'When You Say Nothing At All' had previously enjoyed great success as a moving and soulful country and western ballad, written and performed by three of Nashville's finest, namely singer Keith Whitley and writers Paul Overstreet and Don Schlitz.

Whitley, who had started a career in the music industry at the age of eight, and by twelve already had his own band, looked destined to become one of country and western's biggest stars. However, an ongoing battle with the demon alcohol fuelled by an inherently self-destructive nature made the prospect of Whitley's continuing existence a fragile one. Things looked set to change for the better though, when in 1988 he teamed up with the songwriting duo of Overstreet and Schlitz in the hope of securing that illusive second number one.

The product of their labours, 'When You Say Nothing At All', quite literally came out of nothing. The two writers had spent a fruitless day, searching for a winning composition, never managing to get past a creative brick wall. As Overstreet remarked subsequently, 'We were just joking around humming and saying nothing. As we tried to find another way to say nothing, it led to the song.'

Upon hearing the track, Whitley found himself deeply moved by the song's heartfelt lyrics, feeling it echoed his very life. He immediately went into the studio to record the track. The song entered America's *Billboard* charts at a very respectable number 61 and by Christmas of 1988 it had gained the coveted number one spot, the very thing Whitley had so desired. Finally, Whitley really did look as though he would get to wear country and western's crown. Alas this was not to be, for on 8 May 1989 Whitley's motionless body, was found shortly after midnight. His wife had been away from home and for some reason he had once again felt the call of drink. A postmortem concluded that Whitley had consumed five times the state minimum for intoxication and nearly two times the body's lethal limit. At the time of his death Keith Whitley was thirty-three years of age. He went on to win, albeit posthumously, the Country Music Association Single of the Year.

So, next time you hear 'When You Say Nothing At All', spare a thought for Keith Whitley; he put his whole life into it.

'Whole Lotta Rosie' by AC/DC

Listen to the lyrics and you'll realise that the song concerns a whole lotta woman (42-39-56 so we're told); apparently, the woman in question picked up singer Bon Scott one night, took him back to her pad, and proceeded to make him the twenty-ninth notch on her bedpost that month. Scott was so moved by the experience (as was the earth) that he proceeded to write a song about it.

'SPEAK TO ME PRETTY'
50 Songs with 'Talking Bits'

Long before rap was around, pop singers would talk on their records, even today a few performers like to include spoken passages in their songs.
Here's a list in no particular order of fifty such songs:

'Farewell Is A Lonely Sound'	Jimmy Ruffin
'You're Still The One'	Shania Twain
'Nobody Knows'	Tony Rich
'Hole In My Shoe'	Traffic
'The Green Green Grass Of Home'	Tom Jones
'All I Wanna Do'	Sheryl Crow
'You're Gorgeous'	Babybird
'Ain't No Mountain High Enough'	Diana Ross
'Vindaloo'	Fat Les
'Have You Seen Her?'	The Chi-Lites
'Kites'	Simon Dupree & The Big Sound
'It's You'	Freddy Starr
'Little Does She Know'	The Kursaal Flyers
'I'll Be Home'	Pat Boone
'Heart And Soul'	T'Pau
'Sho' You Right'	Barry White
'A Lover Spurned'	Marc Almond
'The All Seeing I'	The Beat Goes On
'(You're My) Soul And Inspiration'	The Righteous Brothers
'Bag It Up'	Geri Halliwell
'Sugar Baby Love'	The Rubettes
'Come Dancing'	The Kinks
'I'm Still Waiting'	Diana Ross
'Tom-Tom Turnaround'	New World
'Chantilly Lace'	The Big Bopper
'Speedy Gonzales'	Pat Boone
'Girl You Know It's True'	Milli Vanilli
'All Alone Am I'	Brenda Lee
'Guantanamera'	The Sandpipers
'Barbie Girl'	Aqua
'Do You Love Me?'	Brian Poole & The Tremeloes
'Leader Of The Pack'	The Shangri-Las
'Sandy'	John Travolta

'Apeman'	The Kinks
'Rock Island Line'	Lonnie Donegan
'Thong Song'	Sisqó
'Little Darlin' '	The Diamonds
'First Impressions'	The Impressions
'Thorn In My Side'	The Eurythmics
'A Thousand Stars'	Billy Fury
'Surfin' U.S.A.'	Aaron Carter
'Gonna Make You An Offer You Can't Refuse'	Jimmy Helms
'Human'	The Human League
'I've Never Been To Me'	Charlene
'Are You Lonesome Tonight?'	Elvis Presley
'The Price Of Love'	The Everly Brothers
'Give A Little Love'	The Bay City Rollers
'Walking In The Rain With The One I Love'	Love Unlimited
'When A Child Is Born'	Johnny Mathis
'Legend Of Xanadu'	Dave Dee, Dozy, Beaky Mick & Tich

'SONG 2'
Records that Peaked at No. 2 in the Charts
a.k.a. It Should've Been Me!

Here is a list of British number one hits that in our opinion are not among the greatest records ever made. However, these chart-toppers managed to keep over seventy great songs, which under normal circumstances would have made it to number one, off the top spot.

'My Old Man's a Dustman' Lonnie Donegan (14/4/60)
'Fall In Love With You' (Cliff Richard and The Shadows)

'The Good, The Bad And The Ugly' Hugo Montenegro & his Orchestra (27/11/68)
'Eloise' (Barry Ryan)

'Lily The Pink' The Scaffold (18/12/68)
'Ain't Got No – I Got Life' (Nina Simone)

'Lily The Pink' The Scaffold (25/12/68)
'Build Me Up Buttercup' (The Foundations)

'Sugar Sugar' The Archies (1/11/69)
'I'm Gonna Make You Mine' (Lou Christie)

'Sugar Sugar' The Archies (8/11/69–15/11/69)
'Oh Well' (Fleetwood Mac)

'Sugar Sugar' The Archies (22/11/69–29/11/69)
'(Call Me) Number One' (The Tremeloes)

'Sugar Sugar' The Archies (6/12/69)
'Yester-Me, Yester-You, Yesterday' (Stevie Wonder)

'Sugar Sugar' The Archies (13/12/69)
'Ruby Don't Take Your Love To Town' (Kenny Rogers & The First Edition)

'Two Little Boys' Rolf Harris (20/12/69–10/1/70 & 24/1/70)
'Ruby Don't Take Your Love To Town' (Kenny Rogers & The First Edition)

'Two Little Boys' Rolf Harris (17/1/70)
'Suspicious Minds' (Elvis Presley)

'Wand'rin' Star' Lee Marvin (7/3/70)
'I Want You Back' (The Jackson 5)

'Wand'rin' Star' Lee Marvin (14/3/70)
'Let It Be' (The Beatles)

'Back Home' England World Cup Squad (30/5/70)
'Question' (The Moody Blues)

'Grandad Clive Dunn (23/1/71)
'Ride A White Swan' (T.Rex)

'Knock Three Times' Dawn (15/5/71–29/5/71)
'Brown Sugar' (The Rolling Stones)

'Knock Three Times' Dawn (5/6/71)
'Indiana Wants Me' (R.Dean Taylor)

'Ernie (The Fastest Milkman In The West) Benny Hill (11/12/71–
1/1/72)
'Jeepster' (T.Rex)

'Amazing Grace The Pipes And Drums And Military Band Of The Royal
Scots Dragoon Guards (29/4/72–6/5/72)
'Back Off Boogaloo' (Ringo Starr)

'Puppy Love' Donny Osmond (8/7/72–22/7/72)
'Rock And Roll Pt 2' (Gary Glitter)

'Puppy Love' Donny Osmond (29/7/72)
'Sylvia's Mother' (Dr Hook & The Medicine Show)

'Mouldy Ole Dough' Lieutenant Pigeon (21/10/72–28/10/72)
'Donna' (10CC)

'My Ding-A-Ling' Chuck Berry (25/11/72–9/12/72)
'Crazy Horses' (The Osmonds)

'My Ding-A-Ling' Chuck Berry (16/12/72)
'Gudbye T'Jane' (Slade)

'Long-Haired Lover From Liverpool' Little Jimmy Osmond (6/1/73)
'Solid Gold Easy Action' (T.Rex)

'Long-Haired Lover From Liverpool' Little Jimmy Osmond (13/1/73)
'The Jean Genie' (David Bowie)

'Tie A Yellow Ribbon Round The Ole Oak Tree' Dawn featuring Tony Orlando (21/4/73–5/5/73)
'Hello, Hello,I'm Back Again' (Gary Glitter)

'Tie A Yellow Ribbon Round The Ole Oak Tree' Dawn featuring Tony Orlando (12/5/73)
'Hell Raiser' (The Sweet)

'Young Love' Donny Osmond (25/8/73)
'Yesterday Once More' (The Carpenters)

'Young Love' Donny Osmond (1/9/73–8/9/73)
'Dancing On A Saturday Night' (Barry Blue)

'Eye Level' The Simon Park Orchestra (29/9/73–6/10/73)
'Ballroom Blitz' (The Sweet)

'Eye Level' The Simon Park Orchestra (13/10/73)
'My Friend Stan' (Slade)

'Eye Level' The Simon Park Orchestra (20/10/73)
'Daydreamer' (David Cassidy)

'Billy Don't Be A Hero' Paper Lace (23/3/74)
'The Air That I Breathe' (The Hollies)

'The Streak' Ray Stevens (15/6/74)
'Hey Rock And Roll' (Showaddywaddy)

'She' Charles Aznavour (6/7/74–20/7/74)
'Kissing In The Back Row Of The Movies' (The Drifters)

'Whispering Grass' Windsor Davies and Don Estelle (14/6/75)
'Three Steps To Heaven' (Showaddywaddy)

'Save Your Kisses For Me' Brotherhood Of Man (27/3/76)
'Love Really Hurts Without You' (Billy Ocean)

'Save Your Kisses For Me' Brotherhood Of Man (3/4/76–10/4/76)
'You See The Trouble With Me' (Barry White)

'Combine Harvester' The Wurzels (12/6/76)
'Silly Love Songs' (Wings)

'Matchstalk Men and Matchstalk Cats And Dogs' Brian And Michael (8/4/78)
'Denis' (Blondie)

'Matchstalk Men and Matchstalk Cats And Dogs' Brian And Michael (15/4/78)
'I Wonder Why' (Showaddywaddy)

'Theme From M*A*S*H (Suicide Is Painless)' Mash (31/5/80–7/6/80)
'No Doubt About It' (Hot Chocolate)

'Shaddup You Face' Joe Dolce (21/2/81–7/3/81)
'Vienna' (Ultravox)

'Seven Tears' The Goombay Dance Band (3/4/82)
'Just An Illusion' (Imagination)

'Happy Talk' Captain Sensible (10/7/82)
'Abracadabra' (The Steve Miller Band)

'Pass The Dutchie' Musical Youth (25/9/82–2/10/82)
'The Bitterest Pill (I Ever Had To Swallow)' (Jam)

'Pass The Dutchie' Musical Youth (9/10/82)
'Zoom' (Fat Larry's Band)

'Only You' The Flying Pickets (10/10/83–17/10/83)
'Love Of The Common People' (Paul Young)

'Only You' The Flying Pickets (24/12/83–7/1/84)
My Oh My (Slade)

'99 Red Balloons' Nena (10/3/84–17/3/84)
'Joanna' (Kool and The Gang)

'You'll Never Walk Alone' The Crowd (15/6/85)
'Kayleigh' (Marillion)

'Living Doll' Cliff Richard and The Young Ones (5/4/86)
'Wonderful World' (Sam Cooke)

'Rock Me Amadeus' Falco (10/5/86)
'Live To Tell' (Madonna)

'The Chicken Song' Spitting Image (17/5/86–31/5/86)
'On My Own' (Patti LaBelle and Michael McDonald)

'Spirit In The Sky' Doctor and the Medics (7/6/86–14/6/86)
'Holding Back The Years' (Simply Red)

'Every Loser Wins' Nick Berry (1/11/86)
'In The Army Now' (Status Quo)

'Ferry 'Cross The Mersey' Gerry Marsden, Paul McCartney, Holly Johnson, and The Christians (3/6/89)
'Miss You Like Crazy' (Natalie Cole)

'Swing The Mood' Jive Bunny (26/8/89)
'Poison' (Alice Cooper)

'That's What I Like' Jive Bunny (28/10/89–4/11/89)
'Girl I'm Gonna Miss You' (Milli Vanilli)

'You Got It (The Right Stuff)' New Kids On The Block (2/12/89–9/12/89)
'Don't Know Much' (Linda Ronstadt with Aaron Neville)

'Turtle Power' Partners In Cryme (11/8/90)
'Tom's Diner' (DNA featuring Suzanne Vega)

'Itsy Bitsy Teeny Weeny Yellow Polka-Dot Bikini' Bombalurina
(25/8/90)
'Tom's Diner' (DNA featuring Suzanne Vega)

'Itsy Bitsy Teeny Weeny Yellow Polka-Dot Bikini' Bombalurina
(1/9/90–8/9/90)
'Four Bacharach and David Songs' (EP) (Deacon Blue)

'Do The Bartman' The Simpsons (2/3/91)
'Crazy For You' (Remix) (Madonna)

'Doop' Doop (26/3/94)
The Sign (Ace Of Base)

'Doop' Doop (2/4/94)
Streets Of Philadelphia (Bruce Springsteen)

'I Believe / Up On The Roof' Robson and Jerome (1/11/95)
'Wonderwall' (Oasis)

'Barbie Girl' Aqua (1/11/97–8/11/97–22/11/97)
'Torn' (Natalie Imbruglia)

'Flat Beat' Mr Oizo (10/4/99)
'My Name Is' (Eminem)

'Can We Fix It?' Bob The Builder (6/1/01)
'What Makes A Man' (Westlife)

THE MOVIES, TELEVISION AND SHOW BUSINESS

'SING A LITTLE SONG'
75 Songs Recorded by Movie Stars

Just what happens is anyone's guess, but once somebody achieves great success in one arena of life, they begin to believe that all the world is indeed a stage. Film stars are no exception to this rule. John Wayne, for example, was arguably one of the greatest 'western' actors in the history of cinema but what on earth possessed him to pick up a microphone?

Big John is not alone though, as the following list will reveal, in seeing fit to grace us with the sweet serenade of his vocal chords:

John Wayne – America, Why I Love Her
Mae West – Great Balls Of Fire
William Shatner – The Transformed Man
Sissy Spacek – Hangin' Up My Heart
George Segal – The Yama Yama Man
Hayley Mills – Johnny Jingo
Telly Savalas – Some Broken Hearts Never Mend
Virginia McKenna – Two Faces Of Love
Burt Reynolds – Ask Me What I Am
Cheryl Ladd – Good Good Lovin'

Anthony Quinn – Life Itself Will Let You Know
Goldie Hawn – Pitti Pitta
Sidney Poitier – READS Poetry Of The Black Man
Diana Dors – Swingin' Dors
Anthony Perkins – On A Rainy Afternoon
Bette Davis – Miss Bette Davis
Jack Palance – Palance
Honor Blackman – Everything I've Got
Leonard Nimoy – Mr Spock Presents Music From Outer Space
Brigitte Bardot – Sidonie
Eddie Murphy – How Could It Be
Sophia Loren – Bing, Bang, Bong
Robert Mitchum – The Ballad Of Thunder Road
Gina Lollobrigida – La Loa
Jack Lemmon – A Twist Of Lemmon
Jayne Mansfield – Little Things Mean A Lot
David Hemmings – David Hemmings Happens
Cybill Shepherd – I Told Ya I Love Ya, Now Get Out
George Hamilton – By George
Jennifer Lopez – If You Had My Love, Play, Love Don't Cost A Thing
Albert Finney – Albert Finney's Album
Ava Gardner – Loving Dat Man
Dick Van Dyke – Songs I Like
Susan Hampshire – When Love Is True
Kenneth Connor with Glennis Beresford – Much Ado About Love
Joan Collins – Imagine
Ian Carmichael – Girl Crazy
Sondra Locke – I Seek The Night
Yul Brynner – The Gypsy and I
Diana Rigg – Forget Yesterday
Dirk Bogarde – Lyrics For Lovers
Julie Walters – Toy Boys
Joe Pesci (as Joe Ritchie) – Little Joe Sure Can Sing
Joan Crawford – How Long Will It Last
Roger Moore – Where Does Love Go
Farrah Fawcett (as Farrah Fawcett-Majors) – You
James Dean – Jungle Rhythm
Cheryl Ladd – Think It Over
Clint Eastwood – Rowdy
Audrey Hepburn – Moon River
Peter Fonda – Bobby Ogden's Outlaw Blues
Britt Ekland – Do It To Me

David McCallum – The House On Breckenridge Lane
Vanessa Redgrave – Pink Angora
Oliver Reed – The Wild One
Elizabeth Taylor – Send In The Clowns
Robbie Coltrane – New Orleans
John Mills – Young At Heart
Vincent Price – The Monster Mash
James Stewart – Day After Day
Humphrey Bogart – I've Got My Love To Keep Me Warm
Jack Nicholson – Who Is There Among Us Who Knows
Tyrone Power – Chattanooga Choo-Choo
Cary Grant – Did I Remember?
Danny De Vito – They Can't Take That Away From Me
Orson Welles – You Made Me Love You
Rock Hudson – Pillow Talk
Walter Pidgeon – What I'll Do
Michael Caine – Do You Wanna Touch Me (Oh Yeah)
Tom Courtenay – Mrs. Brown You've Got A Lovely Daughter
Laurence Harvey – Camelot
Nanette Newman – Fun Food Factory
Leslie Phillips – Jolly Old Spring
James Stewart and Henry Fonda – Rolling Stone
Orson Welles – I Know What It Is To Be Young

'POP MUZIK'
100 Hits from the Big Screen

Where would we be without music? Well, one thing's for certain, the movies would be a lot less involving, so much so, that the two are seemingly inseparable. When coupled together, music can bring out what is best in film, and vice versa. As an example consider *The Bodyguard* which featured Whitney Houston singing 'I Will Always Love You'. A wonderful song and indeed a quite wonderful film. Honest!

Below are 100 Hits along with the titles of the movies they featured in:

Out Of Reach' by Gabrielle – ***Bridget Jones's Diary***
'Hanky Panky' by Madonna – ***Dick Tracy***
'Unchained Melody' by The Righteous Brothers – ***Ghost*** (a number one hit in the nineties!)
'Take My Breath Away' by Berlin – ***Top Gun***
'My Funny Friend And Me' by Sting – ***The Emperor's New Groove***
'Maneater' by Hall and Oates – ***Runaway Bride***
'Cancer For The Cure' by Eels – ***American Beauty***
'King Of The Road' by Roger Miller – ***Swingers***
'Bad Moon Rising' by Creedence Clearwater Revival – ***An American Werewolf in London***
'No Ordinary Love' by Sade – ***Indecent Proposal***
'There's Always Something There To Remind Me' by Sandie Shaw – ***Letter To Brezhnev***
'What A Wonderful World' by Louis Armstrong – ***Good Morning Vietnam***
'I Don't Want To Miss A Thing' by Aerosmith – ***Armageddon***
'The World Is Not Enough' by Garbage – ***The World Is Not Enough***
'These Boots Are Made For Walking' by Nancy Sinatra – ***Full Metal Jacket***
'I Got You Babe' by Sonny and Cher – ***Buster***
'Stand By Me' by Ben E. King – ***Stand By Me*** (reached number one in the eighties)
'House Of The Rising Sun' by The Animals – ***Casino***
'San Francisco (Be Sure To Wear Some Flowers In Your Hair)' by Scott McKenzie – ***Forrest Gump***
'Love Is All Around' by Wet Wet Wet – ***Four Weddings and a Funeral***
'Picture Of You' by Boyzone – ***Mr. Bean***
'Bohemian Rhapsody' by Queen – ***Wayne's World*** (also number one in the nineties)
'I Do, I Do, I Do, I Do, I Do' by Abba – ***Muriel's Wedding***

'Dream Lover' by Bobby Darin – *Diner*
'Kiss Me' by Sixpence None The Richer – *She's All That*
'I've Never Been To Me' by Charlene – *Priscilla Queen of the Desert*
(reached number one in 1982)
'Lovefool' by Cardigans – *Romeo + Juliet*
'Make Me Smile (Come Up And See Me)' by Steve Harley & Cockney Rebel
– *Velvet Goldmine*
'Without You' by Nilsson – *Casino*
'You're The First The Last My Everything' by Barry White – *Four Weddings and a Funeral*
'Someday' by Eternal – *The Hunchback Of Notre Dame*
'Heart of Glass' by Blondie – *Donnie Brasco*
'Somethin' Else' Eddie Cochran – *Diner*
'Pump Up The Volume' by M.A.R.R.S. – *American Psycho*
'Get Outta My Dreams Get Into My Car' by Billy Ocean – *Striptease*
'When The Going Gets Tough The Tough Get Going' by Billy Ocean – *The Jewel of the Nile*
'Into The Groove' by Madonna – *Desperately Seeking Susan*
'A Groovy Kind of Love' by Phil Collins – *Buster*
'Praise You' by Fatboy Slim – *Cruel Intentions*
'Eye Of The Tiger' by Survivor – *Rocky III*
'I Just Called To Say I Love You' by Stevie Wonder – *The Woman In Red*
'Lady in Red' by Chris De Burgh – *Working Girl*
'Call Me' by Blondie – *American Gigolo*
'Under Pressure' by David Bowie and Queen – *Grosse Pointe Blank*
'All Around The World' by Lisa Stansfield – *Fever Pitch*
'Tainted Love' by Soft Cell – *Coneheads*
'The One And Only' by Chesney Hawkes – *Buddy's Song*
'Gangsta's Paradise' by Coolio featuring L.V. – *Dangerous Minds*
'(Everything I Do) I Do It For You' by Bryan Adams – *Robin Hood: Prince of Thieves*
'I Will Always Love You' by Whitney Houston – *The Bodyguard*
'Show Me Heaven' by Mariah McKee – *Days of Thunder*
'Girls Just Want To Have Fun' by Cyndi Lauper – *To Wong Foo, Thanks For Everything, Julie Newmar*
'Wannabe' by The Spice Girls – *Small Soldiers*
'The Shoop Shoop Song (It's In His Kiss)' by Cher – *Mermaids*
'Steal My Sunshine' by Len – *Go*
'When I Fall In Love' by Nat 'King' Cole – *Mona Lisa*
'Walls Come Tumbling Down' by Style Council – *Billy Elliott*
'Return To Me' by Dean Martin – *Donnie Brasco*
'Hound Dog' by Elvis Presley – *Forrest Grump*

'Ain't No Mountain High Enough' by Marvin Gaye and Tammi Terrell – **_Stepmom_**
'Dream A Little Dream Of Me' by Mama Cass – **_French Kiss_**
'America' by Simon and Garfunkel – **_Almost Famous_**
'Love Song For A Vampire' – Annie Lennox – **_Dracula_**
'Big Spender' by Shirley Bassey – **_Little Voice_**
'Green Onions' by Booker T & The MG's – **_Get Shorty_**
'Mrs. Robinson' by Simon and Garfunkel – **_Forrest Gump_**
'Signed, Sealed, Delivered – I'm Yours' by Stevie Wonder – **_You've Got Mail_**
'Is She Really Going Out With Him' by Joe Jackson – **_There's Something About Mary_**
'Hot Stuff' by Donna Summer – **_The Full Monty_**
'Stuck In The Middle With You' by Stealer's Wheel – **_Reservoir Dogs_**
'Eighteen With A Bullet' by Pete Wingfield – **_Lock, Stock and Two Smoking Barrels_**
'Welcome To The Pleasuredome' by Frankie Goes To Hollywood – **_Toys_**
'Love Is In The Air' by John Paul Young – **_Strictly Ballroom_**
'Have I Told You Lately That I Love You' by Van Morrison – **_One Fine Day_**
'What a Fool Believes' by The Doobie Brothers – **_Frankie and Johnny_**
'Bitch' by Meredith Brooks – **_What Women Want_**
'London's Calling' by Clash – **_Face_**
'Lady Marmalade (Voulez-Vous Coucher Avec Moi Ce Soir?)' by Labelle – **_Carlito's Way_**
'Dude (Looks Like A Lady)' by Aerosmith – **_Wayne's World 2_**
'Waiting For A Star To Fall' by Boy Meets Girl – **_Three Men and a Little Lady_**
'It Must Have Been Love' by Roxette – **_Pretty Woman_**
'Everybody Wants To Rule The World' by Tears for Fears – **_Peter's Friends_**
'Everyday Is A Winding Road' by Sheryl Crow – **_Erin Brockovich_**
'Walking On Sunshine' by Katrina and The Waves – **_Look Who's Talking_**
'I'm So Excited' by Pointer Sisters – **_Working Girl_**
'Change The World' by Eric Clapton – **_Phenomenon_**
'Fashion' by David Bowie – **_Clueless_**
'Good Thing' by Fine Young Cannibals – **_Fever Pitch_**
'Let's Hear It For The Boy' by Deniece Williams – **_Footloose_**
'Moving On Up' by M-People – **_The First Wives Club_**
'Ocean Drive' by Lighthouse Family – **_Jack and Sarah_**
'You Got It' by Roy Orbison – **_Boys On The Side_**
'Beautiful Stranger' by Madonna – **_Austin Powers: The Spy Who Shagged Me_**
'Fantasy' by Mariah Carey – **_Rush Hour_**

'Take A Look Around' by Limp Bizkit – ***Mission Impossible 2***
'Knockin' On Heaven's Door' by Guns N' Roses – ***Days of Thunder***
'Independent Women' by Destiny's Child – ***Charlie's Angels***
'Can't Fight The Moonlight' by LeAnn Rimes – ***Coyote Ugly***
'American Pie' by Madonna – ***The Next Best Thing***
'Pure Shores' by All Saints – ***The Beach***

'FILMSTAR'
Pop Stars on the Big Screen

Like their cinematic counterparts, pop's stars aren't ones to pass up the chance of crossing over and trying their hands at the other's trade. Below is a selection of the best and worst efforts of pop's would-be thespians:

Aerosmith – *Sgt Pepper's Lonely Hearts Club Band* (1978)

Damon Albarn – *Face* (1997)

Gregg Allman – *Rush* (1991)

Herb Alpert – *The Ten Commandments* (1951); *Say One For Me* (1959)

Adam Ant – *Jubilee* (1977); *Love Bites* (1993)

Nicole and Natalie Appleton – *Honest* (2000)

Afrika Bambaataa – *Beat Street* (1984)

The Bee Gees – *Cucumber Castle* (1969)

Björk – *Dancer In The Dark* (2000); *Prêt-à-Porter* (1994)

Melanie Blatt – *Honest* (2000)

Jon Bon Jovi – *The Leading Man* (1996); *Homegrown* (1998); *U-571* (2000); *Pay It Forward* (2000)

Bono – *The Million Dollar Hotel* (2000)

David Bowie – *The Man Who Fell To Earth* (1976); *Just A Gigolo* (1978); *Merry Christmas, Mr. Lawrence* (1983); *The Hunger* (1983); *Absolute Beginners* (1986); *Labyrinth* (1986); *The Last Temptation Of Christ* (1988); *The Linguini Incident* (1992); *Basquiat* (1996)

Brandy – *I Still Know What You Did Last Summer* (1998)

James Brown – *The Blues Brothers* (1980); *Rocky IV* (1985); *When We*

Were Kings (1997); *Blues Brothers 2000* (1998)

Mariah Carey – *The Bachelor* (1999), All That Glitters (2001)

Cher – *Silkwood* (1983); *Mask* (1985); *The Witches Of Eastwick* (1987); *Moonstruck* (1987); *Tea With Mussolini* (1999)

Chicago – *Electra-Glide In Blue* (1973)

Eric Clapton – *Tommy* (1975); *Blues Brothers 2000* (1998)

Phil Collins – *Buster* (1998); *Hook* (1991)

Harry Connick Jr. – *Memphis Belle* (1990); *Little Man Tate* (1991); *Copycat* (1995); *Independence Day* (1996); *Excess Baggage* (1997); *Hope Floats* (1998)

Rita Coolidge – *Pat Garrett And Billy The Kid* (1973)

Alice Cooper – *Sextette* (1978); *Roadie* (1980); *Prince Of Darkness* (1987); *Freddy's Dead: The Final Nightmare* (1991); *Wayne's World* (1992)

Andrea Corr – *The Commitments* (1991); *Evita* (1996)

Elvis Costello – *Spice World* (1997)

Chuck D – *An Alan Smithee Film: Burn Hollywood Burn* (1997)

Roger Daltrey – *Tommy* (1975); *Lisztomania* (1975); *The Legacy* (1975); *Quadrophenia* (1979); *McVicar* (1980); *Buddy's Song* (1991); *Lightning Jack* (1994); *Best* (2000)

Evan Dando – *Reality Bites* (1994)

Ray Davies – *Absolute Beginners* (1986)

Neil Diamond – *The Jazz Singer* (1980)

Bob Dylan – *Pat Garrett And Billy The Kid* (1973); *Hearts Of Fire* (1987)

David Essex – *That'll Be The Day* (1974); *Stardust* (1974); *Silver Dream Racer* (1980)

Gloria Estefan – *50 Violins* (1999)

Fab Five Freddy – *Wild Style* (1982)

Flea – *Less Than Zero* (1987); *Dudes* (1987); *Back To The Future* (1989); *Back To The Future Part II* (1990); *Motorama* (1991); *My Own Private Idaho* (1991); *The Chase* (1994); *The Big Lebowski* (1998); *Fear And Loathing In Las Vegas* (1998); *Psycho* (1998)

Aretha Franklin – *The Blues Brothers* (1980)

Billy Fury – *That'll Be The Day* (1974)

Noel Gallagher – *Mad Cows* (1999)

Art Garfunkel – *Catch-22* (1970); *Carnal Knowledge* (1971)

Stephen Gately – *The Commitments* (1991)

Bob Geldof – *The Wall* (1982); *Spice World* (1997)

Corey Glover – *Platoon* (1986)

Goldie – *The World Is Not Enough* (1999); *Snatch* (2000)

David Gray – *This Year's Love* (1999)

Debbie Harry – *Roadie* (1980); *Videodrome* (1983); *Hairspray* (1988); *Cop Land* (1997)

Richie Havens – *Othello* (1974)

Lauryn Hill – *Sister Act II: Back In The Habit* (1993); *King Of The Hill* (1993)

Jools Holland – *Spice World* (1997)

Whitney Houston – *The Bodyguard* (1992); *Waiting To Exhale* (1995); *The Preacher's Wife* (1996)

Ice Cube – *Boyz N The Hood* (1991); *Trespass* (1992); *Higher Learning* (1995); *Three Kings* (1999); *Next Friday* (2000)

Ice-T – *Breakin'* (1984); *New Jack City* (1991); *Ricochet* (1991); *Trespass* (1992); *Tank Girl* (1994); *Johnny Mnemonic* (1995)

Billy Idol – *The Doors* (1991); *The Wedding Singer* (1998)

Chris Isaak – *Married To The Mob* (1988); *The Silence Of The Lambs* (1991); *Little Buddha* (1993); *That Thing You Do!* (1996)

Janet Jackson – *Poetic Justice* (1993); *Malcolm X* (1992); *Nutty Professor II: The Klumps* (2000)

Michael Jackson – *The Wiz* (1978); *Moonwalker* (1988)

Mick Jagger – *Ned Kelly* (1970); *Performance* (1970); *Freejack* (1992); *Bent* (1997)

Jewel – *Ride With The Devil* (1999)

Elton John – *Tommy* (1975)

Gary Kemp – *The Krays* (1990); *The Bodyguard* (1992); *Killing Zoe* (1994)

Martin Kemp – *The Krays* (1990)

Anthony Kiedis – *F.I.S.T.* (1976); *Less Than Zero* (1987); *Point Break* (1991); *The Chase* (1994)

Kiss – *Detroit Rock City* (1999)

Kris Kristofferson – *Pat Garrett & Billy The Kid* (1973); *A Star Is Born* (1976); *Convoy* (1978); *Heaven's Gate* (1980); *Fire Down Below* (1997); *Blade* (1998)

kd lang – *Salmonberries* (1991)

Lemmy – *Eat The Rich* (1987); *Airheads* (1994)

John Lennon – *How I Won The War* (1967)

Huey Lewis – *Back To The Future* (1985); *Short Cuts* (1993); *Sphere* (1998); *Shadow Of Doubt* (1998)

Little Richard – *Down And Out In Beverly Hills* (1986)

LL Cool J – *The Hard Way* (1991); *Toys* (1992); *Halloween H2O: Twenty Years Later* (1998); *Deep Blue Sea* (1999); *In Too Deep* (1999); *Any Given Sunday* (1999)

Courtney Love – *Sid And Nancy* (1986); *Straight To Hell* (1987); *Basquiat* (1995); *The People Vs. Larry Flynt* (1996); *Feeling Minnesota* (1996); *Man On The Moon* (1999)

Madonna – *A Certain Sacrifice* (1980); *Desperately Seeking Susan* (1985); *Shanghai Surprise* (1986); *Who's That Girl?* (1987); *Bloodhounds Of Broadway* (1989); *Dick Tracy* (1990); *A League Of Their Own* (1992); *Shadows And Fog* (1992); *Body Of Evidence* (1992); *Four Rooms* (1995); *Evita* (1996); *The Next Best Thing* (2000)

Aimee Mann – *The Big Lebowski* (1998)

Marilyn Manson – *Lost Highway* (1997)

Paul McCartney – *Give My Regards To Broad Street* (1984); *Eat The Rich* (1987)

Shane MacGowan – *Eat The Rich* (1987)

MC Shan – *L.A. Story* (1991)

Meat Loaf – *The Rocky Horror Picture Show* (1975); *The Roadie* (1980); *Wayne's World* (1992); *Spice World* (1997); *Crazy In Alabama* (1999); *Fight Club* (1999)

Melle Mel – *Beat Street* (1984)

Bret Michaels – *A Letter From Death Row* (1999)

Bette Midler – *The Rose* (1979); *Down And Out In Beverly Hills* (1986); *Ruthless People* (1986); *Outrageous Fortune* (1987); *Beaches* (1988); *Scenes From A Mall* (1991); *For The Boys* (1991); *Get Shorty* (1995); *The First Wives Club* (1996)

Kylie Minogue – *The Delinquents* (1989); *Street Fighter* (1994); *Bio-Dome* (1996); *Misfits* (1996)

Brian Molko – *Velvet Goldmine* (1998)

Keith Moon – *200 Motels* (1972); *That'll Be The Day* (1974); *Tommy* (1975); *Sextette* (1978)

Alanis Morissette – *Dogma* (1999)

Vince Neil – *The Adventures Of Ford Fairlane* (1990)

Olivia Newton-John – *Grease* (1978); *Xanadu* (1980); *She's Having A Baby* (1988); *In Bed With Madonna* (1991)

Sinéad O'Connor – *Wuthering Heights* (1992); *Butcher Boy* (1997)

Ozzy Osbourne – *Trick Or Treat* (1987); *Private Parts* (1997)

Iggy Pop – *Sid And Nancy* (1986); *The Color Of Money* (1986); *Cry-Baby* (1990); *Hardware* (1990); *Tank Girl* (1994); *Dead Man* (1995); *Crow: City Of Angels* (1996); *Private Parts* (1997)

Prince – *Purple Rain* (1984); *Under The Cherry Moon* (1986); *Graffiti Bridge* (1990)

Queen Latifah – *Jungle Fever* (1991); *House Party 2* (1991); *Juice* (1992); *My Life* (1993); *Sphere* (1998); *Living Out Loud* (1999); *Bringing Out The Dead* (1999)

Busta Rhymes – *Higher Learning* (1995); *Shaft* (2000)

Diana Ross – *Lady Sings The Blues* (1972); *Mahogany* (1975); *The Wiz* (1978)

Shaun Ryder – *The Avengers* (1998)

The Sex Pistols – *The Great Rock 'n' Roll Swindle* (1979)

Tupac Shakur – *Juice* (1992); *Poetic Justice* (1993); *Bullet* (1994); *Above The Rim* (1994); *Gridlock'd* (1996); *Gang Related* (1997)

Will Smith – *Made In America* (1993); *Bad Boys* (1995); *Independence Day* (1996); *Men In Black* (1997); *Enemy Of The State* (1998); *Wild Wild West* (1999); *Men In Black 2* (2001); *Ali* (2001)

The Spice Girls – *Spice World* (1997)

Ringo Starr – *Candy* (1968); *The Magic Christian* (1969); *200 Motels* (1971); *Tommy* (1972); *That'll Be The Day* (1973); *Listzomania* (1975); *Sextette* (1978); *Caveman* (1981); *Give My Regards To Broad Street* (1984)

Sting – *Quadrophenia* (1979); *Dune* (1984); *The Bride* (1985); *Julia & Julia* (1987); *Lock, Stock And Two Smoking Barrels* (1998)

Barbra Streisand – *Funny Girl* (1968); *What's Up Doc?* (1972); *Funny Lady* (1975); *A Star Is Born* (1976); *Yentl* (1983); *The Prince Of Tides* (1991)

James Taylor – *Two-Lane Blacktop* (1971)

Tricky – *The Fifth Element* (1997)

Tina Turner – *Tommy* (1975); *Mad Max Beyond Thunderdome* (1985); *Last Action Hero* (1993)

Usher (Raymond) – *The Faculty* (1998); *She's All That* (1999); *Texas Rangers* (2001)

Vanilla Ice – *Cool As Ice* (1991); *Teenage Mutant Ninja Turtles 2: The Secret Of The Ooze* (1991)

Mark Wahlberg – *Renaissance Man* (1994); *The Basketball Diaries* (1995); *Boogie Nights* (1997); *Three Kings* (1999); *The Yards* (2000); *The Perfect Storm* (2000)

Tom Waits – *The Outsiders* (1983); *The Cotton Club* (1984); *Down By Law* (1986); *Ironweed* (1987); *At Play In The Fields Of The Lord* (1991); *The Fisher King* (1991); *Bram Stoker's Dracula* (1992); *Short Cuts* (1993); *Mystery Men* (1999)

Toyah Wilcox – *Jubilee* (1977); *The Tempest* (1979)

Dennis Wilson – *Two-Lane Blacktop* (1971)

Dwight Yoakam – *Sling Blade* (1996)

Ahmet Zappa – *Pump Up The Volume* (1990)

Dweezil Zappa – *Pretty In Pink* (1986); *The Running Man* (1987); *Jack Frost* (1998)

Frank Zappa – *200 Motels* (1969)

Moon Unit Zappa – *National Lampoon's European Vacation* (1985)

'TELEVISION, THE DRUG OF THE NATION'
Truly Commercial Music

'Sell, Sell, Sell!' – that's the mantra of the television commercial, and what better way to do it than when the commercial concerned is accompanied by a catchy little pop tune?

The following advertisements have all sought to benefit from the inclusion of pop's catchiest hits:

Abbey National – 'Happy Endings (Give Yourself A Pinch)' Lionel Bart
Accurist – 'Give Me Just A Little More Time' Kylie Minogue
Adidas – 'Right Here, Right Now' Fatboy Slim; 'Dive' Propellerheads
Allied Dunbar – 'Let's Face The Music And Dance' Nat 'King' Cole
American Express – 'Blue Monday '88' New Order
Baileys – 'One Way Or Another' Blondie
Boddingtons – 'Back By Dope Demand' King Bee
Brutus Jeans – 'Jeans On' David Dundas
BT Cellnet – 'Beat Goes On' The All Seeing I
Budweiser – 'Ooh La La' Wiseguys
Cadbury's – 'Wonderful Life' Black
Caffrey's – 'Jump Around' House Of Pain (TC5103); 'Clubbed To Death' Rob D; 'Brimful Of Asha' Cornershop (The Norman Cook Remix)
Carling Premier – 'California Dreamin'' Mamas And The Papas; 'Cars (Premier Mix)' Gary Numan; '6 Underground' Sneaker Pimps
Carlsberg – 'Make Me Smile (Come Up And See Me)' Steve Harley And Cockney Rebel; 'An Ubhal As Airde (The Highest Apple)' Runrig; 'They All Laughed' Frank Sinatra
Carphone Warehouse – 'Connected' Stereo MC's
Coca-Cola – 'The First Time' Robin Beck; 'Eat My Goal' Collapsed Lung; 'Hello, Summertime' Bobby Goldsboro; 'It Oughta Sell A Million' Lyn Paul
Daewoo – 'Purple' Crustation with Bronagh Slevin; 'Enter The Monk' Monk & Canatella
Delta Airlines – 'Adiemus' Adiemus
Dulux – 'My Way' Frank Sinatra
Dunlop – 'Venus In Furs' (Live Version) Velvet Underground
Eurostar – 'Sway' Dean Martin
Fiat – '(I Don't Know Why) But I Do' Clarence 'Frogman' Henry; 'Only You' Praise; 'Music To Watch Girls By' Andy Williams

Flora – 'If I Love Ya, Then I Need Ya, If I Need Ya, I Want'cha Around' Eartha Kitt

Ford – 'You Gotta Be (1999 Mix)' Des'ree; 'You Can Go Your Own Way' Chris Rea; 'Bullitt' Lalo Schifrin; 'Born To Be Wild' Steppenwolf

Gap 'Crazy Little Thing Called Love' Dwight Yoakam; 'Blow Up A Go-Go' James Clarke

Guinness – 'We Have All The Time In The World' Louis Armstrong; 'Guaglione' Perez 'Prez' Prado

Honda – 'We Gotta Get Out Of This Place' Space

Impulse – 'Sugar Is Sweeter' CJ Bolland

Jaguar – 'History Repeating' Propellerheads featuring Shirley Bassey

Kenco – 'She Sells Sanctuary' The Cult

Kiss – '(Mucho Mambo) Sway' Shaft

Lancome – 'Everything's Gonna Be Alright' Sweetbox

Lee Jeans – 'Baby Lee' John Lee Hooker; 'Boom Boom' John Lee Hooker

Levi's – 'Novelty Waves' Biosphere; 'It's Written On Your Body' Ronnie Bond; 'Wonderful World' Sam Cooke; 'Don't Be A Dummy' John Du Cann; '(Take A Little) Piece Of My Heart' Erma Franklin; 'Turn On, Tune In, Cop Out' Freak Power; 'I Heard It Through The Grapevine' Marvin Gaye; 'Heart Attack And Vine' Screamin' Jay Hawkins; 'Stand By Me' Ben E. King; 'A Nanny In Manhattan' Lilys; 'The Joker' Steve Miller Band; 'Flat Beat' Mr. Oizo; 'Whine And Grine' Prince Buster; 'Boombastic' Shaggy; 'When A Man Loves A Woman' Percy Sledge; 'Inside' Stiltskin; '20th Century Boy' Marc Bolan and T-Rex; 'Mad About The Boy' Dinah Washington; 'Mannish Boy' Muddy Waters

L'Oreal – 'Encore Une Fois' Sash!

Lucozade – 'Fed Up' House Of Pain

Lynx – 'Bentley's Gonna Sort You Out' Bentley Rhythm Ace

Mastercard – 'Have A Go Hero' Urban DK

Maynard's Wine Gums – 'Hoots Mon' Lord Rockingham's XI

Mercedes – 'The Fun Lovin' Criminal' Fun Lovin' Criminals

Miller – 'What I Like About You' Loop Da Loop

Nat West – 'Rodney Yates' David Holmes

Nike – 'Soul Bossa Nova' Cool, The Fab And The Groovy present Quincy Jones; 'My Way' Shane McGowan; 'Mas Que Nada' Tamba Trio; 'Easy Listening Superstar' Le Hammond Inferno

Nivea – 'Blue Velvet' Bobby Vinton

Orange – 'Loose Fit' Happy Mondays

Paxo – 'I'm In The Mood For Love' Lord Tanamo

Pepsi – 'Lipsmackin' Rock 'N Rollin' ' Peter Blake

Peugeot – 'Fly Away' Lenny Kravitz; 'Baby Please Don't Go' Them; 'Can't Take My Eyes Off You' Andy Williams

Physio Sports – 'Sounds Of Da Police' KRS-One
Renault – 'Keep On Movin'' Soul II Soul; 'Organ Grinder's Swing' Jimmy Smith; 'Run On' Moby
Rolling Rock – 'Drinking In L.A.' Bran Van 3000; 'Drifting Away' Faithless
Rover – 'Going Out Of My Head' Fatboy Slim
Siemens – 'Devil's Trill' Vanessa-Mae
Smile – 'Smile' The Supernaturals
Smirnoff Vodka – 'Tame' Pixies
Soft and Gentle – 'Move Closer' Phyllis Nelson
Sony – 'Days' Kirsty MacColl; 'Rude Boy Rock' Lionrock
Standard Life Assurance – 'Wonderful Life' Black
Strand Cigarettes – 'The Lonely Man Theme' Cliff Adams Orchestra
Sunny Delight – 'Jacques Your Body (Make Me Sweat) ('99 Mix)' Les Rythmes Digitales
Tango – 'Don't You Want Me ('96 Pugilist Mix)' Felix
Tennents Extra – 'Silent Running' Mike And The Mechanics
Toyota – 'The Passenger' Iggy Pop
Vauxhall – 'Original' Leftfield
Volkswagen – 'Young At Heart' Bluebells; 'Sorry But I'm Gonna Have To Pass' Coasters; 'Feeling Good' Nina Simone
Walls Calippo 'My Generation' The Who
Wrigley's Chewing Gum – 'All Right Now' Free
Yellow Pages – 'Days' The Kinks

'CARTOON HEROES'
Pop's 'Toon' Stars

The following pop stars have all allowed themselves to be immortalised in celluloid, and in so doing, become 'toon' stars. The most popular show for pop star appearances has to be Matt Groening's *The Simpsons*, which first aired on American TV in 1989. Since then over 40 musicians have appeared alongside Bart, Lisa, Marge, Homer *et al*:

Paul Anka – as himself in the Simpsons episode, 'Tree House of Horrors IV'

Reginald 'Fieldy' Arvizu (KoRn) – as himself in the *South Park* episode, 'Korn's Groovy Pirate Ship'

Tony Bennett – as himself in the *Simpsons* episode, 'Dancin' Homer'

Bono (U2) – as himself in the *Simpsons* episode, 'The Trash of The Titans'

James Brown – as himself in the *Simpsons* episode, 'Bart's Inner Child'

Joe C (Kid Rock's 3 feet 9 inches rapper) – as himself in the *Simpsons* episode, 'Kill the Alligator and Run'

Johnny Cash – as the voice of 'Coyote' in the *Simpsons* episode, 'El Viaje Misterioso de Nuestro Jomer (The Mysterious Voyage of Our Homer)'

Adam Clayton (U2) – as himself in the *Simpsons* episode, 'The Trash of The Titans'

Billy Corgan (Smashing Pumpkins) – as himself in the *Simpsons* episode, 'Homerpalooza'

David Crosby – as himself in the *Simpsons* episode, 'Marge In Chains'

Roger Daltrey – as himself in the *Simpsons* episode, 'A Tale of Two Springfields'

Jonathan Davis (KoRn) – as himself in the *South Park* episode, 'Korn's Groovy Pirate Ghost Mystery'

The Edge (U2) – as himself in the *Simpsons* episode, 'The Trash of The Titans'

John Entwistle (Who) – as himself in the *Simpsons* episode, 'A Tale of Two Springfields'

Flea (Red Hot Chili Peppers) – as himself in the *Simpsons* episode, 'Krusty Gets Kancelled'

Kim Gordon (Sonic Youth) – as herself in the *Simpsons* episode, 'Homerpalooza'

Christopher Guest – as his alter ego and Spinal Tap guitarist, Nigel Tufnel, in the *Simpsons* episode, 'The Otto Show'

George Harrison – as himself in the *Simpsons* episode, 'Homer's Barbershop Quartet'

Isaac Hayes – *South Park* regular Jerome McElroy aka 'Chef'

Bob Hope – as himself in the *Simpsons* episode, 'Lisa the Beauty Queen'

James Iha (Smashing Pumpkins) – as himself in the *Simpsons* episode, 'Homerpalooza'

Rick James – as himself in the *South Park* Special, 'Chef Aid'

Elton John – as himself in both the *South Park* Special, 'Chef Aid' and the *Simpsons* episode, 'I'm With Cupid'

Tom Jones – as himself in the *Simpsons* episode, 'Marge Gets A Job'

Kid Rock – as himself in the *Simpsons* episode, 'Kill the Alligator and Run'

Cyndi Lauper – as herself in the *Simpsons* episode, 'Wild Barts Can't Be Broken'

Paul and Linda McCartney – as themselves in the *Simpsons* episode, 'Lisa the Vegetarian'

Michael McKean – as his alter-ego and Spinal Tap singer David St Hubbins in the *Simpsons* episode, 'The Otto Show'

Meat Loaf – as himself in the *South Park* Special, 'Chef Aid'

Bette Midler – as herself in the *Simpsons* episode, 'Krusty Gets Kancelled'

Thurston Moore (Sonic Youth) – as himself in the *Simpsons* episode, 'Homerpalooza'

Larry Mullen (U2) – as himself in the *Simpsons* episode, 'The Trash of The Titans'

Willie Nelson – as himself in the *Simpsons* episode, 'Behind The Laughter'

Ozzy Osbourne – as himself in the *South Park* Special, 'Chef Aid'

Dolly Parton – as herself in the *Simpsons* episode, 'Sunday, Cruddy Sunday'

Joe Perry (Aerosmith) – as himself in the *Simpsons* episode, 'Flaming Moe's'

Tito Puente – as himself in the *Simpsons* episode, 'Who Shot Mr. Burns? Part 1' and also 'Who Shot Mr. Burns? Part 2'

Joey, Johnny and Marky Ramone – all as themselves in the *Simpsons* episode, 'Rosebud'

Linda Ronstadt – as herself in the *Simpsons* episode, 'Mr. Plow'

James 'Munkey' Shaffer (KoRn) – as himself in the *South Park* episode, 'Korn's Groovy Pirate Ship'

Harry Shearer – better known as Spinal Tap bassist Derek Smalls, for whom he provided the voice in the *Simpsons* episode, 'The Otto Show'

Britney Spears – as herself in the *Simpsons* episode, 'The Mansion Family'

Ringo Starr – as himself in the *Simpsons* episode, 'Brush With Greatness'

Sting – as himself in the *Simpsons* episode, 'Radio Bart'

Joe Strummer (Clash) – as himself in the *South Park* Special, 'Chef Aid'

Steven Tyler (Aerosmith) – as himself in the *Simpsons* episode, 'Flaming Moe's'

Brian 'Head' Welch (KoRn) – as himself in the *South Park* episode, 'Korn's Groovy Pirate Ship'

Barry White – as himself in the *Simpsons* episode, 'Whacking Day'

Hank Williams Jr – as the Canyonero Singer in the *Simpsons* episodes, 'The Last Temptation of Krusty' and 'Marge Simpson in: "Screaming Yellow Honkers"'

D'arcy Wretzky (Smashing Pumpkins) – as herself in the *Simpsons* episode, 'Homerpalooza'

'LITTLE BIT OF SOAP'
50 Soap Stars Turned Pop Stars

In today's world soap operas or soaps as they are lovingly referred to, have become a mainstay of popular culture. Soaps such as *EastEnders* and *Coronation Street* regularly top the weekly TV viewing figures, and the actors who feature in them have joined the ranks of the nation's favourite celebrities. Such is the appeal of soap stars that they frequently choose to venture beyond the confines of their day-jobs and pursue slightly wackier (and often regrettable) ventures, such as becoming a pop star. Some find success and others find, well, let's just say they find something else.

1. **Robson and Jerome (Soldier Soldier)** 'Unchained Melody' / '(There'll Be Bluebirds Over) The White Cliffs Of Dover'
2. **Nick Berry (EastEnders / Heartbeat)** 'Every Loser Wins'
3. **Cast of Casualty** 'Everlasting Love'
4. **Cast of Grange Hill** 'Just Say No'
5. **Anita Dobson and The Simon May Orchestra (EastEnders)** 'Anyone Can Fall In Love'
6. **Letitia Dean and Paul Medford (EastEnders)** 'Something Outa Nothing'
7. **Coronation Street Cast featuring Bill Waddington (Percy Sugden) / Amanda Barrie and Johnny Briggs (Alma & Mike Baldwin)** 'Always Look On The Bright Side Of Life' / 'Something Stupid'
8. **Michelle Gayle (EastEnders)** 'Sweetness'
9. **Tricia Penrose (Heartbeat)** 'Where Did Our Love Go?'
10. **Barbara Windsor (EastEnders)** – 'Ten Gallon Hat'
11. **Mike Reid (EastEnders)** 'Swinging On A Star'
12. **Kylie Minogue (Neighbours)** 'I Should Be So Lucky' and many, many more
13. **Jason Donovan (Neighbours)** 'Nothing Can Divide Us'
14. **Dannii Minogue (Home And Away)** 'All I Want To Do'
15. **Sally Lindsay (Coronation Street)** 'There's No One Quite Like Grandma' (St Winifred's School Choir)
16. **David Hasselhoff (Knight Rider / Baywatch)** 'If I Could Only Say Goodbye'
17. **Jimmy Nail (Auf Wiedersehen Pet / Spender / Crocodile Shoes)** 'Ain't No Doubt'
18. **Craig McLachlan (Neighbours / Bugs / Home And Away)** 'Mona'

19. **PJ and Duncan (aka Ant and Dec) (Byker Grove)** 'Let's Get Ready To Rhumble'
20. **Malandra Burrows (Emmerdale)** 'Just This Side Of Love'
21. **Martine McCutcheon (EastEnders)** 'Perfect Moment'
22. **Natalie Imbruglia (Neighbours)** 'Torn'
23. **Sean Maguire (Grange Hill / EastEnders / Dangerfield)** 'Someone To Love'
24. **Matthew Marsden (Coronation Street)** 'The Heart's Lone Desire'
25. **Michelle Collins (EastEnders / Sunburn)** 'Sunburn'
26. **Sid Owen (EastEnders)** 'Good Thing Going'
27. **Sid Owen and Patsy Palmer (EastEnders)** 'Better Believe It (Children In Need)'
28. **Kevin Kennedy (Coronation Street)** 'Bulldog Nation'
29. **Dennis Waterman (Minder)** 'I Could Be So Good For You'
30. **Tracy Shaw (Coronation Street)** 'Happenin' All Over Again'
31. **Adam Rickitt (Coronation Street)** 'I Breathe Again'
32. **John Alford (Grange Hill / London's Burning)** 'Smoke Gets In Your Eyes'
33. **Jane McDonald (Cruise)** 'Cruise Into Christmas'
34. **Rebecca Wheatley (Casualty)** 'Stay With Me Baby'
35. **Denise Welch (Soldier, Soldier)** 'You Don't Have To Say You Love Me' / 'Cry Me A River'
36. **Johnny Briggs (Coronation Street)** – 'Living On The Road'
37. **Betty Driver (Coronation Street)** – *The Girl From The Street* (album)
38. **Larry Hagman (Dallas)** – 'Ballad Of The Good Luck Charm'
39. **Jeremy Jackson (Baywatch)** – 'You Can Run'
40. **Arthur Lowe (Coronation Street)** – 'And Yet And Yet'
41. **Ian McShane (Lovejoy)** – 'Harry Brown'
42. **Wendy Richard (with Diana Berry) (EastEnders)** – 'We Had A Dream'
43. **Chris Sandford (Coronation Street)** – 'Not Too Little, Not Too Much'
44. **Michael Elphick (Boon)** – 'Gotcha'
45. **Eddie Grundy (The Archers)** – 'Poor Pig'
46. **David Hasselhoff (Knight Rider / Baywatch)** – 'Lonely Is The Night'
47. **Paul Henry (Crossroads)** – 'Waiting At The Crossroads'
48. **Patrick Duffy (with Mireille Mathieu) (Dallas)** – 'Together We're Strong'
49. **Peter Adamson and Pat Phoenix (Coronation Street)** – 'Two Of Us'
50. **Martin Shaw (Always And Everyone)** – 'Cross My Heart And Hope To Die'

'STARS ON 45'
Showbiz People Who've Made Records

Will we ever be safe? It seems that the whole gamut of celebrities has at one time or another fancied themselves as a bit of pop star. We've already had a look at the film and soap stars. Now it's the turn of the comedians, sportsmen, radio presenters, models, etc, all of whom have attempted to capitalise upon their celebrity status by cutting a record. The horror of it all! Anyway, as something of a warning, we've compiled this list, identifying some of the more dangerous culprits:

Comedians

1. **Russ Abbot** – The Space Invaders Meet The Purple People Eater
2. **Dave Allen** – The Good Earth
3. **Hylda Baker** – Give Us A Kiss
4. **Michael Barrymore** – Kenny The Kangaroo
5. **Victor Borge** – Spring And Autumn
6. **Dora Bryan** – Diamonds Are A Girl's Best Friend
7. **Cannon and Ball** – Everybody's Making It Big But Me
8. **Jimmy Clitheroe** – They All Blame Jim
9. **Norman Collier** – The Singing Chicken
10. **Brian Conley** – Resurrection Shuffle
11. **Kenneth Connor** – Ramona
12. **Phil Cool** – Bridge Over Troubled Water
13. **Harry H. Corbett** – Junk Shop
14. **Ronnie Corbett** – Big Man
15. **Roger De Courcey and Nookie** – Nookie's Song
16. **Jim Davidson** – Silver Threads Amongst The Gold
17. **Freddy (Parrot Face) Davies** – So Lucky
18. **Les Dawson** – Promise Me
19. **Jack Douglas** – Swanee River
20. **Charlie Drake** – Charles Drake 007
21. **Dick Emery** – You're Just As Lovely Today
22. **Derek Guyler** – (You Can't Kill An Old) Desert Rat
23. **Mike Harding** – Disco Vampire
24. **Arthur Haynes** – Not To Worry
25. **Dickie Henderson** – Kalamazoo
26. **Lenny Henry** – Boiled Beef And Carrots

27. **Frankie Howard and June Whitfield** – Up Je T'Aime
28. **Roy Hudd** – The Hole In The Elephant's Bottom
29. **John Inman** – I'm Free
30. **Sidney James** – The 'Ooter Song
31. **Little and Large** – Rock Steady
32. **Bernard Manning** – Everybody's Fool
33. **Spike Milligan** – Purple Aeroplane
34. **Warren Mitchell** – The Writing On The Wall
35. **Morecambe and Wise** – Following You Around
36. **Danny La Rue** – The Counting Song
37. **Tom O'Connor** – Festival Song
38. **Charlie Williams** – Ta Luv
39. **Mike and Bernie Winters** – Fallout Shelter
40. **Mike Yarwood** – Saturday Night At The Crown

Models

1. **Leslie Ash** – Don't Call Me Up Baby
2. **Anne Aston** – I Can't Stop Myself From Loving You Babe
3. **Naomi Campbell** – *Babywoman* (album)
4. **Lorraine Chase** – It's Nice 'Ere Innit?
5. **Nina Carter and Frankie Ward (known as Blonde On Blonde)** – Whole Lotta Love
6. **Sandra Dickinson** – A Big Star In Hollywood
7. **Julie Ege** – Love
8. **Samantha Fox** – Aim To Win
9. **Susan George** – I'll Get Over You
10. **Samantha Juste** – No-One Needs My Love Today
11. **Rula Lenska** – I'm In The Mood For Love
12. **Ami MacDonald** – Ain't Nobody Gonna Touch My Body But My Baby And Me
13. **Erika Roe** – Remember Then
14. **Isla St. Clair** – Songbird
15. **Mandy Smith** – I Just Can't Wait
17. **Linda Thorson** – Here I Am
17. **Twiggy** – Beautiful Dreams

Sportsmen

1. **Muhammad Ali** – I Am The Greatest
2. **Chicago Bears** – Superbowl Shuffle
3. **Nigel Benn** – Stand And Fight
4. **George Best** (with Mary Staven (a former Miss World)) – It Takes Two
5. **Ian Botham** (with Bobby Buck) – Time Out To Care
6. **Jackie Charlton** – Simple Little Things
7. **Linford Christie** – Keep On Running
8. **Brian Clough** – You Can't Win 'Em All
9. **Henry Cooper** – Knock Me Down With A Feather
10. **Jo Durie** – Wimbledon Lawns
11. **Giant Haystacks** – Baby I Need You
12. **Alex 'Hurricane' Higgins** – One-Four-Seven
13. **Tony Jacklin** – *Tony Jacklin Swings Into* (album)
14. **Vinnie Jones** – Woolly Bully
15. **Kevin Keegan** – It Ain't Easy
16. **Evel Knievel** – Why
17. **Meadowlark Lemon** – My Kids
18. **Barry McGuigan** – Somebody To Call My Girl
19. **Freddy Mills** – One For The Road
20. **Gary Player** – *Gary Player Sings* (album)
21. **Peter Shilton and Ray Clemence** – Side By Side
22. **Harvey Smith** – True Love
23. **Billy Walker** – A Certain Smile
24. **Billy Wright** – Sing-Song Just For Kicks
25. **Terry Venables** – What Do You Want To Make Those Eyes At Me For

TV and Radio Presenters

1. **Eamonn Andrews** – The Ship That Never Sailed
2. **Tony Blackburn** (as Big Daddy and the Sugarcanes) – Tomorrow Night
3. **David Bellamy** – Brontosaurus Will You Wait For Me
4. **Keith Chegwin** – I'll Never Fall In Love Again
5. **Simon Dee** – Julie
6. **Noel Edmonds (as Kirk Houston)** – Alcatraz
7. **Kenny Everett and Dave Cash** – Knees
8. **Bruce Forsyth** – Didn't He Do Well

9. **Alan Freeman** – Madison Time
10. **Larry Grayson** – Shut That Door
11. **Hughie Green** – Cuddle Up Closer
12. **Sarah Greene** – Eenie Meenie
13. **David Hamilton** – Have You Heard The News
14. **Derek Jameson** – Do They Mean Us
15. **Bob Monkhouse** – I Remember Natalie
16. **Pete Murray and Brian Matthew** – Gee Ma, I Wanna Go Home
17. **Des O'Connor** – Thin Chow Mein
18. **Mike Read** – Tell Me I'm Wrong
19. **Ted Rodgers** – The Man From Cuckoo
20. **Jimmy Savile** – Ahab The Arab
21. **David Symonds** – Here Is The News
22. **Tommy Vance** – Off The Hook
23. **James Whale** – Bimbo

GUEST STARS

'WITH A LITTLE HELP FROM MY FRIENDS'
Cameo Appearances

It's always good to have friends, especially if they can play the odd bit of guitar or maybe even sing a little.

The following musicians have all made guest appearances (sometimes credited, sometimes not) on the songs of their fellow artists:

Duane Allman – plays slide guitar on Derek And The Dominoes', 'Layla'.

Herb Alpert – can be heard blowing his trumpet on UB40's 1987 hit, 'Rat In Mi Kitchen'.

Average White Band – back Chuck Berry on the gloriously titled, 'My Ding-A-Ling'.

Jeff Beck – plays guitar on Tina Turner's 'Private Dancer'.

Bono – as well as fulfilling production duties on Roy Orbison's 'She's A Mystery To Me', the Irish warbler can also be heard playing guitar.

Kate Bush – can be heard singing away to her little heart's content on Peter Gabriel's 1980s hit 'Games Without Frontiers'.

Ray Charles – apparently Charles can be heard clapping away on the Archies' hit Sugar Sugar.

Cher – hear Cher getting all righteous on 'You've Lost That Lovin' Feeling' by the one and only Righteous Brothers (who weren't actually brothers – see 'Like Sister and Brother' p. 41). She also fulfils a backing role on 'Da Doo Ron Ron' by The Crystals, as well as 'Be My Baby' by The Ronettes. Incidentally all of the above tracks were produced by the legendary Phil Spector who at the time was the employer of Cher's husband Sonny. Finally, she duets (albeit without credit) on Meat Loaf's classic, 'Dead Ringer For Love'.

Neneh Cherry – duets with Matt Johnson, on The The's 'Slow Train To Dawn' from the 1986 album *Infected*.

Eric Clapton – guitar on George Harrison's 'While My Guitar Gently Weeps'; also on Aretha Franklin's 'Good To Me As I Am To You'.

Bootsy Collins – as well as guesting on the latest Fatboy Slim album *Halfway Between the Gutter and the Stars*, the bassist can be heard on James Brown's classic track, 'Get Up I Feel Like Being A Sex Machine (Part 1)'.

Phil Collins – drums on Adam Ant's 'Puss In Boots'.

Thomas Dolby – guests on Belinda Carlisle's *Heaven On Earth*.

Donovan – backing vocals on the Beatles 'Yellow Submarine'.

Michael Douglas – Yes! Michael Douglas the actor. He has a go at singing (backing vocals only) on Billy Ocean's 'When The Going Gets Tough (The Tough Get Going)'.

Bob Dylan – vocals on U2's 'Love Rescue Me'.

Everly Brothers – vocals on Paul Simon's *Graceland* album.

Flea (Red Hot Chili Peppers) – bass on Mick Jagger's *Wandering Spirit*.

Frankie Goes To Hollywood – backing vocals on ABC's hit 'S.O.S.'.

Robert Fripp (King Crimson) – plays guitar on Blondie's *Parallel Lines*.

Dave Gilmour – performs guitar duties on Kate Bush's 'Wuthering Heights'.

George Harrison – guitar on Cream's 'Badge'; lead guitar on Donovan's 'Sunshine Superman'; not forgetting slide guitar on Belinda Carlisle's 'Leave A Light On'.

Whitney Houston – vocals on *Fiyo On The Bayou* by the Neville Brothers.

Michael Jackson – backing vocals on 'Somebody's Watching Me' by Rockwell; also Michael Jackson & Paul McCartney – Ebony and Ivory.

Mick Jagger – backing vocals on Carly Simon's 'You're So Vain'; Jagger can also be heard in a supporting role on the Beatles' 'All You Need Is Love', along with Graham Nash, Keith Moon, Keith Richard, Marianne Faithfull, Garry Leeds, Jane Asher and Patti Boyd!

Billy Joel – plays piano on 'Leader Of The Pack', by the Shangri-Las.

Elton John – vocals on 'Free' by Rick Astley. Dear old Reg also plays piano on the Hollies' ' He Ain't Heavy, He's My Brother'.

Booker T. Jones (Booker T. and The MG's) – Hammond organ on *Grave Dancer's Union* by Soul Asylum.

Chaka Khan – vocals on Robert Palmer's 'Addicted To Love'.

Mark King – the star of Level 42 can be heard slapping his bass on Midge Ure's 'If I Was'.

John Lennon – vocals on David Bowie's 'Fame'. Lennon can also be heard on Elton John's cover of the Beatles hit, 'Lucy In The Sky With Diamonds'.

Little Richard – sings on 'Tears On My Pillow' by New Edition.

Paul McCartney – backing vocals (whispers) on Donovan's 'Mellow Yellow'. While not strictly speaking a cameo appearance, Paul plays not only bass, but drums also on 'The Ballad Of John And Yoko'. John, incidentally plays guitar and piano. The other two Beatles were unavailable at the time of the 1969 recording session. Mr McCartney can also be heard strumming the bass on James Taylor's *Carolina In My Mind*.

Paul's bass can be heard, *sans* Paul, on Wang Chung's 1980s hit 'Dance Hall Days'. During the recording session at London's Abbey Road studios, Wang Chung realised that they lacked one crucial instrument, a left-handed bass guitar. As luck would have it, left-handed bassist Paul McCartney was recording in the next studio at that very moment. He duly agreed to loan them his bass for the recording.

Sandy Nelson – plays drums on the Teddy Bear's' No. 1 US hit, 'To Know Him, Is To Love Him'. The Teddy Bears were formed by legendary producer Phil Spector.

Diana Ross – along with her fellow Supremes provides backing vocals on Marvin Gaye's 'Can I Get A Witness' from 1963.

Luther Vandross – love's very own walrus can be heard singing backing vocals on Chic's, 'Le Freak'.

Rick Wakeman – plays synthesizer on David Bowie's 'Space Oddity'.

Barry White – can be heard tinkling the ivories on Jesse Belvin's American hit, 'Goodnight My Love'. White was aged eleven at the time. An older and of course wiser White can also be heard on Felice Taylor's 'I Feel Love Comin' On', as well as Bob & Earl's 'Harlem Shuffle'.

Brian Wilson – backing vocals on Johnny Rivers's 1975 release of 'Help Me Rhonda'.

Stevie Wonder – plays harmonica on Chaka Khan's 'I Feel For You'.

BAD BOYS (AND GIRLS) OF POP

'FUN LOVIN' CRIMINAL'
Pop's Lawbreakers

Once you achieve fame and fortune, things can get a little tame around town. Celebrity alone no longer holds the allure it once did. When this happens a 'walk on the wildside' seems all the more attractive. Such is the lot of the following stars, all of whom, have found themselves on the wrong side of the law at one time or another.

Chuck Berry

Berry's certainly no Johnny B. Goode. For starters, he was convicted of having sex with an underage hooker in the late fifties, then in 1979 he served four months in the slammer for tax evasion – it seems he'd overlooked a payment in the region of $200,000 regarding his '73 tax return. The sort of mistake we all make. So far, aside from a little paedophilia and some dodgy book-keeping, nothing too bad (not!). However, when Berry chose to open the Southern Air restaurant in Missouri, even seedier goings on occurred. Good old 'ding-a-ling' Chuck saw fit to install a video camera in the ladies' toilets, presumably in the name of customer safety, thereafter recording the more personal moments of some two hundred women, including three minors. In filing charges against Berry, the State Attorney argued that he had made the tapes, 'for the purpose of the entertainment and gratification of the abnormal . . . sexual fetishes and sexual predilections'. The charges against Berry were subsequently dropped, in return for financial compensation to all those concerned.

Danny Bonaduce aka Danny Partridge

Bonaduce's real life shenanigans have been far removed from those of his choirboyesque Partridge Family alter ego. In 1991 he was arrested for assaulting a prostitute in Phoenix, Arizona. It seems Bonaduce had quite literally gotten more than he bargained for, since the 'she' he had chosen to employ was in fact a 'he'. A slightly peeved Bonaduce subsequently demanded a refund, assaulted the transvestite, and fled the scene at a breakneck speed of 125 mph (the limit was 25 mph)!

David Bowie

Bowie's most interesting run-in with the law happened in April 1976. At the time he was going through his 'Thin White Duke' phase (read: 'Thin White Nazi'!). With the horrors of World War II still fresh in their memories, customs officials on the Polish / Russian border therefore took a bleak view of the Duke when he attempted to cross the frontier by train, on his return from Moscow. They were particularly interested in his never-leave-home-without-it' collection of Nazi memorabilia and books. Bowie claimed that he was researching a planned film about the life of Goebbels. Whilst he wasn't arrested, Bowie was detained for several hours as a consequence.

Bobby Brown

Robert Baresford Brown is well known for his fondness of pugilism, something he loves to partake in whenever possible. Once, while walking by a DisneyWorld Club in Orlando, Brown became embroiled in an argument with a white man, who had apparently been staring at him. After a heated exchange of words, culminating, if Brown is to be believed, in the other man spitting at him, Brown's bodyguard knocked the man to the floor, and Brown, always keen to take to the bottle (he's a reformed (?) alcoholic) did just that, hitting the guy with a bottle and nearly removing his ear in the process. Brown subsequently left the scene in a police car, cuffed and under arrest. As a gesture of goodwill he urinated in the squad car and gave its upholstery his seal of approval, carving a four-letter word into it with a pen. Guess that was 'his prerogative'.

Ian Brown

Sweet-talking ex-Stone Roses front man Ian Brown found himself in a spot of bother after threatening to chop the hands off a British Airways stewardess, during a flight from Paris to Manchester. An understanding judge rewarded him with four months inside. Ultimately though, Brown only spent eight weeks in prison, beginning his sentence at Kirkham's open prison, before being transferred to the notorious Strangeways where he served the remainder.

James Brown

In September 1988, a disgruntled Brown charged into an insurance seminar adjacent to his trailer, waving a shotgun at those in attendance; apparently somebody had used his bathroom without asking. Naughty boy! A high-speed police chase ensued, during which Brown attempted to run down two officers who were manning a roadblock. The officers concerned reacted by shooting out the tyres of his truck bringing the Godfather Of Soul to an unexpected stop. Brown was subsequently charged with aggravated assault, carrying a firearm, PCP possession and traffic violations. He was given a six-and-a-half year sentence but made parole after 26 months.

Peter Buck

The REM guitarist found himself in trouble, after an alleged bout of air rage, while on a flight from Seattle to London, prior to the band's appearance at the 'South Africa Freedom Day' concert in London's Trafalgar Square on 29 April 2001.

Buck was charged with two instances of common assault on members of the flight's cabin staff, criminal damage, being intoxicated while on an aircraft, and for a public order offence.

At the time of writing, Buck had been released on £30,000 bail, to enable him to carry out promotional duties in connection with the band's latest album *Reveal*.

Joe Cocker

Cocker and six of his bandmates were arrested in 1972 while in Adelaide for possession of heroin, marijuana and the necessary syringes. If you've ever seen footage of Cocker dancing on stage at Woodstock you'll realise that this all makes perfect sense.

Hugh Cornwell

Strangler Cornwell's collection of natural highs earned him five weeks hard time when he was caught in 1980 with heroin, magic mushrooms, cocaine and pot. Something for every occasion, no less.

Elvis Costello

In 1977, an opportunistic Costello, eager to land a record deal, decided to give an impromptu performance for CBS record execs attending a conference at London's Hilton hotel. Costello made the adjacent street his stage, and as such was arrested and fined for performing without a licence. His gamble paid off though when he was given a record contract several months later.

Steve Craddock (Ocean Colour Scene)

In 1998 Craddock was officially cautioned by police for possession of cocaine. If only he'd 'caught the train' things could have been so different.

David Crosby

While air-bound en route from St Louis to Denver, a stewardess who had been asked to retrieve Crosby's bag from the cargo hold, was shocked to discover that it contained slightly more than just his 'medication'. The sight that greeted her eyes included heroin, cocaine, marijuana and hashish, as well as that all-round panacea – a .22 Magnum. Since it had been Crosby's roadie who had made the request of the stewardess, he and his girlfriend were charged with federal air piracy and promptly carted away, while choirboy Crosby remained at liberty.

John Denver

Four years before his death in 1997, Denver was arrested for drunk driving in his hometown of Aspen, Colorado. He had reacted adversely to the final hearing in his second divorce. Not one to learn his lesson, Denver was caught committing the same offence a year later. It is interesting to note that he once penned a prophetic little number titled, 'Please Daddy (Don't Get Drunk This Christmas)'. There again, they always say that you should write what you know about.

Eminem

No surprises then when rap's latest bad-boy, Eminem aka Marshall Mathers III, found himself in court on gun charges. The rapper had been arrested for brandishing a gun in a Detroit nightclub, in June 2000, during a stand-off with another man, whom Eminem claimed had kissed his wife, Kim. In return for pleading guilty to possession of a firearm, the more serious charge of assault with a deadly weapon was dropped.

As a result of the offence Eminem has been put on probation for two years. The conditions of this, mean that, among other things, he must refrain from drug use, excessive consumption of alcohol, or 'engaging in insulting behaviour'.

Last we heard, Eminem was involved in further court proceedings, this time for brandishing a gun during a confrontation with rival rap act, Insane Clown Posse.

Liam Gallagher

Oasis bad-boy Liam was arrested in November 1996 for possession of cocaine, when stopped by police officers in central London. Charges were ultimately dropped though.

The Grateful Dead

The original 'dead-heads' were arrested for possession of LSD and barbiturates while in New Orleans. Accompanying them at the time was sixties LSD guru and future Grateful Dead soundman Stanley Owsley, who'd built something of a reputation for himself through the manufacture of high quality LSD, which he'd lovingly given names to such as Purple Haze and White

Lightning. Owsley would subsequently give the tabs away at parties known as 'acid tests'; musical accompaniment during these 'trips' often being provided by the Grateful Dead themselves.

George Harrison / Patti Boyd

Police raided Harrison and his then wife's flat on 12 March 1969; they found 120 marijuana joints. However, Harrison claimed that the couple had been framed, since this was also the day of Paul McCartney's marriage to Linda Eastman.

Jimi Hendrix

While on a tour of Scandinavia in 1968, Hendrix was arrested following a fight with his bassist, Noel Redding. During the course of the fight the pair managed to trash their hotel room, as a result of which Hendrix found himself spending a night in a Swedish jail.

Don Henley

Eagle-eyed Don must have failed to notice that the blonde he was partying with one day in 1980 was only sweet sixteen; bet he wished he had, though, when she passed out stark-naked in his flat, drugged up to the eyeballs. Henley was consequently charged with possession of cocaine, Quaaludes (the depressant methaquolone) and pot, as well as contributing to the delinquency of a minor. For his sins Henley was ordered to attend rehab and fined $5,000.

Billy Idol

No doubt young William was on his way to a 'white wedding', when in 1987 NYPD officers found him in possession of $100 worth of crack cocaine, while walking through New York's Greenwich Village. Though arrested, Idol ultimately wasn't charged for the offence.

Janis Joplin

Joplin was arrested in 1969, following a performance in Tampa, Florida, during which she used offensive language while addressing a policeman in attendance at the concert. Apparently the cop had ordered the crowd to calm down. Joplin responded thus, 'Don't fuck with those people!' before finishing with, 'Hey mister, what're you so uptight about? Did you buy a five-dollar ticket?' Joplin was released following payment of a $500 bond; the charges were ultimately dropped.

KRS-One

Rapper Kris Parker was arrested and sentenced for possession of marijuana; he was found with ten bin-bags full of finest home-grown. Smokin'!

Tommy Lee

In 1998 Mötley Crüe drummer, Tommy Lee, was arrested following police response to a 911 call made by his wife, Pamela Anderson. Lee was charged with spousal abuse, child abuse and unlawful possession of a firearm and was subsequently given a six-month jail sentence, placed on probation for three years and ordered to give $5,000 to a shelter for battered women.

Paul and Linda McCartney

A recurring theme of the McCartneys' involvement with the wrong side of the law has been their liking for cannabis, as the following brief synopsis reveals: 1972, the pair are arrested for cannabis possession and fined £800 while in Gothenburg, Sweden; 1973, McCartney is fined £100 for growing cannabis on his farm in Scotland – he claimed that he'd been given the seeds by a fan and as a keen horticulturist had grown them in order to find out exactly what they were; 1975, Linda, charged with possession; and 1980, Paul is caught by customs officers at Tokyo airport, with 219g of, guess what, marijuana in his suitcase. Well, at least he's been consistent.

George Michael

While not one to 'let the sun go down on him' George hasn't always been so choosy. In April 1998, he was caught quite literally with his pants down, when he was arrested and charged with lewd conduct following an impromptu meeting with another man, in the toilets of the Will Rogers Memorial Park in

Beverly Hills. Unfortunately for Michael the other man turned out to be an undercover policeman.

Michael subsequently chose to send up the escapade in his next hit, 'Outside', the video to which featured scenes of two policemen kissing. As a result of which the officer who had arrested Michael attempted to sue the singer for $10 million on the grounds of emotional distress; Officer Rodriguez was particularly troubled by Michael's remarks that he had been set up by someone appearing to be a good looking gay man. The case was dismissed, since Rodriguez, as a public official, was not entitled to compensation due to emotional distress.

Jim Morrison

Throughout his short life Morrison worked tirelessly to create an image as a hard-drinking, drug-taking, trouser-dropping party animal. Well, he succeeded.

In 1967, while waiting to take to the stage in New Haven, Connecticut, Morrison was passing the time of day with a young girl backstage when a patrolling policeman, failing to recognise Morrison ordered the couple to leave, causing the singer to administer his own verbal what-for. The policeman duly maced Morrison. However, once on stage Morrison took the first available opportunity to inform the crowd of his dealings with the police. The police, incensed by this tirade, promptly turned on the house lights and arrested Morrison, charging him with breach of the peace and resisting arrest.

Then, on 1 March 1969, Morrison, during his performance at the Dinner Key Auditorium, Miama, decided to give the audience an added spectacle, his manhood illuminated in all its natural wonder. Although certain members (no pun intended) of the audience might have appreciated his jape, local law enforcement officers felt otherwise. Morrison was arrested and charged with, and subsequently found guilty of, indecent exposure and profanity; the Lizard King appealed against the sentence and the case was pending at the time of his demise.

November 1969; Jim decided to harass a couple of stewardesses while on board a flight from Los Angeles to Phoenix. Morrison and his travelling companion at the time Tom Baker were arrested by the FBI upon landing and charged with public drunkenness and interfering with the flight of an inter- continental aircraft. Luckily for the duo, both charges were dropped when one of the stewardesses changed her testimony.

Once again, Morrison found himself being arrested for public drunken- ness, in August 1970. The singer had been out drinking with a friend when, one or two over the limit, he asked to be dropped off at another friend's house so that he could crash. Morrison banged on the door, only to fall asleep on the porch moments later. Unfortunately for Morrison, it wasn't his friend's porch but that of a 68-year-old woman, who saw fit to call the police.

Jim died eleven months later.

Vince Neil

The festive season of 1984 wasn't a particularly jolly one for the Crüe's Vince Neil; although it was considerably better than that experienced by Hanoi Rocks drummer, Razzle Dingley (who incidentally hailed from the Isle Of Wight). After a hardcore drinking binge, Neil and Dingley, feeling the need for continued sustenance, decided to take a drive down to the local corner shop. Only problem was that Neil, who had elected to drive, was by this stage well over the limit. Things began well, the car started, thereafter they went downhill rapidly. Neil, accelerating too quickly, caused the car to hydroplane as it passed through a puddle of water; within seconds the car had careered head on into an approaching VW. Dingley died within moments of being hit and both passengers of the VW were seriously injured. Neil survived the accident and was convicted of felony vehicular manslaughter; he served twenty days in jail, did two hundred hours community service, several benefit concerts and was ordered to pay $2.6 million in compensation.

The Notorious B.I.G.

When Christopher Wallace aka the Notorious B.I.G was gunned down on 10 March 1997, it was of course a sad day the world over, for with his passing we bade our farewells to a gentleman of gentlemen and a scholar of scholars, as the following episode reveals.

In response to the polite requests of a couple of admiring fans for his autograph, Biggie responded thus; he attacked them with a baseball bat, before chasing down the street after them, issuing death threats as he ran (could he really run?). Even when they reached the safety of their car Biggie would not desist – smashing the windows so as to continue his attack upon them. Biggie was charged with criminal mischief and harassment and, knowing that honesty pays, pleaded guilty as a true gentleman would. R.I.P. Biggie.

Ozzy Osbourne

Metal's ultimate bat-biting madman had one of his finest moments in San Antonio, Texas. Wife Sharon, determined to put Ozzy's alcohol consumption in check, locked all of his clothes in the wardrobe, and confined him to his room. However, Ozzy was not to be deterred; once Sharon was out of the way, he knocked back a bottle of brandy, grabbed one of her dresses, put it on (complete with matching shoes) and headed for the bars. However, at the precise moment he was passing one of the nation's most revered monuments, namely the Alamo, he felt a tremendous pressure on his bladder. Just as he was relieving himself against one of the Alamo's walls, who should choose to pass by but representatives of the local law and order. Ozzy subsequently spent the night in jail for defiling a national monument and being intoxicated in public.

John Phillips (The Mamas and The Papas)

When police officers raided Phillips's Long Island home in 1980, they were greeted by a substantial quantity of amphetamines and opiates. He was charged with conspiracy to distribute narcotics. He was given a five year sentence, though ultimately this was reduced to 250 hours of community service and a spot of lecturing upon the evils of drugs.

Keith Richards

In 1967 Richards was arrested, along with fellow Stone Jagger, plaything Marianne Faithfull and art dealer Robert Fraser, by police officers searching for drugs at his 'Redlands' home. The raid soon became a part of rock 'n 'roll folklore, since it was claimed that at the time Jagger had been helping Ms Faithfull 'work, rest and (most pertinently) play' with the benefit of a Mars bar. However, as Ms Faithfull wrote in her autobiography:

> The Mars Bar was a very effective piece of demonizing. Way out there. It was so overdone, with such malicious twisting of the facts. Mick retrieving a Mars Bar from my vagina, indeed! It was far too jaded for any of us even to have conceived of. It's a dirty old man's fantasy — some old fart who goes to a dominatrix every Thursday afternoon to get spanked. A cop's idea of what people do on acid!

Axl Rose (Guns N' Roses)

Even before adopting the W. Axl Rose persona, Bill Bailey as he used to be known, was always something of a bad boy: Indiana police jailed him more than twenty times while he was still a teenager.

In 1991 while Axl and his cohorts were on stage at Kansas City, Rose spotted a fan committing the most heinous of crimes, unlawful videotaping of the concert. An incensed Rose leaped from the stage, diving into the audience below in an attempt to stop the perpetrator. A riot subsequently broke out among fans, causing some $200,000-worth of damage, as a result of which a warrant was issued for Rose's arrest. However, Rose, who fled the scene immediately, managed to evade capture until a year later, when he was finally arrested at New York's J.F.K. airport, though some deft work by his lawyers meant that he was, to all intents and purposes, exonerated.

David Lee Roth

Former Van Halen frontman Roth was arrested in 1993, complete with ego, for buying $10 worth of weed, from a dealer in N.Y.C.'s Washington Square Park.

Johnny Rotten

Dear, dear Johnny was arrested for his part in a Dublin pub brawl in 1980; though sentenced to three months, he was subsequently acquitted.

S Club 7 – An Alternative 'S Club Party'

On 20 March 2001 all three male members (Bradley McIntosh, John Lee and Paul Cattermole), of the seemingly 'pure as snow' pop band S Club 7, were arrested in the vicinity of London's Covent Garden for possession of cannabis. Metropolitan police officers had apparently smelled the drug, while walking past the boys. They were arrested and taken to Charing Cross police station where they suffered the indignity of the strip-search. A small amount of cannabis was found and all three were formally cautioned.

The band members subsequently issued an apology to their fans.

Snow

Canadian reggae-rapper Snow, who had a hit with 'Informer' in 1993, served time for attempted murder.

Joe Strummer / Topper Headon (both of The Clash)

In 1977 Strummer and Headon were arrested following a spot of direct marketing. They had painted 'The Clash' on a wall in London.

Ike Turner

One time husband of legendary diva Tina, Ike was arrested in 1989 for the sale and possession of cocaine. He served 18 months of his 4 year sentence.

Mark Wahlberg

Before becoming one of the hottest actors around, 'Marky Mark', as the one time rapper used to be known, found himself in a spot of bother back in April 1988. He and several friends had been knocking the beers back. However, when the keg ran dry they were fortunate enough to encounter one Thanh Lam, who by chance had in his possession a couple of cases of beer. With his six pack rippling, Marky Mark knocked the man unconscious. Unfortunately for Mr Wahlberg the even stronger arm of the law wasn't far behind: he ended up serving 45 days at the Deer Island House of Correction, and was placed on probation for two years.

Paul Weller

Old Paul must have been 'Hung Up' on something, when he let loose in his room at the Warwick hotel in Paris in 1997, trashing it in the process. Weller agreed to pay for the damage and was released by the arresting gendarmes.

FAMOUS POP LOCATIONS

'I KNOW A PLACE'
Rock 'n' Roll Landmarks

All things considered, rock has certainly done its bit when it comes to putting places on the map, as anyone living in the vicinity of London's Abbey Road will tell you.

Here's a selection of other notable rock 'n' roll landmarks:

Tittenhurst Park, Bedfordshire: located somewhere between Ascot and Sunningdale, this Georgian Mansion set in a sprawling estate of 72 acres, was home to John Lennon from May 1969 until September 1973. *Imagine* was recorded here, as was the famed footage of John and Yoko in an all-white room.

Stocks Country Club, Aldbury, Hertfordshire: the location for the cover artwork, as featured on the Oasis album, *Be Here Now*.

East Afton Farm, Freshwater, Isle Of Wight: site of the Isle Of Wight's third festival (August 1970), with a lineup including; Jimi Hendrix, The Doors and The Who. Over half a million people made the trip to the Island.

Cavern Club, 10 Mathew Street, Liverpool: legendary venue for The Beatles, who first played there in March 1961. They supposedly went on to play there a further 291 times. The club was closed down by Public Health officials in February 1966, only to open its doors again between July 1966 and May 1973.

The Rainbow, 232 Seven Sisters Road, London: prior to becoming The Rainbow in 1971, the club was known as the Finsbury Park Astoria, during which time acts such as The Beatles and Jimi Hendrix featured on the bill. In fact it was the scene of Jimi's first ever guitar pyrotechnics. In the subsequent Rainbow days, acts such as The Who played there. Famously it was the scene of Eric Clapton's comeback following drugs rehabilitation, and resultant live album, in January 1973.

The Zebra Crossing, Abbey Road, London, NW8: probably one of the most famous landmarks in rock, following its appearance on the cover of The Beatles' 1969 album, later parodied by a besocked Red Hot Chilli Peppers.

Sex, 430 Kings Road, London, SW10: originally opened by Malcolm McLaren and Vivienne Westwood in 1971, the shop was christened 'Sex' in 1975. Popular with rock stars of the time for its outlandish fashion; though probably best remembered for being the place where the idea of The Sex Pistols was conceived. Incidentally, original Pistol bassist and songwriter Glen Matlock worked there.

Apple HQ, 3 Saville Row, London, W1: not only command centre for The Beatles' own record label, but also scene of their legendary impromptu rooftop concert, on 30 January 1969. This was to be their final public appearance as a band.

They're All Saints, everyone of them: All Saints Road, off the Portobello Road, in London's exceptionally trendy W11, was the inspiration for the moniker of one of Britain's greatest all-girl bands, the eponymously named All Saints. Founding members Melanie Blatt and Shaznay Lewis had both worked as backing singers at Metamorphosis Studio which was located, yes you've guessed it, on All Saints Road.

The Factory, Royce Lane, Hulme, Greater Manchester: club owner and label boss, Tony Wilson opened the club in 1978; Joy Division, Big In Japan, Happy Mondays etc. were all to get their start here.

Weller's Stanley Road: Paul Weller took the name of his recent solo album from the street where he lived during his formative years, Stanley Road – Woking – number 8 to be precise.

A COLLECTION OF POSTHUMOUS LISTS

'(DON'T FEAR) THE REAPER'
Rock 'n' Roll Deaths

Death does indeed come to us all, though generally not before time, yet one sector of society seems particularly adept at enjoying a shorter lifespan than most – that of the rock 'n' roll star:

The (Rock 'n') Roll of Honour

Florence Ballard (The Supremes) (30/06/43–21/02/76); cardiac arrest following an overdose of alcohol and pills. Ballard had previously been fired from The Supremes in 1967 as a result of increasing friction between herself and the other members of the group, in particular lead singer Diana Ross. Hard times had ensued, not least of all a failed $8.7 million lawsuit against her former employers, Motown Records.

John Bonham (drummer, Led Zeppelin) (31/05/48–25/09/80); as so many before him, died with honour (among the rock'n'roll fraternity at least), having choked on his own vomit, following a heavy drinking session at Jimmy Page's estate in Windsor. Apparently the unstoppable Bonham had downed some forty measures of vodka before quite literally calling it a day.

Steve Clark (23/04/60–08/01/91); the Def Leppard guitarist had been particularly fond of living the wild life with fellow axeman and bandmate Phil Collen. However, when Collen realised the error of his ways, Clark carried on regardless. Consequently, he was found dead in his Chelsea apartment, following an all-nighter. Cause of death: compression of the brain stem as a result of mixing alcohol with his prescription anti-depressants and painkillers.

Jimi Hendrix (27/11/42–18/09/70); famed for his incendiary riffing and guitar pyrotechnics, Hendrix was found dead in the London flat of his then girlfriend Monika Dannemann, having previously attended a dinner party. Cause of death: inhalation of vomit due to barbiturate intoxication. Upon his return from the party Hendrix had taken nine sleeping tablets, perhaps not the best complement to the wine that he had earlier consumed.

Brian Jones (28/02/42–03/07/69); 'stoner' Brian's life had been on a downward spiral, for some time, with a string of drugs related offences, as well as a stretch in Wormwood Scrubs. It came as little surprise when, having previously been diagnosed as having a poor mental state and suicidal tendencies, Jones was found dead in his swimming pool following a midnight swim, fuelled by a cocktail of alcohol and barbiturates. The coroner concluded death by misadventure.

Terry Kath (31/01/46–23/01/78); a founding member of the band Chicago, the guitarist/vocalist took his life, in a supposed game of Russian Roulette. Kath, with the gun to his head, apparently unaware that it was indeed loaded, pulled the trigger in a bout of unrivalled showmanship. Kath would have been thirty-two in eight days' time.

Paul Kossoff (14/09/50–19/03/76); Free guitarist Kossoff died while 'flying high', though not by his preferred method. At the time of his death he was several thousand feet in the air en route to New York, when his heart and kidney failed following years of increasing drug abuse, in particular heroin.

Phil Lynott (20/08/51–04/01/86); the Thin Lizzy bassist and frontman died, having spent eight days in a coma, following a heroin overdose. By his side in Salisbury General Infirmary were his wife Caroline and father-in-law, TV's Leslie Crowther. The coroner's verdict, 'heart failure and pneumonia following septicaemia'.

Keith Moon (23/08/47–08/09/78); the legendary wildman and Who drummer died from an overdose of Heminevrin, a prescription drug intended to aid in the treatment of alcoholism. That Moon would self-destruct seems somehow inevitable once you consider his penchant for destroying pretty much everything else, hotel rooms (the norm), hotels, cars (Rolls Royces were a particular favourite), swimming pools etc., usually under the guidance of copious amounts of alcohol.

Jim Morrison (08/12/43–03/07/71); ever one to increase his 'perception', Morrison had earned his reputation as a hard drinking, drug-addled student of debauchery the hard way – by being one. No surprises then when Morrison, having quit the Doors and moved to Paris to focus on his poetry, was found dead in his bathtub, an ode to Marat Sade perhaps. Cause of death: heart attack induced by the consumption of drugs.

Bon Scott (09/07/46–20/02/80); the AC/DC frontman died in his car, having drunk a 'whole lotta whiskey' during a night out in Camden, North London. His drinking partner for the night, Alistair Kennear, had driven the inebriated Scott back to his pad in South London, leaving him in the car to sleep it off. Kennear returned later to find Scott still asleep in the car. Scott was pronounced D.O.A. at King's College Hospital. His heart and liver had quite simply given up.

Honourable Mentions

Tommy Bolin (James Gang, Deep Purple) (01/08/51–04/12/76); cause of death: heroin overdose.

Tim Buckley (14/02/47–29/06/75); cause of death: heroin overdose. Buckley had thought he was taking cocaine.

Brian Epstein (19/09/34–27/08/67); cause of death: 'accidental' overdose of sleeping tablets.

Janis Joplin (19/01/43–04/10/70); cause of death: heroin overdose.

Robbie McIntosh (The Average White Band) (25/09/45–23/09/74); cause of death: heroin cut with strychnine (a rat poison). As per Tim Buckley, McIntosh had thought he was taking cocaine.

Gram Parsons (The Byrds, The Flying Burrito Brothers) (05/11/46–19/09/73); cause of death: heroin overdose.

Elvis Presley (08/01/35–16/08/77); cause of death: heart failure due to excessive consumption of drugs, namely butabarbital, codeine, morphine, pentobarbital, placidyl, quaalude, valium, valmid. Not forgetting plenty of burgers and ice cream.

Hillel Slovak (Red Hot Chili Peppers) (13/04/62–25/06/88); cause of death: heroin overdose.

Sid Vicious (10/05/57–02/0279); cause of death: heroin overdose, with heroin procured for him by his mother who didn't want him risking the possibility of arrest. What a thoughtful mom!

Lest We Forget Them

The Drugs Did Work – 10 Drugs Related Deaths

1. **Tim Buckley**, 14 February 1947–End 29 June 1975
2. **Pete Farndon** (The Pretenders) ,2 June 1952–14 April 1983
3. **Andy Gibb**, 5 March 1958–10 March 1988
4. **Shannon Hoon** (Blind Melon), 26 September 1967–21 October 1995
5. **Paul Kossof** (Free), 14 September 1950–19 March 1976
6. **Frankie Lymon**, 30 September 1942–28 February 1968
7. **Gram Parsons**, 5 November 1946–19 September 1973
8. **Rob Pilatus** (Milli Vanilli), 8 June 1965–2 April 1998
9. **David Ruffin** (The Temptations), 18 January 1941–1 June 1991
10. **Johnny Thunders** (New York Dolls), 15 July 1952–23 April 1991

They Left On A Jet Plane – 10 Plane Crash Deaths

1. **John Denver**, 31 December 1943–12 October 1997
2. **Steve Gaines** (Lynyrd Skynyrd), 14 September 1949–20 October 1977
3. **Buddy Holly**, 7 September 1936–3 February 1959
4. **Jimmy King** (Bar-Kays), 1949–9 December 1967
5. **Stevie Ray Vaughan**, 3 October 1954–27 August 1990
6. **Otis Redding**, 9 September 1941–10 December 1967
7. **Randy Rhoads** (Ozzy Osbourne Band), 6 December 1956–20 March 1982
8. **J.P. Richardson aka The Big Bopper**, 24 October 1930–3 February 1959

9. **Aaliyah Dana Haughton**, 16 January 1979–25 August 2001
10. **Ronnie Van Zant** (Lynyrd Skynyrd), January 15, 1949–October 20, 1977

Buddy Holly, the Big Bopper and Richie Valens all perished in the same aircrash. Similarly, Lynyrd Skynyrd's Gaines and Van Zant faced the reaper together.

This Wheel's On Fire – 10 Motoring Deaths

1. **Duane Allman** (Allman Brothers Band), 20 November 1946–29 October 1971
2. **Marc Bolan** (T.Rex), 30 July 1947–16 September 1977
3. **Chris Burton** (Metallica), 10 February 1962–27 September 1986
4. **Harry Chapin**, 7 December 1942–16 July 1981
5. **Eddie Cochran**, 3 October 1938–17 April 1960
6. **Rob Collins** (Charlatans), 12 June 1965–23 July 1996
7. **Jerry Edmonton** (Steppenwolf), 24 October 1946–28 November 1993
8. **Falco**, 19 February 1957–6 February 1998
9. **Cozy Powell**, 29 December 1947–5 April 1998
10. **Dave Prater** (Sam & Dave), 9 April 1937–9 April 1988

Suicide Solutions

1. **Johnny Ace**, 9 June 1929–25 December 1954
2. **Kurt Cobain** (Nirvana), 20 February 1967–5 April 1994
3. **Ian Curtis** (Joy Division), 15 July 1956–18 May 1980
4. **Tom Evans** (Badfinger), 5 June 1947–18 November 1983
5. **Pete Ham** (Badfinger), 27 April 1947–23 April 1975
6. **Donny Hathaway**, 1 October 1945–13 January 1979
7. **Michael Hutchence** (INXS), 22 January 1960–22 November 1997
8. **Phil Ochs**, 19 December 1940–9 April 1976
9. **Danny Rapp** (Danny and the Juniors), 10 May 1941–5 April 1983
10. **Del Shannon**, 30 December 1934–8 February 1990

QUOTES FROM THE STARS

'TALK TALK'
50 of Pop's Finest – Muse, Mumble and Mutter

Though often hailed as the spokespeople of their generation, the stars of rock and pop, would be best advised to confine their thoughts to vinyl, that is if the following quotations are anything to go by:

1. 'I am a mess and you're a mess too. Everyone's a mess – which means, actually, that no one's a mess.' – **Fiona Apple**
2. 'I've never succeeded in reading a book from cover to cover!' – **Victoria Beckham**
3. 'My rule has always been not to have a clue about what I was doing.' – **Björk**
4. 'If you want to torture me, you'd tie me down and force me to watch our first five videos.' – **Jon Bon Jovi** echoes a common thought
5. 'Adolf Hitler was the first pop star. I think he was quite as good as Jagger.' – **David Bowie**
6. 'Hair is the first thing. And teeth the second. Hair and teeth. A man got those two things he's got it all.' – **James Brown**
7. 'I started being really proud of the fact that I was gay even though I wasn't.' – **Kurt Cobain**
8. 'I think I used to be a butterfly. No, a bird! No, birds get chased by cats and butterflies look like bugs when they don't have wings. I guess I was

a dog, 'cos they're able to see what's going on in the world, but they can't express themselves. I think I could see what was going on around me, but I couldn't say or do anything about it.' – **Craig David**

9. 'My dad taught me about music. He used to tap dance.' – **Ray Davies** of The Kinks
10. 'If not me, who then will lead?' – **John Denver**
11. 'Everybody gives off a certain musical note. I think I'm F-sharp. The thing is you can go around and you meet somebody who's in F-sharp, you're in harmony, see. But if you meet somebody who's in F-unng, it's a discord: you don't get on'. – **Donovan**
12. 'Folk singing is just a bunch of fat people.' – **Bob Dylan**
13. Don't do drugs, don't have unprotected sex, don't be violent. Leave that to me.' – people's poet **Eminem**
14. 'Who's gonna be the first to shoot President Bush?' – as pertinent today as it was when first uttered by **Perry Farrel** (of Jane's Addiction) back in 1989
15. 'I wanted a name that would put us first in the phone directory, or second if you count Abba.' – **Martin Fry** of ABC
16. 'We don't have political views . . . I don't think.' – Depeche Mode's **Dave Gahan**
17. 'Don't give me charity . . . you only get in the way with those stupid ideals.' – the King Of Charity himself, **Sir Bob Geldof**
18. 'I hate disco music.' – **Barry Gibb**
19. 'I'm very driven, even though I don't drive.' – **Debbie Gibson**
20. 'Christ was a punk rocker.' – **Billy Idol**
21. 'A lot of Michael's success is due to timing and luck. It could just as easily have been me.' – **Jermaine Jackson**
22. 'We can fly, you know. We just don't know how to think the right thoughts and levitate ourselves off the ground.' – King Of Pop **Michael Jackson** (enough said!)
23. 'I'm one of the best things England's got. Me and the Queen.' – **Mick Jagger** (1)
24. 'I thought we [the Rolling Stones] stood for infinity.' – **Mick Jagger** (2)
25. 'I could be unbelievably horrible and stupid. On tours, I'd get on a plane, then get off it, maybe six or eight times. I'd walk out of a hotel suite because I didn't like the colour of the bedspread. I remember looking out of my room at the Inn On The Park one day and saying, "It's too windy. Can someone please do something about it?"' – **Elton John**
26. 'We want to be the band to dance to when the bomb drops.' – Duran Duran's **Simon Le Bon** – a man who'll do anything to get that elusive next gig

27. 'We're more popular than Jesus now; I don't know which will go first – rock and roll or Christianity.' – **John Lennon**
28. 'Be strong, believe in freedom and in God, love yourself, understand your sexuality, have a sense of humour, masturbate, don't judge people by their religion, colour, or sexual habits, love life and your family.' – **Madonna**
29. 'I consider myself a peasant.' – **Linda McCartney**
30. 'I am the best Keith Moon-type drummer in the world.' – **Keith Moon**
31. 'We always hated being called an art band. I never took art in high school.' – Sonic Youth's **Thurston Moore**
32. 'Erotic politicians, that's what we are. We're interested in everything about revolt, disorder, and all activity that appears to have no meaning.' – **Jim Morrison**
33. 'I realized right away I could write songs, because I could have experiences without even having them.' – **Stevie Nicks**
34. 'All my concerts had no sounds in them; they were completely silent. People had to make their own music in their minds.' – **Yoko Ono**
35. 'When I first went to the Betty Ford Center I was very surprised they didn't have a bar there.' – the bat-biting, dove-devouring **Ozzy Osbourne**
36. 'Six months go by very fast when you're a genius.' – Led Zeppelin's **Robert Plant**
37. 'I get a lot of influences from electric shavers.' – **Iggy Pop**
38. 'I don't know anything about music. In my line, you don't have to.' – **Elvis Presley**
39. 'I'm still that sort to let them wet their knickers on the seats. That's basically what it's all about for me.' – **Cliff Richard**
40. 'The truth is where the truth is and sometimes it's in the candy store.' – **Keith Richards**
41. 'I want to be an artist who is appreciated. Maybe I should do something for cancer research or something.' – **Diana Ross** in a less than 'Supreme' moment
42. 'Rock'n'roll is not so much a question of electric guitars as it is striped pants.' – **David Lee Roth**
43. 'I like Beethoven, especially the poems.' – **Ringo Starr**
44. 'Anybody that walks can sing.' – **Michael Stipe** of REM
45. 'There's nothing like throwing up out of a bus door going sixty-five miles an hour.' – one-time Guns N' Roses guitarist **Izzy Stradlin**; no doubt a sentiment echoed by the drivers of vehicles unfortunate enough to be caught behind the tour-bus during such an outburst
46. 'I'm always trying to figure out why people don't appreciate Duran Duran.' – **Andy Taylor**

47. 'You have to keep busy. After all, no dog's ever pissed on a moving car.'
    – Tom Waits
48. 'Now and then, ideas for songs seem to come from heaven and from
    other places I don't know where the heck they were. Melodies and stuff
    would come from heaven.' **– Brian Wilson**
49. 'You can't look forward and backward at the same time.' **– Coleman
    Young**

And finally . . .

50. 'Rock journalism is people who can't write interviewing people who
    can't talk for people who can't read.' **– Frank Zappa**

'NO MORE MR NICE GUY'
Pop Stars Get Their Claws Out

Sticks and stones may break your bones but names will never hurt you. At least that's what the children's rhyme tells us; le's hope it's true. Tthe stars certainly don't hold their punches when it comes to verbal sparring, as the following comments reveal:

'Bono would love to be six-foot-tall and thin and good-looking. But he's not – he reminds me of a soddin' mountain goat.'
Ian McCulloch of Echo & The Bunnymen.

'[She] needs to get a life.'
Madonna's none too affectionate assessment of dancehall diva Mariah Carey.

'I don't like Bob Dylan. I don't like his attitude or his records . . . All that protest thing was a load of rubbish. I don't hate listening to his records, but I can't stand it when people say he's a genius.'
Sex-bomb Tom (Jones)!

'He's talked himself up his own arse.'
The Who's Roger Daltrey on bandmate and human windmill Pete Townshend.

'Groups like Genesis and Yes are about as exciting as a used Kleenex. It might as well be Tony Bennett.'
Nick Lowe.

'I still love George Harrison as a songwriter in the Beatles, but as a person I think he's a fucking nipple . . . And if you're watching, NIPPLE!'
Liam Gallagher in response to George Harrison's assertion that Oasis are 'rubbish'.

'The Perry Como of punk.'
Johnny Rotten on Billy Idol.

'He's a great singer – but he's not the most masculine guy, is he?'
Alexander O'Neal speaking about Pop's bionic man, Michael Jackson.

'He moves like a parody between a majorette girl and Fred Astaire.'
Truman Capote referring to Mick Jagger.

'I think his greatest achievement was recognising that he was a macho asshole and trying to stop it.'
Sean Lennon on Dad John!

'Britney [Spears] wees all over Christina [Aguilera]! Christina looks like she's mental. She looks like she's a bit of a diva and I think she's losing the plot.'
Victoria Beckham – talent spotter extraordinaire.

'Courtney never bothered to say "hi" to me until I sold a million records.'
Marilyn Manson talking about his 'friendship' with Courtney Love.

'I *acted* vulgar. Madonna *is* vulgar.'
Goddess of the silver-screen, Marlene Dietrich.

'Madonna said I looked like I had a run-in with a lawnmower and that I was about as sexy as a Venetian blind. Now there's a woman that America looks up to as being a campaigner for women, slagging off another woman for not being sexy.'
High-Priestess of Pop (quite literally!), Sinéad O'Connor.

'There's a central dumbness to her.'
Mick Jagger talking about that oh-so-Material Girl.

'Madonna is closer to organised prostitution than anything else.'
Morrissey – claws out.

'The guy's got a girl's name, and he wears makeup. What an original idea.'
Alice Cooper on 'fellow' rocker, Marilyn Manson.

'Sitting around with a bunch of old lesbians writing doesn't sound classical to me. I've written three classical albums.'
Liam Gallagher again, this time commenting on Paul McCartney's classical endeavours.

'Oh God, I hate them. Dishwater!'
Jimi Hendrix on his one-time touring partners, The Monkees.

'Led Zeppelin is just a bunch of stupid idiots who wrote cool riffs.'
Soundgarden's Chris Cornell dispenses a whole lotta love.

'A complete knobhead.'
Noel Gallagher's seemingly fair assessment of brother Liam.

'Presley sounded like Jayne Mansfield looked – blowsy and loud and low.'
Music journalist Julie Burchill: never one to bite her tongue.

'Them touring at their age is like Evita going on tour stuffed in that glass case of hers.'
Lemmy speaking about 'Ever-Ready' rockers, The Rolling Stones.

'The Sex Pistols are like some contagious disease.'
Malcolm McLaren (Sex Pistols' manager).

'She is a piece of licorice [sic] in shoes. She walks into a pool hall and they chalk her head.'
Comedienne Joan Rivers speaking kindly of chanteuse Diana Ross.

'The Spice Girls are like heroin. You know somebody's doin' it, but nobody is willing to admit that it is them.'
Stand-up comedian and actor, Chris Rock.

'Somebody should clip Sting around the head and tell him to stop singing in that ridiculous Jamaican accent.'
Elvis Costello. Say no more!

'. . . Liverpool never produced a decent musician and the Beatles were living proof of it.'
Ian Stewart tells it like it is.

'I'd like to pistol-whip him for about an hour. Though he originally came out against drugs, how many people did he suck?'
Gun-toting American hard-man of rock, Ted Nugent, talking about our own Boy George.

PEER GROUP RECOGNITION

'GLORY DAYS'
The Rock and Roll Hall of Fame

The Rock and Roll Hall of Fame Foundation was formed in 1983 by leading members of the music industry. Its aim – to honour the achievements of those who have made significant contributions beginning in 1986, to the art form which we know as rock and roll music.

Each year select members of the Foundation meet to choose nominees for induction into the Hall of Fame. Nominees are selected from across the music industry, honouring performers and non-performers alike. Non-performers includes such industry professionals as producers, songwriters, DJs, journalists etc. Also honoured, though not necessarily every year, are the 'sidemen' (backing musicians) and the 'early-influences' (artists who preceded rock and roll but were influential in its development).

2001

THE PERFORMERS

Aerosmith
Solomon Burke
The Flamingos

Michael Jackson
Queen
Paul Simon
Steely Dan
Ritchie Valens

THE SIDEMEN

James Burton
Johnnie Johnston

THE NON-PERFORMERS

Chris Blackwell

2000

THE PERFORMERS

Eric Clapton
Earth, Wind & Fire
Lovin' Spoonful
The Moonglows
Bonnie Raitt
James Taylor

THE EARLY INFLUENCES

Nat 'King' Cole
Billie Holiday

THE SIDEMEN

Hal Blaine
King Curtis
James Jamerson
Scotty Moore
Earl Palmer

THE NON-PERFORMERS

Clive Davis

1999

THE PERFORMERS

Billy Joel
Curtis Mayfield
Paul McCartney
Del Shannon
Dusty Springfield
Bruce Springsteen
The Staple Singers

THE EARLY-INFLUENCES

Bob Wills and His Texas Playboys
Charles Brown

THE NON-PERFORMERS

George Martin

1998

THE PERFORMERS

The Eagles
Fleetwood Mac
The Mamas And The Papas
Lloyd Price
Santana
Gene Vincent

THE EARLY INFLUENCES

Jelly Roll Morton

THE NON-PERFORMERS

Allen Toussaint

1997

THE PERFORMERS

The Rascals (Young and Old)
The Bee Gees
Buffalo Springfield
Crosby, Stills and Nash
The Jackson Five
Joni Mitchell
Parliament and Funkadelic

THE EARLY-INFLUENCES

Mahalia Jackson
Bill Monroe

NON-PERFORMERS

Syd Nathan

1996

THE PERFORMERS

David Bowie
Gladys Knight and The Pips
Jefferson Airplane
Pink Floyd

The Shirelles
The Velvet Underground

THE EARLY-INFLUENCES

Little Willie John
Pete Seeger

THE NON-PERFORMERS

Tom Donahue

1995

THE PERFORMERS

The Allman Brothers Band
Al Green
Janis Joplin
Led Zeppelin
Martha and The Vandellas
Neil Young
Frank Zappa

THE EARLY-INFLUENCES

The Orioles

THE NON-PERFORMERS

Paul Ackerman

1994

THE PERFORMERS

The Animals
The Band
Duane Eddy
The Grateful Dead
Elton John
John Lennon
Bob Marley
Rod Stewart

THE EARLY-INFLUENCES

Willie Dixon

THE NON-PERFORMERS

Johny Otis

1993

THE PERFORMERS

Ruth Brown
Cream
Creedence Clearwater Revival
The Doors
Frankie Lymon and The Teenagers
Etta James
Van Morrison
Sly and The Family Stone

THE EARLY-INFLUENCES

Dinah Washington

NON-PERFORMERS

Dick Clark
Milt Gabler

1992

THE PERFORMERS

Bobby 'Blue' Bland
Booker T. and The M.G.'s
Johnny Cash
The Isley Brothers
The Jimi Hendrix Experience
Sam and Dave
The Yardbirds

THE EARLY INFLUENCES
Elmore James
Professor Longhair

THE NON-PERFORMERS

Leo Fender
Bill Graham
Doc Pomus

1991

THE PERFORMERS

LaVern Baker
The Byrds
John Lee Hooker
The Impressions
Wilson Pickett
Jimmy Reed
Ike and Tina Turner

THE EARLY-INFLUENCES

Howlin' Wolf

THE LIFETIME ACHIEVEMENT AWARD

Nesuhi Ertegun

THE NON-PERFORMERS

Dave Bartholomew
Ralph Bass

1990

THE PERFORMERS

Hank Ballard
Bobby Darin
The Four Seasons
The Four Tops
The Kinks
The Platters
Simon and Garfunkel
The Who

THE EARLY-INFLUENCES

Louis Armstrong
Charlie Christian
Ma Rainey

THE NON-PERFORMERS

Gerry Goffin and Carole King
Holland, Dozier and Holland

1989

THE PERFORMERS

Dion
Otis Redding
The Rolling Stones
The Temptations
Stevie Wonder

THE EARLY-INFLUENCES

The Inkspots
Bessie Smith
The Soul Stirrers

THE NON-PERFORMERS

Phil Spector

1988

THE PERFORMERS

The Beach Boys
The Beatles
The Drifters
Bob Dylan
The Supremes

THE EARLY-INFLUENCES

Woody Guthrie
Lead Belly
Les Paul

THE NON-PERFORMERS

Berry Gordy Jr.

1987

THE PERFORMERS

The Coasters
Eddie Cochran
Bo Diddley
Aretha Franklin
Marvin Gaye
Bill Haley
B.B. King
Clyde McPhatter
Ricky Nelson
Roy Orbison
Carl Perkins
Smokey Robinson
Big Joe Turner
Muddy Waters
Jackie Wilson

THE EARLY-INFLUENCES

Louis Jordan
T-Bone Walker
Hank Williams

THE NON-PERFORMERS

Leonard Chess
Ahmet Ertegun
Jerry Leiber and Mike Stoller
Jerry Wexler

1986

THE PERFORMERS

Chuck Berry
James Brown
Ray Charles
Sam Cooke
Fats Domino
The Everly Brothers
Buddy Holly
Jerry Lee Lewis
Elvis Presley
Little Richard

THE EARLY INFLUENCES

Robert Johnson
Jimmie Rodgers
Jimmy Yancey

THE LIFETIME ACHIEVEMENT

John Hammond

THE NON-PERFORMERS

Alan Freed
Sam Phillips

POP STARS WITH TATTOOS

'TATTOOED MILLIONAIRE'
Pop Stars with Tattoos

Appearance is one thing the stars don't have to worry about, at least not when it comes to wearing a suit go to work, or having body piercings, or even the most permanent of all fashion accessories – the tattoo. Here's a list of some of the stars who've elected to become a human canvas and go under the tattoo artist's needle:

Heavenli Abdi (Honeyz)   A tribal sun design around her belly button.

Gregg Allman   A coyote on his lower arm.

Phil Anselmo (Pantera)   Somewhat ironically Pantera's growling frontman has the word 'Unscarred' written across his stomach, as well as numerous other designs.

Nicole Appleton (All Saints)   'Year Of The Tiger' on her waist.

Mel B (Spice Girls)   Never one to be pretentious; Mel has 'Spirit, Heart And Mind' written on her stomach in Japanese.

Sebastian Bach (Skid Row) 'Maria' on his neck.

Travis Barker (Blink-182) Travis has numerous designs, including female nudes on both sides of his chest and a portrait of the Virgin Mary on his arm (dedicated to his mother).

Björk Mad as the proverbial hatter, Björk has an Icelandic compass on her arm. Presumably, in case she gets lost. Though metaphorically speaking maybe she already is!

Melanie Blatt (All Saints) Musical notes on her right shoulder.

Jon Bon Jovi Not one to be modest, the Bon Jovi frontman has the 'Superman' logo on his left shoulder.

Wes Borland (Limp Bizkit) The Limp Bizkit guitarist has the name of his wife 'Heather' on his lower back.

Foxy Brown A Chinese design on her left breast.

Emma Bunton (Spice Girls) 'Baby Spice' has the word 'Baby' on her derrière.

Mel C (Spice Girls) Mel has many tattoos, including: a 'Celtic' arm-band on her right arm; oriental characters signifying 'Women' and 'Strength', i.e. 'Girl Power', on her right shoulder, and the word 'Angel' on her stomach.

Glen Campbell A 'dagger' on his forearm.

Cher Among others, Cher has flower designs on her bottom.

Dixie Chicks All three of the Chicks have little chick

footprints on their feet. All together now; 'Aah!'

Fred Durst (Limp Bizkit)

Aside from single-handedly attempting to bring the red baseball hat to the fore of fashion, Fred has also championed the tattooist's art. He was a tattooist himself before achieving success with Limp Bizkit. Among his various markings, he has an angel on his back, a flower design on his neck, as well as a 'ring' on his left middle finger.

Kian Egan (Westlife)

Kian has a Chinese symbol on his left ankle, apparently meaning 'spirit'.

Eminem

The saviour of rap has 'dog tags' around his neck, the name of his daughter, 'Hailie Jade', on his right arm, as well as the strangely tempting words 'Slit Here' on his right wrist, to mention but a few.

Marianne Faithfull

This sixties wildchild has a 'swallow' on her left wrist.

Flea (Red Hot Chili Peppers)

The Chili Peppers are known for their fondness of tattoos. Flea has many; including the name of his daughter, 'Loesha', on his chest, and a chain of different coloured elephants walking around his arm. Above the elephants he has a portrait of Jimi Hendrix.

Ace Frehley (Kiss)

The Kiss guitarist has 'Ace' on his left arm.

Daryl Hall

A 'star' design on his shoulder.

Geri Halliwell

A 'black panther' on her lower back.

Janet Jackson

Janet has tattoos of Mickey and Minnie Mouse 'together again'.

Kid Rock

The Kid has a Detroit Tiger's 'D' on his right arm.

Tommy Lee (Mötley Crue)

Mr Lee has the word 'Mayhem' on his stomach.

Shaznay Lewis (All Saints)

The Chinese symbol for the year of the rabbit on her right breast.

Brian Littrell (Backstreet Boys)

Backstreet Brian has a 'cross' on his shoulder.

LL Cool J

LL Cool J has the word 'Respect' on his left shoulder, as well as the name 'Mr. Smith' on his right shoulder. His real name is James Todd Smith, in case you were wondering.

Courtney Love

She has a 'fairy with two hearts' on her back, as well as the letter 'K' above her bellybutton.

John Mellencamp

The 'Cougar' has a tattoo of a 'long-haired woman' on his shoulder.

'N Sync

All of the band's members have tattoos of the groups 'flame' design.

Jo O'Meara (S Club 7)

Jo has 'barbed wire' around her arm, a 'butterfly' on her bottom and a 'dolphin' on her hip, plus several others.

Ozzy Osbourne

The Ozzman has a 'hooded ghoul' design on the left side of his chest and a 'Chinese-style beast's head' on the other side. He also has the letters 'OZZY' tattooed on the knuckles of his left hand.

Usher Raymond

Better known to us all as 'Usher'. He has his 'name', pierced by a sword on his left arm.

Henry Rollins	Hard-man of rock, Henry, is partial to the odd tattoo or two. Particularly striking, is the design on his back: the words 'Search and Destroy' surrounded by a flaming sun.
Richie Sambora	Bon Jovi's axe-man has a 'winged-guitar' on his upper right arm.
Tupac Shakur	2 Pac *had* many tattoos, including; the words 'Thug Life' on his stomach and 'Outlaw' on his left arm.
Britney Spears	Britney has a 'fairy' tattooed on her lower back.
Jeff Timmons (98°)	A Chinese symbol for 'Health and Good Luck' on his chest. Jeff also has a symbol for 'God' on his back and the 98° logo on his right arm.
Eddie Van Halen	Eddie has the Van Halen logo and a banner reading 'Wolf' on his right shoulder (Wolf is the name of his son).
Eddie Vedder (Pearl Jam)	The Pearl Jam singer has a 'crossed tomahawk and wrench' design on his right calf.
Donnie Wahlberg (N.K.O.T.B)	Donnie, no longer a 'kid', has a crest with the words 'Wahlberg 1969' drawn on his left shoulder.
Mark Wahlberg	'Marky Mark' reincarnated as an actor, has a portrait of Bob Marley on his shoulders, a 'rosary' around his neck, and a picture of Sylvester and Tweety on his ankle.
Jody Watley	Jody has a 'Cupid' design on her right arm.
Brian 'Head' Welch (KoRn)	The KoRn guitarist has 'Horn' erroneously

tattooed on his body. It is of course, meant to read 'KoRn'; unfortunately the artist, one Frederick Durst, made an irreversible error.

Robbie Williams

Robbie's tattoos include a Maori design on his left arm, a 'Celt Cross' on his leg, and a lion with the legend 'Born To Be Mild' written beneath it, on his right arm.

BRINGING YOU RIGHT UP TO DATE

'MY GENERATION'
21 Facts about the 21st Century

Well, it's finally happened, the 21st Century is upon us, and by way of a little celebration, we've gathered together 21 facts, all concerning pop music since 1 January 2000.

1. **'Pure & Simple'** sold 549,823 copies in its first week alone – the third highest first week sales figures for a single ever, beaten only by Elton John's 'Candle In The Wind 97' and Band Aid's 'Do They Know It's Christmas', both of which were charity singles.

2. **Hearsay's** first single, 'Pure & Simple' was originally written to be the third single for another group of pre-fabricated popsters, all-girl quintet Girlthing.

3. Staying with **Hearsay**, band member Kym Marsh was previously a part of little known group 2db.

4. The Liverpool trio, **Atomic Kitten** became the first band of 2001 to sell more than 100,000 copies of a single, when 'Whole Again' became their first number one hit in February. With its four-week reign at the top, it also became the first single to hold the number one spot for longer than one week. And, as if that isn't enough the Kittens found themselves only the ninth all-girl group in the history of the charts to achieve a number one single.

5. Hardcore Californian badboys **Papa Roach** recorded their debut

album, *Infest*, for the princely sum of $700.

6. The **Beatles** *1* Album, alongside *The Immaculate Collection* by Madonna, shares the honour of 'most consecutive weeks at number one' in the last decade. All in all the Beatles have spent a total of 174 weeks at number one, three times as many as their closest rivals, Abba.

7. Classical chanteuse, **Charlotte Church** became the youngest UK artist to break the top 10 in the American album charts with her album, *Dream A Dream*, in December 2000. Only the week before she found herself turning on the Christmas tree lights at the White House.

8. In the 2000 **New Year Honours** the following members of the musical fraternity were recognised: sax player Courtney Pine (OBE); Virgin's Richard Branson (knighted); songwriter Albert Hammond (whose hits include 'The Air That I Breathe' by the Hollies and 'Don't Turn Around' by Aswad) (OBE); Mark Knopfler (OBE) and Noddy Holder (MBE).

9. As we journey into the 21st Century Pink Floyd's seemingly timeless album, ***Dark Side Of The Moon***, first released in 1973, continues to sell more than half a million copies a year in the US alone.

10. **Gabrielle's** hit record 'Rise' which features a sample of Bob Dylan's classic track 'Knocking On Heaven's Door', was originally recorded using Tracy Chapman's memorable 1988 record 'Fast Car'. Unfortunately, Chapman, who somewhat ironically counts Dylan among her favourite artists, refused permission for the song to be used.

11. The **Geri Halliwell** single 'Bag It Up' featured the talents of eighties pop duo and one-time Wham! backing vocalists, Pepsi and Shirlie.

12. A double dose of **chart history** occurred on 15 April 2000 when the top six slots were all occupied by new entries: previously the record had been for the top five. The new entries in descending order were: 1. 'Fill Me In' by Craig David; 2. 'Flowers' by Sweet Female Attitude; 3. 'A Song For The Lovers' by Richard Ashcroft; 4. 'A Deeper Shade Of Pale' by Steps; 5. 'The Bad Touch' by the Bloodhound Gang; and finally, 6. 'Blow Ya Mind' by Lock 'n' Load. The second piece of chart history relates to Craig David's debut at number one with 'Fill Me In', who in so doing, became the youngest ever UK male solo artist to top the charts.

13. In 2000 the release of **Bon Jovi's** fifth album *Crush*, saw them make chart history when they became one of only five acts to have achieved five consecutive number one albums, namely: Abba, the Beatles, Bon Jovi, Led Zeppelin and Rod Stewart.

14. **Kylie Minogue**'s 29th hit and fifth number one, 'Spinning Around', was co-written by Paula Abdul, nineties hitmaker, choreographer to the stars, and one-time wife of Hollywood leading man Emilio Estevez.

15. Had he lived **John Lennon** would have celebrated his 60th birthday on 9 October 2000.

16. After breaking the top 20 singles chart in 1977 with 'She's Not There', **Santana** had to wait another 23 years to improve upon this feat; however, this time not once but twice with two top 10 hits: 'Smooth' (featuring Matchbox 20's Rob Thomas on vocals) and 'Maria Maria' (with vocals by Product G&B), both within 6 months of each other.

17. British rockers **Toploader**, made history in August 2000 when, as support act to Bon Jovi, they became the last UK act to play at the old Wembley Stadium.

18. For only the third time in 10 years a UK act managed to simultaneously hit number one in the album charts on both sides of the Atlantic: in October 2000, it was **Radiohead** with the release of *Kid A*. The only other acts to have achieved this were the Prodigy, in 1997 with *The Fat Of The Land*, and Pink Floyd before them in 1994 with *The Division Bell*.

19. When **'Independent Women Part 1'** (*Charlie's Angels*) by Destiny's Child knocked LeAnn Rimes 'Can't Fight The Moonlight' (*Coyote Ugly*) off the number one spot in November 2000, it was the second time in the year that one movie song had knocked another off the top of the charts. Earlier in the year Madonna's 'American Pie' (*The Next Best Thing*) took pole position from 'Pure Shores' (*The Beach*) by All Saints. Incidentally, 'Independent Women' was the first time since 1989 ('Eternal Flame' by the Bangles) that an American all-girl group had topped the charts.

20. December 2000, saw Irish supergroup **U2** top the album charts in 32 countries with the release of *All That You Can't Leave Behind*. The band subsequently went on to collect an award 'for outstanding contribution to music' at the Brits ceremony in February 2001.

21. **Eminem** became the first ever rapper to have two number one singles from the same album, with 'Stan' and 'The Real Slim Shady', both of which feature on *The Marshall Mathers LP*.

SIX (HUNDRED) OF THE BEST

'I CAN HEAR MUSIC'
600 Records with a Tale to Tell

Since the publication of the UK's first record chart, on 14 November 1952, the world of popular music has seen the release of literally thousands of songs, some great, some not so great. What constitutes a great song, of course, differs from one person to the next and that as such is the beauty of music.

The following list consists of 600 songs, chosen not only for their musical merit but also for the tale they have to tell. The songs have been selected to reflect the changing trends in pop throughout the history of the chart's 50 year span.

1. 'Here in my Heart' Al Martino (1952)
Became the first male singer to top the charts and first ever number one based on record sales.

2. 'You Belong To Me' Jo Stafford (1952)
Was the first female to make the UK sales charts.

3. 'Blue Tango' Ray Martin (1952)
This South African born orchestra leader was responsible for the first instrumental to make the UK charts

4. 'Zing A Little Zong' Bing Crosby & Jane Wyman (1952)
The famous singer and the big movie star created the first hit duet.

5. 'Glow Worm' The Mills Brothers (1952)
They were actually brothers and became the first group to have a UK hit. The song was written in 1908 for the German operetta, *Lysistrata.*

6. 'Broken Wing' The Stargazers (1953)
Became the first British act to achieve a number one hit in Britain. They were formed in 1949 and one of their members was Dick James who went on to sign The Beatles and Elton John to a publishing deal.

7. 'Limelight' Ron Goodwin (1953)
This became the first movie theme to make the UK charts and was written by Charlie Chaplin.

8. 'Answer Me' David Whitfield/Frankie Laine (1953)
This was the first time the same song, one a British cover, the other the American original hit, were at numbers one and two then exchanged places.

9. 'I Saw Momma Kissing Santa Claus' Jimmy Boyd (1953)
The first Christmas song to make the British charts was this novelty item by actor Jimmy Boyd who earlier the same year had recorded the hit duet, 'Tell Me A Story' with Frankie Laine.

10. 'Dragnet' Ted Heath (1953)
The first TV theme to become a top ten hit in Britain by the bandleader who was responsible for introducing the public to many top singers of the fifties including Dickie Valentine, Lita Rosa and Dennis Lotus.

11. 'Oh Mein Papa' Eddie Calvert / Eddie Fisher (1954)
Eddie Calvert became the first British instrumentalist to top the charts with a tune from a German Language Swiss musical, *Schwartze Hecht.* Eddie Fisher enjoyed some success with the first vocal version of an instrumental hit.

12. 'Such A Night' Johnnie Ray (1954)
First chart hit to get banned not only by the BBC, but also by many American radio stations. However, it still ended up topping the UK charts.

13. 'The Story of Three Loves (Rachmaninoff's 18th Variation)'
Winifred Atwell (1954)
A film theme which became the first classical-based hit. Winifred Atwell was

born in Trinidad and became famous for her honky-tonk piano and sing-along medleys. For this hit she decided to go back to her early days when she studied and played classical music.

14. 'Three Coins in the Fountain' Frank Sinatra (1954)
This was the week that the charts moved from just being a top 12 to a full top 20. Frank Sinatra had the first number one under the new format, which was his first of only two solo UK chart-toppers. The charts changed from top 12 to top 20 on 2 October 1954.

15. 'Sh-Boom' Crew Cuts (1954)
The song was originally recorded earlier in the year by The Chords, but it was Canadian group The Crew-Cuts' version that attracted the attention of the record-buying public and has often been viewed as the first notable move away from the middle of the road sound to that close to rock 'n' roll.

16. 'Sh-boom' Stan Freberg (1954)
For the first time a comedy parody of another hit made the UK charts. Freberg began his show business career recording voices for cartoon characters used in the Warner Brothers movies.

17. 'Rock Around the Clock Bill Haley & His Comets (1955)
The first truly recognised rock 'n' roll hit by the man who, although he began his career as a yodelling cowboy, was one of the great pioneers of the new modern sound of the day. His classic record ended up topping the charts.

18. 'Rose Marie' Slim Whitman (1955)
Held the record for 36 years for the longest stay at number one. It held the top spot for eleven weeks and was finally knocked off the top by Britain's own Jimmy Young and his recording of 'The Man From Laramie'.

19. 'Stranger in Paradise' Tony Bennett / The Four Aces / Tony Martin / Eddie Calvert (1955)
First song to make the top 20 in four different versions in the same week, two other versions also made the charts in the same year by Bing Crosby and Don Cornell.

20. 'The Singing Dogs Medley' Don Charlie's Singing Dogs (1955)
This was the first non-human hit. After spending days recording dog sounds and through the magic of editing, a medley of songs including 'Three Blind Mice' and 'Jingle Bells' came together for this canine group.

21. 'Poor People of Paris' Winifred Atwell (1956)
After the success of the chart being increased from 12 to a top 20 in 1954, eighteen months later it was decided to make a further increase to a top 30. Winifred Atwell with her honky-tonk piano became the first number one when NME increased their charts from 20 to 30 on 14 April 1956.

22. 'Heartbreak Hotel' Elvis Presley (1956)
This was the record that would change the face of the charts, the King of rock 'n' roll had arrived.

23. 'Blue Suede Shoes' Elvis Presley / Carl Perkins (1956)
The classic rock 'n' roll song that probably would have made number one had there not been the two versions competing against each other. The songwriter's original and Elvis's cover. Elvis only just won out with his version ending up at number 9 and Perkins one place below at number 10.

24. 'Why Do Fools Fall In Love' Frankie Lymon & The Teenagers (1956)
The blueprint for up-and-coming black doo-wop groups, Frankie Lymon and his gang were the first of their kind to top the UK charts with their individual sound.

25. 'Love Me Tender' Elvis Presley (1956)
The title track to Presley's very first movie.

26 'Blueberry Hill' Fats Domino (1956)
Another great pioneer of rock 'n' roll who released his first record, 'The Fat Man', back in 1949.

27. 'Singing The Blues' Guy Mitchell / Tommy Steele (1956)
It was the beginning of 1957 when, for three weeks, the two versions of the song exchanged places at the top of the charts.

28. 'Tutti Frutti' Little Richard (1957)
A classic debut hit for one of the most influential singer-songwriters of the fifties. Prior to 'Tutti Frutti', he had recorded several unsuccessful blues tracks with the Billy Wright Orchestra.

29. 'Butterfly' Andy Williams (1957)
A number one hit which was hated so much by the singer, he eventually purchased the rights to the track to keep it off the market. At the same time Andy Williams was in the charts with this song, another version by country star Charlie Gracie was also heading up the top 20.

30. 'Bye Bye Love' The Everly Brothers (1957)
Another fresh new sound to the charts. Don and Phil Everly became known as the world's most famous rock 'n' roll duo.

31. 'When I Fall In Love' Nat 'King' Cole (1957)
One of the all-time classic love songs that is still a favourite at weddings and engagement parties.

32. 'Diana' Paul Anka (1957)
His classic debut hit that found its way to the top of the charts, selling in excess of a million copies in the UK alone. World-wide sales were put at over ten million copies.

33. 'That'll Be The Day' The Crickets (1957)
Another classic debut to reach number one by the group formed to back Buddy Holly, who to this day still tour and release records.

34. 'Peggy Sue' Buddy Holly (1957)
Despite his success with The Crickets, Holly was keen on a solo career as well as continuing to record with his group. To fulfil his wish, Holly was forced to leave his name off all the hits he made with The Crickets.

35. 'Great Balls Of Fire' Jerry Lee Lewis (1957)
The debut chart entry of the man they call 'The Killer' must be one of the most famous rock 'n' roll songs of all time. It was also Jerry Lee's only UK chart-topper despite the hysteria he would create among his fans at all his live concerts.

36. 'Jailhouse Rock' Elvis Presley (1958)
Although Al Martino claims the distinction of being the first performer to enter the sales charts at number one, he was awarded that accolade by default as it was the first chart of its type to be published. Elvis Presley achieved this feat with 'Jailhouse Rock' on the first week's sales.

37. 'The Story Of My Life' Michael Holliday (1958)
The British singer who was greatly influenced by Perry Como. The song became the first UK chart-topper for the now legendary songwriting team, Burt Bacharach and Hal David.

38. 'Magic Moments' Perry Como (1958)
'The Story Of My Life' and 'Magic Moments', became the first two records to reach numbers one and two in the charts that were written by the same

songwriter. Burt Bacharach was the composer and the songs did eventually exchange places.

39. 'Who's Sorry Now?' Connie Francis (1958)
Having recorded a string of flops, Connie Francis was about to be dropped by her label, MGM. This was to be her final release but to everyone's surprise, it went straight to the top of the charts and was the start of her new long and successful recording career.

40. 'When' The Kalin Twins (1958)
Knocking The Everly Brothers' double A-sided hit, 'All I Have To Do Is Dream' / 'Claudette', off the number one spot, they became the first pair of brothers to succeed another pair at the top of the charts.

41. 'It's All In The Game' Tommy Edwards (1958)
Probably the only time in chart history that a number one hit was written by a vice-president of the United States. 'It's All In The Game' was actually written in 1912 by Charles Dawes.

42. 'Move It' Cliff Richard (1958)
Cliff's debut single was originally tucked away as the B-side of 'Schoolboy Crush' which made little impact. Soon after EMI switched sides, the record began climbing the charts and recognised as the first true British rock 'n' roll hit.

43. 'Hoots Mon' Lord Rockingham's XI (1958)
The first rock 'n' roll instrumental to top the UK charts. Lord Rockingham was in fact, successful musical arranger Harry Robinson, and his XI were a bunch of session men who were paid a £10 session fee for playing on this hit that sold over half a million copies.

44. 'To Know Him Is To Love Him' The Teddy Bears (1958)
Phil Spector was a member of this group and this was the first in a long line of successes for him as a record producer.

45. 'It Doesn't Matter Anymore' Buddy Holly (1959)
Prior to The Beatles, Buddy Holly was one of the biggest influences on British pop music. 'It Doesn't Matter Anymore', written by Paul Anka, became the first record to top the charts after the artist's death.

46. 'Living Doll' Cliff Richard (1959)
Giving Cliff a whole string of firsts, his first chart-topper, his first hit from a movie, *Serious Charge*, his first million seller and his first American hit.

47. 'China Tea' Russ Conway (1959)
The first performer to have three singles simultaneously in the top twenty. The other two were 'Side Saddle' and 'Roulette'.

48. 'What Do You Want?' Adam Faith (1959)
Although this was his fourth release, this was his first hit, but it did go all the way to the top.

49. 'What Do You Want To Make Those Eyes At Me For? Emile Ford and The Checkmates (1959)
The only time in chart history that the title of one number one was contained in the title of the record that knocked it off the top spot.

50. 'Good Timin'' Jimmy Jones (1960)
The first chart-topping performer to sing in a falsetto voice.

51. 'Royal Event' Russ Conway (1960)
Russ Conway's seventh top twenty hit was written and recorded to celebrate the birth of Prince Andrew.

52. 'My Old Man's A Dustman' Lonnie Donegan (1960)
Following a TV appearance on Val Parnell's *Sunday Night at the London Palladium*, this record entered the charts at number one, making Donegan the first British act to achieve this feat.

53. 'Cathy's Clown' The Everly Brothers (1960)
The brothers' first release on a new label and also the first record ever issued on Warner Brothers' own label (record number WB 1).

54. 'Apache' The Shadows (1960)
The first backing group to make it to number one and the group that inspired every would-be guitarist in the country.

55. 'Three Steps To Heaven' Eddie Cochran (1960)
This gave the singer his biggest UK hit three months after his death. The first person to the scene of the fatal car crash was then policeman, Dave Dee, later to become the lead singer of Dave Dee, Dozy, Beaky, Mick & Tich.

56. 'Tell Laura I Love Her' Ricky Valence (1960)
The BBC probably enhanced the sales of this single, which was a cover of an American hit by Ray Peterson, because they banned it due to the lyrics about the death of Laura's lover Tommy who died in a stock car race.

57. 'It's Now Or Never' Elvis Presley (1960)
After the release being held up for over six months due to copyright problems, 'It's Now Or Never' became the third single in chart history to enter at number one with advance sales the largest to date of over half a million.

58. 'Save The Last Dance For Me' The Drifters (1960)
Ben E King sang lead vocals on their only American chart-topper. There are more than thirty singers who have, at one time or another, been members of The Drifters.

59. 'Will You Still Love Me Tomorrow?' The Shirelles (1961)
The first female group to have an American chart-topper with this Carole King-Gerry Goffin classic.

60. 'A Hundred Pounds Of Clay' Craig Douglas (1961)
A cover of the American hit by Gene McDaniels. Craig re-recorded his version after the BBC objected to the religious connotations of the original lyrics.

61. 'Blue Moon' The Marcels (1961)
Frowned upon by the song's composer Richard Rodgers who believed that the group had insulted him with their treatment of the song.

62. 'Runaway' Del Shannon (1961)
His co-writer on this hit was Max Crook who played the musitron on the famous instrumental break. The two of them wrote the song by accident while jamming between shows at a local club.

63. 'You Don't Know' Helen Shapiro (1961)
Just forty-nine days away from her fifteenth birthday when Helen Shapiro hit number one, she became the youngest British singer to top the UK charts.

64. 'Johnny Remember Me' John Leyton (1961)
Independent record producer Joe Meek achieved his first number one. Leyton had previously worked as an actor and once played Ginger in the TV series, *Biggles*. This, his first hit, was largely due to his role in the television soap, *HarpersWest One*, when he played pop singer, Johnny St Cyr and was allowed to perform 'Johnny Remember Me'.

65. 'Cupid' Sam Cooke (1961)
One of the biggest influences on soul music even today. This was one of his finest records. In his early days he sang gospel with The Soul Stirrers and once issued a single under the name of Dale Cooke using the pseudonym so that he didn't offend his gospel fans.

66. 'Tower Of Strength' Frankie Vaughan (1961)
The second time in the same year that American singer Gene McDaniels had the rug pulled from under his feet by a British cover version of another of his American hits.

67. 'Take Good Care Of My Baby' Bobby Vee (1961)
Another Carole King-Gerry Goffin song that gave Bobby Vee his only American number one. The singer first came to the public's attention when he had to deputise for Buddy Holly following his fatal plane crash.

68. 'Runaround Sue' Dion & The Belmonts (1961)
Although at the time Dion had a wife named Sue, the song was originally written about a girl named Roberta. Despite having hit after hit in America, Dion's career was put on hold between 1964 and 1968 while he battled against a serious drug addiction.

69. 'Let's Twist Again' Chubby Checker (1962)
This record inspired a whole string of 'twist' hits and new dance crazes to sweep across Europe and America. Checker had previously worked as a chicken plucker during which time he made friends with songwriter, Kal Mann, who wrote or co-wrote many of his American hits including 'Let's Twist Again'.

70. 'Hey Baby' Bruce Channel (1962)
With harmonica played by Delbert McClinton, this record influenced the then unknown John Lennon and Paul McCartney to write 'Love Me Do', the debut hit for their group, The Beatles. In fact, it was McLinton who taught Lennon to play the harmonica during one of their tours.

71. 'Nut Rocker' B.Bumble & The Stingers (1962)
The first number one based on a classical theme (from Tchaikovsky's *Nutcracker Suite*). The group were made up of a variety of session players whose line-up went through many changes over the years. 'Nut Rocker' returned to the UK top twenty in 1972. If Tchaikovsky were alive today, he would turn in his grave.

72. 'Telstar' The Tornados (1962)
Another Joe Meek production and composition, he was inspired by the communications satellite of the same name. This record made The Tornados the first British group to top the American charts.

73. 'Sherry' The Four Seasons (1962)
Bringing a fresh new sound to the charts, the group had previously recorded under the names The Variatones then later as The Four Lovers. In 1962, they emerged as The Four Seasons and 'Sherry' was their first hit to top the American charts.

74. 'Diamonds' Jet Harris & Tony Meehan (1963)
Jet Harris had already had a couple of solo hits but now the two ex-members of The Shadows replaced 'Dance On' by their former group at the top of the charts with their first hit as a duo.

75. 'Please Please Me' The Beatles (1963)
Although their first hit, 'Love Me Do', had made quite an impact, this was the record that was to reshape the sound of the charts all over the world.

76. 'The Wayward Wind' Frank Ifield (1963)
This gave Frank his third consecutive chart-topper, making him the first UK act to achieve this feat.

77. 'How Do You Do It?' Gerry and The Pacemakers (1963)
A song The Beatles rejected made this Liverpudlian group the first from their city to top the charts. (NB Some charts had 'Please Please Me' at number one, but officially it peaked at number two.)

78. 'Summer Holiday' Cliff Richard & The Shadows (1963)
The title song from Cliff's fourth movie about four young transport workers borrowing a red double decker bus to tour the continent, starred, alongside Cliff and The Shadows, Ron Moody, Una Stubbs and Melvyn Hayes.

79. 'From Me To You' The Beatles (1963)
Never mind that The Beatles turned down 'How Do You Do It?', 'From Me To You' knocked Gerry and friends off number one with the record that truly established The Beatles as an act who were here to stay.

80. 'Do You Want To Know A Secret?' Billy J Kramer & The Dakotas (1963)
The first cover of a Beatles song to make the UK top ten. It's interesting to note

that the week ending 13 June, 1963 saw Liverpool represented by the top four records in the charts. The Beatles, Gerry and The Pacemakers, Billy J Kramer & The Dakotas and Billy Fury.

81. 'Sweets For My Sweet' The Searchers (1963)
The first Liverpudlian group not to be managed by Brian Epstein gave record producer and songwriter Tony Hatch his first chart-topper in the UK.

82. 'She Loves You' The Beatles (1963)
Beatlemania really arrived with the group topping the singles, EP and album charts all in the same week.

83. 'Bad To Me' Billy J Kramer and The Dakotas (1963)
The first Lennon and McCartney song to top the charts that hadn't previously been recorded by The Beatles.

84. 'Wipe Out' The Surfaris (1963)
The beginning of the surfing sound with this track that was originally destined to become the 'B' side of one of their records. Now an instrumental anthem.

85. 'Da Doo Ron Ron' The Crystals (1963)
Their second hit really established the Phil Spector produced 'Wall Of Sound'. The Crystals originally worked together recording demos for many of the top songwriters before meeting Spector who knew talent when he saw it.

86. 'Come On' The Rolling Stones (1963)
The Chuck Berry song gave The Rolling Stones their debut hit with their first single release.

87. 'You'll Never Walk Alone' Gerry and The Pacemakers (1963)
Becoming the first act in chart history to reach number one with their first three record releases.

88. 'Be My Baby' The Ronettes (1963)
Another Phil Spector produced hit, became a pop classic. The group began in show business as a dance act called The Dolly Sisters but later recorded as Ronnie and The Relatives before changing their name to The Ronettes. Lead singer Ronnie Bennett married Phil Spector in 1965.

89. 'I Want To Hold Your Hand' The Beatles (1963)
The year's Christmas number one which knocked their previous hit, 'She Loves You' off the top spot, but which held on to the number two position.

90. 'Glad All Over' The Dave Clark Five (1963)
The record was banned by many football grounds because fans were causing damage by stomping their feet in the stands in time with the chorus. The Dave Clark Five replaced The Beatles at the top of the charts which created press speculation that they were about to become bigger than the Fab Four.

91. 'I Only Want To Be With You' Dusty Springfield (1964)
Began her career as a member of The Lana Sisters then went on to have success as a member of her brother Tom's duo, The Springfields. After several hits, she left to pursue a solo career. This became the first hit for Britain's finest white soul singer.

92. 'Needles And Pins' The Searchers (1964)
Written by Sonny Bono who would later become successful as part of Sonny & Cher. This record kept 'I'm The One', by Gerry and The Pacemakers off number one, depriving them of four chart-toppers on the trot.

93. '5-4-3-2-1' Manfred Mann (1964)
The song became the theme to one of television's most popular music shows, *Ready Steady Go*, and helped launch the career of another influential UK act.

94. 'Can't Buy Me Love' The Beatles (1964)
With over a million advance orders, the highest ever recorded in the UK, 'Can't Buy Me Love' became The Beatles' fourth official consecutive chart-topper and their second hit to enter at number one.

95. 'World Without Love' Peter and Gordon (1964)
Again Lennon and McCartney knocked a Lennon and McCartney song off number one. Peter and Gordon replaced 'Can't Buy Me Love' at the top. British-born Peter was Peter Asher who went on to become one of America's top record producers.

96. 'My Guy' Mary Wells (1964)
The first British success for the Motown sound although the company had not yet established its own identity in the UK. Their releases were at this time through EMI's Stateside label.

97. 'My Boy Lollipop' Millie (1964)
The beginnings of the successful ska sound. Millie Small was from Jamaica and followed up 'My Boy Lollipop' with a minor hit, 'Sweet William', before vanishing into obscurity.

98. 'Walk On By' Dionne Warwick (1964)
The Burt Bacharach-Hal David song that established Dionne in the UK and gave her a long and successful working relationship with the two composers.

99. 'House Of The Rising Sun' The Animals (1964)
The first time a record of over four minutes duration hit the top of the charts. Despite hitting the top in the USA, the Americans were less ambitious and edited their version by a minute.

100. 'It's All Over Now' The Rolling Stones (1964)
In truth, with their first number one, written by Bobby and Shirley Womack and originally recorded by The Valentinos, it was just the beginning. The battle was on between The Beatles and The Stones.

101. 'A Hard Day's Night' The Beatles (1964)
The title song from their first full length movie, The Beatles allowed The Stones to enjoy just one week at the top of the charts.

102. 'Doo Wah Diddy Diddy' Manfred Mann (1964)
A song originally recorded by little known black American group, The Exciters gave Manfred Mann their first chart-topper.

103. 'Have I The Right?' The Honeycombs (1964)
Another Joe Meek production and his final chart-topper with the added novelty value of the group having a female drummer in the shape of Honey Lantree.

104. 'You Really Got Me' The Kinks (1964)
Just a classic pop rock song for The Kinks first chart-topper. Their first record was a version of Little Richard's 'Long Tall Sally', and although it failed to make any impact at the time, the original single is now a real collectors' item.

105. 'Rag Doll' The Four Seasons (1964)
Songwriter Bob Gaudio was inspired to write the song after a young girl dressed in rags rushed out to wash his windscreen when he had stopped at traffic lights.

106. 'Oh Pretty Woman' Roy Orbison (1964)
During the Liverpool explosion, Orbison was one of the most successful American singers in the UK. He wrote the number one hit, 'Claudette' for The Everly Brothers and used the money to buy his recording contract with Sun records in order to change labels to Monument where he had all his success in the sixties.

107. '(There's) Always Something There To Remind Me' Sandie Shaw (1964)
Her real name is Sandra Goodrich and she managed to convince Adam Faith that she had talent. It was he who pointed her in the right direction to success by introducing her to his manager, Evie Taylor.

108. 'Baby Love' The Supremes (1964)
The first chart-topper for the Tamla Motown sound who were still without their own label identity in the UK. The Supremes were originally called The Primettes by way of tribute to another group of the time, The Primes, who themselves later changed their name to The Temptations.

109. 'Go Now' The Moody Blues (1964)
Originally a soul hit, recorded by Bessie Banks, The Moody Blues' cover gave them their only UK chart-topper.

110. 'You've Lost That Lovin' Feelin'' The Righteous Brothers (1965)
If you mention record producer Phil Spector, then this is usually the record you most associate with him. Probably one of the best-remembered hits of all time by these two singers who weren't brothers at all, they were Bill Medley and Bobby Hatfield who met at a local club in California.

111. 'It's Not Unusual' Tom Jones (1965)
A song rejected by Sandie Shaw launched the long and successful career of Tom Jones, who began as a vocalist in the group, Tommy Scott & The Senators.

112. 'For Your Love' The Yardbirds (1965)
Although their most successful single, it was reported to have been the reason for Eric Clapton leaving the group. He thought they had become too commercial.

113. 'Stop In The Name Of Love' The Supremes (1965)
Hooray! Finally the Tamla Motown label obtained its own identity in the UK through EMI records, with this, the first release.

114. 'The Times They Are A-Changin'' Bob Dylan (1965)
Although he had a single released prior to 'Times', 'Mixed Up Confusion' was quickly withdrawn because it portrayed the wrong image, so the first official Dylan release saw new beginnings for the protest song from one of the biggest influences in popular music.

115. 'Catch The Wind' Donovan (1965)
Hailed as England's answer to Bob Dylan, Donovan also hit the big-time with his first release, largely due to his regular appearances on one of the UK's top pop TV shows, *Ready, Steady Go.*

116. 'Mr Tambourine Man' The Byrds (1965)
The first successful cover of a Bob Dylan composition launched the career of The Byrds among rumours that most of the band didn't play on this their first hit.

117. 'I Got You Babe' Sonny & Cher (1965)
Any record fan during the sixties will remember the image of this duo performing 'I Got You Babe' on television. They met when Sonny was working as an assistant to Phil Spector and Cher occasionally worked for him as a backing singer.

118. '(I Can't Get No) Satisfaction' The Rolling Stones (1965)
Their fourth consecutive chart-topper and second to be written by Mick Jagger and Keith Richard, it was recorded in Los Angeles and is still claimed by many of their fans to be *the* classic Stones track.

119. 'Eve Of Destruction' Barry McGuire (1965)
The protest song to end all protest songs, and look how right he was. Barry McGuire was first heard singing lead vocals on the 1963 American hit, 'Green Green', by The New Christie Minstrels.

120. 'Hang On Sloopy' The McCoys (1965)
Rick D Zehringer started a group called The McCoys but changed their name to The Rick Z Combo. When they were offered the song, 'My Girl Snoopy', they agreed to record it if the title was changed to 'Hang On Sloopy'. The writers agreed if the group agreed to change their name back to The McCoys. After the recording Rick decided to simplify his own name by changing it to Rick Derringer.

121. 'Get Off Of My Cloud' The Rolling Stones (1965)
This gave The Stones a run of five consecutive chart-toppers, a feat not only equalled but bettered in the UK by . . . yes, you guessed it . . . The Beatles.

122. 'Keep On Running' The Spencer Davis Group (1965)
The group from Birmingham were originally called The Rhythm and Blues Quartet, featuring the outstanding vocal talents of Stevie Winwood. Although they'd achieved minor success with three previous releases, 'Keep On

Running', written by Jamaican born Jackie Edwards gave them their big break and a number one.

123. 'SHA-LA-LA-LA-LEE' The Small Faces (1966)
A well-favoured band by 'the mods', even their name reflected the mod image as a mod was a face. They achieved their first top ten hit with a song written by Kenny Lynch and Mort Shuman.

124. 'The Sun Ain't Gonna Shine Anymore' The Walker Brothers (1966)
Their second UK chart-topper was written by Bob Crewe and Bob Gaudio who were responsible for most of The Four Seasons' hits. The Walker Brothers were another unrelated group of brothers who were Scott Engel, John Maus and Gary Leeds.

125. 'Uptight (Everything's Alright)' Stevie Wonder (1966)
The first appearance in the UK charts for this talented songwriting, producing, performer. He was thirteen years of age (and then known as Little Stevie Wonder), when his first record, 'Fingertips', topped the American charts in 1963. In 1996 he was awarded a Grammy for his lifetime achievement in popular music.

126. 'Lightnin' Strikes' Lou Christie (1966)
The song was co-written by Christie and a clairvoyant named Twyla Herbert, who predicted the chart positions of the songs they wrote together.

127. 'Substitute' The Who (1966)
Although a hugely influential band, they never managed to achieve a UK number one. The original 1961 band were called The Detours and later in 1964 they became The High Numbers releasing a single called 'I'm The Face'. Although it was never a hit, original copies of the single now exchange hands for hundreds of pounds. Keith Moon's exploits on stage, smashing up his equipment began when the band played at a club with a low ceiling and he accidently broke his guitar neck by holding it up too high.

128. 'You Don't Have To Say You Love Me' Dusty Springfield (1966)
One of the great big ballads of the sixties gave Dusty her only UK number one. The song was an English version of an Italian song, 'Io Che No Vivo Senza Te', with English lyrics supplied by Vicki Wickham and Simon Napier-Bell.

129. 'Daydream' The Lovin' Spoonful (1966)
After they made their first record, 'Do You Believe In Magic', they couldn't find a record company interested in their music until Phil Spector came to see them play one evening. Word was out that he was interested and all the record companies started offering deals.

130. 'Strangers In The Night' Frank Sinatra (1966)
From the movie, *A Man Could Get Killed*, this gave Sinatra only his second and final UK solo chart-topper nearly twelve years after his first.

131. 'Wild Thing' The Troggs (1966)
In America, two labels claimed ownership of the hit. As the record soared to the top of the US charts, it became the only number one to be available simultaneously on two different labels.

132. 'California Dreamin'' The Mamas & The Papas (1966)
Although not a huge UK hit, it became a classic. The song was originally recorded as an album track by Barry McGuire with the then un-named Mamas & The Papas providing backing vocals. Later, producer Lou Adler decided to wipe McGuire's vocals and replace it with the groups.

133. 'River Deep – Mountain High' Ike & Tina Turner (1966)
Probably ranking only second to 'You've Lost That Lovin' Feelin'' as the most popular of all Phil Spector productions. The record returned to the top forty nearly three years later in 1969.

134. 'Get Away' Georgie Fame (1966) The first UK chart-topper that was first used in a TV advert to promote a brand of petrol. Georgie Fame was a major force in promoting Rhythm and Blues in the UK and fans used to flock to see him and his band, The Blue Flames play at London's Flamingo club where they would regularly appear.

135. 'Out of Time' Chris Farlowe (1966)
To keep in step with John Lennon and Paul McCartney, and following the theme of anything you can do . . . this Mick Jagger production was the first Jagger–Richards song to top the charts for an act other than The Rolling Stones.

136. 'Reach Out (I'll Be There)' The Four Tops (1966)
The all time classic Tamla Motown track for the group that began life as The Four Aims, but changed their name to the Four Tops because they were getting confused with another act, The Aims Brothers.

137. 'Good Vibrations' The Beach Boys (1966)
An inspired piece of production and songwriting, this track took Brian Wilson over six months to complete, using seventeen separate recording sessions at four different studios at a cost estimated to have been over £10,000 – an amount unheard of in the sixties for producing a single.

138. 'What Becomes Of The Brokenhearted?' Jimmy Ruffin (1966)
Another Motown classic by Ruffin, who, in the early sixties, was offered the lead singer's position with The Temptations, turned it down but recommended his brother, David, who was given the job.

139. 'I'm A Believer' The Monkees (1967)
The first new chart-topper of 1967 launched America's man made super-group with expectations beyond that of The Beatles and The Rolling Stones.

140. 'Hey Joe' Jimi Hendrix (1967)
One of the most influential figures in rock music. He once worked as a backing musician for many big-named acts including Sam Cooke, Little Richard and The Isley Brothers.

141. 'Night Of Fear' The Move (1967)
The first hit for the group from Birmingham which brought a new excitement to the charts with a Roy Wood song based on Tchaikovsky's *1812 Overture*.

142. 'Release me' Engelbert Humperdinck (1967)
The first hit for 'Hump' will always be remembered as the record that kept The Beatles off number one. He took his name from the German composer, Humperdinck, whose only real claim to fame was the opera, *Hansel And Gretel*.

143. 'Penny Lane' / 'Strawberry Fields Forever' The Beatles (1967)
Although this double A-sided hit broke their run of eleven consecutive chart-toppers, peaking at number two, 'Strawberry Fields Forever' was regarded as one of their most innovative productions to date.

144. 'Puppet On A String' Sandie Shaw (1967)
Whether you love it or hate it, no one can deny the kudos it brought Great Britain by winning the Eurovision Song Contest for the first time, achieved by this twenty year old singer.

145. 'Hi Ho Silver Lining' Jeff Beck (1967)
Although not a huge chart hit, this was probably one of the most successful

dance-hall records of all time and the first single from Beck after he left The Yardbirds. Written by Larry Weiss and Scott English, who had a hit in his own right in 1971 with 'Brandy' that re-emerged three and a half years later as 'Mandy' for Barry Manilow.

146. 'A Whiter Shade Of Pale' Procol Harum (1967)
An inspired classic hit in more ways than one, this chart-topper was based on Johann Sebastian Bach's Suite No 3 in D, more popularly known as *Air On A G String*.

147. 'All You Need Is Love' The Beatles (1967)
They couldn't help but keep on making the history books, this was first heard on television via a worldwide linked TV show, 'Our World'.

148. 'She'd Rather Be With Me' The Turtles (1967)
A very underrated group at their very best. Their name was originally spelt Turtyls as a tribute to one of their favourite bands, The Byrds.

149. 'San Francisco (Be Sure To Wear Some Flowers In Your Hair)' Scott McKenzie (1967)
This was the anthem to flower power and announced to the world that the fad was here to stay. It also led the way to a whole string of 'peace brother' styled hits.

150. 'Excerpt From A Teenage Opera' Keith West (1967)
A masterpiece in production from an opera that never existed then, and to this day has never materialised. At the time of recording his hit, Keith West was still lead vocalist with the very 'in' group, Tomorrow.

151. 'I Was Made To Love Her' Stevie Wonder (1967)
A record that was never off the juke boxes all over the country and Stevie's first British top ten hit.

152. 'Groovin'' The Young Rascals (1967)
Their second American chart-topper and one of those magic records that just makes you feel happy. The group were inspired by The Beatles to begin writing their own material.

153. 'Respect' Aretha Franklin (1967)
Written and originally recorded by the late Otis Redding, this was the record that put Aretha firmly on the map in the UK. Her remarkably distinctive voice rightly earned her the title of 'The Queen Of Soul'.

154. 'See Emily Play' Pink Floyd (1967)
Later to become one of the most influential rock bands of all time, Pink Floyd initially made their name with weird and psychedelic songs such as this, which was written by their then lead vocalist Syd Barrett who, soon after, left the group suffering from a nervous breakdown.

155. 'Itchycoo Park' The Small Faces (1967)
Psychedelic music was definitely on the increase, and this Small Faces classic did no damage to flower power, summer love and the big hippy scene. The single returned to the top ten in 1976.

156. 'Flowers In The Rain' The Move (1967)
The first record to be played in its entirety on the BBC's new national pop station, Radio One. However, if one is to be perfectly accurate, Tony Blackburn opened the station with 'Beefeaters', by Johnny Dankworth's orchestra, which he then used daily as his signature tune.

157. 'Massachusetts' The Bee Gees (1967)
The first number one for the group who were, at this point in their career, a five piece band, Barry, Maurice and Robin were supplemented by Australian friends, drummer Colin Peterson and guitarist Vince Melourney.

158. 'Love Is All Around' The Troggs (1967)
The seventh top twenty hit for The Troggs with the Reg Presley song that twenty-seven years later would be transformed into one of the world's biggest selling singles thanks to Wet Wet Wet's version being included on the soundtrack of the movie, *Four Weddings And A Funeral.*

159. 'Baby Now That I've Found You' The Foundations (1967)
Just a great pop song, giving writers Tony Macaulay and John McLeod their first chart-topper. The group were discovered by record shop owner, Barry Class, when he heard them playing in a London club, who then introduced them to Macaulay and McLeod.

160. 'Let The Heartaches Begin' Long John Baldry (1967)
Tony Macaulay and John McLeod managed to knock themselves off number one with another of their compositions. After years of struggling without success, Long John Baldry, who once fronted The Hoochie Coochie Men which also included Rod Stewart, and played in Bluesology with a young Elton John, found his feet and his first hit which went to number one.

161. 'Magical Mystery Tour' (EP) The Beatles (1967)
Made as a TV special for Christmas, the soundtrack EP was kept off the number one spot only by The Beatles themselves and their hit, 'Hello Goodbye'.

162. 'Walk Away Renee' The Four Tops (1967)
Originally recorded by American group, The Left Banke, The Four Tops gave the song the distinctive Motown treatment.

163. 'Everlasting Love' The Love Affair (1968)
Many would pinpoint this record as the blueprint sound for the perfect pop record. Still, the record was surrounded by controversy when it was revealed that Steve Ellis, the lead singer, was the only member of the group to have performed on the disc.

164. 'The Mighty Quinn' Manfred Mann (1968)
The Bob Dylan song became their third and final number one and the only chart-topper with their recently recruited new lead singer, Mike D'Abo.

165. 'Bend Me, Shape Me' Amen Corner (1968)
A cover of the US hit for The American Breed, and another song written by Scott English and Larry Weiss (see no. 146), established the Welsh band Amen Corner in the UK.

166. 'Judy In Disguise (With Glasses)' John Fred & His Playboy Band (1968)
Their only ever hit which was inspired by The Beatles' song, 'Lucy In The Sky With Diamonds'.

167. 'Pictures Of MatchStick Men' Status Quo (1968)
Their first in a long run of successful singles, this was British psychedelia at its best for the group whose previous single, which was released under their former name, Traffic Jam, had the apt title, 'Almost There But Not Quite'.

168. 'Lady Madonna' The Beatles (1968)
Lennon and McCartney wrote the song by way of a tribute to the great Fats Domino, which found a role reversal, Domino himself later recorded the song as a tribute to The Beatles.

169. 'What A Wonderful World' Louis Armstrong (1968)
If it hadn't been for this Louis Armstrong record, 'Simon Says', by the 1910 Fruitgum Company, 'Lazy Sunday', by The Small Faces and 'A Man Without

Love', by Engelbert Humperdink would all have topped the charts. At the age of 67, he still managed to hold the number one spot for four weeks.

171. 'Simon Says' 1910 Fruitgum Company (1968)
One of the very first bubblegum hits, setting the trend for a whole new wave of songs. The group were a studio session band led by songwriter Joey Levine who was responsible for dozens of American hits.

171. 'Jumpin' Jack Flash' The Rolling Stones (1968)
The first number one for The Stones in two years that gave the then somewhat ailing group a new lease of life with this Jimmy Miller produced classic which is still one of the all time great party records.

172. 'Baby Come Back' The Equals (1968)
Their first major hit and indeed a number one, Eddie Grant's former group later became involved in a serious legal dispute with their record company which forced them to stop releasing records for over a year. By the time the dispute was resolved, The Equals were history.

173. 'MacArthur Park' Richard Harris (1968)
A masterpiece created by songwriter Jim Webb who originally wanted American group The Association to record it. At this time it was the longest song to make the top twenty.

174. 'Mony Mony' Tommy James & The Shondells (1968)
Inspired by a flashing sign outside his hotel window for the Mutual Of New York, James took the initials and wrote a song that topped the charts both sides of the Atlantic.

175. 'I Say A Little Prayer' Aretha Franklin (1968)
Aretha scored with the Burt Bacharach–Hal David song where Dionne Warwick's original version failed.

176. 'Hey Jude' The Beatles (1968)
Although still contracted to EMI's Parlophone label, a concession was made and 'Hey Jude' was the first single to be released with an Apple label, The Beatles own company, but carried a Parlophone catalogue number.

177 'Those Were The Days' Mary Hopkin (1968)
The evocative Russian folk song given English lyrics by Gene Raskin, caught the imagination of the great British record buying public. The record sold in excess of four million copies around the world.

178. 'With A Little Help From My Friends' Joe Cocker (1968)
Considered to be among the world's greatest rock singers. In 1968, he took The Beatles' ditty from *Sergeant Pepper*, and turned it into a powerful, soulful classic.

179. 'Eloise' Barry Ryan (1968)
After the success of 'Macarthur Park', and 'Hey Jude', records of long durations started to creep into the charts. Barry's masterful interpretation of his brother Paul's composition remains one of the best remembered for its sensational arrangement by Johnny Arthey.

180. 'Albatross' Fleetwood Mac (1968)
A haunting instrumental that was far removed from the blues tracks expected from Fleetwood Mac, but their change in style established the group's career.

181. 'Dancing In The Street' Martha & The Vandellas (1969)
Originally released in 1964, this re-issue established the record as another to be added to the long list of Tamla Motown classics.

182. 'I Heard it Through The Grapevine' Marvin Gaye (1969)
Although already established as a leader in the Motown family of stars, this was his biggest moment. The record returned to the top ten in 1986 when it was featured in a Levi's jeans television advert.

183. 'The Israelites' Desmond Dekker & The Aces (1969)
The first reggae record to top the UK pop charts and more interestingly, a top ten hit in America where reggae was not being received too well at the time.

184. 'My Way' Frank Sinatra (1969)
What can we say? It still holds the record for the most number of weeks on the chart for any one single, and there have now been more than two hundred different versions of the song, including a duet between Sinatra and Paul Anka who wrote English lyrics to the original French hit by Claude François.

185. 'Pinball Wizard' The Who (1969)
From Pete Townshend's rock opera, *Tommy*, one of the sixties most influential tracks. The song returned to the charts in 1976 when Elton John recorded it for the soundtrack of Ken Russell's movie version of *Tommy*.

186. 'Oh Happy Day' Edwin Hawkins Singers (1969)
True religious gospel records rarely made the charts, but this one caught the record-buying public's eye and became the first major hit in this genre. The

hymn, which dates back to the 18th century, was arranged by Edwin Hawkins for his singers.

187. 'The Ballad Of John and Yoko' (1969)
The final chart-topper for The Beatles, and dedicated to Lennon's recent marriage to Yoko Ono. The record was made with Lennon and McCartney, who played the drums. George and Ringo were nowhere near the studio.

188. 'In The Ghetto' Elvis Presley (1969)
After four years of releasing substandard material mainly due to his movie-making commitments, Presley came back to the charts with this blinding hit.

189. 'Something In The Air' Thunderclap Newman (1969)
The group's only major hit, but what a hit. The Pete Townshend produced record made him the only member of The Who to have a connection with a chart-topper.

190. 'Honky Tonk Women' The Rolling Stones (1969)
Following the anything you can do theory yet again, The Rolling Stones achieved their last UK chart-topper soon after The Beatles.

191. 'Give Peace A Chance' John Lennon & The Plastic Ono Band (1969)
The first Beatle to release a single on his own and achieve a top ten hit. This track was recorded in John and Yoko's bedroom in a hotel in Canada.

192. 'Bad Moon Rising' Creedence Clearwater Revival (1969)
A new brand of music was catching on in America. Originating from the bay area in San Francisco, 'Swamp Rock', was becoming all the rage and Creedence, formerly known as The Golliwogs, were the leaders in promoting the sound.

193. 'Space Oddity' David Bowie (1969)
A classic hit from Bowie after years in the wilderness, releasing records as Davy Jones and The Lower Third and The Mannish Boys. He changed his name to Bowie because of confusion with Davy Jones from The Monkees. 'Space Oddity' returned to the charts in 1975 when it was an even bigger hit, climbing to the top of the charts.

194. 'Sugar Sugar' The Archies (1969)
The first chart-topper by a non-existent group. They were session singers emulating cartoon characters from an American comic strip. This also began a spate of hit records made by session singers who were just in search of a hit.

195. 'Suspicious Minds' Elvis Presley (1969)
Another classic Presley track, proving that he was back on top and taken from his recently recorded Memphis sessions that produced his best album in years, aptly titled, *From Elvis In Memphis*.

196. 'Love Grows (Where My Rosemary Goes)' (1970)
The first chart-topper for songwriter Tony Macaulay, since 'Let The Heartaches Begin'. This was the first British all session group to top the charts. Lead vocals were provided by Tony Burrows, who went on to perform on dozens of other hit records for non existent acts including White Plains, Brotherhood Of Man (who later did become a working act with a different line-up) and The Pipkins.

197. 'I Want You Back' The Jackson Five (1970)
Michael Jackson was just twelve years old when this record entered the charts, however, he made his first public appearance with his brothers at the tender age of five.

198. 'Bridge Over Troubled Water' Simon & Garfunkel (1970)
One of the all-time classic records. The song was originally written by Paul Simon with Aretha Franklin in mind and, although she rejected it in the first instance, she later recorded it and the following year had an American top ten hit. Simon and Garfunkel can claim that they managed to top both the American and British singles and album charts in the same week with 'Bridge Over Troubled Water'.

199. 'Young Gifted And Black' Bob & Marcia (1970)
Arranger, Johnny Arthey who had earlier success with Barry Ryan's 'Eloise', was asked to add strings to this reggae version of the Nina Simone song which she wrote in memory of one of her best friends who died of cancer in her early thirties. The result was the first top ten reggae hit using a full string section.

200. 'In The Summertime' Mungo Jerry (1970)
The biggest selling single of the year and still pops up on those party classic compilations. The band were originally called Good Earth but changed to Mungo Jerry, who was one of the 'Cats' in the T.S. Eliot poem.

201 'All Right Now' Free (1970)
A hit that made periodic returns to the chart over the coming years became an instant rock anthem, taken from the band's best known album, *Fire And Water*.

202. 'Tears Of A Clown' Smokey Robinson & The Miracles (1970)
This song had been tucked away on an album and many years later was discovered by Motown records as a potential hit. They were right, it made number one.

203. 'Give Me Just A Little More Time' Chairman Of The Board (1970)
The incredible talents of the songwriting and production team of Holland-Dozier-Holland who had been responsible for dozens of hits for the Tamla Motown label, set up their own company, Invictus following a long legal dispute with Motown. This was their label's first hit.

204. 'Band Of Gold' Freda Payne (1970)
Following in the footsteps of Chairman Of The Board, Freda Payne gave Invictus their first and only UK chart-topper. Prior to the hit, Payne had been a little known jazz and cabaret singer.

205. '(They Long To Be) Close To You' The Carpenters (1970)
Many versions of this Burt Bacharach–Hal David song had failed prior to The Carpenters making the charts. It was Herb Alpert who brought the song to the attention of Richard and Karen who were signed to his A&M label. The song had been suggested for him to record, but he was convinced they would have a huge hit with it.

206. 'Black Night' Deep Purple (1970)
One of the UK's most influential rock bands. Although this was their debut British hit the band had already achieved a top ten hit in America in 1968 with the Joe South classic 'Hush'.

207. 'Woodstock' Matthews Southern Comfort (1970)
A number one hit then never to be seen in the charts again for this group that covered Joni Mitchell's song about the world's most famous music festival.

208. 'Ride A White Swan' T Rex (1970)
Previously known as Tyrannosaurus Rex, they shortened their name for this and future releases to T Rex, and some considered they had sold out to the commercial scene. However DJs in the discos didn't agree, for when they wanted to get people up on the dance floor, this was the record they would play.

209. 'My Sweet Lord' George Harrison (1971)
The first Beatle to have a solo number one hit, but at a cost. The estate of the

writer of an earlier hit, 'He's So Fine', by The Chiffons, sued Harrison for infringement of copyright.

210. 'It's Impossible' Perry Como (1971)

His last top ten hit was in 1960 and there was no reason to suspect Perry Como would ever return to the charts, but eleven years later, among all the rock and pop, he made a surprise comeback with this middle-of-the-road ballad.

211. 'Your Song' Elton John (1971)

By the time 'Your Song', hit the record stores, Elton John had already released five unsuccessful singles and hope was wearing thin. His new record caught the imagination of DJ Tony Blackburn who then presented BBC Radio 1's powerful breakfast show and made it his record of the week. The rest is history.

212. 'Another Day' Paul McCartney (1971)

The fight was on as each member of The Beatles scored solo success. This was Paul's debut, but stalled at number two. He had to wait another six and a half years for his first number one.

213. 'Brown Sugar' The Rolling Stones (1971)

The Beatles may have split up but The Stones found new beginnings with the first release on their newly formed Rolling Stones label.

214. 'Knock Three Times' Dawn (1971)

Following in the footsteps of their first UK hit, 'Knock Three Times' topped the charts for five weeks. The group were at the time only session singers but, with their chart-topping success, the record company persuaded Tony Orlando, who sang lead vocals, and the rest of the group to form a proper band and go out and tour.

215. 'Co-Co' The Sweet (1971)

Having previously just grazed the charts with 'Funny Funny', The Sweet made a huge impact with their follow up which was to see the beginning of a new musical trend, the era of 'Glam Rock'.

216. 'Get It On' T Rex (1971)

Their second chart-topper of 1971, kicking the year off with 'Hot Love'. 'Get It On' had been recorded in Los Angeles and backing vocals were supplied by Howard Kaylan and Mark Volman of The Turtles fame.

217. 'I'm Still Waiting' Diana Ross (1971)
Another hit largely due to the efforts of DJ, Tony Blackburn. Being a huge Diana Ross fan, he listened intently to her albums and fell in love with this track. He informed her record label that he would make it his record of the week if they released it as a single. He was as good as his word and the record went to number one.

218. 'It's Too Late' Carole King (1971)
With a string of hits to her name as a songwriter, Carole's first success as a performer was in 1962 with her top ten hit, 'It Might As Well Rain Until September'. She then had to wait nearly nine years before she released her classic *Tapestry* album which produced her only other UK hit single, 'It's Too Late'.

219. 'Maggie May' Rod Stewart 1971)
Originally the B-side of 'Reason To Believe' but radio stations started playing 'Maggie' and the record company in their wisdom began promoting the disc as a double A-side.

220. "Cos I Luv You' Slade (1971)
A real 'Supergroup' of the seventies, their previous release, a revival of the Little Richard song, 'Get Down And Get With It', just scraped into the top twenty, but this was their ticket to a long and successful career which gave them a further five number ones.

221. 'Theme From Shaft' Isaac Hayes (1971)
One of the century's most famous instrumental hits (well, almost instrumental, apart from a few lines sung by composer and performer, Hayes), it won an Academy Award for best movie song.

222. 'Son Of My Father' Chicory Tip (1972)
The original version of this was by Georgio Moroder, who later produced hits for Donna Summer, Sparks, Blondie, Human League and many more. Chicory Tip's hit was the first number one to heavily feature synthesiser.

223. 'Without You' Nilsson (1972)
John Lennon once claimed that Harry Nilsson was his favourite singer after hearing his version of The Beatles' song, 'You Can't Do That', on his first album, *Pandemonium Shadow Show*. 'Without You' was composed by Pete Ham and Tom Evans from the group, Badfinger who were signed to The Beatles' Apple label.

224. 'Hold Your Head Up' Argent (1972)
A very influential band in the seventies formed by ex-Zombies keyboard player, Rod Argent. 'Hold Your Head Up', is still considered to be among the best classic rock tracks of all time.

225. 'American Pie' Don McLean (1972)
McLean was such a huge Buddy Holly fan and his death affected him so that it led him to write 'American Pie'. A number one in America but just failed to reach the top in the UK thanks to Chicory Tip and Harry Nilsson.

226. 'Mother And Child Reunion' Paul Simon (1972)
After the break-up of Simon and Garfunkel, Paul released his debut album called simply *Paul Simon* from which this, his first solo single, was released. In actual fact, he had released singles before his association with Art Garfunkel under the name of Jerry Landis.

227. 'Back Off Boogaloo' Ringo Starr (1972)
This completed the set. Now all four Beatles had achieved solo top ten status. The view of the music industry at the time was, however, that Ringo would be the least likely of The Beatles to make it on his own. How wrong they were.

228. 'Vincent' Don McLean (1972)
Deprived of a number one with 'American Pie', and although it only reached number twelve in the States, Don McLean gained his pole position with another classic track this time singing the virtues of the 19th century Dutch artist, Vincent Van Gogh.

229. 'Rock And Roll Pt 2' Gary Glitter (1972)
The success of this record must lie largely with UK DJ, Alan Freeman, who, in spite of having played the record for some fifteen weeks on the trot with still no chart action, refused to give up on this track that he loved. A few weeks later he was rewarded by its chart entry at number six, and Gary Glitter was on his way to becoming a seventies pop hero.

230. 'Puppy Love' Donny Osmond (1972)
His first solo hit and a number one at that. Donny was giving David Cassidy a run for his money as heart-throb of the year.

231. 'Breaking Up Is Hard To Do' The Partridge Family (1972)
One of the biggest shows on British television, the group led by David Cassidy were also selling millions of records around the world . . . Another member of the group, Susan Dey, went on to find fame in the hit American TV series, *LA Law*.

232. 'Betcha By Golly Wow' The Stylistics (1972)
They had failed in the UK with their previous record, 'You Are Everything', (later a hit for Diana Ross and Marvin Gaye), but now The Stylistics' career was established with this great favourite with young lovers.

233. 'School's Out' Alice Cooper (1972)
Amid huge complaints from teachers and parents about this anti-school rocker, and politicians trying to get him banned from touring England, this became the big summer hit of the year.

234. 'How Can I Be Sure?' David Cassidy (1972)
By now Cassidy, who played Keith in the hugely successful TV series, *The Partridge Family*, was the biggest heart throb in the UK His latest single was the revival of a 1967 American top ten hit by The Young Rascals.

235. 'All The Young Dudes' Mott The Hoople (1972)
Ian Hunter was the lead singer with Mott at the time they recorded this song written and produced by David Bowie, a track that to this day remains a pop classic.

236. 'Layla' Derek & The Dominoes (1972)
The all time classic guitar based rock hit for Eric Clapton's band, which had been formed two years previously to play a charity concert in London. They ended up touring Britain and recorded their album, *Layla And Other Assorted Lovers* in America.

237. 'Virginia Plain' Roxy Music (1972)
The band brought a refreshing new sound to the British charts at the height of the 'Glam Rock' period. Produced by Pete Wingfield who would achieve chart success as a performer two years later with 'Eighteen With A Bullet'.

238. 'Donna' 10CC (1972)
The group Hotlegs who had a top ten hit in 1970 with 'Neanderthal Man', metamorphosised into 10CC when Graham Gouldman joined as vocalist. It was Jonathan King who took them the song and gave them their new name.

239. 'Crocodile Rock' Elton John (1972)
Elton proved that he was more than just a ballad writer, now we knew he could also really rock as demonstrated on the first single to be taken from his album, *Don't Shoot Me, I'm Only The Piano Player*. This record established him as an all round performer.

240. 'Crazy Horses' The Osmonds (1972)
With Osmond fans going crazy for their idols all over the world, they amazed their followers with this heavy rocking track.

241. 'You're So Vain' Carly Simon (1972)
One of pop's great mysteries, who was she singing about on her most famous hit, taken from her classic album, *No Secrets*. Carly is the daughter of Richard L Simon, the co-founder of one of the biggest American publishing companies, Simon & Schuster.

242. 'Blockbuster' The Sweet (1973)
Although they were hailed as one of the most successful acts of the glam rock era, they only managed to achieve one chart-topper with this 'Blockbuster'.

243. 'Cum On Feel The Noize' Slade (1973)
The fourth of six UK chart-toppers was probably considered to be Slade's anthem and the favourite among their fans.

244. 'Papa Was A Rolling Stone' The Temptations (1973)
With trends changing, the Tamla Motown label was finding it harder to maintain the consistency of hits they enjoyed in the sixties. However this masterpiece, originally recorded some months previously by label associates, The Undisputed Truth, gave the new kids on the block a run for their money.

245. 'If You Don't Know Me By Now' Harold Melvin & The Blue Notes (1973)
The Philly sound was just beginning to take a hold in Britain and this group, formed in 1954, were among the forerunners of the sound. They had released several records prior to this hit but it was when lead vocalist John Atkins left the group that drummer Teddy Pendergrass was asked to take lead vocals and their fortunes changed.

246. 'Me And Mrs Jones' Billy Paul (1973)
Another classic 'Philly' hit by Billy Paul who had spent a brief spell with Harold Melvin and The Blue Notes before recording this song to which so many people could relate.

247. 'Whisky In The Jar' Thin Lizzy (1973)
Originally a traditional folk song that the group transformed into a rock classic and gave the band their first hit before undergoing a series of personnel changes in the early seventies.

248. 'Killing Me Softly With His Song' Roberta Flack (1973)
Originally recorded by American singer, Lori Lieberman for the Capitol label, the story goes that Roberta Flack was on a flight from Los Angeles to New York when she plugged in the in flight entertainment and heard the song on one of the channels. As soon as she arrived in New York, she set up studio to record the song.

249. 'Love Train' The O' Jays (1973)
Another smash from the 'Philly' stable, this became one of the most established of all the hits.

250. 'And I Love Her So' Perry Como (1973)
Yes, he'd had two previous top twenty hits in the seventies, but with big ballads and easy listening artists well out of vogue, Perry Como comes along with his version of a Don McLean song and climbs all the way to number three in the charts.

251. 'See My Baby Jive' Wizzard (1973)
Roy Wood's new band had achieved chart success with 'Ball Park Incident', but this kitchen sink production and chart-topper really established them for a further five top forty hits.

252. 'Can The Can' Suzi Quatro (1973)
Written by Nicky Chinn and Mike Chapman who had been responsible for all The Sweet hits, the record went all the way to the top for the leather clad Suzi.

253. 'Live And Let Die' Wings (1973)
Paul McCartney's new band were really brought to a larger section of the public when they performed the title song to the latest James Bond movie.

254. 'Life On Mars' David Bowie (1973)
Taken from his 1971 album, *Hunky Dory*, this wonderful Bowie track peaked at number three, the same year his old record label cashed in on his new found success by reissuing an old novelty song recorded by Bowie in the sixties, 'The Laughing Gnome'. Still, he was such a star that even that made the top ten.

255. 'I'm The Leader Of The Gang' Gary Glitter (1973)
Paul Gadd released his first record in 1961 under the name Paul Raven; twelve years later, as Gary Glitter, he finally achieves his first number one.

256. 'Tiger Feet' Mud (1974)
Another Nicky Chinn–Mike Chapman composition gives glam rock band Mud their first UK chart-topper.

257. 'The Air That I Breathe' The Hollies (1974)
With twenty-six top forty hits to their name, The Hollies come up with an absolute masterpiece which was held off number one by 'Billy Don't Be A Hero', by Paper Lace'. No justice in this world.

258. 'Jet' Paul McCartney & Wings (1974)
Another single from the *Band On The Run* album and one of Wings' finest moments.

259. 'Waterloo' Abba (1974)
Completely unknown before the year's Eurovision Song Contest, which they easily won for Sweden with the biggest International hit song ever to come out of the competition. Abba soon became a household name all over the world.

260. 'Sugar Baby Love' The Rubettes (1974)
Wayne Bickerton and Tony Waddington knew they had a hit when they wrote this song. Without an act in mind to record it, they did what many others were doing at the time, put together a group of session singers and went into the studio. With Paul Da Vinci on lead vocals, it became a bigger hit than they ever imagined and a group was quickly put together minus Paul who had settled on a solo career, achieving just one top twenty hit in the same year with 'Your Baby Ain't Your Baby Anymore'.

261. 'This Town Ain't Big Enough For The Both Of Us' Sparks (1974)
The two eccentric brothers, Ron and Russell Mael, brought some very odd music to the charts; this one took the industry by complete surprise.

262. 'Rock Your Baby' George McCrae (1974)
The word was that the song was meant for his wife, Gwen, but she was unable to attend the recording, so George added the vocal instead. Many consider this to be the first disco chart-topper.

263. 'Band On The Run' Paul McCartney & Wings (1974)
The title track from the album became a classic piece of work and a hugely successful single.

264. 'When Will I See You Again' The Three Degrees (1974)
The first and only UK chart-topping single for writer-producers, Kenny Gamble and Leon Huff's Philadelphia International label, thanks to Sheila, Valerie and Fayette, who made up the group that Prince Charles once claimed to be his favourite group.

265. 'I'm Leaving It (All) Up To You' Donny & Marie Osmond (1974)
The first duet by brother and sister, Donny and Marie and a revival of a 1963 American number one by Dale and Grace who covered the original 1957 recording by Don and Dewey.

266. 'Love Me For A Reason' The Osmonds (1974)
This year saw a resurgence of interest in The Osmonds. The family's chart-topper kept brother and sister, Donny and Marie off number one. 'Love Me For A Reason', was written by Johnny Bristol who achieved his only UK hit in the same year with 'Hang On In There Baby'.

267. 'Annie's Song' John Denver (1974)
Dedicated to his wife, Ann Martell, Denver wrote the song in ten minutes while on a skiing holiday in Switzerland when the two were on a trial separation. Unfortunately the couple divorced in 1983 and Denver was killed in a plane he was flying fourteen years later on 12 October 1997.

268. 'Kung Fu Fighting' Carl Douglas (1974)
For years Carl Douglas made records with his group, The Big Stampede, without any success. Record producer Biddu was looking for a singer for a quick session and Douglas was recommended. 'Kung Fu Fighting', was always intended as the B-side and was recorded as a throw away in ten minutes. With the popularity of the Bruce Lee kung fu films at the time, the record topped both the UK and American charts.

269 'You're The First, The Last, My Everything' Barry White (1974)
He had recorded in the sixties under the name of Barry Lee and had worked as a session player and arranger on several big hits, the most famous being Bob and Earl's 'Harlem Shuffle', and Felice Taylor's, 'I Feel Love Comin' On'. The seventies saw the wind of change as Barry became a bigger star in his own right.

270. 'Gonna Make You A Star' David Essex (1974)
With two previous top ten hits behind him, this became the first number one for David Essex who had been trying for success since the mid-sixties, having

released a number of singles on various record labels.

271. 'Killer Queen' Queen (1974)
The track that truly established the sound of Queen, who were to become recognised as one of the greatest rock groups in pop history. During the year, Freddy Mercury released a single under the name of Larry Lurex which was a version of 'I Can Hear Music'. It failed to make any impression on the record buying public, although these days, a copy of the single would sell for more than a hundred pounds.

272. 'You Ain't Seen Nothin' Yet' Bachman-Turner Overdrive (1974)
Written by Randy Bachman, the song was written as a joke for his brother Gary who had a stutter. When they played the track to their record company, they didn't see the funny side, all they could see were dollar signs.

273. 'Down Down' Status Quo (1974)
This became their ninth top forty hit but the only chart-topper of their fifty top-forty-hits' career.

274. 'Streets Of London' Ralph McTell (1974)
A great hit representing the best in British folk music. The song was originally recorded for an album in the late sixties, but McTell decided to re-record it in 1974, adding strings and backing vocals, rewarding himself with a number two hit.

275. 'January' Pilot (1975)
They had previously occupied the top twenty in 1974 with a song called 'Magic', and when this record went to number one it looked as though they were to have a long and successful career. Unfortunately they had two further minor hits then disappeared.

276. 'Make Me Smile (Come Up And See Me)' Steve Harley & Cockney Rebel (1975)
Produced by Alan Parsons who also produced 'January', by Pilot, the record Cockney Rebel dethroned at the top of the charts.

277. 'My Eyes Adored You' Frankie Valli (1975)
The Four Seasons' lead singer decided to go it alone, and not for the first time. In 1971 he made the top twenty with 'You're Ready Now'. This was his biggest solo hit to date but was bettered in 1978 with the title song from the movie, *Grease*.

278. 'Bye Bye Baby' The Bay City Rollers (1975)
Originally called The Saxons but now the hottest band around, Rollermania hit Great Britain as the group topped the charts with a song previously recorded by, would you believe it? Frankie Valli and The Four Seasons.

279. 'Honey' Bobby Goldsboro (1975)
The first time in chart history that the same record reached number two on two separate occasions. Bobby Goldsboro held that position with the same song back in 1968.

280. 'Loving You' Minnie Ripperton (1975)
This pop classic was produced by Stevie Wonder who visited Minnie in hospital on 11 July 1979, the night before she died of cancer at the age of 38.

281. 'I'm Not In Love' 10CC (1975)
When you talk about 10CC, you talk about 'I'm Not In Love'. This was their seventh hit and first number one with a running time of over five minutes.

282. 'The Hustle' Van McCoy (1975)
Well established as a composer, arranger and producer, Van McCoy's 'Hustle' became the big dance craze of 1975 in clubs all around the world. His sudden death from a heart attack in 1979 at the age of 35, stunned the music business.

283. 'Barbados' Typically Tropical (1975)
Two recording engineers, Geoff Calvert and Max West would write and produce their own material in their spare time. They were having a bit of fun with sound effects and a mock reggae rhythm when they came up with 'Barbados'. It became a number one hit but they were unable to repeat the success.

284. 'Can't Give You Anything (But My Love)' The Stylistics (1975)
The remaining members of two disbanded groups, The Percussions and The Monarchs got together to form The Stylistics in the early seventies. This was their biggest moment.

285. 'That's The Way (I Like It)' KC & The Sunshine Band (1975)
One of the biggest disco hits of the year from the band formed in 1973 in Florida by Harry Wayne Casey.

286. 'Bohemian Rhapsody' Queen (1975)
Often voted the best record of all time, was the first record to have a promotional video to accompany its release. With a six minute running time, the record remained at the top of the charts for nine consecutive weeks.

287. 'Mama Mia' Abba (1975)
Strange things happen in chart history but none much stranger than finding that the title of this Abba chart-topper was contained in the lyrics of the previous number one, 'Bohemian Rhapsody'. Remember they sang, 'Mama mia, mama mia'.

288. 'Love Machine' The Miracles (1976)
The only hit achieved by The Miracles after the departure of Smokey Robinson.

289. 'Love To Love You Baby' Donna Summer (1976)
The beginning of a hugely successful career for 'The Queen Of Disco', and her association with writer-producers Georgio Moroder and Pete Bellotte. 'Love To Love You Baby', was originally a seventeen minute piece which was obviously cut down for the single.

290. 'December '63 (Oh What A Night)' The Four Seasons (1976)
Despite having a string of hits to their name, this became their only UK number one.

291. 'Love Really Hurts Without You' Billy Ocean (1976)
Kept off the number one spot by Brotherhood Of Man's 'Save Your Kisses For Me' (England's second Eurovision Song Contest win), this was the record that launched Billy Ocean's successful recording career.

292. 'You To Me Are Everything' The Real Thing (1976)
One of those records you knew would be number one the moment you heard it. The Real Thing hailed from Liverpool and achieved twelve top forty chart entries including remixes of this and other hits.

293. 'Young Hearts Run Free' Candi Staton (1976)
The disco diva from Alabama with her classic floor-filler that returned to the charts in 1999 when she re-recorded it with the group, Source.

294. 'Don't Go Breaking My Heart' Elton John & Kiki Dee (1976)
With sixteen top forty hits to his name, at the beginning of 1976 Elton John had still not achieved his goal of topping the charts. His wish came true through this duet with Kiki Dee, although he probably would have preferred to have done it on his own. He still had to wait another fourteen years for his solo number one.

295. 'Dancing Queen' Abba (1976)
Throughout their recording career, Abba never turned out a bad single, and this was one of their very best and their third consecutive number one. Throughout their career, they managed to top the UK charts on nine separate occasions.

296. 'If You Leave Me Now' Chicago (1976)
A couple of years after they achieved their biggest UK hit, guitarist Terry Kath was killed in a shooting accident, it was believed that he was playing Russian Roulette with a loaded gun. Ironically, the last record on which he played was called 'Baby What A Big Surprise', the line following the title was 'right before my very eyes'.

297. 'Under The Moon Of Love' Showaddywaddy (1976)
Reviving a song produced by Phil Spector and recorded by American singer Curtis Lee in the early sixties, 'Under The Moon Of Love' gave Showaddy-waddy their ninth of twenty-three UK top forty hits, but their only number one.

298. 'Sir Duke' Stevie Wonder (1977)
Stevie's tribute to one of his heroes, Duke Ellington. This was one of his most powerful singles with the blazing brass riffs.

299. 'Free' Deniece Williams (1977)
Began her musical career singing in Stevie Wonder's backing group, Wonderlove, and working as a session singer for many top American stars.

300. 'I Don't Want To Talk About It' Rod Stewart (1977)
One of Rod's most magical moments and released as a double A-side with the revival of the Cat Stevens song, 'The First Cut Is The Deepest' as the other title.

301. 'Ain't Gonna Bump No More' Joe Tex (1977)
The dance craze, 'The Bump' was catching on big time in the UK and this was one of the fans' favourites. Tex was another heart attack casualty, he died on 13 August 1982 at the age of 49.

302. 'God Save The Queen' The Sex Pistols (1977)
Whether you loved them or hated them, there was no denying that they started a whole new trend in pop music. Punk had arrived on the scene.

303. 'So You Win Again' Hot Chocolate (1977)
Their previous thirteen top forty hits had all been written by one or both group members, Errol Brown and Tony Wilson. This, their first number one, was a

Russ Ballard composition whose track record included hits for Limmie and the Family Cookin', Mary Hopkin, Hello and Herman's Hermits.

304. 'I Feel Love' Donna Summer (1977)
The big club record of the year, and will unfortunately be remembered for being at the top of the charts on 16 August of this year, the day Elvis Presley died.

305. 'Baby Don't Change Your Mind' Gladys Knight & The Pips (1977)
The ex-Motown star achieved a top ten hit with this great Van McCoy production and song.

306. 'Way Down' Elvis Presley (1977)
When the record first came out in 1977, it was hardly selling at all. Then everything changed; on 16 August 1977, Presley died and the record shot to the top of the charts.

307. 'Best Of My Love' The Emotions (1977)
The record sold over a million copies and won a Grammy for best R&B vocal performance by a duo, group or chorus.

308. 'Rockin' All Over The World' Status Quo (1977)
Written by John Fogerty and originally recorded by Creedence Clearwater Revival, this became one of Quo's most popular songs.

309. '2-4-6-8 Motorway' Tom Robinson Band (1977)
A huge hit in the clubs and a punk anthem from the group that emerged towards the end of 1977. The following year they made the top twenty with 'Don't Take No For An Answer', before Robinson embarked on a solo career.

310. 'Mull Of Kintyre' Wings (1977)
McCartney's tribute to Scotland became the first record to sell over two million copies just in the United Kingdom and held the record as the biggest seller until 1984.

311. 'Don't It Make My Brown Eyes Blue' Crystal Gayle (1977)
A double Grammy winner for Best Country song and Best Female Country Performance

312. 'Wuthering Height' Kate Bush (1978)
Discovered by Dave Gilmour of Pink Floyd, who played guitar on this chart-

topping single. The record also boosted the sales of the Bronte novel on which the song was based.

313. 'Denis' Blondie (1978)
The song, originally a top ten American hit in 1963 for Randy and The Rainbows, was Blondie's first hit, produced by Mike Chapman who had been co-writer on many earlier hits for The Sweet, Mud and Suzi Quatro.

314. 'Baker Street' Gerry Rafferty (1978)
Just a classic track by the ex-member of Stealers Wheel with probably the most memorable sax solo in pop history played by Ralph Ravenscroft.

315. 'Night Fever' The Bee Gees (1978)
The title song to the movie that produced not only hits for The Bee Gees but also for Tavares and Yvonne Elliman, *Saturday Night Fever*, failed to become the box office smash it should because of its certificate. Youngsters couldn't go and see it without their parents.

316. 'You're The One That I Want' Olivia Newton-John & John Travolta (1978)
From the movie, *Grease*, and a far bigger box office success, it remained the number one movie for six weeks, while the single stayed at the top of the pop charts for nine.

317. 'Dancing In The City' Marshall-Hain (1978)
A great atmospheric record from pop duo, Julian Marshall and Kit Hain. They had one further minor hit, 'Coming Home', before calling it a day.

318. 'Three Times A Lady' Lionel Richie (1978)
The fastest rising hit to date for the Motown label gave the ex-lead singer with the Commodores his first solo chart-topper.

319. 'Grease' Frankie Valli (1978)
Bee Gee Barry Gibb penned the title track to the movie, *Grease*, giving Frankie Valli, still occasional lead singer with The Four Seasons, the biggest solo hit of his career.

320. 'Love Don't Live Here Anymore' Rose Royce (1978)
Their biggest ever hit has been covered by many performers including Madonna and Jimmy Nail who made his top ten debut with the song in 1985.

321. 'Da Ya Think I'm Sexy' Rod Stewart (1978)
One of Rod's most famous hits which returned to the top ten in 1997 when N-Trance revived it and included Rod as guest vocalist.

322. 'YMCA' Village People (1978)
One of the most popular disco number ones in the gay clubs of all time by this group of dancers and singers posing as a Cowboy, an Indian, a Policeman, a Biker, a GI, and a Construction Worker. In 1993, a re-mixed version made the top twenty and in 1994, the song was featured heavily in the movie, 'Wayne's World 2'.

323. 'Hit Me With Your Rhythm Stick' Ian Dury & The Blockheads (1978)
Dury co-wrote the song with another band member, Chas Jankel, who, in 1981, wrote the top twenty hit, 'Ai No Corrida' for Quincy Jones.

324. 'Song For Guy' Elton John (1978)
Elton was so upset when Guy, the office boy at his record company was killed in a motorbike accident, he sat down and wrote this as a tribute.

324. 'Tragedy' The Bee Gees (1979)
'Too Much Heaven' was the first and peaked at number three, 'Tragedy' was the second track to be taken from their album, *Spirits Having Flown* and that went to number one. The song was successfully revived in 1998 by Steps.

326. 'I Will Survive' Gloria Gaynor (1979)
Originally the B-side of a single called 'Substitute', but fortunately club DJ's spotted the gem on the other side and began playing 'I Will Survive'.

327. 'Oliver's Army' Elvis Costello (1979)
The Bee Gees and Gloria Gaynor between them, managed to keep Elvis Costello off the number one spot. The nearest he ever came in his recording career.

328. 'Bright Eyes' Art Garfunkel (1979)
I know you've heard this line before but we love it. This is a song written by a bat about a rabbit. Mike Batt, who wrote the music for The Wombles, wrote and produced this chart-topper for the movie, *Watership Down*.

329. 'Pop Muzik' M (1979)
M was British musician Robin Scott. When he was looking for a pseudonym for his record he was in Paris and, looking out of his hotel window, he saw a

big illuminated 'M' which indicated the entrance to the French Metro, thus M was born.

330. 'Dance Away' Roxy Music (1979)
Taken from their *Manifesto* album, 'Dance Away' became a firm favourite among Roxy fans.

331. 'Ring My Bell' Anita Ward (1979)
Such a big number one hit but then Anita vanished without trace in the UK. She managed one very small hit in America after that with a song called, 'Don't Drop My Love'.

332. 'I Don't Like Mondays' The Boomtown Rats (1979)
In the height of the punk era, Bob Geldof wrote this number one hit after reading about a young woman named Brenda who shot her children because, she claimed, 'I Don't Like Mondays'.

333. 'We Don't Talk Anymore' Cliff Richard (1979)
After topping the charts in 1968 with his Eurovision Song Contest runner up, 'Congratulations', it took Cliff another eleven years to make number one again with one of his best ever singles.

334. 'After The Love Has Gone' Earth, Wind & Fire (1979)
Hailed as one of the most successful black bands in the world, six piece Earth, Wind and Fire, with lead singer, Philip Bailey won a Grammy for Best R&B Song and Best R&B Performance.

335. 'Bang Bang' B.A. Robertson (1979)
Another one of those instant pop songs that just had to be a hit for the man who went on to write hits for many other singers including Cliff Richard.

336. 'Cars' Gary Numan (1979)
A number one hit that was to re-visit the top twenty both in 1987 and 1996 in two more different versions, making Gary Numan the first person to have three hits with the same song which he recorded three times.

337. 'Don't Bring Me Down' Electric Light Orchestra (1979)
The seventeenth successive top forty hit for Jeff Wayne's uniquely sounding group and their biggest hit to date.

338. 'Video Killed The Radio Star' Buggles (1979)
Written by Bruce Wooley, who had previously been a member of The Seekers,

Buggles were Trevor Horn and Geoff Downes. Horne became one of Britain's leading record producers, working with such acts as Frankie Goes To Hollywood, ABC, Seal, Tina Turner and Rod Stewart.

339. 'When You're In Love With A Beautiful Woman' Dr Hook (1979)
Considered the ultimate love song and the most successful record for Dr Hook.

340. 'Don't Stop 'Til You Get Enough' Michael Jackson (1979)
Quincy Jones produced Jackson's first solo album *Off The Wall*. This was the first single.

341. 'Eton Rifles' The Jam (1979)
Considered to be Britain's most successful New Wave Band, this was their ninth top forty hit but the first to make the top ten. A number one was soon to follow.

342. 'Another Brick In The Wall' Pink Floyd (1979)
Although they topped the album charts, Pink Floyd had to wait twenty-two years from the release of their first hit, 'Arnold Layne', before they finally had a number one hit single.

343. 'Nights In White Satin' The Moody Blues (1979)
First released in 1967 and top twenty hit the following year, it made the top ten when it was reissued in 1972, and this year it made its third appearance in the top twenty.

344. 'Funky Towni' Lipps Inc (1980)
With lead vocals sung by Cynthia Johnson, this was the only UK hit for Lipps Inc but the song returned to the top ten when it was remade in 1987 by Australian group, Pseudo Echo.

345. 'Xanadu' Olivia Newton-John & Electric Light Orchestra (1980)
The title song from the film which teamed Olivia with Gene Kelly and is considered to be among the worst films ever made. Its only saving grace was the title song and another hit for Olivia, 'Magic'.

346. 'Ashes To Ashes' David Bowie (1980)
Hailed as the sequel to 'Space Oddity', this became Bowie's second chart-topper and was the first single to be taken from his *Scary Monsters* album.

347. 'One Day I'll Fly Away' Randy Crawford (1980)
Her only previous chart success was as the uncredited voice on the 1979 top ten hit, 'Street Life' by The Crusaders. 'One Day I'll Fly Away' remained at number two for two weeks while 'Feels Like I'm In Love' by Kelly Marie and 'Don't Stand So Close To Me' by The Police took it in turns to hold it off number one.

348. 'My Old Piano' Diana Ross (1980)
Produced by Nile Rodgers and Bernard Edwards who had been responsible for the hits by Chic and Sister Sledge. Ross was not happy with the end results of the tracks they recorded with her and demanded the tapes so she could re-mix them to her liking, which she did to the annoyance of the producers.

349. 'Woman In Love' Barbra Streisand (1980)
Written by Barry and Robin Gibb of The Bee Gees, 'Woman In Love' became a top ten hit in twelve countries and the album, *Guilty*, from which the track was taken, sold in excess of twenty million copies world wide.

350. '(Just Like) Starting Over' John Lennon (1980)
The single reached number one on 20 December 1980 and was the first single to be taken from his forthcoming album, *Double Fantasy*, his first recording in five years. On 8 December John was shot dead outside his New York apartment as he walked home from a recording session.

351. 'Imagine' John Lennon (1980)
In the light of Lennon's death, his former record company decided to reissue the title track from one of his most successful albums. The single was the first new chart-topper of 1981.

352. 'Woman' John Lennon (1981)
The second single to be taken from his *Double Fantasy* album. For the week ending 31 January 1981, Lennon was at number one with 'Imagine' and number two with 'Woman'.

353. 'In The Air Tonight' Phil Collins (1981)
This was the first solo single release by Phil Collins, and was taken from his debut album, *Face Value*. The song was re-mixed in 1988 for a tele-communications TV commercial and returned to the top ten.

354. 'Vienna' Ultravox (1981)
The most famous number two in chart history. It will always be remembered as the record held off number one by the novelty hit, 'Shaddap You Face', by

Joe Dolce. 'Vienna ' was the first hit for Ultravox after founder member John Fox left and was replaced by Midge Ure.

355. 'Jealous Guy' Roxy Music (1981)
Roxy Music's sincere tribute to John Lennon after his death and the band's only number one single.

356. 'This Ole House' Shakin' Stevens (1981)
Originally a number one hit in America 1951 when it was recorded by Rosemary Clooney. The revival gave Stevens his first of four UK chart-toppers.

357. 'Kids In America' Kim Wilde (1981)
The daughter of fifties and sixties heart-throb Marty Wilde, Kim just missed out on reaching number one owing to the huge success of Shakin' Stevens.

358. 'Making Your Mind Up' Bucks Fizz (1981)
Bucks Fizz became the fourth act to win The Eurovision Song Contest for Great Britain, and although it was a strong song, one can't help wondering if they would have done so well if the girls in the group hadn't removed part of their clothing halfway through the song.

359. 'Stand And Deliver' Adam & The Ants (1981)
The eleventh single in chart history to make its first week debut at number one

360. 'Being With You' Smokey Robinson (1981)
After a string of hits as writer, producer and performer with The Miracles, this was Smokey Robinson's first solo hit and indeed, a number one.

361. 'Ghost Town' The Specials (1981)
After the chart-topping success of this single, band members Terry Hall, Neville Staples and Lynval Golding left to form a new group in the shape of Fun Boy Three.

362. 'Happy Birthday' Stevie Wonder (1981)
Kept off the number one spot by 'Green Door', by Shakin' Stevens. No wonder this record became such a huge hit. As the title suggests, hundreds of thousands of people still play this record on that special day.

363. 'Tainted Love' Soft Cell (1981)
An earlier version of the song by Gloria Jones was originally a huge dance hall favourite in the Northern clubs, and the newly formed duo decided that a new

arrangement would be their first single. It reached number one and returned to the top ten when it was reissued in 1991.

364. 'O Superman' Laurie Anderson (1981)
Her only UK hit was an eight-minute haunting epic with Peter Gabriel performing on the track.

365. 'Every Little Thing She Does Is Magic' The Police (1981)
This became their fourth UK chart-topper and their first with new producer, Hugh Padgham.

366. 'When She Was My Girl' The Four Tops (1981)
It was ten years since The Four Tops last had a top ten hit in the UK when 'Simple Game ' hit the number three position. 'When She Was My Girl' also peaked at number three.

367. 'Under Pressure' Queen & David Bowie (1981)
The only track they ever recorded together came about through a chance meeting at a recording studio in Germany. They were all on a break and were fooling around jamming and came up with the song which they immediately recorded.

368. 'Begin The Beguine (Volver A Empezar)' Julio Iglesias (1981)
Before the release of this record, he was virtually unknown in the UK but was a huge star in Spain where he had once been the goalkeeper for the Real Madrid football team before suffering a severe leg injury in a road accident.

369. 'Don't You Want Me?' Human League (1981)
With a year of poor record sales, this became the only 1981 million selling record in the UK.

370. 'Golden Brown' The Stranglers (1982)
After releasing several hard hitting punkish records, The Stranglers surprised their fans with this gentle waltz time song, giving them their biggest hit of their career.

371. 'Arthur's Theme (Best That You Can Do)' Christopher Cross (1982)
The title song to the Dudley Moore movie, *Arthur*. The song was written by Burt Bacharach and Carole Bayer-Sager.

372. 'Town Called Malice' Jam (1982)
The single that kept The Stranglers off number one with 'Golden Brown', this was the third chart-topper for The Jam which was released as a double 'A' side with 'Precious'.

373. 'Ebony and Ivory' Paul McCartney & Stevie Wonder (1982)
This track reunited McCartney with George Martin, his record producer from The Beatles days. Paul and Stevie were in the studio together to record the song but were unable to find time to make the video which they appeared in together only through the art of modern technology.

374. 'The Look Of Love' ABC (1982)
Produced by Trevor Horn, ABC started life as Vice Verca but changed their name for their debut single, 'Tears Are Not Enough'.

375. 'Fame' Irene Cara (1982)
Cara played Coco Hernandez in the original 1980 movie, *Fame* and was asked to perform the title song. Although a hit in America, the song made no impact in the UK. When the TV series was launched, based on the movie, it became an instant smash. Her only other hit was another film theme, the title song from *Flashdance*, but although she sang, she didn't appear.

376. 'Come On Eileen' Dexy's Midnight Runners (1982)
Taken from their album, *Too-Rye-Aye* which were lyrics in the song 'Come On Eileen'. The record also featured a group of violin players called The Emerald Express who were credited on the single.

377. 'Eye Of The Tiger' Survivor (1982)
There had been two successful *Rocky* movies and for *Rocky III*, the producers wanted a new theme. Originally, Queen's 'Another One Bites The Dust' was considered but Jim Peterik and Frankie Sullivan, members of Survivor. ended up writing this number one hit.

378. 'The Bitterest Pill (I Ever Had To Swallow)' Jam (1982)
The success of 'Eye Of The Tiger' kept this Jam classic off the number one spot.

379. 'Zoom' Fat Larry's Band (1982)
'Fat' Larry James and his band made the UK top forty in 1977 with 'Center City' and had another minor hit with 'Boogie Town' in 1979 when they called themselves F.L.B.

380. 'Why?' Carly Simon (1982)
Carly's only really successful venture at making a dance record was produced by Nile Rodgers and Bernard Edwards, those guys from Chic fame.

381. 'Do You Really Want To Hurt Me?' Culture Club (1982)
The first number one by a group whose lead singer made his own dresses and was recognised as the man in drag.

382. 'Heartbreaker' Dionne Warwick (1982)
Her last chart entry was in 1974 when she sang guest vocals on a hit for The Detroit Spinners, 'Then Came You'. Eight years later, the title track from her new album, with songs written and produced by The Bee Gees, became an international hit.

383. '(Sexual) Healing' Marvin Gaye (1982)
Another performer who found himself in the wilderness for over five years. With a change of labels, from Motown to Columbia, Marvin Gaye achieved his biggest hit since 'I Heard It Through The Grapevine'. On 1 April 1984, he was shot dead by his father the day before his 45th birthday.

384. 'You Can't Hurry Love' Phil Collins (1983)
The old Motown classic by The Supremes was given a modern treatment by Phil Collins for inclusion on the soundrack of his new movie, *Buster*.

385. 'Electric Avenue' Eddie Grant (1983)
Although the ex-lead singer with The Equals scored a number one with 'I Don't Wanna Dance', the previous year, this is still considered to have been his best single, which was kept off the number one spot by Men At Work.

386. 'Too Shy' Kajagoogoo (1983)
Discovered by Nick Rhodes of Duran Duran after lead singer Limahl persuaded him to listen to his group. Their debut single, produced by Rhodes and Colin Thurston reached number one, an achievement not then managed by Duran Duran. In 1984, after the departure of Limahl, the group dropped their googoos and were known just as Kaja.

387. 'Billy Jean' Michael Jackson (1983)
The second single to be taken from the *Thriller* album and ironically tells the tale of a woman who tries to blame Jackson for her illegitimate child. *Thriller* became the biggest selling album of all time with world sales in excess of forty million.

388. 'Total Eclipse Of The Heart' Bonnie Tyler (1983)
A number one hit both in the UK and America, the single was produced by Jim Steinman, who had been responsible for many of Meat Loaf's hits.

389. 'Africa' Toto (1983)
One of the all time great singles that quite rightly won six Grammy awards in 1983 including 'Record Of The Year'.

390. 'Sweet Dreams (Are Made Of This)' The Eurythmics (1983)
Annie Lennox and Dave Stewart had previously had hits as members of The Tourists and this, their first major hit as The Eurythmics, hit the number one spot in America but missed out in the UK to Bonnie Tyler.

391. 'Is There Something I should Know?' Duran Duran (1983)
The first number one for Duran Duran, which didn't hang about, the first week of release it entered the charts at number one.

391. 'Let's Dance' David Bowie (1983)
Bowie's fourth UK chart-topper (if you include the duet with Queen) and was the title track from his first album for a new record label. The track was produced by Bowie and Nile Rodgers.

393. 'True' Spandau Ballet (1983)
After eight top forty hits, Spandau Ballet finally achieved a number one with their best ever release.

394. 'Every Breath You Take' The Police (1983)
Sting and his band of men could do no wrong, every record they released was better than the last. This was probably their finest moment, their fifth and final UK chart-topper and their first and only American number one.

395. 'Bad Boys' Wham! (1983)
George and Andrew's third single and their biggest hit to date, held off the number one slot by 'Every Breath You Take'.

396. 'Wherever I Lay My Hat (That's My Home)' Paul Young 1983
He'd experienced chart success in the past with 'Toast', as part of The Streetband, but this was his first solo hit. The revival of a Marvin Gaye 'B' side gave Paul Young the only number one of his career.

397. 'Long Hot Summer' The Style Council (1983)
After the break up of The Jam, Paul Weller's latest band were enjoying their

third successive top twenty hit and probably their record with the most mass appeal to date.

398. 'Come Dancing' The Kinks (1983)
The Kinks had last been in the top twenty in 1972 with 'Supersonic Rocket Ship', eleven years on, they came storming back with this brilliant record which turned out to be their last major hit.

399. 'I'm Still Standing' Elton John (1983)
A great rocker and one of Elton's best records for a long time.

400. 'Red Red Wine' UB40 (1983)
It took UB40 over three years from their first hit to their first number one, and they achieved their goal with a cover of a well-tested Neil Diamond song.

401. 'Karma Chameleon' Culture Club (1983)
The second and final chart-topper for Boy George and his group.

402 'Uptown Girl' Billy Joel (1983)
The only UK chart-topper of his career but the song was to return to number one eighteen years later with its revival by Westlife.

403. 'Say Say Say' Paul McCartney & Michael Jackson (1983)
Two of the biggest stars in the world team up for an attempt at topping the charts with a duet, but run out of steam at number two. Paul and Jacko just lose out to Billy Joel, who is still doing unbeatable business with 'Uptown Girl'.

404. 'Love Of The Common People' Paul Young (1983)
Paul's second biggest hit of his career revived a song that reggae singer, Nicky Thomas took to number nine in the charts in 1970. Two records held Paul off the number one spot, Billy Joel's 'Uptown Girl', was still going strong, while Paul still held on to the number two position as The Flying Pickets claimed number one.

405. 'Only You' The Flying Pickets (1983)
The year's Christmas number one and amazingly, the song had reached number two only eighteen months earlier for Yazoo. The Flying Pickets became the first totally *a capella* group to top the charts.

406. 'Relax' Frankie Goes To Hollywood (1984)
Trevor Horn produced one of the great music sensations of the eighties. The record had been out for several weeks and was hanging around the lower end

of the charts. When the BBC imposed an all out ban on the record brought about by D.J. Mike Read, the record sold in its thousands.

407. 'Madonna' Holiday (1984)
How many people could have realised how big a star Madonna would become when she achieved her first chart success with this single?

408. 'Jump' Van Halen (1984)
Became one of the fastest selling singles of the eighties in America, this rock anthem topped the US charts for eight weeks. Any rock fan would recognise the single from the picture sleeve of a baby with angel wings and holding a cigarette.

409. 'It's Raining Men' The Weather Girls (1984)
'The Two Tons Of Fun' was the name Izora Redman-Armstead and Martha Wash gave themselves when they worked as backing singers for many of the top American recording artists. They changed their name to The Weather Girls when they released this single which despite not making the American charts, became a UK top ten hit. The song was successfully revived in 2001 and taken to the top of the charts by Geri Halliwell.

410. 'Wake Me Up Before You Go Go' Wham (1984)
Their first chart-topper and the beginnings of rumours that Andrew Ridgeley and George Michael may soon be going their own ways.

411. 'Careless Whisper' George Michael (1984)
The only hit song written by George Michael which also credited Andrew Ridgeley. This was the first solo single from George, although in America, where it also topped the charts, the single credits were Wham featuring George Michael.

412. 'Pride (In The Name Of Love)' U2 (1984)
This was the first U2 single from their album, *Under A Blood Red Sky* and their first product for nearly eighteen months.

413. 'Drive' The Cars (1984)
One of the all time classic soft rock hits which made the top ten twice inside a year. In 1985, the single was used as backing music for footage shot for 'Live Aid', showing the poverty in Africa. The line in the song, 'who's gonna plug their ears when you scream', was drowned out by a piercing yell from a small child. This so moved Ric Ocasek, the lead singer of The Cars and composer of the song, that he donated all future royalties from 'Drive' to 'Live Aid'.

414. 'I Feel For You' Chaka Khan (1984)
Written by Prince, 'I Feel For You' was a UK number one and featured Stevie Wonder on harmonica and a rap by Melle Mel.

415. 'Do They Know It's Christmas?' Band Aid (1984)
Until 1997, this was the biggest selling single ever in the UK and the first where every penny went to the charity including, thanks mainly to Bob Geldof, the record company's profits.

416. 'I Want To Know What Love Is' Foreigner (1984)
Although many of their fans considered they had sold out with this easy listening ballad, it became an international smash. The single featured The New Jersey Mass Choir and included extra vocal support form Jennifer Holliday and Tom Bailey from The Thompson Twins.

417. '1999 Little Red Corvette' Prince (1985)
A double A-side of two of his earlier records.Both had been released in 1983 and neither had done particularly well. But following the success of 'Purple Rain' this re-release saw the single climb to number two, just held off number one by Foreigner.

418. 'Dancing In The Dark' Bruce Springsteen (1985)
Another single that hadn't fared too well with its initial release the previous year. The reissue of one of Bruce's best ever songs took him to number four in the UK charts and two places higher in America.

419. 'Every Time You Go Away' Paul Young (1985)
Paul's only American chart-topper was written by Daryl Hall, and was first featured on the Hall and Oates 1981 album, *Voices*.

420. 'Easy Lover' Philip Bailey & Phil Collins (1985)
Phil Collins produced the debut solo album, *Chinese Wall*, for Philip Bailey after he left Earth, Wind And Fire. During one of the sessions, it was decided to try this joint composition by Phil and Phil, as a duet.

421. 'We Are The World' USA For Africa (1985)
In the wake of the British-instigated Band Aid by Bob Geldof, Harry Belafonte decided to launch a similar appeal in America. Geldof himself joined the host of stars who gave their support to the song written by Michael Jackson and Lionel Richie. The record was premiered simultaneously on over 500 radio stations throughout the world on 5 April 1985.

422. '19' Paul Hardcastle (1985)
This international hit referred to the average age of the American soldiers called up to fight in the Vietnam War, the subject matter brought about many protests from the older generation.

423. 'A View To A Kill' Duran Duran (1985)
The final outing for Roger Moore as James Bond saw the title song performed by Duran Duran and held off the number one spot for three weeks by Paul Hardcastle.

424. 'I'm On Fire / Born In The U.S.A.' Bruce Springsteen (1985)
It's quite incredible to note that such a huge star has never topped the UK or American charts. These two titles issued as a double A-side and taken from his *Born In The U.S.A*, album were considered among his finest works.

425 'There Must Be An Angel (Playing With My Heart)'
Eurythmics (1985)
Their eighth top forty chart entry gave The Eurythmics their first number one.

426. 'We Don't Need Another Hero (Thunderdome)' Tina Turner (1985)
The third Mad Max movie not only starred Tina Turner but also featured her performing the title song over the soundtrack.

427. 'Into The Groove' Madonna (1985)
With her sixth top twenty entry, Madonna finally achieved her first number one in the UK with a song featured in her movie, *Desperately Seeking Susan*. Oddly, the track was never released as a single in America.

428. 'Dancing In The Street' David Bowie & Mick Jagger (1985)
The two superstars made a special video of this old Martha And The Vandellas classic for the broadcast of 'Live Aid'.

429. 'Money For Nothing' Dire Straits (1985)
The second single to be taken from their platinum album, *Brothers In Arms*, was written by Mark Knopfler and Sting who also sang on the track. The video that accompanied the song will always be remembered for all its clever computer graphics.

430. 'Take On Me' A-Ha (1985)
The first hit for A-Ha and, after the huge success of Abba, they became the second Scandinavian group whose name read the same backwards as forwards.

431. 'Road To Nowhere' Talking Heads (1985)
Despite a huge fan base, this was Talking Heads' only UK top ten hit, although they achieved two top twenty entries with 'Once In A Lifetime' and 'And She Was'.

432. 'Saving All My Love For You' Whitney Houston (1985)
Originally an album track by the two ex-Fifth Dimension singers, Marilyn McCoo and Billy Davis Jnr, who scored with their only UK hit, 'You Don't Have To Be A Star (To Be In My Show)', in 1977. Whitney's first hit couldn't do better than reach number one.

433. 'West End Girls' The Pet Shop Boys (1985)
The Pet Shop Boys, Neil Tennant and Chris Lowe, had released a version of 'West End Girls', a year earlier with little success. This new version took them right to the top.

434. 'Walk Of Life' Dire Straits (1986)
The fourth single from the *Brothers In Arms* album, the title track being the third, was a dedication to all street buskers of London.

435. 'The Sun Always Shines on TV' A-Ha (1986)
With 'Take On Me' having been held off the number one spot for three weeks by 'The Power Of Love' by Jennifer Rush, A-Ha managed to achieve top billing with their second hit.

436. 'Chain Reaction' Diana Ross (1986)
Having waited nearly fifteen years since her last chart-topper, 'I'm Still Waiting', Diana Ross reigned supreme again with this Bee Gees composition and second single from the album, *Eaten Alive*.

437. 'Manic Monday' The Bangles (1986)
Written by Prince under the pseudonym of Christopher. Prince had heard the girls' first album and had been impressed, he contacted them and offered 'Manic Monday'. Ironically, it was Prince's own record, 'Kiss', that held The Bangles' single off the number one spot in America.

438. 'Wonderful World' Sam Cooke (1986)
Co-written by Cooke with Lou Adler and Herb Alpert, under his wife's maiden name, Barbara Campbell, the record was first released in 1960 and was a moderate hit. Twenty-two years after his death, the song climbed to number two in the charts after being heavily featured in a big TV campaign to promote blue jeans.

439. **'Sledgehammer'** Peter Gabriel (1986)
The animation and visual effects on the video that accompanied this single must have induced thousands of extra sales for this big hit single from the *So* album.

440. **'Holding Back The Years'** Simply Red (1986)
Written by Mick Hucknall before he had formed Simply Red, the single, when first released in 1983, made little impact. Three years later it was a different story; it was reissued due to interest in America and it peaked at number two held off the top by the revival of 'Spirit In The Sky' by Doctor & The Medics.

441. **'The Lady In Red'** Chris De Burgh (1986)
A record you either love or hate, dedicated to his wife, the mums went out and bought it in their thousands. I think I'm going to scream, it's just come on the radio again.

442. **'You Can Call Me Al'** Paul Simon (1986)
Three years after his marriage to Carrie Fisher, Paul Simon completed probably the best album of his career, *Graceland* which featured this mammoth single. The video featured Simon look a like, comedy star Chevvy Chase.

443. **'All I Ask Of You'** Cliff Richard & Sarah Brightman (1986)
A wonderful show tune from the musical, *Phantom Of The Opera*, written by Andrew Lloyd-Webber, Charles Hart and Richard Stilgoe.

444. **'Reet Petite'** Jackie Wilson (1986)
Another of the year's highly successful reissues, first released in 1957 when it made number six in the charts. Twenty-nine years later and just over two years after his death, the single finally topped the UK charts with the help of a memorable video using putty like animation characters.

445. **'I Knew You Were Waiting (For Me)'** Aretha Franklin & George Michael (1987)
Aretha Franklin had never before or since had a record at number one in the UK. This single topped both the UK and American charts as well as fulfilling a lifelong ambition for George Michael to sing with Aretha.

446. **'Stand By Me'** Ben E King (1987)
One of the all-time classic soul records was first released in 1961 by this ex-lead singer with The Drifters. The record just scraped into the lower end of the charts at that time but almost twenty-six years later, topped the charts after being used in a huge jeans commercial on British television.

447. 'When A Man Loves A Woman' Percy Sledge (1987)
A very similar story to Ben E King. Another soul classic which was one of the most distinctive, classic soul tracks of the century. Although believed to have been written by Sledge, the composer credits are Cameron Lewis and Arthur Wright, who were members of his group at the time and created the song's arrangement at a moment's notice for him to perform at a gig. First released in 1966 and reaching number four, through the mighty power of TV advertising, Sledge had a new lease of life in the top ten in 1987.

448. 'Nothing's Gonna Stop Us Now' Starship (1987)
Written by Diane Warren and Albert Hammond, the song was featured in the movie *Mannequin*, which was all about a dummy in a shop window coming to life. The record became one of the biggest selling singles of the year.

449. 'Always' Atlantic Starr (1987)
An American chart-topper for a song written some five years before it was recorded. It was the debut single from their first album release for Warner Brothers, *All In The Name Of Love*.

450. 'Alone' Heart (1987)
Writers Billy Steinberg and Tom Kelly who had been responsible for hits by Cyndi Lauper and Madonna, had previously recorded this song themselves several years earlier with a different arrangement under the name I-Ten on an album called, *Taking A Cold Look*. They rewrote part of the song and submitted it to Heart who had a number one in the USA.

451. 'Never Gonna Give You Up' Rick Astley (1987)
He'd never had a hit before in his life, then suddenly, there he was with a number one both in the UK and America. Not only did this single lift the career of Rick Astley, but also firmly established the team of Mike Stock, Matt Aitken and Pete Waterman as Britain's number one songwriting and production team.

452. 'Bad' Michael Jackson (1987)
The second hit single and title track from the album, *Bad*. The previous single, the number one hit, 'I Just Can't Stop Loving You' featured singer Siedah Garrett who was credited on the sleeve but not on the label.

453. 'You Win Again' The Bee Gees (1987)
Having being absent from the top twenty for over seven years, The Bee Gees made a return with this electrifying chart-topper.

454. 'China In Your Hand' T'Pau (1987)
This single became the 600th record to top the British sales chart. The group, who took their name from a character in the TV series *Star Trek* were turned down by almost every major UK record label before they signed with Siren.

455. 'Got My Mind Set On You' George Harrison (1987)
Originally recorded in the States during the sixties, George Harrison, after over seven years, makes a return to the charts with a modern arrangement of this oldie.

456. 'Heaven Is A Place On Earth' Belinda Carlisle 1987
Belinda came from a family of seven children and, at one stage of her life, decided to drop out of society and could be seen dressed in old rags and dustbin liners and sitting at the side of the road, much to the horror of her parents. Fortunately she met up with and became the lead singer of the girl group The Go-Go's before finding solo success.

457. 'Sign Your Name' Terence Trent D'Arby (1988)
It was Belinda Carlisle that kept this single from topping the UK charts. It was the third single to be taken from his number one debut album , *Introducing The Hard Line According To Terence Trent D'Arby*.

458. 'Everywhere' Fleetwood Mac (1988)
Taken from their multi-million selling album, *Rumours*, Fleetwood Mac had undergone more personnel changes than the London Underground. This was their biggest hit since 'Oh Well' in 1969 and it's incredible to think that such a successful act only managed one chart-topping single. In the UK it was 'Albatross' and, in America, 'Dreams' topped the charts in 1977.

459. 'Perfect' Fairground Attraction (1988)
The group that brought Eddi Reader to the attention of the public topped the charts with this, their first single The follow up, 'Find My Love', was also a top ten hit, then they had two very minor chart entries before going their separate ways.

460. 'I Don't Want To Talk About It' Everything But The Girl (1988)
Proving you can't keep a good song down, Everything But The Girl take the song that gave Rod Stewart a number one hit in 1977 back into the top ten, peaking at number three.

461. 'He Ain't Heavy . . . He's My Brother' The Hollies (1988)
First released in 1969 when it made the top ten, the reissue gave The Hollies

only their second and final number one of their career thanks to its use in a beer commercial on television. It took over twenty-three years from their first number one, 'I'm Alive', to the next time they held the pole position.

462. 'Teardrops' Womack & Womack (1988)
The successful husband and wife team of Cecil and Linda Cooke Womack. They recently adopted the names Zeriija (Linda) and Zekkariyas (Cecil) after travelling to Nigeria where they discovered their historical roots with the Zekkariyas tribe.

463. 'Desire' U2 (1988)
Just over seven years after their first hit, U2 finally make it to the top of the charts with the first single to be taken from their fourth number one album, *Rattle And Hum.*

464. 'Girl You Know It's True' Milli Vanilli (1988)
What a commotion developed when Milli Vanilli went on tour and it was discovered that the group appearing on stage were not the singers on the original record.

465. 'Orinoco Flow' Enya (1988)
Once a member of the successful Irish group Clannad, Enya left the group in 1982 to pursue a solo career. Her song relating to a famous river in South America gave her a number one hit.

466. 'The First Time' Robin Beck (1988)
The song was used extensively in a Coca-Cola advert on television and, on this occasion, the song was written for the commercial. The exposure was enough to send the record to the top of the charts. Unfortunately it did very little for Robin Beck's career; after that she was never heard of in the charts again.

467. 'Need You Tonight' Inxs (1988)
The band's biggest hit which was held off the top spot by Robin Beck. The group's lead singer, Michael Hutchence was found dead through hanging in an Australian hotel room in Sydney on 22 November 1997.

468. 'Mistletoe And Wine' Cliff Richard (1988)
The enormous Christmas hit for this year made Cliff Richard the only act to achieve a number one hit in four decades, but wait, it gets even better.

469. **'Something's Gotten Hold Of My Heart'** Marc Almond & Gene Pitney (1989)
Originally, Marc Almond invited Pitney to sing a few backing vocals on the song that the American had himself taken into the top ten twenty-two years earlier. When it came to record the song, they worked so well together, it was decided to turn it into a duet. A number one in the UK, but the record was never released in America on the grounds that the song had already been a hit in 1967 for Pitney.

470. **'The Living Years'** Mike & The Mechanics (1989)
Their biggest hit was held off the number one spot for three weeks by Marc Almond and Gene Pitney. A huge tragedy hit the group in 2001 when their lead singer, Paul Young died suddenly.

471. **'You Got It'** Roy Orbison (1989)
After a twenty year absence from the charts, Roy Orbison looked all set for a healthy revival of his career with the enormous success of this Jeff Lynne produced hit and his work with The Travelling Wilburys. Unfortunately it was not to be, he died from a massive heart attack on 6 December, 1988.

472. **'Belfast Child'** Simple Minds (1989)
After 'Hey Jude', this became the second longest track to top the charts, being twenty seconds short of seven minutes. The song was the first and only number one single for the group who based the song on an old traditional song, 'She Moved Through The Fair'.

473. **'Like A Prayer'** Madonna (1989)
Her nineteenth top twenty hit and sixth number one. However, it wasn't all good news for the lady, the video for 'Like Prayer' was considered blasphemous and a soft drinks company for whom she had been hired to make a series of TV commercials, immediately dropped her from the project after only one screening of the ad.

474. **'Eternal Flame'** The Bangles (1989)
The song, co-written by the group's lead singer Susanna Hoffs with Billy Steinberg and Tom Kelly, is a tribute to the eternal flame burning over Elvis Presley's Memphis grave. A few months after the release of this chart-topping single, the group broke up, although there have been strong rumours that they might be reforming in the near future. In 2001 Atomic Rubber took the song to the number one spot in the UK.

475. 'Beds Are Burning' Midnight Oil (1989)
The only top ten hit achieved by this Australian band and originally called The Farm. They have always had a reputation for being rebels and from the beginning have insisted on total artistic control over their material.

476. 'Sweet Child O' Mine' Guns N' Roses (1989)
The song was a dedication to Erin Everly, the daughter of Phil from The Everly Brothers. She was the current girlfriend of Axl Rose and the single which topped the American charts was an edited version from their album, *Appetite For Destruction*. The edit itself upset Rose and he was often heard commenting on how much he hated it during press interviews.

477. 'Toy Soldiers' Martika (1989)
An American number one, Martika had previously appeared in the 1982 film version of the musical *Annie*. In 1991, she had another top ten hit on both sides of the Atlantic with a song written by Prince, 'LoveÚ7Thy Will Be Done'.

478. 'Sowing The Seeds Of Love' Tears For Fears (1989)
Although they achieved sixteen top forty hits, they never managed that elusive number one. This song had shades of The Beatles and The Electric Light Orchestra.

479. 'Right Here Waiting' Richard Marx (1989)
Taken from his second album, *Repeat Offender*, Marx had already scored three number ones in America, including 'Right Here Waiting', by the time it made the top ten in the UK. It was his first major hit and a track he didn't want to include on the album for personal reasons.

480. 'Girl I'm Gonna Miss You' Milli Vanilli (1989)
Despite all the controversy over the group not being who the fans thought they were, they still managed to achieve an even bigger hit than 'Girl You Know It's True'.

481. 'All Around The World' Lisa Stansfield (1989)
She began her career as presenter of the eighties children's television series, *Razzamatazz*. She left the show to form the group Blue Zone. 'All Around The World', was her second solo single; apart from hitting the top in the UK, she became only the second white performer to achieve a number one in the American R&B charts.

482. 'Nothing Compares 2 U' Sinead O' Connor (1990)
Written by Prince, he recorded his own version for an album in 1984, then a

year later he produced another treatment with a group called The Family. Five years later, Sinead produced her own chart-topping recording of the song.

483. 'How Am I Supposed To Live Without You?' Michael Bolton (1990)

Originally an American top twenty hit in 1983 for Laura Branigan, Michael Bolton, who'd been in the music business for over twenty years, decided to record his version of his own composition which topped the American charts and became a huge hit all around Europe.

484. 'Killer' Adamski (1990)

Adamski's second hit and only number one featured the vocal talents of Seal, who himself re-recorded the song the following year and took it back into the top ten

485. 'Sacrifice / Healing Hands' Elton John (1990)

Finally, Elton John achieved his first solo number one after a wait of nearly twenty-nine years since his first hit. The two songs are reissues of his previous two singles, neither at the time even made it into the top forty.

486. 'It Must Have Been Love' Roxette (1990)

The biggest hit from the Richard Gere/Julia Roberts hit film, *Pretty Woman*, of that year. Roxette returned to the top ten just over three years later with a reissue of the single.

487. 'Show Me Heaven' Maria McKee (1990)

Used on the soundtrack of the Tom Cruise/Robert Duvall/Nicole Kidman movie, *Days Of Thunder*. Prior to this hit, McKee had written the chart-topping 'A Good Heart', for Feargal Sharkey some five years earlier, thus making her the first female to have achieved a number one hit for herself and another act. 'Show Me Heaven' became a minor hit again in 1995 for Australian singer, Tina Arena.

488. 'Ice Ice Baby' Vanilla Ice (1990)

This single made its debut in the charts at number three, breaking all records for the highest position for a new act to have entered the top forty. The song borrowed the bass line from Queen and David Bowie's hit, 'Under Pressure'. He was also the first solo rap artist to top the British and American charts.

489. 'Saviour's Day' Cliff Richard (1990)

We told you it would get even better (see no. 468), Cliff's second Christmas number one in three years gave him the unbeatable record of having topped the charts in all five decades.

490. 'All Together Now' The Farm (1990)
Believe it or not, The Farm were formed in 1983 by Peter Hooton, but it wasn't until 1990 that they achieved their first top forty hit with 'Groovy Train'. Their biggest hit, 'All Together Now', was based on the classical piece, *Canon in D* by the 17th century composer, Johann Pachelbel.

491. 'Innuendo' Queen (1991)
The title track to Queen's sixteenth top ten album and third chart-topper, had a running time of six minutes and twenty-five seconds, just twenty-five seconds longer than their biggest ever hit, 'Bohemian Rhapsody'.

492. 'Should I Stay Or Should I Go?' The Clash (1991)
Yet another record to become a huge hit second time around thanks to a TV advert. The Clash single, first released in 1982 topped the charts after being seen in the commercial for Levi's jeans.

493. 'Sit Down' James (1991)
Through an early interest by Morrissey, James managed to get a recording contract with Factory records based in their hometown, Manchester. In 1990, they signed to the Fontana label and had three minor hits before they reissued an earlier recording, 'Sit Down', which became their biggest hit to date.

494. '(Everything I Do) I Do It For You' Bryan Adams (1991)
Taken from the soundtrack of the movie, *Robin Hood: Prince Of Thieves*, this single still holds the record for the number of weeks at number one where it remained for a total of sixteen weeks, bypassing the previous record held since 1955 by Slim Whitman and his chart-topping 'Rose Marie'.

495. 'Wind Of Change' The Scorpions (1991)
Usually associated with loud rock music, this German band toured the Soviet Union in the early nineties and the experience inspired lead singer Klaus Meine to write this gentle ballad that became a worldwide hit.

496. 'The Fly' U2 (1991)
Joining forces with Iron Maiden and Queen, U2 became the third act of 1991 to enter the charts at number one, although three more followed with Michael Jackson, George Michael and Elton John's duet and Queen for the second time in the year with their Christmas number one and a reissue of 'Bohemian Rhapsody', which became the first record to top the charts on two separate occasions.

497. 'Black Or White' Michael Jackson (1991)
This was the first single to be taken from his first album in four years, in fact it was a double album, *Dangerous*. The track featured a momentous guitar solo by Slash from Guns N' Roses.

498. 'Smells Like Teen Spirit' Nirvana (1991)
One of the real classic tracks of the nineties from this exciting new grunge band. Written by lead singer Kurt Cobain who shot himself to death on 5 April, 1994. The track was taken from their album, *Nevermind*.

499. 'Stay' Shakespear's Sister (1992)
Ex-Bananarama singer, Siobhan Fahey enjoyed twenty-three top forty hits with her previous group, but with Shakespear's Sister this was the only time she made it to number one.

500. 'My Girl' The Temptations (1992)
First released in 1965, but it was the Otis Redding version that was the hit in Britain. Reissued to tie in with the movie of the same name starring Macaulay Culkin, The Temptations just failed to make number one because they couldn't jump over Shakespear's Sister.

501. 'Tears In Heaven' Eric Clapton (1992)
One of Clapton's best songs and the saddest. With lyrics by Will Jennings, it was written as a tribute to his late son, Conor, who fell to his death from a balcony window in a New York apartment block.

502. 'Why?' Annie Lennox (1992)
Since winding down The Eurythmics, this became the first solo hit for Annie Lennox which was taken from her album *Diva*. She has since got back together with Dave Stewart to record new material.

503. 'Beauty And The Beast' Celine Dion and Peabo Bryson (1992)
The title song from the Disney animated movie gave Peabo Bryson his second top ten hit duet of his career. He never managed to succeed with a solo single, his last chart appearance being in 1983 with Roberta Flack. In 1993, he scored yet again with the theme from another Disney film, *Aladdin*, called 'A Whole New World', and this time the duet was with Regina Bell.

504. 'End Of The Road' Boyz II Men (1992)
This single spent thirteen weeks at the top of the American charts, the longest stay of any record in chart history. The record was previously held by Elvis Presley with his eleven week run for his 1956 double A-sided hit, 'Don't Be

Cruel', and 'Hound Dog'. Boyz II Men were finally knocked off the top spot by a record that meant nothing in the UK, 'How Do You Talk To An Angel', by The Heights.

505. 'Would I Lie To You?' Charles And Eddie (1992)
Charles and Eddie are Charles Pettigrew and Eddie Chacon from California. They managed to top the UK charts for two weeks before Whitney Houston settled there for the year's Christmas number one.

506. 'I Will Always Love You' Whitney Houston (1992)
Written and originally recorded by Dolly Parton, Whitney Houston enjoyed ten weeks at the top of the charts, the longest stay by any female artist. The song was featured in Whitney's movie with Kevin Costner, *The Bodyguard.*

507. '(Take A Little) Piece Of My Heart' Erma Franklin (1992)
Aretha's little sister originally released this amazing soul single in 1967 to considerable airplay but no chart action. Twenty-five years later, the song was picked up for a big advertising campaign for Levi's jeans, Erma's record company re-issued the single and she achieved her only UK hit.

508. 'Oh Carolina' Shaggy (1993)
His debut hit, which samples Henry Mancini's 'Peter Gunn Theme', a hit twice for Duane Eddy, once in 1958 as a solo guitarist, then again in 1986 with The Art Of Noise, set the way for a revival of reggae music in the UK.

509. 'Are You Going My Way?' Lenny Kravitz (1993)
Kravitz came from a showbiz family, his father was a TV producer and his mother an actress. In 1990, he wrote and produced Madonna's top ten hit, 'Justify My Love'. 'Are You Going My Way?', was the title track from his 1993 chart-topping album.

510. 'Young At Heart' The Bluebells (1993)
Written by 'Bluebell' Bobby Hodgens and 'Bananarama's' Siobhan Fahey, the song was originally a top ten hit when it was first released in 1984. The song became a 1993 chart-topper after it was used in a TV commercial to advertise a brand of car long after the group had broken up. They briefly reformed for a couple of television appearances.

511. 'All That She Wants' Ace Of Base (1993)
Another successful product from Sweden, the Bergren family consisting of sisters Marlin and Jenny and brother Jonas, together with electronic pro-grammer Ulf Ekberg, made up Ace Of Base, whose number one single took

over a year to finally get released in the UK after achieving international success.

512. 'Dreams' Gabrielle (1993)
Taken from her album, *Find A Way*, her first hit took her right to the top of the charts. Recently Gabrielle revealed that the eyepatch and dark glasses are no gimmick, she actually lost an eye some years ago.

513. 'What Is Love?' Haddaway (1993)
This Trinidadian-born performer started his own company, in Germany arranging fashion shows and photographic sessions. 'What Is Love' was just pipped at the post to be number one by Gabrielle's 'Dreams'.

514. 'Pray' Take That (1993)
After nine previous releases and five top twenty chart entries, Take That, the new pop sensation of the nineties, finally top the charts with 'Pray'.

515. 'Living On My Own' Freddy Mercury (1993)
This was a reworking of a 1985, minor hit by Freddy from his solo album, *Mr Bad Guy*. The record gave him his first solo chart-topper, nearly two years after his death.

516. 'Relight My Fire' Take That featuring Lulu (1993)
A reworking of a failed Dan Hartman track from the late seventies. The original Hartman recording featured a female vocal part, so the group decided to recreate the feel by inviting Lulu to sing guest vocals; the result was a second chart-topper for Take That.

517. 'I'd Do Anything For Love (But I Won't Do That)' Meat Loaf (1993)
After a nine year absence from the top twenty, Meat Loaf came storming back with his first chart-topper and debut single from his new album, *Bat Out Of Hell II*.

518. 'Runaway Train' Soul Asylum (1993)
The record was used to help promote a huge campaign both in the UK and America to try and reunite lost and runaway children with their families; photographs of some of the missing children were used in their video.

519. 'Things Can Only Get Better' D:Ream (1994)
The meeting up of Peter Cunnah and club DJ, Al McKenzie, led them to form D:Ream. 'Things Can Only Get Better', was originally the follow up to their

debut single, 'U R The Best Thing'. A year later, a new improved Paul Oakenfold mix resulted in a number one placing.

520. 'Without You' Mariah Carey (1994)
Previously a number one hit in 1972 for Harry Nilsson, Mariah Carey's cover made her the first solo female artist in the UK to enter the charts at number one.

521. 'All For Love' Bryan Adams, Rod Stewart and Sting (1994)
A number one in America but held off the top spot in the UK by D:Ream. The song was written for the soundtrack of the Disney movie *The Three Musketeers*, starring Kiefer Sutherland and Charlie Sheen.

522. 'Streets of Philadelphia' Bruce Springsteen (1994)
Featured on the soundtrack of the movie, *Philadelphia*, starring Tom Hanks and Denzel Washington, this Oscar winning song gave Bruce his first UK top ten hit in nearly nine years.

523. 'Mmm Mmm Mmm Mmm' The Crash Test Dummies (1994)
The Canadian rock band from Winnipeg took this novelty song from their album *God Shuffled His Feet*, which they co-produced with Talking Heads' Jerry Harrison.

524. 'Love Is All Around' Wet Wet Wet (1994)
Featured in the movie, *Four Weddings And A Funeral*, this revival of the Troggs' 1967 hit became the second-longest-running stay for a single at the top of the charts. With fifteen weeks at number one, if it had remained in pole position for one more week, it would have tied with Bryan Adams. However, the drop was blamed on the record company deleting the record that week.

525. '7 Seconds' Youssou N'Dour featuring Neneh Cherry (1994)
This multilingual duet between Neneh Cherry and Senegalese, Youssou N'Dour, who had previously worked with Peter Gabriel on an extensive American tour, brought a efreshing new sound to the charts.

526. 'All I Wanna Do' Sheryl Crow (1994)
Crow got her first real show business break as a backing singer to Michael Jackson on the *Bad*, tour. This was her second single from her debut album, *Tuesday Night Music Club*.

527. 'Stay Another Day' East 17 (1994)
They took their name from their home town's postal code, Walthamstow in

London. They created an image of being badly behaved which finally resulted in their downfall after this chart-topping single. Lead singer Brian Harvey was asked to leave the group after making comments supporting the use of drugs.

528. 'Think Twice' Celine Dion (1994)
The longest climb to number one for ten years since 'The Power Of Love' by Jennifer Rush. It entered the top forty at number 30 for the week ending 12 November and finally made it to number one twelve weeks later.

529. 'Turn On, Tune In, Cop Out' Freak Power (1995)
First released in 1993 to attract little interest when it scraped into the lower end of the charts. Then this Norman Cook production was picked up for yet another Levi's jeans television commercial, which led to the record climbing to number three. By this time, Cook had gone on to bigger and better things, working with such acts as The Housemartins, Beats International and as Fatboy Slim.

530. 'Love Can Build A Bridge' Cher, Chrissie Hynde, and Neneh Cherry with Eric Clapton (1995)
Originally recorded by American country act, The Judds, the song was used as the 1995 Comic Relief single and became the first number one single to credit Eric Clapton in over thirty years of his career.

531. 'Back For Good' Take That (1995)
Written by Gary Barlow and premiered at the 1995 Brits Awards. Ironically, soon after this song had given Take That their sixth chart-topper, there were strong rumours about their break up. It was confirmed in February the following year that the group would be going their separate ways.

532. 'Chains' Tina Arena (1995)
Born in Melbourne, Australia, Philopina Arena achieved international success with her debut single. In the late nineties, she took the lead in the West End production of Andrew Lloyd-Webber's musical, *Whistle Down The Wind*.

533. 'Alright' Supergrass (1995)
Released as a double A-side with 'Time', Supergrass launched their recording career the previous year with the much acclaimed, 'Caught By The Fuzz', a song about being busted by the police for possession of drugs. The video accompanying 'Alright', was filmed in Portmeirion in North Wales, where the entire sixties cult TV series, *The Prisoner* was made.

534. 'Country House' Blur (1995)
In the sixties it was The Beatles against The Rolling Stones fighting it out for the number one spot. In the nineties, Blur took on Oasis and on this occasion it was Blur who kept 'Roll With It' by the opposition at number two.

535. 'I'll Be There For You' The Rembrandts (1995)
The theme song to the ever popular TV series, *Friends*. The single returned to the top ten just twenty months later in 1997 when it was reissued to tie in with the start of another new series.

536. 'Gangsta's Paradise' Coolio (1995)
The first truly hard-hitting, street rap to top the charts. It was based on a Stevie Wonder album track, 'Pastime Paradise'. Coolio, from Los Angeles, California, was joined on this chart-topper by gospel singer LV; the song was featured in the Michelle Pfeiffer movie, *Dangerous Minds*.

537. 'Wonderwall' Oasis (1995)
A song named after a George Harrison album, this was the song that put Oasis firmly on the map, but they were held off the number one spot by Robson and Jerome's double A-side, 'I Believe' and 'Up On The Roof'. 'Wonderwall' peaked at number two again some six weeks after Oasis had dropped out of the charts in a bizarre version by The Mike Flowers Pops.

538. 'Earth Song' Michael Jackson (1995)
Many music fans would have been grateful to Jackson because it was this 'green' track that kept The Mike Flowers Pops from topping the charts. However, 1995 brought Jacko his own share of problems, when he performed it at the 1995 Brit awards, Pulp's Jarvis Cocker invaded the stage in protest at Jackson's Messiah white outfit.

539. 'Free As A Bird' The Beatles (1995)
An unreleased Beatles track from the sixties gave the group their first new title to make the charts in thirteen years after extensive production work by Jeff Lynne.

540. 'Jesus To A Child' George Michael (1996)
After a long battle with his old record company, Epic, George Michael finally released a new single on a new label. His debut for Virgin entered the charts at number one replacing Michael Jackson's 'Earth Song', which ironically was on Epic.

541. 'Spaceman' Babylon Zoo (1996)
The group were the brainchild of writer-producer Jas Mann, and this, their debut single, entered the charts at number one on the back of it being selected for a Levi's jeans TV commercial. It became the sixth chart-topper to be used in their ads.

542. 'Lifted' The Lighthouse Family (1996)
First released the previous year to little success, but this re-mixed version from their debut album, *Ocean Drive*, became their first top ten hit. The song was chosen by the Labour party as their anthem for the 2001 General Election.

543. 'Don't Look Back In Anger' Oasis (1996)
The charts for the week of 2 March will always be remembered by Oasis fans as the week four of their old singles entered the top seventy-five for the second time. This followed their appearance at the Brit awards to win in three categories. 'Don't Look Back In Anger' made its chart debut at number one.

544. 'How Deep Is Your Love?' Take That (1996)
The group's farewell single before their break-up became their eighth number one and also the eighth Bee Gees composition to top the chart.

545. 'Firestarter' The Prodigy (1996)
The tenth consecutive single to enter the charts at number one and their first new product in two years, saw dancer Keith Flint on vocals for the first time.

546. 'Killing Me Softly' The Fugees (1996)
The first time since 1965 that a record fell off the number one spot only to return a week later. This is a reworking of the 1973 hit by Roberta Flack from this group who took their name by shortening the word 'refugees'. The record made its chart debut at number one and since then all three members of the band, plus Wyclef Jean and Lauryn Hill, have gone on to enjoy solo success.

547. 'Forever Love' Gary Barlow (1996)
The first ex-member of Take That to achieve solo success, Barlow made his impressive debut at number one with his own composition. Robbie was close behind, but his first single, 'Freedom', was kept off the number one spot by The Spice Girls.

548. 'Wannnabe' The Spice Girls (1996)
A new pop sensation who become the first British all girl group to top the charts. They did it within two weeks of the record being released, and there it remained for seven whole weeks.

549. 'E-Bow The Letter' REM (1996)
The first single from their new album, *New Adventures In Hi-Fi*, became the biggest single of the group's career.

550. 'Setting Sun' The Chemical Brothers (1996)
Their fourth chart entry and first number one which entered the charts at number one, featured Oasis man Noel Gallagher on lead vocals.

551. 'Words' Boyzone (1996)
Take That's last chart-topper was a cover of a Bee Gees song and so was Boyzone's first. Although the single sold almost a quarter of a million copies in the first week of release and entered the charts at number one, many Bee Gees fans readily pointed out that they had left out some of the original lyrics of the song. The single just remained at the top of the charts for one week as it was replaced by the second release by The Spice Girls, 'Say You'll Be There'.

552. 'Say What You Want' Texas (1997)
A brilliant new single from the Glasgow based group formed by John McElhone, who had enjoyed previous chart success with Altered Images and Hipsway. This was their second top ten single despite a wait of eight years since their debut, 'I Don't Want A Lover'.

553. 'Discotheque' U2 (1997)
Their third number one single, and although probably not their best, it should be noted that chart history was made the week it entered at number one (15/2/97), for the first time ever, six of the top ten were new entries. Apart from U2, the third ex-Take That member, Mark Owen, made number three with his debut, 'Clementine', then there was 'Barrel Of A Gun' by Depeche Mode, 'Ain't Talkin' 'Bout Dub' by Apollo Four Forty, the delightfully titled 'She Makes My Nose Bleed' by Mansun, and 'Novocaine For The Soul' by Eels.

554. 'Hush' Kula Shaker (1997)
The fifth hit for the group revived an old Joe South song that was recorded as the debut single in the sixties by rock legends Deep Purple. Group member Crispian Mills is the son of actress Hayley Mills and director Roy Boulting.

555. 'Mama / Who Do You Think You Are?' The Spice Girls (1997)
The first act in chart history to top the charts with their first four consecutive releases. All four of their hits were taken from their debut album, *Spice*.

556. 'I Believe I Can Fly' R Kelly (1997)
Everyone believed that R Kelly had been kept off the number one spot by The
Spice Girls, however, he dropped down to number five the week The Chemical
Brothers hit the top for the second time with, 'Block Rockin' Beats', they held
the spot for one week only to be overtaken by Mr Kelly. The song was featured
in the movie, *Space Jam*, starring Michael Jordan. Another song from the
same movie, 'Fly Like An Eagle', by Seal, also made it's top twenty chart debut
the same week.

557. 'Love Won't Wait' Gary Barlow (1997)
The ex-Take That star achieved his second number one with a song written by
Shep Pettibone and the uncredited Madonna. The week it went to number one
(10/5/97), more chart history was created. With the faster turnaround of
singles, for the first time all top three records were new entries: Barlow at
number one, George Michael at two with 'Star People '97' and 'Love Is The
Law' by The Seahorses at three.

558. 'You're Not Alone' Olive (1997)
After three previous attempts at making the top forty, Olive finally broke
through with a re-mixed version of a song they previously released a year
earlier. Entering the charts at number one, the founder member, keyboard
player Tim Kellett, who once played with Simply Red, recorded and mixed all
the group's material in his home studio in Derbyshire.

559. 'Time To Say Goodbye' Sarah Brightman & Andrea Bocelli
(1997)
A completely out of place single for the top ten in the nineties, but this record
was bought in its thousands around the world. Bocelli was one of Italy's
brightest new opera stars and the record became the biggest selling single in
history in Germany. The single was held off the number one spot by Olive and
Eternal's 'I Wanna Be The Only One'.

560. 'I'll Be Missing You' Puff Daddy & Faith Evans (1997)
The single was released by way of a tribute to the late Notorious B.I.G, who
had been shot dead outside a nightclub earlier in the year. The record was
based on the 1983 chart-topper by The Police, 'Every Breath You Take'.

**561. 'Candle In The Wind / Something About The Way You Look
Tonight'** Elton John (1997)
'Something About The Way You Look Tonight', had been released a few weeks
earlier but was withdrawn and reissued as a double A-side along with Elton's
tribute to Princess Diana which sold more than three-quarters of a million

copies on the week of release, and ended up being the biggest selling UK single in chart history.

562. 'All Around The World' Oasis (1998)
Entering the charts at number one, this was their fourth chart-topper and second number one from their album *Be Here Now*. Running at twenty seconds short of ten minutes, it became the longest running single ever to top the UK charts and the second time that particular song title had been number one, the first was Lisa Stansfield in 1989, although a completely different song.

563. 'My Heart Will Go On' Celine Dion (1998)
The main theme from the year's biggest box office movie, *Titanic* and Oscar winner for best song. Celine's single dropped from number one after its first week, only to return to the top two weeks later for one more week at the top, the very week that the top three positions were all held by female singers, the first time in this decade.

564. 'Brimful Of Asha' Cornershop (1998)
Although first issued during the middle of 1997, with six weeks of national radio airplay prior to its release, the 1998 re-mix by Norman Cook finally made it to the top of the charts on its first week of release.

565. 'Frozen' Madonna (1998)
Although she managed nineteen top ten hits in eight years, this became Madonna's first number one since 'Vogue', in 1990. Her tally of forty top ten hits to date made her by far the most successful female chart artist of all time.

566. 'You're Still The One' Shania Twain (1998)
The lady who brought a renewed interest to country music in the UK with this brilliant single. Shania, which means 'I'm On My Way' in the Ojibwa Indian language, a tribe from which she is a descendent, is married to leading record producer Robert John 'Mutt' Lange, who has been responsible for not only his wife's hits but also Bryan Adams, Foreigner and many more.

567. 'How Do I Live?' LeAnn Rimes (1998)
The debut UK hit from the fifteen year old singer from Jackson Mississippi, became the biggest selling Country single in history. A year earlier, the song had been an American hit for Trisha Yearwood and was featured in the movie *Con Air*, starring Nicolas Cage.

568. 'No Matter What' Boyzone (1998)
Their twelfth top ten hit and fourth number one was taken from the musical, *Whistle Down The Wind*, written by Andrew Lloyd-Webber and Jim Steinman. By pure coincidence, another single in the top ten with Boyzone was 'Life Is A Flower' by Ace Of Base which also contained the line 'Whistle Down The Wind' as part of the lyric.

569. 'Bootie Call' All Saints (1998)
Apart from being their third consecutive number one and their biggest-selling number one to date, 'Bootie Call' was another landmark in chart history becoming the 800th single to top the UK sales chart.

570. 'Believe' Cher (1998)
By far the longest run with seven weeks at the top of the charts in 1998, the title track from the album of the same name became Cher's nineteenth solo UK top forty hit and her second chart-topper. At the age of fifty-two, it made her the oldest female singer to reach number one. It took six British songwriters to compose 'Believe' which was, in fact, constructed from two separate incomplete songs.

571. 'Praise You' Fatboy Slim (1999)
Fatboy Slim, aka Norman Cook achieved his third chart-topper with his third reincarnation at the beginning of 1999. In 1986 he was part of The Housemartins who reached number one with 'Caravan Of Love', and four years later he was back again as one of Beats International who rocketed to the top with 'Dub Be Good To Me'. He had other top twenty hits as a member of Freak Power in 1995 and Pizzaman in 1996.

572. 'Maria' Blondie (1999)
Just over eighteen years previously, Blondie achieved their last number one with 'The Tide Is High' and that's how long they had to wait to repeat that success. After a long absence from the recording scene, the group decided to re-form and this was their first new single in seventeen years.

573. 'Baby One More Time' Britney Spears (1999)
Her debut single became the biggest first week seller of any new artist in chart history, shifting just under half a million copies on its release. At the age of seventeen, she became the youngest artist ever to sell a million copies in the UK alone with a first record.

574. 'Music To Watch Girls By' Andy Williams (1999)
First released in 1967 when it crept quietly in and out the lower end of the chart. The song was originally written as an instrumental and recorded by The Bob Crewe Generation for an American Pepsi-Cola TV ad. Thirty-three years later, Andy Williams was back in the UK top ten for the first time in twenty-six years with a re-release of his vocal version of the song which was used in a television ad for the Fiat Punto car.

575. 'Flat Beat' Mr Oizo (1999)
Probably the most famous instrumental in many a year thanks to yet another television campaign, this time promoting Levi's new Sta-Prest line. Mr Oizo is Quentin Dupieux and the first French act in twenty-five years to top the UK charts, when Charles Aznavour was at number one with 'She'.

576. 'My Name Is' Eminem (1999)
The debut single for this white boy rapper, who was soon to become the hottest property in the music business, climbed to the number two position, just held off by Mr Oizo. The protégé of Dr Dre took his name from the initials of his real name, Marshall Mathers, and has contributed vocals to several successful hip-hop projects.

577. 'Everybody's Free (To Wear Sunscreen)' Baz Luhrmann (1999)
Australian actor and film director Luhrmann was responsible for the hit movies *Ballroom Dancing* and the 1996 remake of *Romeo And Juliet*, the latter featuring the 1991 top ten hit by Rozalla, 'Everybody's Free (To Feel Good)', the song on which this, his number one hit, was based.

578. 'Livin' La Vida Loca' Ricky Martin (1999)
Ricky, who once appeared in the American TV soap series, *General Hospital*, spent five weeks at the top of the American charts and three weeks in the UK with this single.

579. 'When You Say Nothing At All' Ronan Keating (1999)
A song originally recorded by Country singer Paul Overstreet, who also co-wrote the song, and later by Keith Whitley and then by Alison Krauss. This was the debut solo hit for the ex-Boyzone Ronan Keating who had achieved fifteen consecutive top five hits including six chart-toppers with his former group.

580. 'If I Let You Go' Westlife (1999)
Dethroning their manager from the number one position, Westlife achieved their second consecutive chart-topper. Earlier in the year they became the first

boy band to enter the charts at number one with their debut single, 'Swear It Again'. Co managed by Ronan Keating of Boyzone fame, this became the tenth hit by an Irish band to top the UK charts in the past year.

581. 'Mi Chico Latino' Geri Halliwell (1999)

Ex-Spice Girl, Ginger, or as she became known, Geri Halliwell became the first member of one of the most successful acts of the nineties to achieve a solo number one hit with the twenty-fifth new chart-topper of 1999. The song, which she co-wrote, like twenty-two other chart-toppers throughout the year, only managed to hold the top spot for one week.

582. 'Pure Shores' All Saints (2000)

Taken from the soundtrack of the movie, *The Beach*, and their next album, *Saints and Sinners*, 'Pure Shores' replaced 'Go Let It Out' by Oasis at the top of the charts which was sweet revenge for the girls whose 'Never Ever', was knocked off number one back in 1998 by 'All Around The World', the fourth Oasis chart-topper.

583. 'Smooth' Santana featuring Rob Thomas (2000)

Originally released a few months earlier to a luke warm reception in the UK, 'Smooth' was taken from the award winning album of the same name, and after the chart-topping success in America with the single, the record was reworked in Britain and became Santana's first top twenty hit in over twenty-two years.

584. 'Fill Me In' Craig David (2000)

David originally found it almost impossible to get a record deal, first coming to the public's attention with his work with Artful Dodger. This, his first solo single, entered the charts at number one making him the youngest solo singer to top the charts in twelve years. He also went to number one the week the chart had all top six singles as new entries, another first for the history books.

585. 'Day And Night' Billie (2000)

The Swindon-born lass, with her final release as Billie because from this point on in her career she would be known as Billie Piper. She also became the youngest female singer to achieve three number one hits in the UK and she achieved it in her first five releases.

586. 'It Feels So Good' Sonique (2000)

Originally released in time for the 1998 Christmas market when it hovered around the lower regions of the top forty, the 2000 re-release of this single by the former lead singer with S'Express reached number eight in the American charts earlier in the year and topped the UK charts for three weeks.

587. 'Babylon' David Gray (2000)
Gray had been releasing material in the UK for many years without success, even 'Babylon' had been previously available as a single. Then suddenly the media took a huge interest in this talented artist and proved that perseverance can pay off in the end.

588. 'Breathless' The Corrs (2000)
The group were discovered by their manager, John Hughes, who was helping movie director Alan Parker find musicians to appear in his movie, *The Commitments*, in which Andrea was given an acting role. The Corrs achieved their first UK number one with 'Breathless', their tenth top forty chart entry.

589. 'We Will Rock You' Five & Queen (2000)
Although treated by Queen fans as one of the group's signature songs, it had never before been a hit, it hadn't even been an A-side. It was originally on the B-side of their 1977 top ten hit, 'We Are The Champions'. By using the original Queen recording, Five achieved their ninth chart-topper and second number one.

590. 'Groovejet (If This Ain't Love)' Spiller (2000)
Every so often a record comes along that just can't fail to be number one, and this was one of those records. A great song in its own right but given an enormous amount of extra exposure on BBC television several times a day as the music for one of their huge promotion campaigns for their networks. 'Groovejet' was originally an instrumental, but with the extra vocals by Sophie Ellis-Baxter, this has become a classic pop track.

591. 'Music' Madonna (2000)
This gave Madonna the all time record for being the first female in chart history to achieve ten number ones in her fifty-one hit's career. Earlier in 2000 she had topped the charts with 'American Pie', beating the chart position of the original 1972 Don McLean version by one place. Madonna's revival of the pop classic was used in the movie, *The Next Best Thing*, in which she starred with Rupert Everett.

592. 'Who Let The Dogs Out' The Baha Men (2000)
A huge American hit by this U.S. based group who are of Bahamian descent and who had been releasing records with little success for over ten years. It was also the first record in two years to enter the charts outside the top ten and then claw its way into it where it continued to yo-yo up and down for thirteen weeks, selling more copies than any other record in the year 2000 without reaching number one.

593. 'Dancing In The Moonlight' Toploader (2000)
Although it first entered the charts towards the end of 2000, it wasn't until February 2001 that it finally managed to climb into the top ten, something that was virtually unheard of for the past five years. The song was originally recorded in the sixties by an unknown group called High Broom and there have been several versions since, none of which made the charts.

594. 'Love Don't Cost A Thing' Jennifer Lopez (2001)
Her first single from the album *J-Lo*, was produced by Birmingham-born Ric Wake, who had previously been associated with hits for Mariah Carey, Taylor Dayne and Celine Dion.

595. 'Whole Again' Atomic Kitten (2001)
The ninth all female group in chart history to achieve a number one hit. With four weeks at the top of the charts, this was their fifth chart entry, all of which were featured on their debut album, *Right Now*, which, following the success of this single, was subsequently repackaged to contain new material including their follow-up hit.

596. 'Here With Me' Dido (2001)
Following her successful collaboration with Eminem on the single 'Stan', Dido's single from her debut album, *No Angel*, shot into the top ten on its week of release.

597. 'It Wasn't Me' Shaggy featuring Rikrok (2001)
The track featuring Ricardo 'Rickrok' Ducent was from Shaggy's American chart-topping album *Hot Shot*. The release of the single was brought forward in the UK because thousands of import copies were being sold at nearly double the price, enough to have put it into the lower regions of the top forty prior to its official UK release.

598. 'Pure And Simple' Hear'Say (2001)
Success brought about by a TV series watched by over ten million viewers, which showed how a new pop group were put together and groomed for success. Fortunately for the producers, it worked and Hear'Say achieved a chart-topper with this, their first release. They also broke all records by selling over half a million copies in their first week of release, more than any other first time act to the charts.

599. 'What Took You So Long?' Emma Bunton (2001)
The fourth ex-member of The Spice Girls to achieve a number one, making the group the first act in history where four members of a group have achieved

chart-topping solo singles. The Beatles held the record until this point, but it was Ringo Starr who let them down by falling one place short of the top in 1972 with 'Back Off Boogaloo'.

600. 'Don't Stop Movin'' S Club 7 (2001)

The third number one for S Club 7 who knocked Destiny's Child off the top spot for the second time. 'Don't Stop Movin'' replaced 'Survivor' at the top of the charts, and towards the end of 2000, they dethroned 'Independent Woman', with their Children In Need hit, 'Never Had A Dream Come True'.

BRITS, OSCARS AND OTHER BAUBLES

'CELEBRATION'
Music Awards

The first significant awards ceremony to be held which sought specifically to honour those working in the music industry, was the Grammys on 4 May 1959. The top award (album of the year) went to Henry Mancini for *Peter Gunn*.

Since then several other award ceremonies have come into being, including our very own Brit awards which began in 1977.

In this chapter we list all of the major music-related awards to be given on an annual basis; the Brits, the Grammys, the MTV, the Academy Awards (Oscars) and the Golden Globe awards.

BRIT AWARDS

2001

Best Female Sonique

Best Male Robbie Williams

Best Group Coldplay

Best Pop Act Westlife

Best Album *Parachutes* by Coldplay

Best Newcomer A1

Best Dance Act Fatboy Slim

Best Single 'Rock DJ' from *Sing When You're Winning* – Robbie Williams

Best Video 'Rock DJ' from *Sing When You're Winning* – Robbie Williams

Best International Female Madonna

Best International Male Eminem

Best International Group U2

Best International Newcomer Kelis

Best Soundtrack *American Beauty*

Outstanding Contribution to British Music U2

2000

Best Female Beth Orton

Best Male Tom Jones

Best Group Travis

Best Pop Act Five

Best Album *The Man Who* – Travis

Best Newcomer S Club 7

Best Dance Act The Chemical Brothers

Best Single 'She's The One' – Robbie Williams

Best Video 'She's The One' – Robbie Williams

Best International Female Macy Gray

Best International Male Beck

Best International Group TLC

Best International Newcomer Macy Gray

Best Soundtrack *Notting Hill*

Special Award – Best-Selling British Live Act Steps

Outstanding Contribution to British Music Spice Girls

1999

Best Female Des'ree

Best Male Robbie Williams

Best Group Manic Street Preachers

Best Album *This Is My Truth Tell Me Yours* – Manic Street Preachers

Best Newcomer Belle & Sebastian

Best Dance Act Fatboy Slim

Best Single 'Angels' – Robbie Williams

Best Video 'Millennium' – Robbie Williams

Best International Female Natalie Imbruglia

Best International Male Beck

Best International Group The Corrs

Best International Newcomer Natalie Imbruglia

Best Soundtrack *Titanic*

Outstanding Contribution to British Music Eurythmics

1998

Best Female Shola Ama

Best Male Finley Quaye

Best Group The Verve

Best Album *Urban Hymns* – The Verve

Best Newcomer Stereophonics

Best Dance Act Prodigy

Best Single 'Never Ever' – All Saints

Best Video 'Never Ever' – All Saints

Best International Female Björk

Best International Male Jon Bon Jovi

Best International Group U2

Best International Newcomer Eels

Best Soundtrack *The Full Monty*

1997

Best Female Gabrielle

Best Male George Michael

Best Group Manic Street Preachers

Best Album *Everything Must Go* – Manic Street Preachers

Best Newcomer Kula Shaker

Best Dance Act Prodigy

Best Single 'Wannabe' – Spice Girls

Best Video 'Say You'll Be There' – Spice Girls

Best International Female Sheryl Crow

Best International Male Beck

Best International Group Fugees

Best International Newcomer Robert Miles

Best Soundtrack *Trainspotting*

1996

Best Female Annie Lennox

Best Male Paul Weller

Best Group Oasis

Best Album *What's The Story Morning Glory* – Oasis

Best Newcomer Supergrass

Best Dance Act Massive Attack

Best Single 'Back For Good' – Take That

Best Video 'Wonderwall' – Oasis

Best International Female Alanis Morissette

Best International Male The Artist Formerly Known As Prince

Best International Group Bon Jovi

Best International Newcomer Alanis Morissette

Best Soundtrack *Batman Forever*

1995

Best Female Eddi Reader

Best Male Paul Weller

Best Group Blur

Best Album *Park Life* – Blur

Best Newcomer Oasis

Best Dance Act M People

Best Single 'Parklife' – Blur

Best Video 'Parklife' – Blur

Best International Female k.d. lang

Best International Male The Artist Formerly Known As Prince

Best International Group REM

Best International Newcomer Lisa Loeb

Best Soundtrack *Pulp Fiction*

1994

Best Female Dina Carroll

Best Male Sting

Best Group Stereo MC's

Best Album *Connected* – Stereo MC's

Best Newcomer Gabrielle

Best Dance Act M People

Best Single 'Pray' – Take That

Best Video 'Pray' – Take That

Best International Female Björk

Best International Male Lenny Kravitz

Best International Group Crowded House

Best International Newcomer Björk

Best Soundtrack *The Bodyguard*

1993

Best Female Annie Lennox

Best Male Mick Hucknall

Best Group Simply Red

Best Album *Diva* – Annie Lennox

Best Newcomer Tasmin Archer

Best Single 'Could It Be Magic' – Take That

Best Video 'Stay' – Shakespears Sister

Best International Group REM

Best International Newcomer Nirvana

Best Soundtrack *Wayne's World*

1992

Best Female Lisa Stansfield

Best Male Seal

Best Group The KLF & Simply Red

Best Album *Seal* – Seal

Best Newcomer Beverley Craven

Best Single 'These Are The Days Of Our Lives' – Queen

Best Video 'Killer' – Seal

Best International Group U2

Best International Newcomer PM Dawn

Best Soundtrack *The Commitments*

1991

Best Female Lisa Stansfield

Best Male Elton John

Best Group The Cure

Best Album *Listen Without Prejudice Vol. I* – George Michael

Best Newcomer Betty Boo

Best Single 'Enjoy The Silence' – Depeche Mode

Best Video 'A Little Time' – The Beautiful South

Best International Group INXS

Best International Newcomer MC Hammer

Best Soundtrack *Twin Peaks*

1990

Best Female Annie Lennox

Best Male Phil Collins

Best Group Fine Young Cannibals

Best Album *The Raw & The Cooked* – Fine Young Cannibals

Best Newcomer Lisa Stansfield

Best Single 'Another Day In Paradise' – Phil Collins

Best Video 'Lullaby' – The Cure

Best International Group U2

Best International Newcomer Neneh Cherry

Best Soundtrack *Batman*

1989

Best Female Annie Lennox

Best Male Phil Collins

Best Group Erasure

Best Album *First Of A Million Kisses* – Fairground Attraction

Best Newcomer Bros

Best Dance Act – Fairground Attraction

Best Single 'Perfect' – Fairground Attraction

Best Video 'Smooth Criminal' – Michael Jackson

Best International Group U2

Best International Newcomer Tracy Chapman

Best Soundtrack *Buster*

1988

Best Female Alison Moyet

Best Male George Michael

Best Group Pet Shop Boys

Best Album *Nothing Like The Sun* – Sting

Best Newcomer Wet Wet Wet

Best Single 'Never Gonna Give You Up' – Rick Astley

Best Video *True Faith* – New Order

Best International Group U2

Best International Newcomer Terence Trent D'Arby

Best Soundtrack *Phantom Of The Opera*

1987

Best Female Kate Bush

Best Male Peter Gabriel

Best Group Five Star

Best Album *Brothers In Arms* – Dire Straits

Best Newcomer The Housemartins

Best Single 'West End Girls' – Pet Shop Boys

Best Video 'Sledgehammer' – Peter Gabriel

Best International Group The Bangles

Best Soundtrack *Top Gun*

1986

Best Female Annie Lennox

Best Male Phil Collins

Best Group Go West

Best Album *No Jacket Required* – Phil Collins

Best Newcomer Go West

Best Single 'Everybody Wants To Rule The World' – Tears For Fears

Best Video 'Every Time You Go Away' – Paul Young

Best International Group Huey Lewis & The News

1985

Best Female Alison Moyet

Best Male Paul Young

Best Group Wham!

Best Album *Diamond Life* – Sade

Best Newcomer Frankie Goes To Hollywood

Best Single 'Relax' – Frankie Goes To Hollywood

Best Video 'Wild Boys' – Duran Duran

Best Soundtrack *Purple Rain*

1984

Best Female Annie Lennox

Best Male David Bowie

Best Group Culture Club

Best Album *Thriller* – Michael Jackson

Best Newcomer Paul Young

Best Single 'Karma Chameleon' – Culture Club

1983

Best Female Kim Wilde

Best Male Paul McCartney

Best Group Dire Straits

Best Album *Love Songs* – Barbra Streisand

Best Newcomer Yazoo

Best Single 'Come On Eileen' – Dexy's Midnight Runners

1982

Best Female Randy Crawford

Best Male Cliff Richard

Best Group The Police

Best Album *King Of The Wild Frontier* – Adam & The Ants

Best Newcomer Human League

Best Single 'Tainted Love' – Soft Cell

1977

Best Female Shirley Bassey

Best Male Cliff Richard

Best Group The Beatles

Best Album *Bridge Over Troubled Water* – Simon & Garfunkel

Best Newcomer Julie Covington

Best Single 'Bohemian Rhapsody' – Queen

MTV EUROPE AWARDS

2000

Best Male Ricky Martin

Best Female Madonna

Best Group Backstreet Boys

Breakthrough Artist Blink 182

Best Dance Madonna

Best Hip Hop Eminem

Best Pop All Saints

Best R&B Jennifer Lopez

Best Rock Red Hot Chili Peppers

Best Song 'Rock DJ' – Robbie Williams

Best Album *Marshall Mathers LP* by Eminem

Best Dutch Kane

Best French Modjo

Best German Guano Apes

Best Italian Subsonic

Best Nordic Bomfunk MC's

Best Polish Kazik

Best Spanish Dover

Best UK & Ireland Westlife

1999

Best Male Will Smith

Best Female Britney Spears

Best Group Backstreet Boys

Breakthrough Artist Britney Spears

Best Dance Fatboy Slim

Best Hip Hop Eminem

Best Pop Britney Spears

Best R&B Whitney Houston

Best Rock The Offspring

Best Song 'Baby One More Time' – Britney Spears

Best Album *Boyzone: By Request* – Boyzone

Best Video Blur – 'Coffe and TV'

Best German Xavier Naidoo

Best Italian Elio E Le Storie Tese

Best Nordic Lene Marlin

Best UK & Ireland Boyzone

Free Your Mind Bono

1998

Best Male Robbie Williams

Best Female Madonna

Best Group Spice Girls

Breakthrough Artist All Saints

Best Dance Prodigy

Best Pop Spice Girls

Best Rap Beastie Boys

Best Rock Aerosmith

Best Song 'Torn' – Natalie Imbruglia

Best Album *Ray of Light* by Madonna

Best Video Massive Attack – 'Tear Drop'

Select Central Thomas D – Franka Potente

Select UK & Ireland Five

Select North Eagle Eye Cherry

Select Southern Bluvertigo

Free Your Mind B92 (independent Serbian Radio Station)

1997

Best Male Jon Bon Jovi

Best Female Janet Jackson

Best Group Spice Girls

Breakthrough Artist Hanson

Best Alternative Prodigy

Best Dance Prodigy

Best Live U2

Best R & B Blackstreet

Best Rap Will Smith

Best Rock Oasis

Best Song 'MMMBop' – Hanson

MTV Select Prodigy's 'Breathe'

Free Your Mind The Landmine's Survivors' Network

1996

Best Male George Michael

Best Female Alanis Morissette

Best Group Oasis

Breakthrough Artist Garbage

Best Dance Prodigy

Best Rock The Smashing Pumpkins

Best Song 'Wonderwall' – Oasis

MTV Amour 'Get Down' – Backstreet Boys

Free Your Mind The Buddies & Carers of Europe

1995

Best Male Michael Jackson

Best Female Björk

Best Group U2

Breakthrough Artist Dog Eat Dog

Best Live Act Take That

Best Rock Bon Jovi

Best Dance East 17

Best Song The Cranberries – 'Zombie'

Best Director Michel Gondry – Massive Attack's 'Protection'

Free Your Mind Greenpeace

1994

Best Male Bryan Adams

Best Female Mariah Carey

Best Group Take That

Breakthrough Artist Crash Test Dummies

Best Dance The Prodigy

Best Rock Aerosmith

Best Song '7 Seconds' – Youssou N'Dour and Nenah Cherry

Best Cover Gun – 'Word Up

Best Director Mark Pellington – Whale's 'Hobo Humpin' Slobo Babe'

Free Your Mind Amnesty International

MTV VIDEO

2000

Video of the Year 'The Real Slim Shady' – Eminem

Male Video 'The Real Slim Shady' – Eminem

Female Video 'Try Again' – Aaliyah

Group Video 'All The Small Things' – Blink 182

Dance Video 'Waiting For Tonight' – Jennifer Lopez

Rap Video 'Forgot About Dre' – Dr. Dre featuring Eminem

Rock Video 'Break Stuff' – Limp Bizkit

R&B Video 'Say My Name' – Destiny's Child

Hip Hop Video 'Thong Song' – Sisqo

Pop Video 'Bye Bye Bye' – N Sync

New Artist In A Video 'I Try' – Macy Gray

Viewers' Choice 'Bye Bye Bye' – N Sync

Video Vanguard Red Hot Chili Peppers

1999

Video of the Year 'Doo Wop (That Thing)' – Lauryn Hill

Male Video 'Miami' – Will Smith

Female Video 'Doo Wop (That Thing)' – Lauryn Hill

Group Video 'No Scrubs' – TLC

Dance Video 'Livin' La Vida Loca' – Ricky Martin

Rap Video 'Can I Get A . . . ' – Jay-Z

Rock Video 'Freak On A Leash' – Korn

R&B Video 'Doo Wop (That Thing)' – Lauryn Hill

1998

Video of the Year 'Ray Of Light' – Madonna

Male Video 'Just The Two Of Us' – Will Smith

Female Video 'Ray Of Light' – Madonna

Group Video 'Everybody (Backstreet's Back)' – Backstreet Boys

Rap Video 'Gettin' Jiggy Wit It' – Will Smith

Alternative 'Time Of Your Life (Good Riddance)' – Green Day

Rock Video 'Pink' – Aerosmith

R&B Video 'The Boy Is Mine' – Brandy & Monica

1997

Video of the Year 'Virtual Insanity' – Jamiroquai

Male Video 'Devil's Haircut' – Beck

Female Video 'You Were Meant For Me' – Jewel

Group Video 'Don't Speak' – No Doubt

Rap Video 'Hypnotize' – The Notorious B.I.G.

Alternative Video 'What I Got' – Sublime

Hard Rock Video 'Falling in Love (Is Hard on the Knees)' – Aerosmith

R&B Video 'I'll Be Missing You' – Puff Daddy

1996

Video of the Year 'Tonight Tonight' – Smashing Pumpkins

Male Video 'Where It's At' – Beck

Female Video 'Ironic' – Alanis Morissette

Group Video 'Big Me' – Foo Fighters

Rap Video 'Gangsta's Paradise' – Coolio

Alternative Video '1979' – Smashing Pumpkins

Hard Rock Video 'Until It Sleeps' – Metallica

R&B Video 'Killing Me Softly With His Song' – Fugees

1995

Video of the Year 'Waterfalls' – TLC

Male Video 'You Don't Know How It Feels' – Tom Petty

Female Video 'Take A Bow' – Madonna

Group Video 'Waterfalls' – TLC

Rap Video 'Keep Their Heads Ringin' – Dr. Dre

Alternative Video 'Buddy Holly' – Weezer

Hard Rock Video 'More Human Than Human' – White Zombie

R&B Video 'Waterfalls' – TLC

Video Vanguard R.E.M.

1994

Video of the Year 'Cryin' ' – Aerosmith

Male Video 'Mary Jane's Last Dance' – Tom Petty

Female Video 'If' – Janet Jackson

Group Video 'Cryin' ' – Aerosmith

Rap Video 'Doggy Dogg World' – Snoop Doggy Dogg

Alternative Video 'Heart-Shaped Box' – Nirvana

Metal/ Hard Rock Video 'Black Hole Sun' – Soundgarden

R&B Video 'Whatta Man' – Salt-n-Pepa with En Vogue

Video Vanguard Tom Petty

1993

Video of the Year 'Jeremy' – Pearl Jam

Male Video 'Are You Gonna Go My Way' – Lenny Kravitz

Female Video 'Constant Craving' – k.d. lang

Group Video 'Jeremy' – Pearl Jam

Rap Video 'People Everyday' – Arrested Development

Alternative Video 'Jeremy' – Pearl Jam

R&B Video 'Free Your Mind' – En Vogue

1992

Video of the Year 'Right Now' – Van Halen

Male Video 'Tears In Heaven' – Eric Clapton

Female Video 'Why' – Annie Lennox

Group Video 'Even Better Than The Real Thing' – U2

Rap Video 'Tennessee' – Arrested Development

Metal / Hard Rock Video 'Enter Sandman' – Metallica

Alternative Video 'Smells Like Teen Spirit' – Nirvana

Video Vanguard Guns N' Roses

1991

Video of the Year 'Losing My Religion' – R.E.M.

Male Video 'Wicked Game' – Chris Isaak

Female Video 'Love Will Never Do (Without You)' – Janet Jackson

Group Video 'Losing My Religion' – R.E.M.

Rap Video 'Mama Said Knock You Out' – LL Cool J

Metal/ Hard Rock Video 'The Other Side' – Aerosmith

Alternative Video 'Been Caught Stealing' – Jane's Addiction

Video Vanguard Bon Jovi

1990

Video of the Year 'Nothing Compares 2 U' – Sinead O'Connor

Male Video 'The End Of The Innocence' – Don Henley

Female Video 'I Do Not Want What I Haven't Got' – Sinead O'Connor

Group Video 'Love Shack' – B-52s

Rap Video 'U Can't Touch This' – M.C. Hammer

Metal/ Hard Rock Video 'Water Song' / 'Janie's Got A Gun' – Aerosmith

Video Vanguard Janet Jackson

1989

Video of the Year 'This Note's For You' – Neil Young

Male Video 'Veronica' – Elvis Costello

Female Video 'Straight Up' – Paula Abdul

Group Video 'Cult Of Personality' – Living Colour

Rap Video 'Parents Just Don't Understand' – DJ Jazzy Jeff and The Fresh Prince

Heavy Metal Video 'Sweet Child O' Mine' – Guns N' Roses

Video Vanguard George Michael

1988

Video of the Year 'Need You Tonight' – INXS

Male Video 'U Got The Look' – Prince

Female Video 'Lu.k.a' – Suzanne Vega

Group Video 'Need You Tonight' – INXS

Video Vanguard Michael Jackson

1987

Video of the Year 'Sledgehammer' – Peter Gabriel

Male Video 'Sledgehammer' – Peter Gabriel

Female Video 'Papa Don't Preach' – Madonna

Group Video 'Wild Wild Life' – Talking Heads

Video Vanguard Peter Gabriel, Julien Temple

1986

Video of the Year 'Money For Nothing' – Dire Straits

Male Video 'Addicted To Love' – Robert Palmer

Female Video 'How Will I Know' – Whitney Houston

Group Video 'Money For Nothing' – Dire Straits

Video Vanguard Madonna, Zbigniew Rybeznski

1985

Video of the Year 'Boys Of Summer' – Don Henley

Male Video 'I'm On Fire' – Bruce Springsteen

Female Video 'What's Love Got To Do With It' – Tina Turner

Group Video 'We Are The World' – USA For Africa

Video Vanguard David Byrne, Kevin Godley and Lol Creme, Russell
Mulcahy

1984

Video of the Year 'You Might Think' – The Cars

Male Video China Girl – David Bowie

Female Video 'Girls Just Want To Have Fun' – Cyndi Lauper

Group Video 'Legs' – ZZ Top

Video Vanguard The Beatles, David Bowie, Richard Lester

ACADEMY AWARDS

Best Song

This award was not introduced until the 22nd Oscars

2000 'Things Have Changed' from *Wonder Boys* – Bob Dylan
1999 'You'll Be In My Heart' from *Tarzan* – Phil Collins
1998 'When You Believe' from *The Prince of Egypt* – Stephen Schwartz
1997 'My Heart Will Go On' from *Titanic* – James Horner, Will Jennings
1996 'You Must Love Me' from *Evita* – Andrew Lloyd Webber, Tim Rice
1995 'Colors of the Wind' from *Pocahontas* – Alan Menken, Stephen Schwartz
1994 'Can You Feel The Love Tonight' from *The Lion King* – Elton John, Tim Rice
1993 'Streets of Philadelphia' from *Philadelphia* – Bruce Springsteen
1992 'A Whole New World' from *Aladdin* – Alan Menken, Tim Rice
1991 'Beauty and the Beast' from *Beauty and the Beast* – Howard Ashman, Alan Menken
1990 'Sooner or Later (I Always Get My Man)' from *Dick Tracy* – Stephen Sondheim
1989 'Under the Sea' from *The Little Mermaid* – Howard Ashman, Alan Menken
1988 'Let the River Run' from *Working Girl* – Carly Simon
1987 '(I've Had) The Time of My Life' from *Dirty Dancing* – John DeNicola, Donald Markowitz, Franke Previte
1986 'Take My Breath Away' from *Top Gun* – Giorgio Moroder, Tom Whitlock
1985 'Say You, Say Me' from *White Nights* – Lionel Richie
1984 'I Just Called To Say I Love You' from *The Woman in Red* – Stevie Wonder
1983 'Flashdance . . . What a Feeling' from *Flashdance* – Irene Cara, Keith Forsey, Giorgio Moroder
1982 'Up Where We Belong' from *An Officer and a Gentleman* – Will Jennings, Jack Nitzsche, Buffy Sainte-Marie
1981 'Arthur's Theme (Best That You Can Do)' from *Arthur* – Peter Allen, Burt Bacharach, Christopher Cross, Carole Bayer Sager
1980 'Fame' from *Fame* – Michael Gore, Dean Pitchford
1979 'It Goes Like It Goes' from *Norma Rae* – Norman Gimbel, David Shire

1978 'Last Dance' from *Thank God It's Friday* – Paul Jabara

1977 'You Light Up My Life' from *You Light Up My Life* – Joseph Brooks

1976 'Evergreen (Love Theme from a Star Is Born)' from *A Star Is Born* – Barbra Streisand, Paul Williams

1975 'I'm Easy' from *Nashville* – Keith Carradine

1974 'We May Never Love Like This Again' from *The Towering Inferno* – Joel Hirschhorn, Al Kasha

1973 'The Way We Were' from *The Way We Were* – Alan Bergman, Marilyn Bergman, Marvin Hamlisch

1972 'The Morning After' from *The Poseidon Adventure* – Joel Hirschhorn, Al Kasha

1971 'Theme From Shaft' from *Shaft* – Isaac Hayes

1970 'For All We Know' from *Lovers and Other Strangers* – James Griffin, Fred Karlin, Robb Royer

1969 'Raindrops Keep Fallin' On My Head' from *Butch Cassidy and the Sundance Kid* – Burt Bacharach, Hal David

1968 'The Windmills of Your Mind' from *The Thomas Crown Affair* – Alan Bergman, Marilyn Bergman, Michel Legrand

1967 'Talk to the Animals' from *Doctor Dolittle* – Leslie Bricusse

1966 'Born Free' from *Born Free* – John Barry, Don Black

1965 'The Shadow of Your Smile' from *The Sandpiper* – Johnny Mandel, Paul Francis Webster

1964 'Chim Chim Cher-Ee' from *Mary Poppins* – Richard M Sherman, Robert B Sherman

1963 'Call Me Irresponsible' from *Papa's Delicate Condition* – Sammy Cahn, James Van Heusen

1962 'Days of Wine and Roses' from *Days of Wine and Roses* – Henry Mancini, Johnny Mercer

1961 'Moon River' from *Breakfast at Tiffany's* – Henry Mancini, Johnny Mercer

1960 'Never On Sunday' from *Never On Sunday* – Manos Hadjidakis

1959 'High Hopes' from *A Hole in the Head* – Sammy Cahn, James Van Heusen

1958 'Gigi' from *Gigi* – Alan Jay Lerner, Frederick Loewe

1957 All The Way' from *The Joker Is Wild* – Sammy Cahn, James Van Heusen

1956 'Whatever Will Be, Will Be (Que Sera, Sera)' from *The Man Who Knew Too Much* – Ray Evans, Jay Livingston

1955 'Love Is A Many-Splendored Thing' from *Love Is A Many-Splendored Thing* – Sammy Fain, Paul Francis Webster

1954 'Three Coins In The Fountain' from *Three Coins In The Fountain* – Sammy Cahn, Jule Styne

1953 'Secret Love' from *Calamity Jane* – Sammy Fain, Paul Francis Webster

1952 'High Noon (Do Not Forsake Me, Oh My Darlin')' from *High Noon* – Dimitri Tiomkin, Ned Washington

1951 'In The Cool, Cool, Cool Of The Evening' from *Here Comes The Groom* – Hoagy Carmichael, Johnny Mercer

1950 'Mona Lisa' from *Captain Carey, U.S.A.* – Ray Evans, Jay Livingston

1949 'Baby, It's Cold Outside' from *Neptune's Daughter* – Frank Loesser

GOLDEN GLOBE AWARDS

'Best Song'

This award began in 1961.

2000 'Things Have Changed' from *Wonder Boys* – Bob Dylan

1999 'You'll Be In My Heart' from *Tarzan* – Phil Collins

1998 'The Prayer' from *Quest for Camelot* – David Foster, Carole Bayer Sager, Alberto Testa (Italian translation), Tony Renis (Italian translation)

1997 'My Heart Will Go On' from *Titanic* – James Horner, Will Jennings

1996 'You Must Love Me' from *Evita* – Andrew Lloyd Webber, Tim Rice

1995 'Colors of the Wind' from *Pocahontas* – Alan Menken, Stephen Schwartz

1994 'Can You Feel the Love Tonight' from *The Lion King* – Elton John, Tim Rice

1993 'Streets of Philadelphia' from *Philadelphia* – Bruce Springsteen

1992 'A Whole New World' from *Aladdin* – Alan Menken, Tim Rice

1991 'Beauty and the Beast' from *Beauty and the Beast* – Alan Menken, Howard Ashman

1990 'Blaze of Glory' from *Young Guns II* – Jon Bon Jovi

1989 'Under the Sea' from *The Little Mermaid* – Alan Menken, Howard Ashman

1988 'Two Hearts' from *Buster* – Lamont Dozier, Phil Collins; together with 'Let the River Run' from *Working Girl* – Carly Simon

1987 '(I've Had) The Time of My Life' from *Dirty Dancing* – Frank Previte, John De Nicola, Donald Markowitz

1986 'Take My Breath Away' from *Top Gun* – Giorgio Moroder, Tom Whitlock

1985 'Say You, Say Me' from *White Nights* – Lionel Richie

1984 'I Just Called to Say I Love You' from *Woman in Red* – Stevie Wonder

1983 'Flashdance . . . What a Feeling' from *Flashdance* – Giorgio Moroder, Keith Forsey, Irene Cara

1982 'Up Where We Belong' from *An Officer and a Gentleman* – Jack Nitzsche, Buffy Sainte-Marie, Will Jennings

1981 'Arthur's Theme (Best That You Can Do)' from *Arthur* – Burt Bacharach, Carole Bayer Sager, Christopher Cross, Peter Allen

1980 'Fame' from *Fame* – Michael Gore, Dean Pitchford

1979 'The Rose' from *The Rose* – Amanda McBroom

1978 'Last Dance' from *Thank God It's Friday* – Paul Jabara

1977 'You Light Up My Life' from *You Light Up My Life* – Joseph Brooks

1976 'Evergreen (Love Theme from A Star is Born)' from *A Star is Born* – Paul Williams, Barbra Streisand

1975 'I'm Easy' from *Nashville* – Keith Carradine

1974 'Benji's Theme (I Feel Love)' from *Benji* – Euel Box, Betty Box

1973 'The Way We Were' from *The Way We Were* – Marvin Hamlisch, Alan Bergman, Marilyn Bergman

1972 'Ben' from *Ben* – Walter Scharf, Don Black

1971 'Life Is What You Make It' from *Kotch* – Marvin Hamlisch, Johnny Mercer

1970 'Whistling Away the Dark' from *Darling Lili* – Henry Mancini, Johnny Mercer

1969 'Jean' from *The Prime of Miss Jean Brodie* – Rod McKuen

1968 'The Windmills of Your Mind' from *The Thomas Crown Affair* – Michel Legrand, Alan Bergman, Marilyn Bergman

1967 'If Ever I Should Leave You' from *Camelot* – Frederick Loewe

1966 'Strangers In the Night' from *A Man Could Get Killed* – Bert Kaempfert, Charles Singleton, Eddie Snyder

1965 'Forget Domani' from *The Yellow Rolls-Royce* – Riz Ortolani, Norman Newell

1964 'Circus World' from *Circus World* – Dimitri Tiomkin, Ned Washington

1963 No Award.

1962 No Award.

1961 'Town Without Pity' from *Town Without Pity* – Dimitri Tiomkin, Ned Washington

GRAMMYS – GENERAL

2000

Record of the Year 'Beautiful Day' – U2

Album of the Year *Two Against Nature* – Steely Dan

Song of The Year 'Beautiful Day' – U2

Best New Artist Shelby Lynne

1999

Record of the Year 'Smooth' – Santana

Album of the Year *Supernatural* – Santana

Song of The Year 'Smooth' – Itaal Shur and Rob Thomas

Best New Artist Christina Aguilera

1998

Record of the Year 'My Heart Will Go On' – Celine Dion

Album of the Year *The Miseducation Of Lauryn Hill* – Lauryn Hill

Song of The Year 'My Heart Will Go On' – James Horner and Will Jennings

Best New Artist Lauryn Hill

1997

Record of the Year 'Sunny Came Home' – Shawn Colvin

Album of the Year *Time Out of Mind* – Bob Dylan

Song of The Year 'Sunny Came Home' – Shawn Colvin

Best New Artist Paula Cole

1996

Record of the Year 'Change the World' – Eric Clapton

Album of the Year *Falling Into You* – Celine Dion

Song of The Year 'Change the World' – Gordon Kennedy, Wayne Kirkpatrick and Tommy Sims

Best New Artist LeAnn Rimes

1995

Record of the Year 'Kiss From a Rose' – Seal

Album of the Year *Jagged Little Pill* – Alanis Morissette

Song of The Year 'Kiss From a Rose' – Seal

Best New Artist Hootie & the Blowfish

1994

Record of the Year 'All I Wanna Do' – Sheryl Crow

Album of the Year *MTV Unplugged* – Tony Bennett

Song of The Year 'Streets of Philadelphia' – Bruce Springsteen

Best New Artist Sheryl Crow

1993

Record of the Year 'I Will Always Love You' – Whitney Houston

Album of the Year *The Bodyguard* – Whitney Houston

Song of The Year 'A Whole New World (Theme From Aladdin)' – Alan Menken and Tim Rice

Best New Artist Toni Braxton

1992

Record of the Year 'Tears in Heaven' – Eric Clapton

Album of the Year *Unplugged* – Eric Clapton

Song of The Year 'Tears in Heaven' – Eric Clapton

Best New Artist Arrested Development

1991

Record of the Year 'Unforgettable' – Natalie Cole with Nat King Cole

Album of the Year *Unforgettable* – Natalie Cole with Nat King Cole

Song of The Year 'Unforgettable' – Irving Gordon

Best New Artist Marc Cohn

1990

Record of the Year 'Another Day in Paradise' – Phil Collins

Album of the Year *Back on the Block* – Quincy Jones

Song of The Year 'From a Distance' – Julie Gold

Best New Artist Mariah Carey

1989

Record of the Year 'Wind Beneath My Wings' – Bette Midler

Album of the Year *Nick of Time* – Bonnie Raitt

Song of The Year 'Wind Beneath My Wings' – Larry Henley and Jeff Silbar

No New Artist award this year

1988

Record of the Year 'Don't Worry Be Happy' – Bobby McFerrin

Album of the Year *Faith* – George Michael

Song of The Year 'Don't Worry Be Happy' – Bobby McFerrin

Best New Artist Tracy Chapman

1987

Record of the Year 'Graceland' – Paul Simon

Album of the Year *Joshua Tree* – U2

Song Of The Year 'Somewhere Out There' – James Horner, Barry Mann and Cynthia Weil

Best New Artist Jody Watley

1986

Record of the Year 'Higher Love' – Steve Winwood

Album of the Year *Graceland* – Paul Simon

Song of The Year 'That's What Friends Are For' – Burt Bacharach and Carole Bayer Sager

Best New Artist Bruce Hornsby and the Range

1985

Record of the Year 'We Are the World' – USA for Africa

Album of the Year *No Jacket Required* – Phil Collins

Song of The Year 'We Are the World' – Michael Jackson and Lionel Richie

Best New Artist Sade

1984

Record of the Year 'What's Love Got to Do With It' – Tina Turner

Album of the Year *Can't Slow Down* – Lionel Richie

Song of The Year 'What's Love Got to Do With It' – Graham Lyle and Terry Britten

Best New Artist Cyndi Lauper

1983

Record of the Year 'Beat It' – Michael Jackson

Album of the Year *Thriller* – Michael Jackson

Song of The Year 'Every Breath You Take' – Sting

Best New Artist Culture Club

1982

Record of the Year 'Rosanna' – Toto

Album of the Year *Toto IV* – Toto

Song of The Year 'Always on My Mind' – Johnny Christopher, Mark James and Wayne Carson

Best New Artist Men at Work

1981

Record of the Year 'Bette Davis Eyes' – Kim Carnes

Album of the Year *Double Fantasy* – John Lennon and Yoko Ono

Song of The Year 'Bette Davis Eyes' – Donna Weiss and Jackie DeShannon

Best New Artist Sheena Easton

1980

Record of the Year 'Sailing' – Christopher Cross

Album of the Year *Christopher Cross* – Christopher Cross

Song of The Year 'Sailing' – Christopher Cross

Best New Artist Christopher Cross

1979

Record of the Year 'What a Fool Believes' – Doobie Brothers

Album of the Year *52nd Street* – Billy Joel

Song of The Year 'What a Fool Believes' – Doobie Brothers

Best New Artist Rickie Lee Jones

1978

Record of the Year 'Just the Way You Are' – Billy Joel

Album of the Year *Saturday Night Fever* – The Bee Gees

Song of The Year 'Just the Way You Are' – Billy Joel

Best New Artist A Taste of Honey

1977

Record of the Year 'Hotel California' – Eagles

Album of the Year *Rumours* – Fleetwood Mac

Song of The Year (tie) 'Love Theme From A Star Is Born' – Barbra Streisand and Paul Williams,

Song of The Year (tie) 'You Light Up My Life' – Joe Brooks

Best New Artist Debby Boone

1976

Record of the Year 'This Masquerade' – George Benson

Album of the Year *Songs in the Key of Life* – Stevie Wonder

Song of The Year 'I Write the Songs' – Bruce Johnston

Best New Artist Starland Vocal Band

1975

Record of the Year 'Love Will Keep Us Together' – The Captain & Tennille

Album of the Year *Still Crazy After All These Years* – Paul Simon

Song of The Year 'Send in the Clowns' – Stephen Sondheim

Best New Artist Natalie Cole

1974

Record of the Year 'I Honestly Love You' – Olivia Newton-John

Album of the Year *Fulfillingness' First Finale* – Stevie Wonder

Song of The Year 'The Way We Were' – Marilyn and Alan Bergman and Marvin Hamlisch

Best New Artist Marvin Hamlisch

1973

Record of the Year 'Killing Me Softly With His Song' – Roberta Flack

Album of the Year *Innervisions* – Stevie Wonder

Song of The Year 'Killing Me Softly With His Song' – Norman Gimbel and Charles Fox

Best New Artist Bette Midler

1972

Record of the Year 'The First Time Ever I Saw Your Face' – Roberta Flack

Album of the Year *The Concert for Bangla Desh* – George Harrison and Friends

Song of The Year 'The First Time Ever I Saw Your Face' – Ewan MacColl

Best New Artist America

1971

Record of the Year 'It's Too Late' – Carole King

Album of the Year *Tapestry* – Carole King

Song of The Year 'You've Got a Friend' – Carole King

Best New Artist Carly Simon

1970

Record of the Year 'Bridge Over Troubled Water' – Simon & Garfunkel

Album of the Year *Bridge Over Troubled Water* – Simon & Garfunkel

Song of The Year 'Bridge Over Troubled Water' – Paul Simon

Best New Artist The Carpenters

1969

Record of the Year 'Aquarius/Let the Sunshine In' – The Fifth Dimension

Album of the Year *Blood, Sweat & Tears* – Blood, Sweat & Tears

Song of The Year 'Games People Play' – Joe South

Best New Artist Crosby, Stills and Nash

1968

Record of the Year 'Mrs. Robinson' – Simon & Garfunkel

Album of the Year *By the Time I Get to Phoenix* – Glen Campbell

Song of The Year 'Little Green Apples' – Bobby Russell

Best New Artist José Feliciano

1967

Record of the Year 'Up, Up and Away' – The Fifth Dimension

Album of the Year *Sgt. Pepper's Lonely Hearts Club Band* – The Beatles

Song of The Year 'Up, Up and Away' – Jimmy L. Webb

Best New Artist Bobbie Gentry

1966

Record of the Year 'Strangers in the Night' – Frank Sinatra

Album of the Year *Sinatra – A Man and His Music* – Frank Sinatra

Song of The Year 'Michelle' – John Lennon and Paul McCartney

No Best New Artist this year

1965

Record of the Year 'A Taste of Honey' – Herb Alpert & Tijuana Brass

Album of the Year *September of My Years* – Frank Sinatra

Song of The Year 'The Shadow of Your Smile' (Love Theme From The Sandpiper) – Paul Francis Webster & Johnny Mandel

Best New Artist Tom Jones

1964

Record of the Year 'The Girl From Ipanema' – Stan Getz and Astrud Gilberto

Album of the Year *Getz/Gilberto* – Stan Getz and Joao Gilberto

Song of The Year 'Hello, Dolly!' – Jerry Herman

Best New Artist The Beatles

1963

Record of the Year 'The Days of Wine and Roses' – Henry Mancini

Album of the Year *The Barbra Streisand Album* – Barbra Streisand

Song of The Year 'The Days of Wine and Roses' – Henry Mancini and Johnny Mercer

Best New Artist Swingle Singers

1962

Record of the Year 'I Left My Heart in San Francisco' – Tony Bennett

Album of the Year *The First Family* – Vaughn Meader

Song of The Year 'What Kind of Fool Am I' – Leslie Bricusse and Anthony Newley

Best New Artist Robert Goulet

1961

Record of the Year 'Moon River' – Henry Mancini

Album of the Year *Judy at Carnegie Hall* – Judy Garland

Song of The Year 'Moon River' – Henry Mancini

Best New Artist Peter Nero

1960

Record of the Year 'Theme From A Summer Place' – Percy Faith

Album of the Year *The Button Down Mind of Bob Newhart* – Bob Newhart

Song of The Year 'Theme From Exodus' – Ernest Gold

Best New Artist Bob Newhart

1959

Record of the Year 'Mack the Knife' – Bobby Darin

Album of the Year *Come Dance With Me* – Frank Sinatra

Song of The Year 'The Battle of New Orleans' – Jimmy Driftwood

Best New Artist Bobby Darin

1958

Record of the Year 'Nel Blu Dipinto di Blu (Volare)' – Domenico Modugno

Album of the Year *The Music From Peter Gunn* – Henry Mancini

Song of The Year 'Nel Blu Dipinto di Blu (Volare)' – Domenico Modugno

No Best New Artist award this year

GRAMMYS – ROCK & POP

2000

Best Rock Song 'With Arms Wide Open' – Creed

Best Rock Album *There Is Nothing Left To Lose* – Foo Fighters

Best Pop Album *Two Against Nature* – Steely Dan

Best Male Rock Vocal Performance 'Again' – Lenny Kravitz

Best Female Rock Vocal Performance 'There Goes The Neighborhood' – Sheryl Crow

Best Male Pop Vocal Performance 'She Walks This Earth' (Soberana Rose) – Sting

Best Female Pop Vocal Performance 'I Try' – Macy Gray

Best Rock Performance by a Duo or Group 'Beautiful Day' – U2

Best Pop Performance by a Duo or Group 'Cousin Dupree' – Steely Dan

Best Alternative Music Performance 'Kid A' – Radiohead

Best Hard Rock Performance 'Guerilla Radio' – Rage Against The Machine

Best Metal Performance 'Elite' – Deftones

Best Pop Collaboration Performance With Vocals 'Is You Is, Or Is You Ain't (My Baby)?' – B.B. King & Dr John

Best Rock Instrumental Performance 'The Call Of The Ktulu' – Metallica with San Francisco Symphony Orchestra

Best Pop Instrumental Performance 'Caravan' – The Brian Setzer Orchestra

1999

Best Rock Song 'Scar Tissue' – Red Hot Chili Peppers

Best Rock Album *Supernatural* – Santana

Best Pop Album *Brand New Day* – Sting

Best Male Rock Vocal Performance 'American Woman' – Lenny Kravitz

Best Female Rock Vocal Performance 'Sweet Child O' Mine' – Sheryl Crow

Best Male Pop Vocal Performance 'Brand New Day' – Sting

Best Female Pop Vocal Performance 'I Will Remember You' – Sarah McLachlan

Best Rock Performance by a Duo or Group 'Put Your Lights On' – Santana feat. Everlast

Best Pop Performance by a Duo or Group 'Maria Maria' – Santana feat. The Product G&B

Best Alternative Music Performance 'Mutations' – Beck

Best Hard Rock Performance 'Whiskey In The Jar' – Metallica

Best Metal Performance 'Iron Man' – Black Sabbath

Best Pop Collaboration Performance With Vocals 'Smooth' – Santana feat. Rob Thomas

Best Rock Instrumental Performance 'The Calling' – Santana feat. Eric Clapton

Best Pop Instrumental Performance 'El Farol' – Santana

1998

Best Rock Song 'Uninvited' – Alanis Morissette

Best Rock Album *The Globe Sessions* – Sheryl Crow

Best Pop Album *Ray of Light* – Madonna

Best Male Rock Vocal Performance 'Fly Away' – Lenny Kravitz

Best Female Rock Vocal Performance 'Uninvited' – Alanis Morissette

Best Male Pop Vocal Performance 'My Father's Eyes' – Eric Clapton

Best Female Pop Vocal Performance 'My Heart Will Go On' – Celine Dion

Best Rock Performance by a Duo or Group 'Pink' – Aerosmith

Best Pop Performance by a Duo or Group 'Jump Jive An' Wail' – Brian Setzer Orchestra

Best Alternative Music Performance 'Hello Nasty' – Beastie Boys

Best Hard Rock Performance 'Most High' – Jimmy Page & Robert Plant

Best Metal Performance 'Better Than You' – Metallica

Best Pop Collaboration Performance With Vocals 'I Still Have That Other Girl' – Elvis Costello & Burt Bacharach

Best Rock Instrumental Performance 'The Roots of Coincidence' – Pat Metheny

Best Pop Instrumental Performance 'Sleepwalk' – Brian Setzer Orchestra

1997

Best Rock Song 'One Headlight' – The Wallflowers

Best Rock Album *Blue Moon Swamp* – John Fogerty

Best Pop Album *Hourglass* – James Taylor

Best Male Rock Vocal Performance 'Cold Irons Bound' – Bob Dylan

Best Female Rock Vocal Performance 'Criminal' – Fiona Apple

Best Male Pop Vocal Performance 'Candle In The Wind 1997' – Elton John

Best Female Pop Vocal Performance 'Building a Mystery' – Sarah McLachlan

Best Rock Performance by a Duo or Group 'One Headlight' – The Wallflowers

Best Pop Performance by a Duo or Group 'Virtual Insanity' – Jamiroquai

Best Alternative Music Performance 'OK Computer' – Radiohead

Best Hard Rock Performance 'The End is the Beginning is the End' – Smashing Pumpkins

Best Metal Performance 'Aenema' – Tool

Best Pop Collaboration Performance With Vocals 'Don't Look Back' – John Lee Hooker & Van Morrison

Best Rock Instrumental Performance 'Block Rockin' Beats' – The Chemical Brothers

Best Pop Instrumental Performance 'Last Dance' – Sarah McLachlan

1996

Best Rock Song 'Give Me One Reason' – Tracy Chapman

Best Rock Album *Sheryl Crow* – Sheryl Crow

Best Pop Album *Falling Into You* – Celine Dion

Best Male Rock Vocal Performance 'Where It's At' – Beck

Best Female Rock Vocal Performance 'If It Makes You Happy' – Sheryl Crow

Best Male Pop Vocal Performance 'Change the World' – Eric Clapton

Best Female Pop Vocal Performance 'Un-Break My Heart' – Toni Braxton

Best Rock Performance by a Duo or Group 'So Much To Say' – Dave Matthews Band

Best Pop Performance by a Duo or Group 'Free as a Bird' – Beatles

Best Alternative Music Performance ''Odelay' – Beck

Best Hard Rock Performance 'Bullet With Butterfly Wings' – Smashing Pumpkins

Best Metal Performance 'Tire Me' – Rage Against the Machine

Best Pop Collaboration Performance With Vocals 'When I Fall in Love' – Natalie Cole & Nat King Cole

Best Rock Instrumental Performance 'SRV Shuffle' – Jimmie Vaughan & Eric Clapton

Best Pop Instrumental Performance 'The Sinister Minister' – Bela Fleck & the Flecktones

1995

Best Rock Song 'You Oughta Know' – Alanis Morissette

Best Rock Album *Jagged Little Pill* – Alanis Morissette

Best Pop Album *Turbulent Indigo* – Joni Mitchell

Best Male Rock Vocal Performance 'You Don't Know How It Feels' – Tom Petty

Best Female Rock Vocal Performance 'You Oughta Know' – Alanis Morissette

Best Male Pop Vocal Performance 'Kiss From a Rose' – Seal

Best Female Pop Vocal Performance 'No More I Love You's' – Annie Lennox

Best Rock Performance by a Duo or Group 'Run-around' – Blues Traveler

Best Pop Performance by a Duo or Group 'Let Her Cry' – Hootie & the Blowfish

Best Alternative Music Performance 'MTV Unplugged in New York' – Nirvana

Best Hard Rock Performance 'Spin The Black Circle' – Pearl Jam

Best Metal Performance 'Happiness In Slavery' – Nine Inch Nails

Best Pop Collaboration Performance With Vocals 'Have I Told You Lately That I Love You' – The Chieftans w/ Van Morrison

Best Rock Instrumental Performance 'Jessica' – The Allman Brothers Band

Best Pop Instrumental Performance 'Mariachi Suite' – Los Lobos

1994

Best Rock Song 'Streets of Philadelphia' – Bruce Springsteen

Best Rock Album *Voodoo Lounge* – The Rolling Stones

Best Pop Album *Longing In Their Hearts* – Bonnie Raitt

Best Male Rock Vocal Performance 'Streets of Philadelphia' – Bruce Springsteen

Best Female Rock Vocal Performance 'Come To My Window' – Melissa Etheridge

Best Male Pop Vocal Performance 'Can You Feel the Love Tonight' – Elton John

Best Female Pop Vocal Performance 'All I Wanna Do' – Sheryl Crow

Best Rock Performance by a Duo or Group 'Crazy' – Aerosmith

Best Pop Performance by a Duo or Group 'I Swear' – All-4-One

Best Alternative Music Performance 'Dookie' – Green Day

Best Hard Rock Performance 'Black Hole Sun' – Soundgarden

Best Metal Performance 'Spoonman' – Soundgarden

Best Pop Collaboration Performance With Vocals 'Funny How Time Slips Away' – Al Green & Lyle Lovett

Best Rock Instrumental Performance 'Marooned' – Pink Floyd

Best Pop Instrumental Performance 'Cruisin'' – Booker T. & the MGs

1993

Best Rock Song 'Runaway Train' – Soul Asylum

Best Rock Vocal Performance Solo 'I'd Do Anything For Love (But I Won't Do That)' – Meat Loaf

Best Male Pop Vocal Performance 'If I Ever Lose My Faith In You' – Sting

Best Female Pop Vocal Performance 'I Will Always Love You' – Whitney Houston

Best Rock Performance by a Duo or Group 'Livin' On The Edge' – Aerosmith

Best Pop Performance by a Duo or Group 'A Whole New World (Aladdin's Theme)' – Peabo Bryson & Regina Belle

Best Alternative Music Performance 'Zooropa' – U2

Best Hard Rock Performance 'Plush' – Stone Temple Pilots

Best Metal Performance 'I Don't Want to Change the World' – Ozzy Osbourne

Best Rock Instrumental Performance 'Sofa' – Steve Vai

Best Pop Instrumental Performance 'Barcelona Mona (from the 1992 Summer Olympics)' – Bruce Hornsby & Branford Marsalis

1992

Best Rock Song 'Layla' – Eric Clapton

Best Male Rock Vocal Performance 'Unplugged' – Eric Clapton

Best Female Rock Vocal Performance 'Ain't It Heavy?' – Melissa Etheridge

Best Male Pop Vocal Performance 'Tears in Heaven' – Eric Clapton

Best Female Pop Vocal Performance 'Constant Craving' – k.d. lang

Best Rock Performance by a Duo or Group 'Achtung Baby' – U2

Best Pop Performance by a Duo or Group 'Beauty and the Beast' – Celine Dion & Peabo Bryson

Best Alternative Music Performance 'Bone Machine' – Tom Waits

Best Hard Rock Performance 'Give It Away' – Red Hot Chili Peppers

Best Metal Performance 'Wish' – Nine Inch Nails

Best Rock Instrumental Performance 'Little Wing' – Stevie Ray Vaughan & Double Trouble

Best Pop Instrumental Performance 'Beauty and the Beast' – Richard Kaufman

1991

Best Rock Song 'Soul Cages' – Sting

Best Rock Vocal Performance, Solo 'Luck of the Draw' – Bonnie Raitt

Best Male Pop Vocal Performance 'When a Man Loves a Woman' – Michael Bolton

Best Female Pop Vocal Performance 'Something to Talk About' – Bonnie Raitt

Best Rock Performance by a Duo or Group "Good Man Good Woman' – Bonnie Raitt & Delbert McClinton

Best Pop Performance by a Duo or Group 'Losing My Religion' – R.E.M.

Best Alternative Music Performance 'Out Of Time' – R.E.M.

Best Hard Rock Performance 'For Unlawful Carnal Knowledge' – Van Halen

Best Metal Performance 'Metallica' – Metallica

Best Rock Instrumental Performance 'Cliffs of Dover' – Eric Johnson

Best Pop Instrumental Performance 'Robin Hood: Prince of Thieves' – Michael Kamen

1990

Best Male Rock Vocal Performance 'Bad Love' – Eric Clapton

Best Female Rock Vocal Performance 'Black Velvet' – Alannah Myles

Best Male Pop Vocal Performance 'Pretty Woman' – Roy Orbison

Best Female Pop Vocal Performance 'Vision of Love' – Mariah Carey

Best Rock Performance by a Duo or Group 'Janie's Got a Gun' – Aerosmith

Best Pop Performance by a Duo or Group 'All My Life' – Linda Ronstadt & Aaron Neville

Best Alternative Music Performance 'I Do Not Want What I Haven't Got' – Sinead O'Connor

Best Hard Rock Performance 'Time's Up' – Living Colour

Best Metal Performance 'Stone Cold Crazy' – Metallica

Best Rock Instrumental Performance 'D/FW' – The Vaughan Brothers

Best Pop Instrumental Performance 'Twin Peaks Theme' – Angelo Badalementi

1989

Best Male Rock Vocal Performance 'The End of the Innocence' – Don Henley

Best Female Rock Vocal Performance 'Nick of Time' – Bonnie Raitt

Best Male Pop Vocal Performance 'How Am I Supposed To Live Without You' – Michael Bolton

Best Female Pop Vocal Performance 'Nick of Time' – Bonnie Raitt

Best Rock Performance by a Duo or Group 'Traveling Wilburys Volume One' – Traveling Wilburys

Best Pop Performance by a Duo or Group 'Don't Know Much' – Linda Ronstadt & Aaron Neville

Best Hard Rock Performance 'Cult of Personality' – Living Colour

Best Metal Performance 'One' – Metallica

Best Rock Instrumental Performance 'Jeff Beck's Guitar Shop with Terry Bozzio and Tony Hymas' – Jeff Beck

Best Pop Instrumental Performance 'Healing Chant' – Neville Brothers

1988

Best Male Rock Vocal Performance 'Simply Irresistable' – Robert Palmer

Best Female Rock Vocal Performance 'Tina Live in Europe' – Tina Turner

Best Male Pop Vocal Performance 'Don't Worry Be Happy' – Bobby McFerrin

Best Female Pop Vocal Performance 'Fast Car' – Tracy Chapman

Best Rock Performance by a Duo or Group 'Desire' – U2

Best Pop Performance by a Duo or Group 'Brasil' – Manhattan Transfer

Best Hard Rock/Metal Performance 'Crest of a Knave' – Jethro Tull

Best Rock Instrumental Performance 'Blues For Salvador' – Carlos Santana

Best Pop Instrumental Performance 'Close-Up' – David Sanborn

1987

Best Rock Vocal Performance, Solo 'Tunnel of Love' – Bruce Springsteen

Best Male Pop Vocal Performance 'Bring On The Night' – Sting

Best Female Pop Vocal Performance 'I Wanna Dance with Somebody (Who Loves Me)' – Whitney Houston

Best Rock Performance by a Duo or Group 'The Joshua Tree' – U2

Best Pop Performance by a Duo or Group '(I've Had) The Time of My Life' – Jennifer Warnes w/ Bill Medley

Best Rock Instrumental Performance 'Jazz From Hell' – Frank Zappa

Best Pop Instrumental Performance 'Minute By Minute' – Larry Carlton

1986

Best Male Rock Vocal Performance 'Addicted to Love' – Robert Palmer

Best Female Rock Vocal Performance 'Back Where You Started' – Tina Turner

Best Male Pop Vocal Performance 'Higher Love' – Steve Winwood

Best Female Pop Vocal Performance 'The Broadway Album' – Barbra Streisand

Best Rock Performance by a Duo or Group 'Missionary Man' – Eurythmics

Best Pop Performance by a Duo or Group 'That's What Friends Are For' – Dionne & Friends

Best Rock Instrumental Performance 'The Peter Gunn Theme' – Art of Noise featuring Duane Eddy

Best Pop Instrumental Performance 'Top Gun' – Steve Stevens & Harold Faltermeyer

1985

Best Male Rock Vocal Performance 'The Boys of Summer' – Don Henley

Best Female Rock Vocal Performance 'One of the Living' – Tina Turner

Best Male Pop Vocal Performance 'No Jacket Required' – Phil Collins

Best Female Pop Vocal Performance 'Saving All My Love For You' – Whitney Houston

Best Rock Performance by a Duo or Group 'We Are The World' – U.S.A. for Africa

Best Pop Performance by a Duo or Group 'Money For Nothing' – Dire Straits

Best Rock Instrumental Performance 'Escape' – Jeff Beck

Best Pop Instrumental Performance 'Miami Vice Theme' – Jan Hammer

1984

Best Male Rock Vocal Performance 'Dancing In The Dark' – Bruce Springsteen

Best Female Rock Vocal Performance 'Better Be Good To Me' – Tina Turner

Best Male Pop Vocal Performance 'Against All Odds' – Phil Collins

Best Female Pop Vocal Performance 'What's Love Got To Do With It?' – Tina Turner

Best Rock Performance by a Duo or Group 'Purple Rain' – Prince & the Revolution

Best Pop Performance by a Duo or Group 'Jump (For My Love)' – The Pointer Sisters

Best Rock Instrumental Performance 'Cinema' – Yes

Best Pop Instrumental Performance 'Ghostbusters' – Ray Parker Jr.

1983

Best Male Rock Vocal Performance 'Beat It' – Michael Jackson

Best Female Rock Vocal Performance 'Love is a Battlefield' – Pat Benatar

Best Male Pop Vocal Performance 'Thriller' – Michael Jackson

Best Female Pop Vocal Performance 'Flashdance. . .What a Feeling' – Irene Cara

Best Rock Performance by a Duo or Group 'Synchronicity' – The Police

Best Pop Performance by a Duo or Group 'Every Breath You Take' – The Police

Best Rock Instrumental Performance 'Brimstone & Treacle' – Sting

Best Pop Instrumental Performance 'Being With You' – George Benson

1982

Best Male Rock Vocal Performance 'Hurt So Good' – John Cougar

Best Female Rock Vocal Performance 'Shadows of the Night' – Pat Benatar

Best Male Pop Vocal Performance 'Truly' – Lionel Richie

Best Female Pop Vocal Performance 'You Should Hear How She Talks About You' – Melissa Manchester

Best Rock Performance by a Duo or Group 'Eye of the Tiger' – Survivor

Best Pop Performance by a Duo or Group 'Up Where We Belong' – Joe Cocker & Jennifer Warnes

Best Rock Instrumental Performance 'D.N.A.' – A Flock of Seagulls

Best Pop Instrumental Performance 'Chariots of Fire' (Dance Version) – Ernie Watts

1981

Best Male Rock Vocal Performance 'Jessie's Girl' – Rick Springfield

Best Female Rock Vocal Performance 'Fire and Ice' – Pat Benatar

Best Male Pop Vocal Performance 'Breakin' Away' – Al Jarreau

Best Female Pop Vocal Performance 'Lena Horne: The Lady and Her Music' – Lena Horne

Best Rock Performance by a Duo or Group 'Don't Stand So Close To Me' – The Police

Best Pop Performance by a Duo or Group 'The Boy From New York City' – Manhattan Transfer

Best Rock Instrumental Performance 'Behind My Camel' – The Police

Best Pop Instrumental Performance 'Theme From Hill Street Blues' – Larry Carlton & Mike Post

1980

Best Male Rock Vocal Performance 'Glass Houses' – Billy Joel

Best Female Rock Vocal Performance 'Crimes of Passion' – Pat Benatar

Best Male Pop Vocal Performance 'This Is It' – Kenny Loggins

Best Female Pop Vocal Performance 'The Rose' – Bette Midler

Best Rock Performance by a Duo or Group 'Against The Wind' – Bob Seger & The Silver Bullet Band

Best Pop Performance by a Duo or Group 'Guilty' – Barbra Streisand & Barry Gibb

Best Rock Instrumental Performance 'Regatta De Blanc' – The Police

Best Pop Instrumental Performance 'One On One' – Bob James & Earl Klugh

1979

Best Male Rock Vocal Performance 'Gotta Serve Somebody' – Bob Dylan

Best Female Rock Vocal Performance 'Hot Stuff' – Donna Summer

Best Male Pop Vocal Performance '52nd Street' – Billy Joel

Best Female Pop Vocal Performance 'I'll Never Love This Way Again' – Dionne Warwick

Best Rock Performance by a Duo or Group 'Heartache Tonight' – Eagles

Best Pop Performance by a Duo or Group 'Minute By Minute' – Doobie Brothers

Best Rock Instrumental Performance 'Rockestra Theme' – Wings

Best Pop Instrumental Performance 'Rise' – Herb Alpert

1978

Best Male Pop Vocal Performance 'Copacabana (At the Copa)' – Barry Manilow

Best Female Pop Vocal Performance 'You Needed Me' – Anne Murray

Best Pop Performance by a Duo or Group 'Saturday Night Fever' – Bee Gees

Best Pop Instrumental Performance 'Children of Sanchez' – Chuck Mangione Group

1977

Best Male Pop Vocal Performance 'Handy Man' – James Taylor

Best Female Pop Vocal Performance 'Love Theme from A Star Is Born (Evergreen)' – Barbra Streisand

Best Pop Performance by a Duo or Group 'How Deep Is Your Love' – Bee Gees

Best Pop Instrumental Performance 'Star Wars' – John Williams

1976

Best Male Pop Vocal Performance 'Songs in the Key of Life' – Stevie Wonder

Best Female Pop Vocal Performance 'Hasten Down The Wind' – Linda Ronstadt

Best Pop Performance by a Duo or Group 'If You Leave Me Now' – Chicago

Best Pop Instrumental Performance 'Breezin'' – George Benson

1975

Best Male Pop Vocal Performance 'Still Crazy After All These Years' – Paul Simon

Best Female Pop Vocal Performance 'At Seventeen' – Janis Ian

Best Pop Performance by a Duo or Group 'Lyin' Eyes' – Eagles

Best Pop Instrumental Performance 'The Hustle' – Van McCoy

1974

Best Male Pop Vocal Performance 'Fulfillingness' First Finale' – Stevie Wonder

Best Female Pop Vocal Performance 'I Honestly Love You' – Olivia Newton-John

Best Pop Performance by a Duo or Group 'Band on the Run' – Paul McCartney & Wings

Best Pop Instrumental Performance 'The Entertainer' – Marvin Hamlisch

1973

Best Male Pop Vocal Performance 'You are the Sunshine of My Life' – Stevie Wonder

Best Female Pop Vocal Performance 'Killing Me Softly With His Song' – Roberta Flack

Best Pop Performance by a Duo or Group 'Neither One of Us (Wants to Be the First to Say Goodbye)' – Gladys Knight & the Pips

Best Pop Instrumental Performance 'Also Sprach Zarathustra' (2001) – Deodato

1972

Best Male Pop Vocal Performance 'Without You' – Nilsson

Best Female Pop Vocal Performance 'I Am Woman' – Helen Reddy

Best Pop Performance by a Duo or Group 'Where Is The Love' – Donny Hathaway & Roberta Flack

Best Pop Instrumental Performance 'Black Moses' – Isaac Hayes

Best Pop Instrumental Performance 'Outa-Space' – Billy Preston

1971

Best Male Pop Vocal Performance 'You've Got a Friend' – James Taylor

Best Female Pop Vocal Performance 'Tapestry' – Carole King

Best Pop Performance by a Duo or Group 'Carpenters' – The Carpenters

Best Pop Instrumental Performance 'Smackwater Jack' – Quincy Jones

1970

Best Contemporary Instrumental 'Theme from Z and Other Film Music' – Henry Mancini

Best Contemporary Song 'Bridge Over Troubled Water' – Simon & Garfunkel

Best Contemporary Vocal Performance By a Group 'Close To You' – The Carpenters

Best Contemporary Vocal Performance, Female 'I'll Never Fall In Love Again' – Dionne Warwick

Best Contemporary Vocal Performance, Male 'Everything Is Beautiful' – Ray Stevens

1969

Best Contemporary Instrumental 'Variations on a Theme' – Eric Satie by Blood, Sweat & Tears

Best Contemporary Performance By a Chorus 'Love Theme from Romeo & Juliet' – Percy Faith

Best Contemporary Song 'Games People Play' – Joe South

Best Contemporary Vocal Performance By a Group 'Aquarius/Let the Sunshine In' – 5th Dimension

Best Contemporary Vocal Performance, Female 'Is That All There Is' – Peggy Lee

Best Contemporary Vocal Performance, Male 'Everybody's Talkin'' – Nilsson

1968

Best Contemporary Pop Performance, Chorus 'Mission Impossible/Norwegian Wood (Medley)' – Alan Copeland Singers

Best Contemporary Pop Performance, Instrumental 'Classical Gas' – Mason Williams

Best Pop Performance by a Duo or Group 'Mrs. Robinson' – Simon & Garfunkel

Best Contemporary Pop Vocal Performance, Female 'Do You Know The Way to San Jose' – Dionne Warwick

Best Contemporary Pop Vocal Performance, Male 'Light My Fire' – Jose Feliciano

1967

Best Contemporary Album *Sgt. Pepper's Lonely Hearts Club Band* – The Beatles

Best Contemporary Female Solo Vocal Performance 'Ode to Billie Joe' – Bobbie Gentry

Best Contemporary Group Performance (Vocal or Instrumental) 'Up, Up and Away' – 5th Dimension

Best Contemporary Male Solo Vocal Performance 'By The Time I Get to Phoenix' – Glen Campbell

Best Contemporary Single 'Up, Up and Away' – 5th Dimension

Best Instrumental Performance 'Chet Atkins Picks The Best' – Chet Atkins

Best Performance By a Chorus 'Up, Up and Away' – 5th Dimension

Best Performance By a Vocal Group 'Up, Up and Away' – 5th Dimension

Best Vocal Performance, Female 'Ode to Billie Joe' – Bobbie Gentry

Best Vocal Performance, Male 'By The Time I Get to Phoenix' – Glen Campbell

1966

Best Contemporary Group Performance (Vocal or Instrumental) 'Monday, Monday' – Mamas & The Papas

Best Contemporary Recording 'Winchester Cathedral' – The New Vaudeville Band

Best Contemporary Solo Vocal Performance, Male or Female 'Eleanor Rigby' – Paul McCartney (Beatles)

Best Instrumental Performance 'What Now My Love' – Herb Alpert & the Tijuana Brass

Best Performance By a Chorus 'Somewhere My Love' – Ray Conniff Singers

Best Performance By a Vocal Group 'A Man and A Woman' – Anita Kerr Singers

Best Vocal Performance, Female 'If He Walked Into My Life' – Eydie Gorme

Best Vocal Performance, Male 'Strangers in the Night' – Frank Sinatra

1965

Best Contemporary Performance, Group (Vocal or Instrumental) 'Flowers on the Wall' – Statler Brothers

Best Contemporary R&B Vocal Performance, Female 'I Know a Place' – Petula Clark

Best Contemporary Single 'King of the Road' – Roger Miller

Best Contemporary Vocal Performance, Male 'King of the Road' – Roger Miller

Best Instrumental Performance 'A Taste of Honey' – Herb Alpert & the Tijuana Brass

Best Performance By a Chorus 'Anyone for Mozart?' – Swingle Singers

Best Performance By a Vocal Group 'We Dig Mancini' – Anita Kerr Singers

Best Vocal Performance, Female 'My Name is Barbra' – Barbra Streisand

Best Vocal Performance, Male 'It Was A Very Good Year' – Frank Sinatra

1964

Best Instrumental Performance 'Pink Panther' – Henry Mancini

Best Performance By A Chorus 'Swingle Singers Going Baroque' –
Swingle Singers

Best Performance By A Vocal Group 'A Hard Day's Night' – The Beatles

Best Rock And Roll Recording 'Downtown' – Petula Clark

Best Vocal Performance, Female 'People' – Barbra Streisand

Best Vocal Performance, Male 'Hello, Dolly' – Louis Armstrong

1963

Best Performance By a Chorus 'Bach's Greatest Hits' – Swingle Singers

Best Performance By a Vocal Group 'Blowin' In The Wind' – Peter,
Paul & Mary

Best Performance By an Orchestra, For Dancing 'This Time By
Basie! Hits of the 50's & 60's' – Count Basie

**Best Performance By an Orchestra/Instrumentalist with Orchestra
Primarily Not Jazz or For Dancing** 'Java' – Al Hirt

Best Rock and Roll Recording 'Deep Purple' – April Stevens & Nino
Tempo

Best Vocal Performance, Female *The Barbra Streisand Album* – Barbra
Streisand

Best Vocal Performance, Male 'Wives and Lovers' – Jack Jones

1962

Best Performance By a Chorus 'Presenting the New Christy Minstrels' –
The New Christy Minstrels

Best Performance By a Vocal Group 'If I Had a Hammer' – Peter, Paul & Mary

Best Performance By an Orchestra, For Dancing 'Fly Me To The Moon Bossa Nova' – Joe Harnell

Best Performance By an Orchestra/Instrumentalist with Orchestra, Primarily Not Jazz or for Dancing 'The Colorful Peter Nero' – Peter Nero

Best Rock and Roll Recording 'Alley Cat' – Bent Fabric

Best Solo Vocal Performance, Female 'Ella Swings Brightly With Nelson Riddle' – Ella Fitzgerald

Best Solo Vocal Performance, Male 'I Left My Heart in San Francisco' – Tony Bennett

1961

Best Performance By a Chorus 'Great Band With Great Voices' – Johnny Mann Singers

Best Performance By a Vocal Group 'High Flying' – Lambert, Hendricks and Ross

Best Performance By an Orchestra For Dancing 'Up a Lazy River' – Si Zentner

Best Performance By an Orchestra For Other Than Dancing 'Breakfast at Tiffany's' – Henry Mancini

Best Rock and Roll Recording 'Let's Twist Again' – Chubby Checker

Best Solo Vocal Performance, Female 'Judy at Carnegie Hall' – Judy Garland

Best Solo Vocal Performance, Male 'Lollipops and Roses' – Jack Jones

1960

Best Performance By a Band For Dancing 'Dance With Basie' – Count Basie

Best Performance By a Chorus 'Songs of the Cowboy' – Norman Luboff Choir

Best Performance By a Pop Single Artist 'Georgia on My Mind' – Ray Charles

Best Performance By a Vocal Group 'We Got Us' – Eydie Gorme & Steve Lawrence

Best Performance By an Orchestra (Other Than For Dancing) 'Mr Lucky' – Henry Mancini

Best Vocal Performance, Album, Female *Mack The Knife – Ella in Berlin* – Ella Fitzgerald

Best Vocal Performance, Album, Male *Genius of Ray Charles* – Ray Charles

Best Vocal Performance, Single Record or Track, Female 'Mack The Knife' – Ella Fitzgerald

Best Vocal Performance, Single Record or Track, Male 'Georgia on My Mind' – Ray Charles

1959

Best Performance By a Dance Band 'Anatomy of a Murder' (Motion Picture) – Duke Ellington

Best Performance By a Top 40 Artist 'Midnight Flyer' – Nat King Cole

Best Performance By a Vocal Group or Chorus 'Battle Hymn of the Republic' – Mormon Tabernacle Choir

Best Performance By an Orchestra 'Like Young' – André Previn & David Rose

Best Vocal Performance, Female 'But Not For Me' – Ella Fitzgerald

Best Vocal Performance, Male 'Come Dance With Me' – Frank Sinatra

1958

Best Performance By a Dance Band 'Basie' – Count Basie

Best Performance By a Vocal Group or Chorus 'That Old Black Magic' – Keely Smith & Louis Prima

Best Performance By an Orchestra 'Billy May's Big Fat Brass' – Billy May

Best Vocal Performance, Female 'Ella Fitzgerald Sings The Irving Berlin Song Book' – Ella Fitzgerald

Best Vocal Performance, Male 'Catch a Falling Star' – Perry Como

GRAMMYS – R&B AND SOUL

2000

Best Female R&B Vocal Performance 'He Wasn't Man Enough' – Toni Braxton

Best Male R&B Vocal Performance 'Untitled (How Does It Feel)' – D'Angelo

Best R&B Album *Voodoo* – D'Angelo

Best R&B Performance By A Duo Or Group With Vocal 'Say My Name' – Destiny's Child

Best R&B Song 'Say My Name' – Destiny's Child

Best Traditional R&B Vocal Album *Ear-Resistible* – The Temptations

1999

Best Female R&B Vocal Performance 'It's Not Right But It's Okay' – Whitney Houston

Best Male R&B Vocal Performance 'Staying Power' – Barry White

Best R&B Album *Fanmail* – TLC

Best R&B Performance By A Duo Or Group With Vocal 'No Scrubs' – TLC

Best R&B Song 'No Scrubs' – Written by Kevin Briggs, Kandi Burruss & Tameka Cottle

1998

Best Female R&B Vocal Performance Doo Wop (That Thing) – Lauryn Hill

Best Male R&B Vocal Performance 'St Louis Blues' – Stevie Wonder

Best R&B Album *The Miseducation Of Lauryn Hill* – Lauryn Hill

Best R&B Performance By A Duo Or Group With Vocal 'The Boy Is Mine' – Monica and Brandy

Best R&B Song 'Doo Wop (That Thing)' – Lauryn Hill

Best Traditional R&B Vocal Performance 'Live! One Night Only' – Patti LaBelle

1997

Best Female R&B Vocal Performance 'On and On' – Erykah Badu

Best Male R&B Vocal Performance 'I Believe I Can Fly' – R. Kelly

Best R&B Album *Baduizm* – Erykah Badu

Best R&B Performance By A Duo Or Group With Vocal 'No Diggity' – Blackstreet

Best R&B Song 'I Believe I Can Fly' – R. Kelly

1996

Best Female R&B Vocal Performance 'You're Makin' Me High' – Toni Braxton

Best Male R&B Vocal Performance 'Your Secret Love' – Luther Vandross

Best R&B Album *Words* – Tony Rich Project

Best R&B Performance By A Duo Or Group With Vocal 'Killing Me Softly With His Song' – Fugees

Best R&B Song 'Exhale (Shoop Shoop)' – Written by Babyface performed by Whitney Houston

1995

Best Female R&B Vocal Performance 'I Apologize' – Jeffrey Cohen and Anita Baker

Best Male R&B Vocal Performance 'For Your Love' – Stevie Wonder

Best R&B Album *Crazysexycool* – TLC

Best R&B Performance By A Duo Or Group With Vocal 'Creep' – TLC

Best R&B Song 'For Your Love' – Stevie Wonder

1994

Best Female R&B Vocal Performance 'Breathe Again' – Toni Braxton

Best Male R&B Vocal Performance 'When Can I See You' – Babyface

Best R&B Album *II* – Boyz II Men

Best R&B Song 'I'll Make Love To You' – Babyface

1993

Best R&B Performance By A Duo Or Group With Vocal 'No Ordinary Love' – Sade

Best R&B Song 'That's The Way Love Goes' – Jimmy Jam, Terry Lewis and Janet Jackson

Best R&B Vocal Performance, Female 'Another Sad Love Song' – Toni Braxton

Best R&B Vocal Performance, Male 'A Song For You' – Ray Charles

1992

Best R&B Instrumental Performance 'Doo-Bop' – Miles Davis

Best R&B Performance By A Duo Or Group With Vocal 'End Of The Road' – Boyz II Men

Best R&B Song 'End Of The Road' – Written by L.A. Reid, Daryl Simmons and Babyface

Best R&B Vocal Performance, Female 'The Woman I Am' – Chaka Khan

Best R&B Vocal Performance, Male 'Heaven And Earth' – Al Jarreau

1991

Best R&B Performance By A Duo Or Group With Vocal 'Cooleyhighharmony' – Boyz II Men

Best R&B Song 'Power Of Love / Love Power' – Marcus Miller, Luther Vandross and Teddy Vann

Best R&B Vocal Performance, Female 'How Can I Ease The Pain' – Lisa Fischer

Best R&B Vocal Performance, Female 'Burnin'' – Patti LaBelle

Best R&B Vocal Performance, Male 'Power Of Love' – Luther Vandross

1990

Best R&B Performance By A Duo Or Group With Vocal 'I'll Be Good To You' – Chaka Khan & Ray Charles

Best R&B Song 'U Can't Touch This' – Rick James, Alonzo Miller & M.C. Hammer

Best R&B Vocal Performance, Male 'Here And Now' – Luther Vandross

Best R&B Vocal Performance, Female 'Compositions' – Anita Baker

1989

Best R&B Instrumental Performance 'African Dance' – Soul II Soul

Best R&B Performance By A Duo Or Group With Vocal – 'Back To Life' – Soul II Soul & Caron Wheeler

Best R&B Song 'If You Don't Know Me By Now' – Written by Leon Huff & Kenny Gamble

Best R&B Vocal Performance, Female 'Giving You The Best That I Got' – Anita Baker

Best R&B Vocal Performance, Male 'Every Little Step' – Written by Bobby Brown

1988

Best R&B Instrumental Performance (Orchestra, Group Or Soloist) 'Light Years' – Chick Corea

Best R&B Performance By A Duo Or Group With Vocal 'Love Overboard' – Gladys Knight And The Pips

Best R&B Song 'Giving You The Best That I Got' – Anita Baker, Skip Scarborough & Randy Holland

Best R&B Vocal Performance, Female 'Giving You The Best That I Got' (single) – Anita Baker

Best R&B Vocal Performance, Male 'Introducing The Hardline According To Terence Trent D'Arby' – Terence Trent D'Arby

1987

Best R&B Instrumental Performance (Orchestra, Group Or Soloist) 'Chicago Song' – David Sanborn

Best R&B Performance By A Duo Or Group With Vocal 'I Knew You Were Waiting (For Me)' – Aretha Franklin & George Michael

Best R&B Song 'Lean On Me' – Bill Withers

Best R&B Vocal Performance, Female 'Aretha' (album) – Aretha Franklin

Best R&B Vocal Performance, Male 'Just To See Her' – Smokey Robinson

1986

Best R&B Instrumental Performance (Orchestra, Group Or Soloist) 'And You Know That' – Yellojackets

Best R&B Performance By A Duo Or Group With Vocal 'Kiss' – Prince And The Revolution

Best R&B Song 'Sweet Love' – Anita Baker, Louis A Johnson & Gary Bias

Best R&B Vocal Performance, Female 'Rapture' – Anita Baker

Best R&B Vocal Performance, Male 'Living In America' – James Brown

1985

Best R&B Instrumental Performance, Orchestra, Group Or Soloist 'Musician' – Ernie Watts

Best R&B Performance By A Duo Or Group With Vocal 'Nightshift' – Commodores

Best R&B Song 'Freeway Of Love' – Jeffrey Cohen & Narada Michael Walden

Best R&B Vocal Performance, Female 'Freeway Of Love' – Aretha Franklin

Best R&B Vocal Performance, Male 'In Square Circle' – Stevie Wonder

1984

Best R&B Instrumental Performance 'Sound System' – Herbie Hancock

Best R&B Performance By A Duo Or Group With Vocal 'Yah Mo B There' – James Ingram & Michael McDonald

Best R&B Song 'I Feel For You' – Written by Prince, performed by Chaka Khan

Best R&B Vocal Performance, Female 'I Feel For You' – Chaka Khan

Best R&B Vocal Performance, Male 'Caribbean Queen (No More Love On The Run)' – Billy Ocean

1983

Best New R&B Song 'Billie Jean' – Michael Jackson

Best R&B Instrumental Performance 'Rockit' – Herbie Hancock

Best R&B Performance By A Duo Or Group With Vocal 'Ain't Nobody' – Chaka Khan & Rufus

Best R&B Vocal Performance, Female 'Chaka Khan' – Chaka Khan

Best R&B Vocal Performance, Male 'Billie Jean' – Michael Jackson

1982

Best R&B Instrumental Performance 'Sexual Healing' (Instrumental Version) – Marvin Gaye

Joint Winners Best R&B Performance By A Duo Or Group With Vocal 'Let It Whip' – Dazz Band

Best R&B Performance By A Duo Or Group With Vocal 'Wanna Be With You' – Earth, Wind And Fire

Best R&B Song 'Turn Your Love Around' – Written by Bill Champlin, performed by George Benson

Best R&B Vocal Performance, Female 'And I Am Telling You I'm Not Going' – Jennifer Holliday

Best R&B Vocal Performance, Male 'Sexual Healing' -Marvin Gaye

1981

Best R&B Instrumental Performance 'All I Need Is You' – David Sanborn

Best R&B Performance By A Duo Or Group With Vocal 'The Dude' – Quincy Jones

Best R&B Song 'Just The Two Of Us' – William Salter, Bill Withers & Ralph MacDonald

Best R&B Vocal Performance, Female 'Hold On I'm Comin" – Aretha Franklin

Best R&B Vocal Performance, Male 'One Hundred Ways' – James Ingram

1980

Best R&B Instrumental Performance 'Off Broadway' – George Benson

Best R&B Vocal Performance, Male 'Give Me The Night' – George Benson

Best R&B Song 'Never Knew Love Like This Before' – Written by Reggie Lucas & James Mtume

Best R&B Performance By A Duo Or Group With Vocal 'Shining Star' – Manhattans

Best R&B Vocal Performance, Female 'Never Knew Love Like This Before' – Stephanie Mills

1979

Best R&B Instrumental Performance 'Boogie Wonderland' (Instrumental) – Earth Wind And Fire

Best R&B Vocal Performance By A Duo Group Or Chorus 'After The Love Has Gone' – Earth, Wind And Fire

Best R&B Song 'After The Love Has Gone' – David Foster, Jay Graydon & Bill Champlin

Best R&B Vocal Performance, Male 'Don't Stop 'til You Get Enough' – Michael Jackson

Best R&B Vocal Performance, Female 'Deja Vu' – Dionne Warwick

1978

Best R&B Vocal Performance, Male 'On Broadway' – George Benson

Best R&B Instrumental Performance 'Runnin'' – Earth, Wind & Fire

Best R&B Vocal Performance By A Group 'All 'n All' – Earth, Wind & Fire

Best R&B Song 'Last Dance' – Paul Jabara

Best R&B Vocal Performance, Female 'Last Dance' – Donna Summer

1977

Best R&B Instrumental Performance 'Q' – Brothers Johnson

Best R&B Vocal Performance By A Group 'Best Of My Love' – The Emotions

Best R&B Vocal Performance, Female 'Don't Leave Me This Way' – Thelma Houston

Best R&B Song 'You Make Me Feel Like Dancing' – Leo Sayer & Vini Poncia

Best R&B Vocal Performance, Male 'Unmistakably Lou' – Lou Rawls

1976

Best R&B Instrumental Performance 'Theme From Good King Bad' – George Benson

Best R&B Vocal Performance, Female 'Sophisticated Lady (She's A Different Lady)' – Natalie Cole

Best R&B Vocal Performance By A Duo, Group Or Chorus 'You Don't Have To Be A Star (To Be In My Show)' – Marilyn McCoo & Billy Davis Jr

Best R&B Song 'Lowdown' – David Paich & Boz Scaggs

Best R&B Vocal Performance, Male 'I Wish' – Stevie Wonder

1975

Best R&B Song 'Where Is The Love' – Written by Harry Wayne Casey, Richard Finch, Willie Clarke & Betty Wright, performed by Roberta Flack and Donny Hathaway

Best R&B Vocal Performance, Male 'Living For The City' – Ray Charles

Best R&B Vocal Performance, Female 'This Will Be' – Natalie Cole

Best R&B Vocal Performance By A Duo, Group Or Chorus 'Shining Star' – Earth, Wind And Fire

Best R&B Instrumental Performance 'Fly, Robin, Fly' – Silver Convention

1974

Best R&B Vocal Performance, Female 'Ain't Nothing Like The Real Thing' – Aretha Franklin

Best R&B Instrumental Performance 'The Sound Of Philadelphia' – MFSB & Bobby Martin

Best R&B Vocal Performance By A Duo, Group or Chorus 'Tell Me Something Good' – Rufus

Best R&B Vocal Performance, Male 'Boogie On Reggae Woman' – Stevie Wonder

Best R&B Song 'Living For The City' – Stevie Wonder

1973

Best R&B Vocal Performance, Female 'Master Of Eyes' – Aretha Franklin

Best R&B Vocal Performance By A Group 'Midnight Train To Georgia' – Gladys Knight And The Pips

Best R&B Instrumental Performance 'Hang On Sloopy' – Ramsey Lewis

Best R&B Vocal Performance, Male 'Superstition' – Stevie Wonder

Best R&B Song 'Superstition' – Stevie Wonder

1972

Best R&B Vocal Performance, Female 'Young, Gifted & Black' – Aretha Franklin

Best R&B Vocal Performance, Male 'Me & Mrs Jones' – Billy Paul

Best R&B Instrumental Performance 'Papa Was A Rolling Stone' – Paul Riser and The Temptations

Best R&B Song 'Papa Was A Rolling Stone' – Written by Barrett Strong & Norman Whitfield

Best R&B Vocal Performance By A Group 'Papa Was A Rolling Stone' – Paul Riser and The Temptations

1971

Best R&B Vocal Performance, Female 'Bridge Over Troubled Water' – Aretha Franklin

Best R&B Vocal Performance, Male 'A Natural Man' – Lou Rawls

Best R&B Performance By A Duo Or Group, Vocal Or Instrumental 'Proud Mary' – Ike & Tina Turner

Best R&B Song 'Ain't No Sunshine' – Bill Withers

1970

Best R&B Performance By A Duo Or Group, Vocal Or Instrumental 'Didn't I (Blow Your Mind This Time)' – Delfonics

Best Rhythm & Blues Song 'Patches' – Written by Ronald Dunbar & General Johnson, performed by Clarence Carter

Best R&B Vocal Performance, Female 'Don't Play That Song' – Aretha Franklin

Best R&B Vocal Performance, Male 'The Thrill Is Gone' – B.B. King

1969

Best R&B Instrumental Performance 'Games People Play' – King Curtis

Best R&B Vocal Performance, Female 'Share Your Love With Me' – Aretha Franklin

Best R&B Vocal Performance By A Duo Or Group 'It's Your Thing' – The Isley Brothers

Best R&B Vocal Performance, Male 'The Chokin' Kind' – Joe Simon

Best R&B Song 'Color Him Father' – Written by Richard Spencer, performed by The Winstons

1968

Best R&B Performance, Female 'Chain Of Fools' – Aretha Franklin

Best R&B Vocal Performance, Male '(Sittin' On) The Dock Of The Bay' – Otis Redding

Best R&B Song '(Sittin' On) The Dock Of The Bay' – Otis Redding & Steve Cropper

Best R&B Performance By A Duo Or Group Vocal Or Instrumental 'Cloud Nine' – The Temptations

1967

Best R&B Song 'Respect' – Aretha Franklin

Best R&B Performance, Vocal or Instrumental, Duo or Group 'Soul Man – Sam And Dave

Best R&B Vocal Performance, Female 'Respect' – Aretha Franklin

Best R&B Vocal Performance, Male 'Dead End Street' – Lou Rawls

1966

Best R&B Recording 'Crying Time' – Ray Charles

Best R&B Solo Vocal Performance, Male Or Female 'Crying Time' – Ray Charles

Best R&B Group Performance, Vocal Or Instrumental 'Hold It Right There' – Ramsey Lewis

1965

Best R&B Recording 'Papa's Got A Brand New Bag' – James Brown

1964

Best R&B Recording 'How Glad I Am' – Nancy Wilson

1963

Best R&B Recording 'Busted' – Ray Charles

1962

Best R&B Recording 'I Can't Stop Loving You' – Ray Charles

1961

Best R&B Recording 'Hit The Road Jack' – Ray Charles

1960

Best R&B Recording 'Let The Good Times Roll' – Ray Charles

1959

Best R&B Recording 'What A Difference A Day Makes' – Sarah Vaughan

1958

Best R&B Recording 'Tequila' – The Champs

GRAMMYS – RAP & HIP HOP

2000

Best Rap Album *The Marshal Mathers* LP – Eminem

Best Rap Solo Performance 'The Real Slim Shady' – Eminem

Best Rap Performance By A Duo Or Group 'Forget About Dre' – Dr Dre featuring Eminem

1999

Best Rap Album *The Slim Shady LP* – Eminem

Best Rap Solo Performance 'My Name Is' – Eminem

Best Rap Performance By A Duo Or Group 'You Got Me' – The Roots featuring Erykah Badu

1998

Best Rap Album *Vol. 2 . . . Hard Knock Life* – Jay-Z

Best Rap Solo Performance 'Gettin' Jiggy Wit It' – Will Smith

Best Rap Performance By A Duo Or Group 'Intergalactic' – Beastie Boys

1997

Best Rap Album *No Way Out* – Puff Daddy And The Family

Best Rap Solo Performance 'Men In Black' – Will Smith

Best Rap Performance By A Duo Or Group 'I'll Be Missing You' – Puff Daddy and Faith Evans featuring 112

1996

Best Rap Album *The Score* – Fugees

Best Rap Solo Performance 'Hey Lover' – LL Cool J

Best Rap Performance By A Duo Or Group 'Tha Crossroads' – Bone Thugs-N-Harmony

1995

Best Rap Album *Poverty's Paradise* – Naughty By Nature

Best Rap Solo Performance 'Gangsta's Paradise' – Coolio

Best Rap Performance By A Duo Or Group 'I'll Be There For You' / 'You're All I Need To Get By' – Method Man featuring Mary J. Blige

1994

Best Rap Solo Performance 'U.N.I.T.Y.' – Queen Latifah

Best Rap Performance By A Duo Or Group 'None Of Your Business' – Salt-N-Pepa

1993

Best Rap Solo Performance 'Let Me Ride' – Dr. Dre

Best Rap Performance By A Duo Or Group 'Rebirth Of Slick (Cool Like Dat)' – Digable Planets

1992

Sir Mix-A-Lot Best Rap Solo Performance 'Baby Got Back' – Sir Mix-A-Lot

Best Rap Performance By A Duo Or Group 'Tennessee' – Arrested Development

1991

Best Rap Solo Performance 'Mama Said Knock You Out' – LL Cool J

Best Rap Performance By A Duo Or Group 'Summertime' – D.J. Jazzy Jeff And The Fresh Prince

1990

Best Rap Solo Performance 'U Can't Touch This' – M.C. Hammer

Best Rap Performance By A Duo Or Group 'Back On The Block' – Kool Moe Dee, Ice-T, Melle Mel, Big Daddy Kane, Quincy Jones, Quincy D. III

1989

Best Rap Performance 'Bust A Move' – Young MC

1988

Best Rap Performance 'Parents Just Don't Understand' – D.J. Jazzy Jeff And The Fresh Prince

GRAMMYS - COUNTRY

2000

Best Bluegrass Album *The Grass Is Blue* – Dolly Parton

Best Country Album *Breathe* – Faith Hill

Best Country Collaboration With Vocals 'Let's Make Love' – Faith Hill and Tim McGraw

Best Country Instrumental Performance 'Leaving Cottondale' – Alison Brown With Béla Fleck

Best Male Country Vocal Performance 'Solitary Man' – Johnny Cash

Best Country Song 'I Hope You Dance' – Written by Mark D. Sanders & Tia Sillers, performed by Lee Ann Womack

Best Female Country Vocal Performance 'Breathe' – Faith Hill

Best Country Performance By A Duo Or Group With Vocal 'Cherokee Maiden' – Asleep At The Wheel

1999

Best Bluegrass Album *Ancient Tones* – Ricky Skaggs and Kentucky Thunder

Best Country Album *Fly* – Dixie Chicks

Best Country Collaboration With Vocals 'The Gold Rush' – Emmylou Harris, Linda Ronstadt & Dolly Parton

Best Country Instrumental Performance 'Bob's Breakdowns' – Asleep At The Wheel

Best Country Performance By A Duo Or Group With Vocal 'Ready To Run' – Dixie Chicks

Best Country Song 'Come On Over' – Written by Shania Twain & R.J. Mutt Lange

Best Male Country Vocal Performance 'Choices' – George Jones

Best Female Country Vocal Performance 'Man! I Feel Like A Woman!' – Shania Twain

1998

Best Bluegrass Album *Bluegrass Rules!* – Ricky Skaggs and Kentucky Thunder

Best Country Album *Wide Open Spaces* – Dixie Chicks

Best Country Collaboration With Vocals 'Same Old Train' – Clint Black, Pam Tillis, Dwight Yoakam & Earl Scruggs

Best Country Instrumental Performance 'A Soldier's Joy' – Randy Scruggs & Vince Gill

Best Country Performance By A Duo Or Group With Vocal 'There's Your Trouble' – Dixie Chicks

Best Country Song 'You're Still The One' – Written by Robert John Mutt Lange & Shania Twain

Best Female Country Vocal Performance 'You're Still The One' – Shania Twain

Best Male Country Vocal Performance 'If You Ever Have Forever In Mind' – Vince Gill

1997

Best Bluegrass Album *So Long So Wrong* – Alison Krauss and Union Station

Best Country Album *Unchained* – Johnny Cash

Best Country Collaboration With Vocals 'In Another's Eyes' – Trisha Yearwood & Garth Brooks

Best Country Instrumental Performance 'Little Liza Jane' – Alison Krauss and Union Station

Best Country Performance By A Duo Or Group With Vocal 'Looking In The Eyes Of Love' – Alison Krauss and Union Station

Best Country Song 'Butterfly Kisses' – Bob Carlisle & Randy Thomas

Best Female Country Vocal Performance 'How Do I Live' – Trisha Yearwood

Best Male Country Vocal Performance 'Pretty Little Adriana' – Vince Gill

1996

Best Bluegrass Album *True Life Blues: The Songs Of Bill Monroe* – Todd Phillips

Best Country Album *The Road To Ensenada* – Lyle Lovett

Best Country Collaboration With Vocals 'High Lonesome Sound' – Vince Gill & Alison Krauss and Union Station

Best Country Instrumental Performance 'Jam Man' – Chet Atkins

Best Country Song 'Blue' – Written by Bill Mack, performed by LeAnn Rimes

Best Country Vocal Performance By A Duo Or Group With Vocal 'My Maria' – Brooks And Dunn

Best Female Country Vocal Performance 'Blue' – LeAnn Rimes

Best Male Country Vocal Performance 'Worlds Apart' – Vince Gill

1995

Best Bluegrass Album *Unleashed* – Nashville Bluegrass Band

Best Country Album *The Woman In Me* – Shania Twain

Best Country Instrumental Performance 'Hightower' – Asleep At The Wheel

Best Country Collaboration With Vocals 'Somewhere In The Vicinity Of The Heart' – Shenandoah

Best Country Performance By A Duo Or Group With Vocal 'Here Comes The Rain' – Mavericks

Best Country Song 'Go Rest High On That Mountain' – Vince Gill

Best Female Country Vocal Performance 'Go Rest High On That Mountain' – Alison Krauss

Best Male Country Vocal Performance 'Go Rest High On That Mountain' – Vince Gill

1994

Best Bluegrass Album *The Great Dobro Sessions* – Jerry Douglas & Tut Taylor

Best Country Album *Stones In The Road* – Mary-Chapin Carpenter

Best Country Instrumental Performance 'Young Thing' – Chet Atkins

Best Country Performance By A Duo Or Group With Vocal 'Blues For Dixie' – Lyle Lovett & Asleep At The Wheel

Best Country Song 'I Swear' – Performed by John Michael Montgomery, written by Frank J. Meyers & Gary Baker

Best Country Vocal Collaboration 'I Fall To Pieces' – Aaron Neville & Trisha Yearwood

Best Female Country Vocal Performance 'Shut Up And Kiss Me' – Mary-Chapin Carpenter

Best Male Country Vocal Performance 'When Love Finds You' – Vince Gill

1993

Best Bluegrass Album *Waitin' For The Hard Times To Go* – Nashville Bluegrass Band

Best Country Instrumental Performance 'Red Wing' – Eldon Shamblin & Johnny Gimble, Chet Atkins, Vince Gill, Marty Stuart, Asleep At The Wheel

Best Country Performance By A Duo Or Group With Vocal 'Hard Workin' Man' – Brooks And Dunn

Best Country Song 'Passionate Kisses' – Lucinda Williams

Best Country Vocal Collaboration 'Does He Love You' – Reba McEntire & Linda Davis

Best Female Country Vocal Performance 'Passionate Kisses' – Mary-Chapin Carpenter & Linda Davis

Best Male Country Vocal Performance 'Ain't That Lonely Yet' – Dwight Yoakam

1992

Best Bluegrass Album *Every Time You Say Goodbye* – Alison Krauss and Union Station

Best Country Instrumental Performance 'Sneakin' Around' – Jerry Reed & Chet Atkins

Best Country Performance By A Duo Or Group With Vocal 'Emmylou Harris and The Nash Ramblers At The Ryman' – Emmylou Harris & The Nash Ramblers

Best Country Song 'I Still Believe In You' – Vince Gill & Jarvis

Best Country Vocal Collaboration 'The Whiskey Ain't Workin'' – Travis Tritt & Marty Stuart

Best Female Country Vocal Performance 'I Feel Lucky' – Mary-Chapin Carpenter

Best Male Country Vocal Performance 'I Still Believe In You' – Vince Gill

1991

Best Bluegrass Album *Spring Training* – Carl Jackson & John Starling

Best Country Instrumental Performance 'The New Nashville Cats' – Mark O'Connor

Best Country Performance By A Duo Or Group With Vocal 'Love Can Build A Bridge' – The Judds

Best Country Song 'Love Can Build A Bridge' – Written by John Jarvis, Naomi Judd & Paul Overstreet

Best Country Vocal Collaboration 'Restless' – Ricky Skaggs, Steve Wariner & Vince Gill

Best Female Country Vocal Performance 'Down At The Twist And Shout' – Mary-Chapin Carpenter

Best Male Country Vocal Performance 'Ropin' The Wind' – Garth Brooks

1990

Best Bluegrass Recording 'I've Got That Old Feeling' – Alison Krauss

Best Country Instrumental Performance 'So Soft, Your Goodbye' – Mark Knopfler & Chet Atkins

Best Country Performance By A Duo Or Group With Vocals 'Pickin'
On Nashville' – Kentucky Headhunters

Best Country Song 'Where've You Been?' – Don Henry & Jon Vesner

Best Country Vocal Collaboration 'Poor Boy Blues' – Mark Knopfler &
Chet Atkins

Best Female Country Vocal Performance 'Where've You Been' – Kathy
Mattea

Best Male Country Vocal Performance 'When I Call Your Name' –
Vince Gill

1989

Best Bluegrass Recording 'The Valley Road' – Bruce Hornsby & Nitty
Gritty Dirt Band

Best Country Instrumental Performance 'Amazing Grace' – Randy
Scruggs

Best Country Performance By A Duo Or Group With Vocal 'Will The
Circle Be Unbroken Volume Two' – Nitty Gritty Dirt Band

Best Country Song 'After All This Time' – Rodney Crowell

Best Country Vocal Collaboration 'There's A Tear In My Beer' – Hank
Williams Sr. & Hank Williams Jr

Best Female Country Vocal Performance 'Absolute Torch And Twang'
– k.d. lang

Best Male Country Vocal Performance Lyle Lovett And His Large Band
– Lyle Lovett

1988

Best Bluegrass Album *Southern Flavor* – Bill Monroe

Best Country Collaboration With Vocals 'Crying' – Roy Orbison & k.d. lang

Best Country Instrumental Performance 'Sugarfoot Rag' – Asleep At The Wheel

Best Country Performance By A Duo Or Group With Vocal 'Give A Little Love' – Judds (Naomi Judd & Wynonna Judd)

Best Country Song 'Hold Me' – Written by Robert John Mutt Lange & K.T. Oslin

Best Female Country Vocal Performance 'Hold Me' – K.T. Oslin

Best Male Country Vocal Performance 'Old 8x10' – Randy Travis

1987

Best Country Instrumental Performance 'String Of Pearls' – Asleep At The Wheel

Best Country Performance By A Duo Or Group With Vocal 'Trio' – Dolly Parton, Linda Ronstadt & Emmylou Harris

Best Country Song 'Forever And Ever, Amen' – Don Schlitz & Paul Overstreet performed by Randy Travis

Best Country Vocal Performance, Duet 'Make No Mistake, She's Mine' – Kenny Rogers & Ronnie Milsap

Best Female Country Vocal Performance '80's Ladies' – K.T. Oslin

Best Male Country Vocal Performance 'Always and Forever' – Randy Travis

1986

Best Country Instrumental Performance, Orchestra Group Or Soloist 'Raisin' The Dickins' – Ricky Skaggs

Best Country Performance By A Duo Or Group With Vocal 'Grandpa (Tell Me 'Bout The Good Old Days)' – Judds (Wynona Judd & Naomi Judd)

Best Country Song 'Grandpa (Tell Me 'Bout The Good Old Days)' – Jami Ohara, performed by Judds (Wynona Judd & Naomi Judd)

Best Female Country Vocal Performance 'Whoever's In New England' – Reba McEntire

Best Male Country Vocal Solo Performance 'Lost In The Fifties Tonight' – Ronnie Milsap

1985

Best Country Instrumental Performance 'Cosmic Square Dance' – Chet Atkins & Mark Knopfler

Best Country Performance By A Duo Or Group With Vocal 'Why Not Me?' – Judds (Wynnona & Naomi Judd)

Best Country Song 'Highwayman' – Written by Jimmy L Webb, performed by The Highwaymen

Best Country Vocal Performance, Female 'I Don't Know Why You Don't Want Me' – Rosanne Cash

Best Male Country Vocal Performance 'Lost In The Fifties Tonight' (In The Still Of The Night) – Ronnie Milsap

1984

Best Country Instrumental Performance 'Wheel Hoss' – Ricky Skaggs

Best Country Performance By A Duo Or Group With Vocal 'Mama He's Crazy' – Judds (Naomi Judd & Wynnona Judd)

Best Country Song 'City Of New Orleans' – Written by Steve Goodman, Performed by Willie Nelson

Best Female Country Vocal Performance 'In My Dreams' – Emmylou Harris

Best Male Country Vocal Performance 'That's The Way Love Goes' – Merle Haggard

1983

Best Country Instrumental Performance 'Fireball' – The New South Ricky Skaggs, J.D. Crowe, Jerry Douglas & Tony Rice

Best New Country Song 'Stranger In My House' – Written by Mike Reid, Performed by Ronnie Milsap

Best Country Performance By A Duo Or Group With Vocal 'The Closer You Get' – Alabama

Best Female Country Vocal Performance 'A Little Good News' – Anne Murray

Best Male Country Vocal Performance 'I.O.U.' – Lee Greenwood

1982

Best Country Instrumental Performance 'Alabama Jubilee' – Roy Clark

Best Country Performance By A Duo Or Group With Vocal 'Mountain Music' – Alabama

Best Country Song 'Always On My Mind' – Willie Nelson

Best Female Country Vocal Performance 'Break It To Me Gently' – Juice Newton

Best Male Country Vocal Performance 'Always On My Mind' – Willie Nelson

1981

Best Country Instrumental Performance 'Country' – After All These Years – Chet Atkins

Best Country Performance By A Duo Or Group With Vocal 'Elvira' – The Oak Ridge Boys

Best Country Song '9 To 5' – Dolly Parton

Best Female Country Vocal Performance, '9 To 5' – Dolly Parton

Best Male Country Vocal Performance '(There's) No Gettin' Over Me' – Ronnie Milsap

1980

Best Country Instrumental Performance 'Orange Blossom Special / Hoedown' – Gilley's Urban Cowboy Band

Best Country Performance By A Duo Or Group 'That Lovin' You Feelin' Again' – Roy Orbison & Emmylou Harris

Best Country Song 'On The Road Again' – Willie Nelson

Best Female Country Vocal Performance 'Could I Have This Dance' – Anne Murray

Best Male Country Vocal Performance 'He Stopped Loving Her Today' – George Jones

1979

Best Country Instrumental Performance 'Big Sandy / Leather Britches' – Merle Watson & Doc Watson

Best Country Song 'You Decorated My Life' – Kenny Rogers

Best Country Vocal Performance By A Duo Or Group 'The Devil Went Down To Georgia' – Charlie Daniels Band

Best Female Country Vocal Performance 'Blue Kentucky Girl' – Emmylou Harris

Best Male Country Vocal Performance 'The Gambler' – Kenny Rogers

1978

Best Country Instrumental Performance 'One O'Clock Jump' – Asleep At The Wheel

Best Country Song 'The Gambler' – Kenny Rogers

Best Country Vocal Performance By A Duo Or Group 'Mamas Don't Let Your Babies Grow Up To Be Cowboys' – Waylon Jennings & Willie Nelson

Best Female Country Vocal Performance 'Here You Come Again' – Dolly Parton

Best Male Country Vocal Performance 'Georgia On My Mind' – Willie Nelson

1977

Best Country Instrumental Performance Hargus 'Pig' Robbins

Best Country Song 'Don't It Make My Brown Eyes Blue' – Crystal Gayle

Best Country Vocal Performance By A Duo or Group 'Heaven's Just A Sin Away' – The Kendalls

Best Female Country Vocal Performance 'Don't It Make My Brown Eyes Blue' – Crystal Gayle

Best Male Country Vocal Performance 'Lucille' – Kenny Rogers

1976

Best Country Instrumental Performance 'Chester And Lester' – Les Paul & Chet Atkins

Best Country Song 'Broken Lady' – Larry Gatlin

Best Country Vocal Performance By A Duo Or Group 'The End Is Not In Sight (The Cowboy Tune)' – Amazing Rhythm Aces

Best Female Country Vocal Performance 'Elite Hotel' – Emmylou Harris

Best Male Country Vocal Performance '(I'm A) Stand By My Woman Man' – Ronnie Milsap

1975

Best Country Instrumental Performance 'The Entertainer' – Chet Atkins

Best Country Song '(Hey Won't You Play) Another Somebody Done Somebody Wrong Song' – B.J. Thomas

Best Country Vocal Performance By A Duo Or Group 'Lover Please' – Kris Kristofferson & Rita Coolidge

Best Female Country Vocal Performance 'I Can't Help It (If I'm Still In Love With You)' – Linda Ronstadt

Best Male Country Vocal Performance 'Blue Eyes Crying In The Rain' – Willie Nelson

1974

Best Country Instrumental Performance 'The Atkins-Travis Traveling Show' – Merle Travis & Chet Atkins

Best Country Song 'A Very Special Love Song' – Written by Billy Sherrill & Norris Wilson, performed by Ricky Skaggs

Best Country Vocal Performance By A Duo Or Group 'Fairytale' – Pointer Sisters

Best Female Country Vocal Performance 'Love Song' – Anne Murray

Best Male Country Vocal Performance, 'Please Don't Tell Me How The Story Ends' – Ronnie Milsap

1973

Best Country Instrumental Performance 'Dueling Banjos' – Steve Mandell & Eric Weissberg

Best Country Song 'Behind Closed Doors' – Charlie Rich

Best Country Vocal Performance By A Duo Or Group 'From The Bottle To The Bottom' – Kris Kristofferson & Rita Coolidge

Best Female Country Vocal Performance 'Let Me Be There' – Olivia Newton-John

Best Male Country Vocal Performance 'Behind Closed Doors' – Charlie Rich

1972

Best Country Instrumental Performance 'Charlie McCoy/The Real McCoy' – Charlie McCoy

Best Country Song 'Kiss An Angel Good Mornin'' – Charley Pride

Best Country Vocal Performance By A Group 'Class Of '57' – The Statler Brothers

Best Female Country Vocal Performance 'Happiest Girl In The Whole USA' – Donna Fargo

Best Male Country Vocal Performance 'Charley Pride Sings Heart Songs' – Charley Pride

1971

Best Country Instrumental Performance 'Snowbird' – Chet Atkins

Best Country Song 'Help Me Make It Through The Night' – Kris Kristofferson

Best Country Vocal Performance By A Duo 'After The Fire Is Gone' – Loretta Lynn & Conway Twitty

Best Female Country Vocal Performance 'Help Me Make It Through The Night' – Sammi Smith

Best Male Country Vocal Performance 'When You're Hot, You're Hot' – Jerry Reed

1970

Best Country Instrumental Performance 'Me & Jerry' – Jerry Reed & Chet Atkins

Best Country Song 'My Woman, My Woman, My Wife' – Marty Robbins

Best Country Vocal Performance By A Duo Or Group 'If I Were A Carpenter' – Johnny Cash & June Carter

Best Female Country Vocal Performance, 'Rose Garden' – Lynn Anderson

Best Male Country Vocal Performance 'For The Good Times' – Ray Price

1969

Best Country Instrumental Performance 'The Nashville Brass Featuring Danny Davis Play More Nashville Sounds' – The Nashville Brass With Danny Davis

Best Country Song 'A Boy Named Sue' – Shel Silverstein

Best Country Vocal Performance By A Duo Or Group 'Mac Arthur Park' – The Kimberlys & Waylon Jennings

Best Female Country Vocal Performance 'Stand By Your Man' – Tammy Wynette

Best Male Country Vocal Performance 'A Boy Named Sue' – Johnny Cash

1968

Best Country Performance, Duo Or Group, Vocal Or Instrumental 'Foggy Mountain Breakdown' – Flatt & Scruggs

Best Country Song 'Little Green Apples' – Bobby Russell

Best Female Country Vocal Performance 'Harper Valley P.T.A.' – Jeannie C. Riley

Best Male Country Vocal Performance 'Folsom Prison Blues' – Johnny Cash

1967

Best Country & Western Recording 'Gentle On My Mind' – Glen Campbell

Best Country & Western Song 'Jackson' – Johnny Cash & June Carter

Best Country & Western Solo Vocal Performance, Female 'I Don't Wanna Play House' – Tammy Wynette

Best Country & Western Solo Vocal Performance, Male 'Gentle On My Mind'– Glen Campbell

1966

Best Country & Western Recording 'Almost Persuaded' – David Houston

Best Country & Western Song 'King Of The Road' – Roger Miller

Best Female Country & Western Vocal Performance 'Almost Persuaded' – David Houston

Best Male Country & Western Vocal Performance 'Don't Touch Me' – Jeannie Seely

1965

Best Country & Western Album *King Of The Road* – Roger Miller

Best Country & Western Single 'King Of The Road' – Roger Miller

Best Country & Western Song 'King Of The Road' – Roger Miller

Best Female Country & Western Vocal Performance 'Queen Of The House' – Jody Miller

Best Male Country & Western Vocal Performance 'King Of The Road' – Roger Miller

Best New Country & Western Artist The Statler Brothers

1964

Best Country & Western Album *Dang Me / Chug-A-Lug* – Roger Miller

Best Country & Western Single 'Dang Me' – Roger Miller

Best Country & Western Song 'Dang Me' – Roger Miller

Best Female Country & Western Vocal Performance 'Here Comes My Baby' – Dottie West

Best Male Country & Western Vocal Performance 'Love Song' – Roger Miller

Best New Country & Western Artist Roger Miller

1963

Best Country & Western Recording 'Detroit City' – Bobby Bare

1962

Best Country & Western Recording 'Funny Way Of Laughin'' – Burl Ives

1961

Best Country & Western Recording 'Big Bad John' – Jimmy Dean

1960

Best Country & Western Performance 'El Paso' – Marty Robbins

1959

Best Country & Western Performance 'Battle Of New Orleans' – John Horton

1958

Best Country & Western Performance 'Tom Dooley' – Kingston Trio

BIBLIOGRAPHY / REFERENCES

BOOKS

Rock' n' Roll Confidential (1984) Penny Stallings – Vermilion

Singer Songwriters (1994) – Dave DiMartino – Billboard Books

The Ultimate Lists Book (1998) Geoff Tibballs (compiler) – Carlton Books Limited

The Oxford Companion to Popular Music (1991) Peter Gammond – Oxford University Press

Rock – The Rough Guide (1996) Jonathan Buckley and Mark Ellingham plus contributing editors – Rough Guides Limited

The NME Rock 'n' Roll Years (1990) John Tobler (consultant editor) – The Hamlyn Publishing Group Ltd

Who Wrote That Song (1988) Dick Jacobs – Betterway Publications Inc.

Encyclopaedia of Rock (1987) Phil Hardy and Dave Laing – Macdonald & Co (Publishers) Ltd

Rock and Pop – Day by Day (1992) Frank Laufenberg – Blandford

On this Day in Rock (1993) John Tobler – Simon & Schuster

Rock Day By Day (1987) Steve Smith & The Diagram Group – Guinness Books

The NME Encyclopaedia of Rock (1977) Nick Logan and Bob Woffinden – Salamander Books Ltd

Blues Who's Who (1979) Sheldon Harris – Da Capo

Billboards Hottest Hot 100 Hits (1995) Fred Bronson – Billboard Books

The Rolling Stone Encyclopaedia of Rock & Roll (1983) John Pareles and Patricia Romanowski (editors) – Rolling Stone Press

The Guinness Encyclopedia of Popular Music (1992) (compiled and edited by Colin Larkin) – Guinness Publishing Ltd

Q Encyclopedia of Rock Stars (1996) Dafydd Rees & Luke Crampton – Dorling Kindersley

The Virgin Encyclopedia of Nineties Music (2000) Colin Larkin – Virgin Books

The Penguin Encyclopedia of Popular Music (1989) Donald Clarke (ed.) – Viking

Rock On: The Illustrated Encyclopedia of Rock 'n' Roll: The Modern Years: 1964-Present (1978) Norman N. Nite – Thomas Y. Crowell, Publishers

The Encyclopedia of Pop, Rock & Soul (1989) Irwin Stambler – Macmillan London Limited

1990 Recordiary 70's & 80's Music (1989) Dave Mcaleer – Dataday

Rock Chronicle – A 365 Day-By-Day Journal Covering 25 Years of Rock History (1982) Dan Formento – Sidgwick & Jackson Limited

The Gold Record (1978) Lucy Emerson – Fountain Publishing Co., Inc.

What Was The First Rock 'n' Roll Record? (1992) Jim Dawson & Steve Propes – Faber and Faber

Who Sang What on the Screen (1984) Alan Warner – Angus & Robertson Publishers

The Grammys: The Ultimate Unofficial Guide to Music's Highest Honor (1999) Thomas O'Neil and Peter Bart – Perigee Books

The Big Book of Show Business Awards (1997) David Sheward – Billboard Books

Tele Tunes 2000 (2000) Mike Preston – Mike Preston Music

Who's Who in Country Music (1993) Hugh Gregory – Weidenfelf And Nicolson

Billboard Top 1000 Singles (1986) Joel Whitburn – Billboard Publications Inc.

Classic Albums (1991) John Pidgeon and the estate of the late Roger Scott – BBC Books

30 Years of Number 1's (1990) Phil Swern and Shaun Greenfield – BBC Books

Rock Bottom – The Book of Pop Atrocities (1981) M Raker – Proteus (Publishing) Ltd

NME Who's Who in Rock & Roll (1991) John Tobler (editor) – Hamlyn Publishing Group Ltd

Top Pop Singles 1955 – 1993 (1994) Joel Whitburn – Record Research Inc. (TPS)

British Hit Singles (13th Edition) (2000) David Roberts (Managing Editor) –

Guinness World Records Ltd

Billboard Top 10 Charts 1958–1997 (1998) Joel Whitburn – Record Research Inc.

The Billboard Book of Number One Hits (1998) Fred Bronson – Billboard Books

The Billboard Book of Number One Adult Contemporary Hits (1999) Wesley Hyatt – Watson-Guptill Publications

MTV-Cyclopedia (1997) Nick Duerden, Ian Gittins, Shaun Phillips – Carlton Books Limited

The Name of the Game (1986) Glenn A. Baker – GRR/Pavilion

The New Book of Rock Lists (1994) Dave Marsh & James Bernard – Sidgwick & Jackson

Q Encyclopedia of Rock Stars (1996) Dafydd Rees & Luke Crampton – Dorling Kindersley Limited

The Virgin Encyclopedia of Nineties Music (2000) Colin Larkin – Virgin Books

Rock Confidential (2000) Coral Amende – Plume

Rock Names from A to Z (1994) Adam Dolgins – Pan Macmillan Limited

The Complete Book of the British Charts, Singles and Albums (2000) Tony Brown, Jon Kutner & Neil Warwick – Omnibus Press

Boy Power (1999) Billboard Books

Girl Power (1999) Billboard Books

MAGAZINES

Music Week
Q
NME
Billboard
Smash Hits

Brutally he tw_____ _____ until she cried out with pain.

'Doon't you want to know wheer your fuckin' brother is?'

She nodded, but remained silent, and kept her head bent down to avoid his eyes, knowing that he was waiting for some look or gesture or word from her which he would claim was threatening and use as an excuse to launch a vicious assault.

'Your precious brother is in the 'orspital. He might be dead by now,' he informed her with brutal glee.

'Oh no!' Eva felt sick and faint, and the shock momentarily overlaid her fear of her husband. She demanded desperately, 'What happened? How bad is he hurt? When did it happen?'

He grinned, happy with the effect his news had had, and released her wrist to pick up his mug of beer.

Introduction

The summer of 1914 was the summer of a dream. Long, hot sunlit days followed unbrokenly one after the other. The people of this story believed that despite the uncertainties and traumas of their own lives the secure and ordered world that they lived in would never change . . . But the thunderclouds of war were gathering, and before the summer ended that secure and ordered world would be changed forever.

1

Chapter One

Redditch, Worcestershire. May 1914.

The afternoon meeting of the United Methodist Sunday School was drawing to its close.

> 'Jesus, Friend of little children,
> Be a friend to me;
> Take my hand and ever keep me
> Close to Theeeee . . .'

The children's voices soared high and sweet but on this Sunday afternoon Josie Kitson took no pleasure from the melodious chorus. She bent low over the keyboard, her fingers moving automatically across the yellowed ivory keys, her mind troubled by an ever-increasing nervousness. She sensed the man's eyes upon her, but could not bring herself to lift her head and meet his gaze.

I should never have promised him! she thought regretfully. I shouldn't have done it.

Clement Hulme stared over the heads of the singing children, hungry impatience gnawing within him as he studied the slender figure seated at the upright piano. That impatience drove him to instruct loudly, 'Go straight to the last verse, children.'

They obeyed the instruction.

> '. . . Never leave me or forsake me
> Ever be my Friend,
> For I need Thee from life's dawning
> Toooo itsss ennnnddd. Aaaamennnn . . .'

3

The hymn ended and Hulme gabbled quickly through the closing prayer and dismissed the Sunday School class.

'Shall I collect the hymnbooks, Mister Hulme,' a small girl offered.

Hulme shook his head and told her curtly, 'No thank you, get off home with you.'

He shepherded the chattering children out of the large room, and with a sigh of relief bolted the door behind them.

The young woman was still seated upon the piano stool as he went eagerly towards her. Her head was bowed, her hands clasped together upon her lap.

Her body stiffened as she felt his hands come around her from behind and clasp her breasts, and she was lifted from the stool. His wet lips sucked the side of her throat and he crushed his lower body against her buttocks.

Fear swept through her as he roughly turned her to him, and she tried to draw her face back from his greedy mouth.

'No, Clem! No, don't do this. Please! Please, Clem.'

He ignored her protests, his breathing harsh and rapid as he told her huskily, 'I love you, Josie, and you love me. We both want this. I've waited so long. I love you. I love you.'

His hands tugged at her long skirt and petticoat, lifting them around her hips, and his fingers feverishly clutched the soft warm skin beneath her drawers, and sought to penetrate between her thighs.

'No!' Tears sprang into her eyes, and fear caused her to struggle violently.

A scowl twisted his full lips and he hissed furiously, 'You promised. You promised to let me. If you really loved me you'd let me.'

Guilt and distress coursed through her, and she fell silent, and momentarily her struggles ceased.

He glared questioningly at her, his face flushed and glowing in the sunlight that streamed through the tall windows.

'You were lying to me, weren't you? You were lying when you told me that you loved me,' he challenged aggressively. 'You've just been playing with me. Just leading me on to make a fool of me.'

She shook her head. 'No, Clem, no. I do love you. You know that I do.'

'Then why are you acting like this?' he demanded.

'What if you make me pregnant?' she retorted.

'Don't talk like a fool. I'll take precautions.' He pulled out a small tin from his pocket. 'I brought this with me.'

While she stared with wide, shocked eyes, he opened the tin and extracted a piece of sponge which smelled of strong vinegar and had a long trailing thread attached to it.

Then his mouth clamped upon hers once more, and he bore her beneath him to the floor. His weight crushed her and she felt weak and powerless against his strength. His hand moved down her belly and his fingers entered her moistness, and despite her fear she experienced a thrill of sexual excitement. He drew her drawers down and his legs parted her thighs. Again his fingers entered her, and she felt the cold wetness of the sponge pushed deep inside her flesh.

'There now, sweetheart, it'll be safe now. It'll be safe,' he panted hoarsely. 'Now let me love you, darling. Let me love you.'

After a momentary resistance she surrendered to the long-denied, overwhelming hungers of her flesh and ceased from struggling against him. Then his hard maleness thrust into her, and sharp pain lanced through her. Grunting, he drove deep within her, and as his excitement increased so his hips pounded harder and harder upon her.

'I love you, Josie. I love you,' he panted into her ear. And she felt as if she were suffocating as his wet mouth smothered her own.

Her eyes were tightly closed, and at first she gasped and whimpered beneath his brutal onslaught, then her pain gradually became mingled and overlaid with sweaty, breathless lust. She clutched his shoulders with hooked fingers, crying out and rearing her hips against him as thrills of ecstasy shuddered through her. She heard him emit a harsh, guttural cry, and the pounding abruptly ceased.

No, don't stop. Don't stop! She wanted him to go on, but instead she felt him pull out from her flesh, and his crushing weight lift from her, and instead of fulfilment she experienced a momentary resentment of frustration.

Curiously she waited for some tremendous feeling to overwhelm her. Some deep emotional reaction to this entry into full womanhood. But there was only a strange numbness in her mind, and a sense of detachment, as if what had just happened to her was of no real importance.

'Come on, get up and straighten your clothes. What if somebody comes knocking on the door? I'll be ruined!'

His voice was laced with panic and she opened her eyes, and blinked puzzledly up at him. He was standing, feverishly tucking his shirt into his trousers and buttoning up his flies.

'Get up, Josie, damm you! What if somebody comes?' Anger was in his voice, and fear in his eyes. 'I'll be ruined if you're seen like this. Cover yourself up, can't you. Make yourself look decent.'

She raised herself up on her elbows and shamed embarrassment flooded through her as she saw the white nakedness of her belly and thighs. Her face flamed as she struggled to her feet and pulled out the piece of sponge, which he snatched from her.

'I'll get rid of this.' He walked away towards the toilet and she hurriedly readjusted her clothing.

When he returned, he pulled a large handkerchief from his pocket and mopped his sweating face, then ran his hands over his head, smoothing his pomaded hair. His fingers moved restlessly to straighten his tie and clothing, and he questioned anxiously, 'How do I look? Am I tidy?'

She was unable to comprehend his changed attitude. The abrupt transformation from eager, powerful lover to impatient, fearful stranger.

'Yes, you're tidy.'

He stared at her suspiciously, and she felt driven to ask, 'Why do you look at me like that?'

He shook his head and muttered, 'It's nothing.' But still his eyes were questioning, and she persisted.

'What's the matter, Clem?'

He shrugged and replied petulantly, 'Well, if you must know, it's the way you're acting. You're so cool and calm, it's hard to believe that this was your first time.'

Indignation sparked, and she grimaced as the sore wetness between her legs made its presence unpleasantly noticeable. She answered sharply, 'It was my first time, Clem. And you know very well it was.'

6

He was much calmer himself now that they were both properly dressed.

'Turn round,' he instructed, and frowned as he saw the dust on the back of her dark dress. 'Have you got a brush with you?'

'No,' she told him.

He shook his head as if to deplore her lack of forethought, and then tried to clean the dust from her clothing with his hands, muttering angrily beneath his breath as he slapped and brushed.

'There, that will have to do. If anyone notices, you must tell them that you brushed against a wall or something.'

Then he saw that the knees of his trousers were also coated with dust, and frantically scrubbed at the stains with his hands, while she watched with a hint of a bleak, sardonic smile quirking her lips.

This was not the way she had dreamed that her first experience of physical love would be, or how her lover would behave.

'Don't just stand there,' he snapped impatiently. 'Go and unbolt the door.'

She did as he said, and when she returned he appeared to be in better temper.

'There now, if anyone comes they won't think anything's amiss, will they? Come on, let's collect the hymnbooks and leave the place tidy.'

Silently Josie joined him in collecting the books and arranging them in neat piles upon the table which stood before the serried rows of benches. As she moved she felt the discomfort of ravaged intimate flesh, but to her own perplexity the strange partial numbness of emotion persisted. It was as if this body that she inhabited was nothing to do with her, and what had just happened to it was of no personal concern.

By the time the books had all been collected and stacked, Clement Hulme was humming happily to himself.

He put on his bowler hat and they walked to the door. Before he opened it he pulled her hard against him and kissed her passionately, his hands cupping her rounded buttocks, fingers kneading the firm flesh.

7

She stood passively, her arms at her sides, and he pulled his head back, annoyed at her lack of response.

'What's the matter?'

'Nothing,' she told him quietly.

He opened his mouth as if to speak, but before he could do so she pointed out, 'I have to go, Clem. My mother will want to know why I'm so late.'

Frowning, he nodded. 'All right.'

The street outside the chapel was quiet and deserted and the shadows cast by the sun were already beginning to lengthen. But both of them were well aware that from behind the net curtains of the houses, curious eyes could be observing them.

'It's best we part here, Josie.' He lifted his hat in farewell. 'Will you be at the service tonight?'

She shrugged indifferently. 'I don't know. It depends on how well Mother is feeling.'

He stared doubtfully at her.

'Are you feeling all right? Are you angry with me? Did I hurt you?'

She shook her head to the questions, then turned and walked away from him.

For a moment he continued to stare after her with doubtful eyes, then, frowning, went off in the opposite direction.

'Where have you been, Josie? Just look at the time. I've had the table laid for more than an hour. Really, it's too bad of you. This pot of tea will have to be thrown away. It's gone cold. It's such a dreadful waste.' Dorothy Kitson's voice was shrill with resentment as she flustered around the table, where a sparse meal was set out upon a starched, pristine white cloth.

'You could have started without me, Mother,' Josie told her.

The older woman's plump, pasty face assumed an expression of affront. 'Start without you? Why, the very idea of it. Good-class families take their meals together, my girl. Only low and common people eat in relays. I don't know where you get your ideas from, I really don't. Not from me, that's for sure. Why are you so late anyway?'

With sardonic amusement Josie wondered how her mother would react if she were to tell her, I'm late because Clement

Hulme has been having sexual intercourse with me on the chapel floor . . .

Aloud she explained, 'I was helping Mr Hulme to clear up after the class had finished. There was more to do than usual.'

'Helping Mr Hulme.' The older woman seemed pleased. 'That man is a saint! He really is a true Christian. How he copes with that wife of his and all those children I just do not know. And he works so hard for the chapel! He's a saint, he really is. A model husband and father. It's a pity there aren't more men like him.'

Now, suddenly, all the strange numbness of emotion abruptly disappeared and terrible guilt flooded through Josie. She felt her face flush with hot shame as the squalid reality of what had just happened between herself and the man struck home.

'I'll not be a minute,' she blurted, and rushed out of the room and up the stairs to hide her shame and guilt from her mother's searching eyes.

In her own bedroom she sank down on to her knees and buried her face in her hands. Tears stung her eyes and a sob tore from her throat.

What have I done? she castigated herself in bitter remorse. Dear God, what have I done? I'm nothing but a slut. A dirty slut.

She rocked backwards and forwards upon her knees, trying desperately to stifle her sobs, fearful that her mother would discover her like this.

Oh God, forgive me! Forgive me, she begged silently. I'll never do it again. Never . . .

But even as she promised, the memory of how Clem Hulme had felt inside her invaded her mind, and despite all her efforts, it persisted and strengthened, and with bitter self-disgust she was forced to acknowledge that he had awakened an appetite that she was not sure she would be able to suppress.

'Josie? Josie?' her mother shrilled up the stairs. 'What are you doing up there? I'm waiting to start.'

The young woman drew a long, shuddering breath and fought to control the tremor in her voice.

'All right, Mother, I'm coming.'

She rose and went to stare anxiously into the mirror of her

9

dressing table, and the yellowed glass showed her reddened, puffy eyes.

'Josie, are you coming or not?' Again the shrill demand echoed, and again the young woman answered.

'I'm coming, just wait a moment, can't you?'

She splashed cold water from the jug on the washstand and rubbed her face hard with the towel. The rough treatment brought the blood to her face and cheeks and the resultant flush served to disguise her reddened eyes a little.

Dorothy Kitson peered suspiciously at her daughter when she seated herself at the table.

'You're all red in the face, and your eyes are puffed up. Have you been crying?'

Josie forced a smile. 'No, of course not. It's my hay fever, I think. I was sneezing on the way home from chapel.'

After a moment the older woman nodded. 'Yes, I'm not surprised. I've never known it to be so hot and dry this early in the year.'

The two women ate their meagre meal of bread and butter and tea without speaking, and Josie was grateful for the silence. She thought on what had happened between herself and Clement Hulme in the chapel schoolroom, and once more resolved that it must never happen again. When she thought of the man's wife and children, her guilt was so intense that a lump came to her throat and she could not swallow the bread in her mouth and had to gulp from her cup of tea to wash the food down her gullet.

Yet still the memories tormented her of how she had reacted to his loving. Of the ravening desires that had dominated her. Of the exquisite lustful pleasure that had thrilled through her body.

'Josie? What's the matter with you, girl?' The older woman's loud shout brought a flustered Josie back to her present surroundings.

'What is it, Mother?'

'I've asked you a question twice, and you've just ignored me,' her mother stated indignantly. 'Is that hayfever affecting your senses, girl?'

Josie took a firm grip on her wandering thoughts, and asked, 'What was the question, Mother?'

'I asked you who's taking the service tonight? I hope it's Mr Hulme. I like the hymns he chooses. The Reverend Mullins preaches a good sermon, but he chooses all the hymns that I don't like. I'm in the mood for a lively tune.'

The prospect of seeing Clement Hulme filled Josie with sudden dread.

'Did you want to go to chapel tonight, then?'

'That's what I'm saying, isn't it?' the older woman challenged petulantly.

Normally Josie would have behaved as a dutiful daughter and obediently pushed her mother's wheelchair up the series of hills that intervened between their home and the Methodist Chapel. But tonight she could not face the prospect of returning to the scene of her shame, and being forced to see and speak with Clement Hulme. She felt that if she was to do so then in some way she would betray herself, and all the world would recognise what had happened between them.

She shook her head and blurted out, 'I'm sorry, Mother. But I'm not well enough to go to chapel with you this evening. My hay fever is making me feel really ill. I'll have to go to bed after I've cleared up here.'

The pasty fat face opposite her displayed sudden fury. 'You selfish little wretch! You mean, selfish little wretch!'

The familiar tirade began, and went on, and on, and on, and Josie Kitson sat with bowed head and endured as she had endured so often in the past.

But this time she did not weaken and give way to her mother's demands. Instead, when the older woman at last tired and fell silent, Josie cleared the table and washed up the soiled plates and utensils, then wished her mother goodnight, and went to her bed.

It was still light outside, and in her shadowed room the young woman took off her clothes and unpinned her long hair, letting it fall about her shoulders. Then she went to stand before her mirror and stared at the reflection of her face and naked body. She was not pretty, but she had good teeth and clear blue eyes, and her light brown hair was lustrous, her skin without blemish. Her slender body was shapely, hips rounded, breasts high and firm. Without vanity she considered that she was not unattractive. Yet the only man who had ever professed to love her was Clement Hulme.

I'm twenty-six, and the only lover I've ever known is a married man, she thought with guilty remorse, which after a moment became tinged with resentment at the injustice of life.

Since childhood she had prayed nightly before sleep. As she had grown older the prayer had become more of a habit than any deep expression of faith. But tonight she prayed with an intensity and need that she had not experienced for long years. She prayed that God would help her to be strong enough to break with Clement Hulme. That she would be strong enough to control the hungers of her flesh.

Comforted, she lay down, and eventually slept. But with that sleep came vivid dreams, and her body moved restlessly, and from her parted lips came moans of pleasure as in that phantom world she once more surrendered to the passionate embraces of her lover.

Chapter Two

At five minutes to nine o'clock on Monday morning the pupils and staff of the Bridge Street Council School assembled for prayers in the large, vaulted main hall. The boys were ranked on the right side of the hall, the girls on the left, and the infants in front, while the senior pupil monitors guarded the entrance to prevent latecomers sneaking in, or reluctant attenders sneaking out.

Led by the school and boys' headmaster, James Parnell, the staff filed into the hall and mounted the low platform at its far end. Josie Kitson took her normal position slightly to the right rear of the girls' headmistress, Camelia Blunt, a middle-aged, angular spinster, whose grim expression masked a gentle heart.

'Silence!' Parnell bellowed, and the chorus of coughing and mutterings instantly hushed.

The headmaster bore a distinct facial resemblance to the reigning monarch, King George V, and secretly gloried in that fact, even heightening the resemblance by trimming his hair, beard and moustache in the style favoured by the 'Sailor King'.

'Let us pray.' Parnell bowed his head and clasped his hands together in front of his chest, but his bulging blue eyes continued to sweep over the assembly, and the pupils dutifully closed their own eyes, bowed their heads and clasped their hands before their faces.

'Our Father which art in Heaven, Hallowed be Thy Name . . .'

After the Lord's Prayer, Parnell then offered up his own personal prayer to the Deity, begging the Lord to shower his blessings on 'Their most Gracious Majesties, King George and

Queen Mary. On the Prime Minister and the Government. On the British Empire. On the Great and Good. On the Judiciary. On the Royal Navy. On the Army. On the Clergy. On the Managing Committee of the Bridge Street School. On all the various benefactors of the Bridge Street School . . .' The list seemed endless, and there were restless shufflings from the body of the hall.

At last the prayer ended, and the children let out a heartfelt 'Amen!'

But no one attempted to let their hands fall, or to open their eyes, until Parnell ordered, 'Stand to attention!'

Hands flashed down to sides, eyes opened, heads and bodies stretched to stiff erectness.

Satisfied, Parnell ordered, 'Stand at ease.'

The relaxation engendered a sudden outburst of chattering, provoking a bellow of 'Silence!'

And a hush fell again.

'I have some announcements to make. Pay attention all of you. The school nurse will be carrying out an inspection today. I hope therefore that your standards of personal hygiene have improved from her previous inspection.'

Many children exchanged troubled looks of foreboding.

Now James Parnell's bulging blue eyes became fierce. 'Sergeant Sinclair has reported to me that certain boys absconded from the drill period on Friday afternoon. He has also reported that other boys were insolent, inattentive and lazy . . . The following boys will therefore report to my study immediately after their class roll-calls.'

He read out a list of names, and the designated boys grimaced at each other in fearful consternation, knowing that this dread summons meant that their tender buttocks would soon be feeling the painful lash of the long, thick leather strap that hung on the wall behind the headmaster's desk.

'Now, to turn to worthier matters.' A smile wreathed the headmaster's lips and he drew himself up to his full height of six feet. 'You all know what we celebrate on the twenty-fourth day of this month. The twenty-fourth of May is Empire Day.' His eyes gleamed with pride. 'On that day, together with their most Gracious Majesties, and all the other citizens of our great family of nations, we shall celebrate the glory of our empire.

14

The greatest empire the world has ever known. The empire on which the sun never sets. Our nation holds dominion over the oceans of the world, and our flag flies on every continent. Over palm and pine, prairie and forest, mountain and coral strand. We are the rulers of countless millions of less fortunate breeds. Our wealth and power exalt us above all other nations in this world, and God has given us the right to rule . . .'

Josie Kitson listened to the familiar oration with mixed feelings. She was a patriot and proud to be British, but she could not help but wonder what benefits from the ownership of this mightiest of empires accrued to these children of the poor who were ranked before her. Her gaze wandered across the close-packed ranks. She saw the ragged clothing, the pallid features and stunted bodies of the undernourished and sickly, the matted, unbrushed hair, the ingrained dirt on necks and faces. She knew the fetid hovels that many of these children dwelt in, the dire ignorance and poverty that were their birthrights.

'. . . You are the children of that empire. You are the imperial race . . .' Parnell's voice thundered, and his eyes gleamed with pride and passion. 'Someday you boys and girls may be called upon to stand forth in your empire's defence. To defend it against the attacks of the wicked foreign tyrants who wish for our downfall and ruin. When that day comes, I am confident that you will not shame your brave forefathers, who time and time again took up arms in England's cause and destroyed her enemies. Until that day of battle comes you must all conduct yourselves so that you are worthy to bear the name of English boys and English girls.'

He raised both arms on high and thundered, 'Now then, school, let us give three hearty cheers for the red, white and blue . . . Hip hip hip . . .'

'Hurraayyy, hurraayyy, hurraayyy . . .' the childish voices screamed in enthusiastic concert.

Then Parnell dismissed the assembly and the children streamed out excitedly into the playground, where they would be remustered into their classes by the teachers and marched into their respective classrooms.

As Josie Kitson moved about the playground collecting her infant class together, Camelia Blunt came to her.

'Miss Kitson, Miss Ward will take over your class today. I want you to superintend the girls at the nurse's inspection.'

'Very well, ma'am,' Josie agreed.

The older woman smiled sympathetically. 'I know it's not the pleasantest of duties, Miss Kitson. But some of our girls become quite upset during the course of the inspection. That's why I want you to supervise them. Some of our other ladies lack the necessary experience to deal with any such upsets. The nurse will be in the rear classroom of the main hall. Perhaps you could check to see if she has arrived. If so, then directly after roll-call you may take the first batch of girls in to her. I suggest we commence with Standard Three.'

'Very well, ma'am.' Josie hurried into the main hall where the monitors were busily dragging the movable partitions across to divide the hall into separate classrooms. She saw the white dress of the nurse ahead of her, and turned back.

When she returned with the first group of ten-year-old girls the nurse was sitting at a desk, with a large ledger open before her. On a small table by her side was set out a collection of bottles and small tin basins. Her grim-looking, rawboned female assistant was standing to one side of the table, pulling on a pair of rubber gloves and donning a long, enveloping rubber apron.

The nurse was dour-faced and heftily built. She frowned at the incomers and ordered brusquely, 'Line up in single file facing that wall there.'

The girls dutifully obeyed.

'No chattering,' the nurse ordered unnecessarily, because no girl was making any attempt to talk to another.

'When my assistant comes to you, you are to shout out your name and your address.'

She nodded to the rawboned woman, who moved to the end of the line of small girls.

Josie experienced a fleeting sense of pity as she looked along the line. Each girl was wearing a smock pinafore over her clothing, grey, or white, or dark blue in colour. It was possible to judge the quality of the home care the girls received from the condition of the pinafores, and of their long hair. All too many of the garments were dirty and ragged, and the hair matted and greasy.

16

Because Josie customarily taught the infants she did not know many of these girls by name, or even by sight. But her attention was drawn to one girl halfway along the line. While her neighbours were short for their age, she was tall and upright. Her long blonde hair shone with brushing. Her white pinafore, although threadbare, was clean and well pressed. Her skin glowed with health and cleanliness.

Who can you be? Josie was intrigued.

'What's your name and address, girl?' the raw-boned assistant demanded from the first girl in the line, who answered meekly, 'It's Agatha, miss. Agatha Oats.'

'Address?'

'I lives in Hill Street, miss.'

'Speak up, I can't hear that mumbling,' the nurse shouted irritably.

The small, stunted child became visibly nervous. She gulped hard, then piped in a high-pitched voice, 'Me name's Agatha Oats, miss, and I lives in Hill Street.'

'What number?' the nurse wanted to know, and the child shook her head helplessly.

'What number, you stupid girl?' the nurse shouted angrily.

Josie's indignation boiled at this bullying. Although she did not know the girl or her address, she intervened to save her from further harassment. 'The child lives at number eighteen, Hill Street,' she told the woman sharply.

The nurse nodded a surly acknowledgement and noted the details in the ledger.

Agatha Oats cried out in pain as the assistant roughly tugged and pulled at her matted hair, scowling as she informed the nurse, 'Bad infestation, Sister! She's filthy dirty!' She roughly shook the girl by the hair, causing the child to cry out loudly in distress. 'You filthy little tyke! Take your dress off . . .'

The girl began to weep, and fumbled for the tie strings of her pinafore, while the assistant moved on to the next child in line.

The rough handling continued as the inspection progressed, and few girls escaped some harsh censure from either the nurse or her assistant. Josie fumed as she watched, helpless to intervene.

Then it was the turn of the blonde-haired girl to be inspected.

17

'Marie Gurden. Number six court, Edward Street,' she called out in a clear tone, and Josie was struck by the strange accent. The girl didn't sound English. Her accent was like that of an American whom Josie had met and talked with some years previously.

The assistant completed the head examination and then moved back to the start of the line to begin checking the bodies of those girls she had ordered to undress.

Josie's pity intensified as she saw the embarrassment and shame of the selected girls. For the most part their bodies were painfully thin, and on their dirty, pallid skins many bore the discolorations of bruising, and the pustules and scabs of vermin bites.

The inspection was completed, and the treatment commenced. The assistant doused the lice-infested scalps with strong-smelling crude kerosene oil, and used an ether spray on the body parts. Then she instructed, 'When you get home you must wash your hair and body, and apply some soothing ointment. And you must tell your mothers to bake your clothes in the oven. The heat must be at least two hundred degrees Fahrenheit.'

The wan faces stared at her in blank incomprehension.

'Very well. We're ready for the next group,' the nurse informed Josie, who nodded curtly and ushered the girls out.

As the group walked back to their own classroom Josie asked the blonde-haired girl, 'Where are you from, Marie? You're not English, are you?'

The girl smiled, displaying another rarity among the children of Bridge Street School, a set of sound white teeth.

'I am English, miss. But I've been raised in Canada. My pa brought me back here a few weeks since.'

Josie was interested, and would have liked to question the girl further, but time was pressing, so she merely smiled and told her, 'Well, I hope you'll enjoy being back in the mother country.'

The girl mock-pouted, and with a mischievous grin answered, 'I don't think that those two back there were behaving very motherly, were they, miss? They were acting more like Cinderella's ugly sisters.'

Josie tried to look stern at such a display of disrespect

towards authority, but could not help smiling fleetingly in rueful agreement. However, she still warned the girl sharply, 'Don't speak like that about your elders, Marie. Show respect.'

But the girl had noted the fleeting smile, and only grinned cheerfully.

The hours passed and Josie was grateful to be kept busy shepherding the parties of girls back and forth. It helped her to keep at bay the troubling memory of what had happened between herself and Clement Hulme the previous afternoon. But inevitably that memory intruded, and during the midday break from noon until two o'clock, she did not follow her usual custom and join the other teachers in the small room which they used as their rest place, but instead put on her hat and coat and wandered out of the school. Facing the front gates were long, grimy Edward Street and Britten Street stretching southwards. To her left was the large factory of William Woodfield and the bustling railway goods yard. She turned to her right and walked along the pathway which led between the factory yard of the cable works and the newly cultivated allotments, and onwards to the fields beyond.

The day was warm and pleasant, and as she left the industrial enclave behind her so the air lost its smoky pollution and became clear and sweet to breathe. Birds sang in the hedgerows and flowers shed their scent, but Josie was unconscious of these natural delights. Her mind was filled with anxiety and regret.

The sharp visual image of Clement Hulme's face and body imposed itself upon her, and she found herself wondering why she had ever imagined that she was so madly in love with him. She did not find him particularly physically attractive. He was middle-aged and overweight, with a protuberant paunch and heavy jowls, and his teeth were ill-shaped and discoloured. His manner radiated enormous self-conceit, and she knew that he was both avaricious and mean. He was overbearing and contemptuous towards those beneath him in the social scale, and obsequious to those above him.

She felt a sense of bewilderment. He is everything that I dislike in a man, and yet I surrendered to him. When he took hold of me I wanted him.

A surge of disgust for her own bodily appetites suddenly overwhelmed her.

19

I'm a slut! A whore!

She wanted to punish herself, to inflict pain on her treacherous body, which had so betrayed her with its hunger for a man's loving.

But even as she berated herself, she could feel the insidious, unholy stirrings in her groin, the swelling of her breasts and the tautening of her nipples as she remembered how his manhood had filled the aching emptiness within her, and momentarily there came again the raging lust which had transformed her into a mindless creature of flesh, blind to everything but the need to satisfy that terrible, ravenous sexual hunger.

'God help me,' she groaned aloud as she realised that if in this moment Clement Hulme was to come upon her and take her in his arms, she would once more surrender.

The awful awareness filled her with an unreasoning panic, and she turned and hurried back towards the close-packed buildings, as if to seek sanctuary beneath their smoky pall.

'Oh there you are, Josie. I was wondering where you'd got to.' Emily Burgess, head of the infants school smiled, and patted the empty chair beside her in invitation. She was a plump little woman in her late thirties, with bright, birdlike eyes and a generous mouth on which laughter seemed to be hovering constantly.

The rest room was half empty; only Emily and two male teachers were present. As Josie sat down and removed her broad-brimmed flowered hat, the other woman smiled again, and nodding towards the two men, stage-whispered, 'You're just in time for Mr Billington's declaration of war against the Kaiser.'

Josie giggled, and Howard Billington, a young, fresh-featured, athletic-looking man, scowled and said sharply, 'Oh, very funny, Miss Burgess. Very witty indeed!'

The second man, Thomas Mould, laughed, then coughed heavily and snatching a large handkerchief from his pocket buried his face in its capacious folds until the fit of coughing ceased. His eyes were worried as he briefly stared into the handkerchief, before folding it up and returning it to his pocket.

The two women exchanged pitying glances. Thomas Mould,

barely thirty, yet appearing twenty years older, was suffering from the onset of consumption.

'Pray, do continue, Mr Billington,' Emily invited with a teasing smile. 'I'm sure Miss Kitson is all agog to hear what you intend doing to the Kaiser.'

'You may mock as much as you please, Miss Burgess.' The young man was very serious. 'But I happen to be in a position to know that unless we strike first, Kaiser Wilhelm and the German General Staff will launch a surprise attack against us. More than likely it will be an invasion. Landings of German troops will take place all along the Norfolk and Suffolk coasts.'

The plump woman widened her eyes in assumed horror and gasped, 'Goodness, Mr Billington! That is terrifying news. Where did you obtain such information?'

He shook his head and assumed an air of mystery. 'You know that I can't divulge my sources, Miss Burgess. It's a military secret.'

'Then how did you come by it?' she challenged.

He smiled at her with a superior air. 'Well, Miss Burgess, I'm a military man, am I not?'

Billington was a gunner in the local artillery battery of the Territorial Army.

Josie was hard put to keep from giggling. She thought that her friend was very cruel to torment this young man, as she so frequently did. But at the same time she enjoyed seeing his pompous conceit deflated.

When Emily did not reply, Howard Billington visibly preened in triumph, and stroked the soldierly moustache of which he was inordinately proud.

Then the plump little woman asked him innocently, 'This secret information, Mr Billington. Were all you Territorials informed of it?'

He nodded carelessly.

'Then why am I not allowed to know it? After all, I'm sure that some of your comrades have already told their wives or friends.'

He frowned sternly. 'If they have, then they'll be in very hot water. Very hot water indeed. I wouldn't hesitate to shoot any man that I found behaving so treacherously.'

21

'That seems very extreme, Mr Billington,' Emily protested.'

The young man puffed out his chest and announced portentously, 'When our country is in such extreme peril, Miss Burgess, then we military men have a duty to mete out extreme punishments to those who would betray us.'

The little woman looked very perturbed, and murmured, 'Oh dear, Mr Billington. You have placed me in an extremely difficult position.'

'How?' He stared in blank puzzlement.

She shook her head, and muttered, as if in distress, 'I hold a man's life in my hands. Oh dear me! What shall I do? What shall I do?'

His face mirrored his own uncertainty. 'I don't understand, Miss Burgess.'

Josie was struggling to keep from bursting into laughter, as her friend began to wring her hands as if under terrible stress.

'What shall I do?' Emily implored the ceiling. 'What shall I do? I hold a man's life in my hands.' She looked directly at Howard Billington, and beseeched him, 'You could not be so ruthless, surely, Mr Billington, as to shoot a traitor?'

After a moment's hesitation, he nodded and stated vehemently, 'I am a soldier, Miss Burgess. And a soldier must do his duty. I shall never shirk doing my duty.'

For some moments Emily bit her lip in indecision. Then she nodded her head, and declared firmly, 'Very well, Mr Billington. I also will do my duty. You have made me feel ashamed to do otherwise.'

'Good show!' the young man applauded.

'Thank you, Mr Billington,' Emily gushed gratefully, and now Josie did erupt with laughter and buried her face in her hands. It took her several seconds to control herself, and then she apologised.

'I'm sorry, it's my hay fever. It sometimes attacks me like this.'

Billington scowled suspiciously before Emily intervened to draw his attention back to herself.

'I am going to do my duty, as you have advised me to, Mr Billington. I am going to name the traitor who has been telling people the details of this secret information you are guarding.'

His eyes widened with shock, and he gasped, 'Who is it?'

Emily rose to her feet, and flung out one arm to point at his face, then declaimed dramatically, 'He is an officer. His name is Major William Tunbridge. He's my neighbour. And he told his wife, and she told me. The secret information is the content of a lecture which was given to senior army officers by a Professor Smythe concerning a hypothetical German landing on the east coast. Shoot him, Mr Billington. He is the traitor.'

Howard Billington sagged back into his chair and exclaimed, 'But he's my battery commander. I can't shoot him!'

'Then I will!' Emily declared.

Josie looked at the young man's horrified expression and burst into laughter again. Thomas Mould was holding his sides and choking with glee, and Howard Billington's face darkened with fury.

'Oh, that's very funny, Miss Burgess!' he exclaimed witheringly. 'Very witty indeed!'

He jumped to his feet and stormed out of the room, slamming the door behind him with a resounding crash.

'You're too cruel to him, Emily,' Josie gasped out between peals of laughter.

Laughing herself, the little woman replied, 'It serves the pompous young fool right. He thinks that we women are simpletons who don't know anything at all about what's going on in the world. And that he can tell us any nonsensical tale and we'll believe him.'

Thomas Mould was suddenly racked by another fit of coughing, and this sobered the two women, who hurried to support his heaving body, and to fetch him a cup of water to sip at when his coughing had subsided.

Serious now, Josie asked her friend, 'Do you think that there will be a war between us and Germany, Emily? Do you, Thomas? I know that the papers are always going on about the arms race between us, and how the Germans are catching us up in naval construction, and the Kaiser keeps making threats against us. But surely it can't lead to war, can it?'

Emily looked suddenly sad. 'I pray to God that it won't. I

lost my eldest brother in the Boer War. I don't want to lose my younger brothers in another war.'

'What do you think, Thomas?' Josie turned to him.

He shrugged his bowed shoulders. 'I really don't know. But I don't think that the Kaiser would be stupid enough to fight the French Army and the British Navy together. And then there are the Russians. They're allied to France. No, I don't really think that Germany will attack any of us.'

Josie thought of her own brother, who was serving in the Royal Navy with the Mediterranean Fleet.

'Oh God, I hope that there won't be a war. I can't bear to think of it.'

The dread prospect filled her thoughts for the remainder of that day. And yet, despite her fear of war, a vague tingling of excitement hovered in the depths of her mind. A European war would have a radical effect upon millions of people's lives, perhaps even bring change into her own seemingly pointless existence.

Chapter Three

Life suddenly became difficult for Josie Kitson. Normally many of her evenings were filled by chapel activities. She regularly attended, or helped at, the weekday services, the Society of Christian Endeavour, the Band of Hope, the charitable Clothing Club. It was not that she was devoutly religious, or even particularly interested in these chapel activities, but she needed to get out of the stifling confines of her home, and away from her mother's constant nagging and complaining, and these functions had been her means of escape, of gaining brief respites. Now, they were suddenly denied her, because she dreaded having to see and talk with Clement Hulme again. So she stayed at home in the evenings, telling her mother that she did not feel well enough to go to the chapel, and spending the long lonely hours in her bedroom, trying to read or do embroidery, but instead mostly finding herself gazing unseeingly through the net curtains of her window, her mind filled with imaginings and visual images that both troubled and excited her.

She was sufficiently honest with herself to admit that she was not in any physical fear of Clement Hulme. She knew the man well enough to know that if she was firm and determined in refusal, then he would eventually accept that their relationship was over. Her fear was of herself, and what she perceived to be her own weakness. Whenever she had leisure to be by herself and do nothing, then sexual desire insidiously invaded her mind and body, tormenting her until at times she feverishly sought to satisfy her cravings by caressing herself and rubbing her body against the long, hard bolster on her bed. Relief would come with shudderings of physical ecstacy, and bitter shame and remorse would then assail her that she could surrender to what she considered her shameful lusts in such a sordid and bestial manner.

Her mother constantly badgered her at every opportunity, refusing to accept her claims to be unwell, sneering that if she was well enough to go to work then she was well enough to go to chapel, demanding to be told the real reason why she had so abruptly ceased her normal pattern of activity. Josie endured the badgering in silence, but there were times when she was driven almost beyond the limits of her endurance, and felt like screaming at the woman to leave her alone.

The curtailment of her chapel activities also brought her to the realisation of just how empty her life really was. She had no close friends. No one in whom she could confide, no one with whom she could share her doubts and troubles, her joy and laughter.

That's why I go to the chapel really, isn't it? she admitted sadly. I go there purely and simply to fill the emptiness in my life. Not because I love God. Not because I enjoy going there. Not because I find any real camaraderie, or joy. I go there only to fill empty hours.

Her work did give her some pleasure. She enjoyed the small children. But the brief hours at school passed all too quickly, and then with a sinking heart she trudged wearily back to this house, and her carping, complaining, nagging, bitter-mouthed mother.

When she awoke on Saturday morning, Josie lay in her narrow bed and glumly faced yet another interminable day. This morning she would have to go up into the town with her mother and do the shopping, pushing the heavy, fat body in the clumsy wheelchair up the long sloping hill. Wrestling the chair through shop doorways and thronging crowds while her mother constantly whined and complained about prices, and goods, and Josie's clumsiness in handling the chair.

The old cow can walk well enough when it suits her, Josie thought resentfully, then felt guilty. Dorothy Kitson's hip joints were arthritic, and she could not really walk any distance above a few yards.

Josie thought enviously of her brother John, far away in the Mediterranean. He had joined the Royal Navy as a boy, and was now a chief petty officer.

26

I wish I'd been born a man. I'd be far away from here.

'Josie? Josie? Aren't you up yet? It's late.' Her mother came through the bedroom door, her fat, sallow face frowning. 'You know I like to get to the shops early, girl. How can you be so selfish? Lying there as if there was nothing to do. Get up, will you?'

Josie sighed heavily, and pushed the bedclothes from her and rose from the bed.

As she poured cold water from the big jug into the basin on the washstand, she suddenly had a cheering thought.

On alternate Saturday afternoons Dorothy Kitson exchanged visits with her sister, Josie's Aunt Clara. Today it was the turn of Clara to act as hostess. Josie would take her mother to her aunt's house, and leave her there until late evening, when she would go and collect her and bring her back home.

She smiled gratefully. I'll be free of her for hours.

Her mood lightened by this prospect, she felt almost happy as she washed her hands and face, then dressed and went downstairs to begin the day.

The long slope of Beoley Road ran eastwards from the central plateau of the town, bottoming at the ford and footbridge across the River Arrow, then continuing on through farmland to its junction with the ancient Roman military road known as Icknield Street, some two miles from the town centre.

Josie and her mother lived in an isolated terrace of houses standing several hundred yards further on from the ford and footbridge. The sun was high and hot as she pushed her mother's wheelchair down towards the ford. Once there Dorothy Kitson, grumbling and wheezing, dismounted and made her ponderous way across the low wooden bridge, leaning heavily on her walking stick and stopping every couple of yards to voice loud complaints about her daughter's cruelty in making her walk. Josie followed across the narrow boarding, dragging the wheelchair behind her. On the other side Dorothy Kitson slumped back into the chair, and Josie began the long, laborious ascent of Beoley Road.

Even before she had reached the halfway point of the long hill, Josie's leg muscles were aching, and she was breathing hard. Her face was hot and flushed with exertion, and beneath the tight bodice of her dark dress her skin was damp with sweat. But she was able to accept all these discomforts with equanimity. Because she was travelling towards several hours of precious freedom. Once the shopping was completed she would take her mother to her aunt's house, and leave her there until the early evening.

The Saturday market was in full swing when they arrived. The long lines of stalls, stretching along Market Place, which bordered the south flank of St Stephen's churchyard faced shops whose keepers bitterly resented this weekly influx of rivals, because the stallholders undercut their prices.

'Come on now, what'll you give me for this fine china teapot? Did you say a shillin' madam? What? You didn't? Then it must have been that pretty lady next to you who made the offer.'

'Buy my carrots, they're loverly!'

'Oranges, two for a penny, five for twopence! Lemons the same. Don't look so sour, missus, else people 'ull think I'm selling you wi' the lemons!'

'I've got silks, I've got satins, I've got cloth fit for a queen to wear, and all of it chape! Dirt chape! I'm a fool to meself tó be giving it away at these prices! Come on now, here's bargains for you, silk straight from China, satin straight from India, and you can have me as well for a tanner, and I'm straight from Brum!'

'Rabbits, fresh killed this morning. Rabbits, fresh killed this morning.'

'Fish, fish, fish! Eels, eels, eels! Crabs, crabs, crabs!'

Hoarse-voiced hucksters cried their wares, bantered and cajoled.

Small children pointed, and begged for sweets, and capered joyfully while their mothers haggled and bartered. Stray dogs scavenged in the thick sawdust below the meat stalls, rooting out the discarded scraps of gristle and fat and bolting them hungrily, while wary, half-starved cats patrolled the fish stalls, seeking their moment to pounce. Ragged urchins prowled, searching the littered ground for carelessly dropped coins, and cheekily begging broken biscuits, stale cakes, crushed buns from the confectioners' stalls.

Josie loved the hustle and bustle of the market, its vibrant life, its colourful characters. But her mother hated it, and always complained long and bitterly when Josie insisted on passing through it on the way to the shops that Dorothy patronised.

At the central crossroads of the town Josie turned south along Evesham Street, the town's main thoroughfare. Although not as thronged as the marketplace, there were still many shoppers, and she was constantly forced to halt and ask gossiping men and women to make way for the chair. At times people greeted her or her mother, some being the parents of the children Josie taught. These latter spoke to Josie respectfully, wanting to know how their child was behaving at school and progressing with lessons. Josie always took pains to praise the child's behaviour and scholastic ability, and the parents would smile with gratification. She was continually surprised at the respect the majority of the poorer people of the town showed towards her profession, and how much they appeared to value her opinions as to their offspring. She knew from conversations with the older teachers at her school that this majority respect for teachers was of comparatively recent growth. According to the oldest teachers, her profession had once been derided and despised by many. But following the introduction of the board schools in the 1870s it was becoming more elevated in the eyes of the general public.

Althought Josie was not vain or arrogant, she still enjoyed these manifestations of respect, and it always boosted her confidence to receive them.

The shopping took little time. Their purchases of food and household necessities were frugal, with bread and potatoes their dietary mainstay. Since her father's death Josie had supported the household on her wages. Of course her mother received the small old-age pension, the Lloyd George, as the local humorists referred to it, naming it for the politician who had introduced it in 1908. But Dorothy Kitson hoarded the few shillings of her pension, refusing to part with any of it, because she wanted to save towards her funeral.

There were times when Josie wondered ironically if her mother planned on having a state funeral, because the old woman was so insistent on guarding every penny.

Aunt Clara lived close to the town centre, in Easemore Road, which was situated by the northern apex of the recreation garden. It was with relief that Josie trundled the wheelchair down its gentle slope. The road was one of the superior residential areas of the town, and Dorothy Kitson bitterly resented the fact that her sister had a better address than she did. There were several buildings of some pretension in Easemore Road: the technical institute and secondary school, the large St Stephen's church hall, the artillery drill hall, the Conservative and Union Club. This last-named was the gathering place of the self-regarded male élite of the town: local politicians, industrialists, business and professional men, shopkeepers and managerial staff, who met there to drink and gossip, play billiards, and generally relax from their multitudinous cares and responsibilities. It was also a discreet and secretive haven for those men, like Clement Hulme, who occasionally needed to break their vows of temperance and take a soothing drink or two.

As the week progressed Hulme had become increasingly anxious about Josie's absence from the chapel activities. The young woman had become an obsession with him, and the memory of her smooth, firm body, and how she had reacted to his lovemaking, had kept him in a state of extreme sexual tension. In an effort to ease that tension he had attempted to have sex with his wife on three occasions during the past week, but each time her flaccid body, wrinkled skin and decaying teeth had repulsed him, and he had rolled away from her, unable to continue, and lain sleepless through the long, dark hours of the night, yearning desperately for Josie Kitson.

He had wanted to go to her home, using chapel business as an excuse, and confront her, demand to know why she was avoiding him. But the fear of the possible consequences of such an action held him back. He knew that her mother watched Josie like a hawk, and that the old woman's shrewd, suspicious mind might well divine his real reasons for calling on her daughter. Hulme valued his respectable position in local society. He knew very well that should any scandal besmirch him, he could very possibly lose everything that he had worked and struggled to achieve during his lifetime. He would be cast out from the chapel, where he was a powerful figure; and since his father-in-law was a very influential local councillor, and

30

the Electric Light Company was owned by the council, he would almost certainly lose his position there also. As much as he desired Josie Kitson, and hungered for her body, he had too much to lose by acting rashly.

The worry of her avoidance of him, and the strain of wanting and yearning for her, had finally driven him to seek solace in the bottle. But even here caution ruled him. His occasional ventures to the Union Club were carefully planned and timed, so that there would be no likelihood of any reports of his backsliding reaching the ears of the chapel elders. He had used the Electric Light Company's business affairs to cover his presence at the club today, letting it be known that he was coming here to interview potential customers among the regular clientele.

In the empty snug room he drank several glasses of whisky and soda. The fragrant amber liquid warmed his belly and for a time at least soothed his tensions. But then, as the effect of the spirit began to overcome him, his thoughts inevitably turned to Josie, and he felt the familiar tumescence stirring in his groin as he pictured her smooth white belly and rounded thighs.

Perhaps she'll come to chapel tomorrow, he wished desperately.

In a vain effort to distract himself he walked to the small window that overlooked Easemore Road and stared out. He suddenly sucked in his breath and exhaled it gustily in surprise. Josie Kitson was passing by on the opposite side of the road, pushing her mother in the wheelchair. In a flurry of excitement he unlatched the window and pushed it wide, opening his mouth to call to her. Then he suddenly realised what he was doing, and slammed the window shut once more.

You dammed fool! he berated himself. Are you mad? Just think of what people will say if you go shouting after her like an idiot.

For some time he stood watching her slender, shapely body moving further away from him, and his desperate yearning and lust for her became too strong to be held in check any longer. He was going to speak with her, no matter what risks he might run.

He went out from the club building, and saw that the wheelchair was now several scores of yards down Easemore

31

Road. At first he was puzzled as to what the couple were doing here in this part of the town. Then he recalled that Dorothy Kitson had a relative of some sort living in this road.

That's what they're doing, he decided. They're visiting their relative.

Confirmation of this theory was almost immediately offered as the wheelchair came to a halt and then entered the front gate of one of the houses.

Hulme scowled in frustration. She might be inside there for hours.

He remained where he was, staring down at the distant house, undecided as to what he might do, even considering momentarily the thought of calling at the house himself. He was able to dismiss that wild notion without much difficulty. That course of action would be real madness. But still he didn't want to move from here while there might be a chance of somehow contriving to speak with her.

Then he saw the slender figure in the dark dress and broad-brimmed flowered hat come out of the entrance gate and begin to walk back in his direction. His heart leapt, but some instinct made him remain motionless, half hidden from her view by the wall of the Union Club.

As she neared him he noticed the two bulging string bags she was carrying, and then she had turned away from him along a newly constructed roadway which would lead her back to the Beoley Road.

Again his memory sparked. Josie had once told him that on certain Saturdays she would leave her mother at her aunt's house for several hours before returning to collect her. He remembered how her eyes had sparkled as she related how much she appreciated the precious hours of freedom from naggings and complaints.

She's taking the shopping home with her. She'll be alone there, he realised, and now he moved to follow her route.

He longed to hurry and overtake her, but again instinct held him back from doing so. She could so easily snub him in the street, and he could not risk any sort of scene in public view.

I'll wait until she's back in her home, and then I'll go there.

With this plan in mind, he contented himself with following her at a distance.

32

Josie's initial relief at being free of her mother soon gave way to a sense of frustration as she slowly trudged beneath the hot sun carrying the bags, which seemed to become heavier with each succeeding step. She had gained a few precious hours of freedom, but what could she really do with them? She could go for a solitary walk along the country lanes. She could sit in the solitude of her home and read a book, or do embroidery. She could write a letter to her distant brother, and try to fill the empty silence that surrounded her with the imaginary sound of his voice.

What's the use of having some freedom if I've no one to share it with? she asked herself dejectedly.

The mere physical act of walking, and seeing other people passing by, helped to keep her sense of acute solitude at bay. But when she finally reached her home and entered its cool, clinically clean silence, loneliness engulfed her like an all-enveloping shroud, and she experienced a bleak despair.

Laying the bags down, she seated herself on a chair at the table and took off her hat to lay it aside. The silence of the room oppressed her, but she was gripped by an overwhelming lethargy and could not summon the necessary resolution to find something to do which would at least create an illusion of time being well spent.

I'm so lonely, she thought sadly. So very very lonely.

Then came the knocking on the rear door of the house.

Startled, she rose and went to open it, and found Clement Hulme standing there.

He took off his bowler hat and stood bare-headed in the posture of a supplicant, pleading in low, urgent tones.

'Please, Josie, don't send me away. I need to see you and to talk with you so badly. This last week has been terrible. I've been so lonely without you, there've been moments when I've felt that I was the last living creature on this earth.'

Josie stood gazing at his flushed face, and conflicting emotions battled within her. It was as if two entities were arguing in her mind, and she could hear and sympathise with both of their conflicting arguments.

'Send him away, he's no good for you.'

'But he's so sad and lonely.'

'There'll only be trouble come of this affair.'

'But I can't help feeling sorry for him.'

'He's a married man, with children.'

'His wife doesn't love him, and he doesn't love her. And we aren't harming his children.'

'He just wants to use you for his sexual pleasures.'

'No, it's not only for sex that he wants me. He truly loves me.'

'How can you be sure of that?'

'Just look at him now, how humble he is, how sad he looks. Of course he loves me.'

'But you don't love him, do you?'

'I don't know. I just don't know. But I need someone. I'm so very, very lonely. I need to be loved by someone. I can't spend my life living like a nun. I need to be loved and needed by someone . . .'

She reached out her hand, and as he snatched it eagerly and pressed kisses upon it, she drew him into the house, and closed the door.

Chapter Four

At half past eight o'clock on Monday morning, Clement Hulme, assistant manager of the Redditch Electric Light Company, leaned back in his chair and his fingers toyed with the heavy gold watch chain that stretched across his protuberant paunch.

His eyes examined the tall, lean, shabbily dressed man standing cap in hand before the desk, and he sucked his front teeth reflectively.

'You want work, do you? Where have you been working till now?'

'I was in Canada, sir. I've only come back from there a few weeks past,' the tall man told him.

Hulme showed some surprise. 'Canada, you say? It's Canada you've just come back from, is it?'

'Yes, sir,' the tall man confirmed.

'What brought you back?'

'My wife died, so I brought my little girl back here where we have family. We'd no relatives in Canada, and if anything happened to me there'd be no one to look after her.'

'Hadn't you got any friends there who could have looked after her?' Hulme's tone was hectoring, and the tall man's eyes hardened slightly. But he replied politely.

'No, sir. We'd had to move around quite a lot to get work. So we didn't get the chance to make any close friends.'

'Hmmm!' The manager pursed his thick lips as he considered that explanation. Then he asked, 'What's your name?'

'Gurden, sir . . . Caleb Gurden.'

'Caleb Gurden?' Hulme ejaculated a scoffing snort of laughter. 'Caleb Gurden? Funny sort of name that, isn't it?'

Resentment flashed in Caleb Gurden's eyes but his expression remained impassive.

Hulme made a great show of examining the other man's shabby clothing, then stated contemptuously, 'Well, Caleb Gurden, you don't look as if you made any sort of fortune in Canada, judging by what you're wearing. How old are you?'

'Thirty-one,' Gurden replied.

'Have you done stoking before?'

'No, but I know that I can do it.'

The manager sneered openly. 'I wish I had a penny for every layabout I've heard make that claim.' His tone became aggressive. 'Why should I believe you?'

Caleb Gurden's spirit was being sorely tried by this ignorant, hectoring bully before him. But he was desperate for work, and so he crushed down the anger boiling within him and answered meekly, 'If you'll give me the chance, sir, I'll be able to prove to you that I can do the work.'

Hulme stared long and hard, as if seeking some spark of rebellion in the man. Then, appearing satisfied that he had asserted complete dominance, he nodded and ordered brusquely, 'Go across to the boiler house. Tell the foreman I sent you.'

'Thank you, sir.' Caleb Gurden felt almost elated with relief. 'Who shall I ask for, sir? What's the foreman's name?'

Hulme was staring down at the open ledger on the desk in front of him, and he ignored the questions.

Caleb Gurden allowed a flicker of contempt to pass across his face as he turned and left the office.

He walked across the cinder-covered yard to the big, grimy-walled boiler house. The sunlight was veiled by the clouds of black-grey smoke pouring out of the tall chimney. The metallic clattering of steam-driven reciprocation generators sounded from within the walls, and when he went down the stone steps into the hot darkness of the subterranean room, the sulphuric fumes assailed his lungs, and the stench of wet coal and hot oil filled his nostrils. As he neared the row of three huge boilers, the heat from their open fire doors blasted him, and he halted to stare at the two ragged figures, etched black against the dazzling glare of the fires, as they wielded the twelve-foot-long steel clinker rakes, thrusting the tools backwards and forwards through the white-hot beds of coals to draw out the ashes and allow fresh oxygen to penetrate.

'Who're you when you'm about?' a harsh voice bellowed into Caleb's ear, and he swung to confront a burly, broad-featured, walrus-moustached man who wore a bowler hat pushed back on his bullet head, and a greasy three-piece suit.

Caleb explained his errand, and the burly man nodded and grinned, displaying a mouthful of decayed teeth.

'You'm very welcome,' the man chuckled hoarsely, and his breath stank of stale beer. 'I'm Ned Hands. I'm the foreman. Cummon over 'ere a minute.'

He led Caleb away from the boilers towards a large wooden box that stood against a wall. From the box he lifted a broad-bladed, long-helved shovel.

'Theer you be.' He handed the shovel to Caleb and then jerked his head towards the boilers. 'Goo on, get stuck in. The lads 'ull show you what's to be done.' He winked drolly and tapped the side of his bulbous nose with a dirty forefinger. 'I can smell the ones who aren't able to do it.'

Caleb could not help but smile. 'You must have a powerful nose if you can smell anything other than this stink in here.'

Hands chuckled. 'That's just it, matey, we'se all got a different stink, aren't us? And my nose can tell the difference.'

Caleb, still smiling at the man's humour, walked back to the boilers, where the two men had closed the fire doors and now stood watching him approach.

As he reached them, one said sourly, 'You wun't be happy for very long, mate. You'll be grinning the other side o' your face when you'se had a taste o' this bleedin' job.'

Caleb nodded. 'You could be right. What do I have to do?'

The man pointed to the boilers. 'See them 'oppers? You'se got to keep 'um full o' coal. They feeds it into the furnace. You can start shovelling, and I'll show you what else 'as to be done 'as we goes on.'

Caleb peered through the gloom and saw that adjacent to each boiler's fire doors there stood a six-foot-high steel hopper. In front of each hopper was a great heap of coal which was replenished from the yard by fresh supplies being tipped from carts down the chutes which were over the heaps.

37

'When you'm shovelling, take care that you don't get underneath the chutes. You'll have a load o' coals dropped on you else,' the sour man warned.

'If I was you I'd take your jacket off, mate,' the second man advised. 'It's bloody warm work. You can put it over theer, wheer we puts our'n.'

'Thanks.' Caleb removed his jacket and cap and hung them from the protruding nails in the filthy corner, where there was a bench, and an upturned packing case to serve as a table. Then he went to the nearest hopper and began to work.

Each shovel-load of coal had to be thrown six feet in the air to pass over and into the open top of the hopper. Caleb's first few loads were thrown clumsily and the coal hit the top edges of the steel sides and came back down on him. The wet lumps of coal thudded on his head and shoulders, and he hissed with pain and annoyance.

'No, mate, do it like this.' The sour man took the shovel from him and demonstrated the smooth, fluid lift and throw with the final flick of the wrists which sent the coal soaring in compact unity up and over the top edge of the hopper.

'Thanks.' Caleb was sincere in his gratitude, and within a very short time had caught the knack and was able to send the shovel-loads soaring neatly and accurately.

For a while he found himself exhulting in this new-found manual skill, but then the gruelling work started to strain muscles that during his long weeks of enforced idleness had become soft and slack, and he found himself panting with effort.

Conscious of the fact that he was being observed for any signs of weakness, his fierce pride would not allow him to display such, and he gritted his teeth and forced his toiling body on and on and on, for hour after hour without respite. As soon as one hopper was filled he moved to its neighbour, and then to the next, and then back to the first. The skin on the palms of his hands blistered and the blisters burst, and blood mingled with the sweat and coal dust and his palms felt as if they were on fire.

Just when he thought he would not be able to continue any longer, the sour man gripped his arm and told him, ''Ave a breather, mate.' He nodded towards the filthy corner where the bench and makeshift table stood, and asked, ''As you brought any grub wi' you?'

Caleb's hunger gnawed painfully as he shook his head.

The sour man scowled and emitted a gusting sigh of disgust. Then he went to his ragged jacket hanging on one of the nails and from its pocket took a small bundle wrapped in dirty rag, and a beer bottle stopped with a cork. He pushed the bottle and bundle into Caleb's hands.

''Ere, get this down you. When you'se had it I'll show you the water gauges and the inlet valves, and how to use the rake and keep the fire sweet.'

He walked away and began shovelling coal into the nearest hopper, and Caleb gratefully sank down upon the bench. His stomach rumbled audibly as he eagerly drank the cold tea that the bottle contained, and then unwrapped the rag from the thick slices of bread and dripping. He tore wolfishly at the food, chewing hurriedly and bolting the mouthfuls down in an effort to satisfy his ravenous hunger, hardly tasting the greasy dripping or the stale bread.

After he had eaten, and drunk again from the bottle, he felt renewed strength, and he rose and went to the sour man.

'Thank you very much for the food. I really needed it.'

The sour man grinned bleakly. 'Ahr, so does every poor bugger who comes to work 'ere. Now let's show you what else you 'as to do.'

He demonstrated how to use the clinker rake, and then watched while Caleb thrust and pulled the heavy iron tool through the bed of flaming coals, urging his pupil, 'That's it, mate. Now shift that piece theer, and break up that soddin' lump. Get the bed nice and level.'

The tremendous heat scorched Caleb's exposed face and arms and hands, and he could not help but flinch back as spurts of superheated fumes belched out from the open steel fire doors.

'You'll get used to it,' the sour man encouraged, and when satisfied that his pupil had mastered the job, showed Caleb the water gauges and the valves which he had to operate to feed the boilers with fresh supplies of water.

'You must watch the water levels very careful. If you lets 'um get too low you'll have a bleedin' blow-up, and there wun't be enough o' you left to fill a soddin' match-box.'

Caleb paid very careful attention, and when satisfied that he had understood what the man had showed him, said, 'Thanks, I reckon I've got it.'

'All right, mate, you can knock off now. Go and see Ned Hands and he'll tell you what shifts you'm on.'

Caleb found the foreman sitting in a small wooden lean-to situated on the outside wall of the boiler house. The man had a jug of beer in front of him, from which he took frequent gulps as he explained to Caleb, 'You doon't get paid for the hours you'se done today. It's counted as your schooling for the job. Now you'll be working day shifts and night shifts, a fortnight about. When we'se got the full numbers o' stokers the day shift is nine hours and the night shift is eleven hours.'

He chuckled merrily. 'But we aren't never going to have the full numbers o' stokers, so you'll be working straight twelve-hour shifts for six days or nights, and a six-hour shift on the seventh day or night.' The broad features grinned drolly. 'I know the Lord God laboured six days and rested on the seventh, but he weren't working for the Redditch Electric Light Company. You'll get fourpence three farthings an hour. So for the seventy-eight hours you'll earn thirty shillings. Which aren't so bad considering.'

Considering what? Caleb was tempted to ask, but knowing discretion to be the better part of valour, he merely nodded silently.

'Wheer does you live?' the man wanted to know.

'Edward Street,' Caleb informed him.

'Oh, you aren't got too far to walk then.' Hands grinned and quipped, 'I takes it you am walking, aren't you? You doon't own a carriage and pair?'

Caleb returned the grin. 'The only pair I own are on my feet, Mister Hands.'

The fat man chuckled and banged his great hobnailed boots on the ground. 'Ahr, you'm like me then. Shanks's pony's my only bloody transport as well. Right then, be here at a quarter to six tomorrow morning.'

The electric works were situated on the eastern edge of the raised plateau on which the central portion of the hilly town

40

was built, and feeling as physically tired as he was, Caleb was grateful that he had no hills to climb on his journey back to Edward Street.

But despite his weariness and the aching of his strained muscles, his spirits were considerably higher than they had been earlier that day. He had found work, and he would now be able to rent a small house for himself and his daughter to live in. At present they were lodging in the cramped home of his younger sister Eva and her husband and swarm of children, and although he was grateful for his sister's kindness in giving him shelter, he had found the past weeks a tremendous strain. Eva's husband, Alfred Payne, was a drunken, brutal bully, and Caleb disliked him heartily.

He frowned now at the thought of the man. Although while he, Caleb, had been staying with them Alfred Payne had not been physically violent towards Eva, Caleb knew without doubt that he customarily battered her and the children. Although Eva vehemently denied that her husband used violence towards her, Caleb could see the scars of old beatings upon her face, and upon the faces and bodies of her children, and the fear that she and they could not hide when Payne was drunk or ill-tempered. Caleb's big hands clenched as he thought of these things, and he silently promised his sister, If that bastard ill-treats you or your kids again now I'm back living in this town, he'll have to answer to me for it.

He trudged steadily through the town centre, past the great steepled parish church of St Stephen in its tree-shaded graveyard, and went over the central crossroads and down steep Unicorn Hill towards the railway station at its foot, over the railway bridge and then into Edward Street, with its factories and workshops belching filthy smoke and fumes from tall chimneys and flakings of soot which drifted down upon the terraces and courts of the mean hovels.

Caleb had always found it incongruous that in this, his home town, industrial slums such as Edward Street and its neighbours stood only a score of yards from the large houses and carefully landscaped gardens of the wealthy. And just beyond those large houses stretched lushly wooded hillsides and fecund farmland.

As he entered the low covered entryway which led into the

41

court where his sister lived, Caleb grimaced as he breathed in the fume-laden air, laced with the stench of rotting refuse and animal and human ordure, and cursed the fate that had forced him to bring his beloved daughter back to this slum.

But when he went into the cramped tenement he smiled with genuine pleasure at the sight of his ten-year-old daughter Marie sitting on a broken-backed wooden chair, her younger nephews and nieces crowding around her as she told them a story.

She looked up at his entrance, and said gravely, 'You're very dirty, Pa.'

As he smiled down at her small, delicate features, softly framed by long, loose, flowing blonde hair, he marvelled at her ever-increasing resemblance to her mother, and a poignant yearning flooded through him, causing a lump to rise in his throat. He had loved his wife very dearly, and still grieved for her.

He swallowed hard, and told her, 'I've found a job, sweetheart. We're going to have a home of our own again very soon.'

He glanced at the grimy faces of the small children staring up at him, and chuckled at their solemnity.

'And you'll be able to invite these ladies and gentlemen to take tea with you. To eat jelly and cakes and drink lots of ginger beer.'

Radiant grins overlaid the solemn stares.

Marie rose and came to him, and he bent to kiss her smooth cheek. She whispered into his ear, 'I don't want the kids to know, Pa, but I'm really glad that we're leaving here. I really am.'

He briefly hugged her slender body close to him, and whispered back, 'And I'm glad, sweetheart. I'm really glad as well.'

'I won't have to invite Uncle Alfred to tea, will I, Pa?' she whispered with concern.

'No,' he breathed emphatically. 'No, you won't. You'll only invite who you want to invite. I won't let anybody come to our house who you don't want there.'

She chuckled with delight, and then released herself from his arms. 'I'll take the kids out of the way while you bath yourself, Pa.'

She turned back to the children. 'Come on then, kids. I'll take you all for a walk. We'll go up to the woods.'

With excited cries of pleasure they gathered around her once more, and she led them away.

Caleb took a tin bucket from the tiny back scullery and went out into the court to fill it at the standpipe, the only water supply for the six tenements which clustered around the yard. The standpipe was in the corner next to the ash box, and behind the ash box were situated the two water closets which were shared by the court's inhabitants. One of them had overflowed and the stench of urine and excreta turned Caleb's stomach, hardened though he was to bad smells.

Back in the scullery he stripped to the skin and cleaned his teeth. Then, using a piece of rag as a flannel, he soaped and washed his head and body. By the time he had finished, the remaining water in the bucket was blackened and scummed.

He still did not feel thoroughly clean, but knew that his brother-in-law would be home shortly, and that he did not have time to fetch fresh water and repeat his makeshift bathing. He sighed heavily, but then consoled himself with the thought that soon he would be in his own house, and then he would be able to maintain his high standards of personal hygiene.

He had just finished dressing in his only other clothes, a clean cotton shirt, woollen vest and long drawers, topped by a rough serge jacket and trousers, when Alfred Payne came into the house.

Payne was a powerfully built man, a couple of years older than Caleb. He was a bricklayer by trade, and when in work earned good money. But very little of his earnings went to support his wife and children. Most of his money was spent in the public houses of the town.

Alfred Payne now bitterly regretted allowing his brother-in-law to come and lodge in his home, although initially he had been more than willing to take him in. He had anticipated that his wife's brother would be as meek and submissive as she herself was, and had looked forward to having someone new to bully and exploit. But to his dismay, instead of a meek, timid male version of Eva, there had arrived instead a hard-eyed, tough-looking man whose manner and appearance Payne had found distinctly intimidating.

The antipathy between the two men was mutual, but violent bully though he was, Payne was wary of his brother-in-law and reluctant to risk angering him. Caleb himself felt no such reluctance, but he had to consider his sister's feelings, and he accepted her wishes that he should not quarrel with her husband. So the two men treated each other with bleak civility.

'Caleb.'

'Alfred.'

They nodded at each other in greeting.

Payne slung his bag of tools into the corner of the room and slouched down on to the ramshackle wooden armchair next to the fireless grate. His clothing, boots and skin were thick with the lime and mortar of his work, and his jaw and throat were thickly stubbled with a three-day-old beard. His body stank of stale sweat, and his breath reeked vilely.

Caleb could not keep the gleam of disgust from his eyes as he looked at his sister's husband. He knew that the man would not change his clothes, wash or shave before the end of the working week, and even then would only make a token effort towards cleanliness. He thought of how dainty and fastidious his younger sister had been as a girl, and his heart bled within him.

What in hell's name did she ever see in this filthy pig? he asked in silent bemusement.

'Her's bloody late, aren't her?' Payne growled irritably.' I wants summat to ate afore I goes out. Her's supposed to be bringing some fish and chips home wi' her. I expect her's stood bloody canking, instead o' getting back wheer her belongs.'

Caleb's anger smouldered, but he kept himself under control. His sister worked long hours in a factory, paying an elderly neighbour to care for her children during her absence. Then she had to come home and look after her children, and this worthless husband who would not lift a finger to help her. Every penny that she earned went into the upkeep of her home and to feed and clothe her children, and she knew no leisure. The hours she was not at the factory she spent in washing, cleaning, mending, cooking. Her life was virtual slavery, and the only rewards that she ever received from Alfred Payne for the sacrifices she made were hard words and harder blows.

44

As he thought about these things Caleb felt the increasing urge to smash the other man to a pulp, and in the end that urge became so overwhelming that he was forced to go out of the house before he surrendered to it.

He walked slowly up the street. Work had finished for the day and men and women were returning homewards. He pleasantly greeted some of those he knew, others he bleakly ignored. Caleb knew from bitter experience how hard life was for the people who dwelt in this mean street. He respected those amongst them who struggled to do the best they could for their families. He despised those who ill-treated their wives, neglected their children, wasted what small amounts of money they earned on drinking and gambling. Not that he was a puritan. He enjoyed drink and tobacco and the occasional wager himself. But he believed that those pleasures should only be taken after the obligations to wives and children had been met. He thought that it was a contemptible thing for a man to buy drinks for the landlord of a public house when that same man's children were running around the streets hungry and shoeless. Because he was prepared to openly voice such views, he was not regarded as easy company by many men, and so tended to be somewhat solitary in his life. A state of affairs which he did not seek, but was able to accept with equanimity.

Among the oncoming shawled women and shabbily clothed men he sighted his sister's small, frail figure hurrying with bent head towards him. He smiled and halted, and as she neared him called, 'Hello, Eva.'

Her careworn face lighted when she saw him.

'Oh, Caleb, you're not gone out already, are you? I've brought you some fish and chips.'

She lifted the newspaper parcel she was carrying in her arms beneath her shawl. 'They're fresh out of the pan. But there was ever such a long queue. That's why I'm late.' Her face clouded with sudden apprehension. 'Is he home yet?'

Caleb could not help frowning as he nodded.

'Oh my God!' she exclaimed anxiously. 'He'll go mad because I'm late with his food.'

'No he won't,' Caleb assured her grimly. 'I'll see to that.'

They walked on side by side, and Caleb was forced to

lengthen his steps to keep up with her hurried pace. She was almost running in her anxiety to get home.

'Come on, Caleb,' she urged fearfully. 'Walk faster.'

He wanted to force her to slow down, to make the man wait. But he hadn't the heart to do so, and he quickened his pace.

'Are the kids in?' she panted.

'No. Marie's taken them up the woods. But she'll have them back before dark, so you've no need to worry.

'She's a lovely kid, Caleb.' Eva's tone was warm and tender. 'God was good to you when he gave you Marie.'

'I know.' He nodded, then told her tentatively, 'I've got a job. Stoking at the Electric Light works. I start tomorrow on the day shift.'

She came to an abrupt halt and turned her thin face to look up at him.

'Does that mean that you'll be leaving me then?' She sounded apprehensive.

He nodded reluctantly, knowing that she did not want him to leave her home. Although his being there did not ease her workload, his presence was a comforting shield against the violence of her husband, and gave her someone to talk and laugh with.

'I'll really miss you and Marie,' she said wistfully. 'It's been lovely having you both with me.'

'Hey, it's only to another house I'll be moving. I'm not going off abroad again. You'll be seeing all that you want to of me and Marie. You can be sure of that.'

She took solace from this promise, and smiled. 'Good. Now let's get home quick and eat this fish and chips.'

Chapter Five

The morning air was fresh and cool, and Caleb Gurden enjoyed the walk to the Electric Light Company. Even at that early hour there were many men going to their employments and the public houses that Caleb passed were already open and doing good business, as men called in for a glass of ale or a tot of spirits. As he walked along Red Lion Street, which led from the Church Green towards his destination, he came to two public houses standing almost opposite each other, the Red Lion and the White Lion. From the doorway of the White Lion he heard his name called, and he looked across the street to see his foreman, Ned Hands, beckoning to him.

'Cummon in 'ere, Caleb.'

Caleb crossed the street and Ned Hands led him into the bar, smoky and noisy with drinkers. Standing at the bar counter were the two stokers he had met the previous day. They nodded in greeting. The sour-featured one introduced himself.

'Me name's Henry Jacobs, but everybody calls me Sailor on account o' me being an old navy man. And this 'un is called TeeTee, on account he took the vow once.'

'What's you having, Caleb? It's Sailor's round,' Ned Hands invited.

Caleb didn't really want to drink anything at this early hour, but loath to offend by refusal, he accepted. 'I'll just have a half of stout, please.'

''Alf o' stout?' Hands stared in mock horror. 'I daren't ask for a 'alf o' stout in this bar, my bucko. I'd ne'er live it down. You'll have to 'ave a pint.'

Caleb shrugged, then looked up at the clock. 'It's twenty to six. I thought you wanted me in work by a quarter to.'

The foreman's dirty forefinger tapped the side of his bulbous

47

purple nose, and he grinned and winked slyly. 'You doon't want to pay any attention to that bleedin' clock, matey. It's always fast this time o' the mornin'.'

The drinks were placed on the counter before them, and the foreman lifted his pint pot and drained it in a series of noisy gulps, then belched noisily and slammed the pot down on the counter.

'Cummon, Caleb, it's your shout. You needn't worry if you aren't got any money on you. I'se already told the landlord to open your slate. You can settle up on payday.'

Caleb was not happy to hear this, but knew better than to dispute with the foreman. Times were hard, and jobs were few and far between. He desperately needed to work, and if that meant he had to buy the foreman drinks, then he would put up with that. In these days of heavy unemployment he knew that if he refused, he would very quickly be out of a job, and Hands would fill his place with another more amenable man.

He called for another round, for Hands, Sailor and TeeTee, but didn't buy for himself. Hands drained this pint just as quickly, and it was TeeTee's turn to buy.

Caleb refused, but the others all took another.

Hands's expression was surly, and tension entered the atmosphere as he challenged Caleb aggressively, 'Aren't you a drinking man, then?'

Caleb smiled easily and replied, 'Not really. But I don't mind buying a drink for friends.' He turned and shouted to the landlord, 'Give my mates another round on my slate, will you? No more for me, though.'

The tension that had so quickly arisen between them abruptly disappeared, and Ned Hands clapped Caleb on the shoulder and told the other men, 'Theer, didn't I tell you that this bloke 'ud be a good 'un? I can smell good blokes a mile off, and the minute I smelled this 'un 'ere, I knew he was a good 'un.'

It was well past six o'clock when the four men left the bar and walked the rest of the distance to the Electric Light works.

There was only a single stoker on duty, and Hands explained to Caleb, 'In the summertime there aren't much demand at night, so we only 'as one boiler operating. One bloke can handle that by hisself.'

The night man scowled as he smelt the drink fumes wafting from the newcomers, but he said nothing, only took his coat and cap from the nails in the wall and walked out.

'Miserable bastard, he is!' Hands made a lewd gesture at the man's retreating back. 'Fuckin' teetotaller he is. Stingy bugger 'udn't buy you a drink, not if you was dying wi' thirst, he 'udn't. But he wun't be 'ere much longer. I'm getting rid o' the miserable bleeder just as soon as I can get somebody else in for his job. I can't stand bleedin' teetotallers or stingy buggers, I can't.'

He left Caleb and went to check the various gauges, and Caleb hung up his coat and cap then joined the other two stokers in shovelling coal into the hoppers.

As the two shut-down boilers were refired and the daytime consumption of electricity increased, the pace of the work quickened, and soon Caleb was sweating and his muscles were feeling the strain of the merciless demands made upon them.

During the course of the day Sailor imparted a few facts to Caleb. Each boiler consumed three hundredweight of coal every twenty minutes, which meant that the stokers must pitch twenty-seven hundredweight of coal six feet high into the hoppers each hour. During a twelve-hour shift that totalled over sixteen tons of coal. On top of this they must constantly rake and trim the fires, and replenish the water supplies to the boilers. Caleb could well understand why there was such a high turnover of stokers. Only the very strongest and toughest men could withstand the cumulative effects of such gruelling toil for long periods of time.

He also learned more about his new workmates. Sailor was in his late forties. He had served twenty-two years in the Royal Navy, and his hairy arms and torso were covered with tattoos etched in ports all over the world. Upon his discharge some years previously he had married a much younger woman, and she presented him with a new baby every year. The small pension he received from the navy was not enough to support a family, and so he was forced to slave his days away here in the boiler room. TeeTee was a younger man, about the same age as Caleb himself. He also was married and had a large family to support. As he came to know them better, Caleb developed a great liking for both men. Sailor's sour expression masked a ready humour, and a generous nature, and TeeTee was a simple-souled, good-tempered man. Both of them reciprocated Caleb's liking for them, as they came to appreciate that he was a hard-working, straight-speaking individual, who was pleasant and easy to get along with.

Within a few days Caleb's muscles regained their tone and hardened to the work, and by the time his first payday came along, he had fully established his place in the workforce.

Payday was Saturday, and Sailor told him that it was the custom for Ned Hands to collect all the wages from the works office and pay them out in the public house after the shift finished at six o'clock.

Caleb grinned wryly. He had managed to avoid any further morning drinking sessions in the White Lion by taking a different, longer route. His workmates had advised him to do this. They themselves only went into the public house because they were neighbours of Ned Hands and he called for them at their homes each morning.

'I'll have to buy Ned a few extra rounds then, to make up for the ones I've haven't bought him in the mornings,' he said to Sailor.

The man's battered features were as sour as ever. 'He's a cadging bastard, is Hands. But he's not so bad as some of the bosses I know of. At least he'll shout his round when he's got money, and there's a lot of bosses who never, ever pays their round. Only trouble is, he's usually spent all his bloody wages by Monday or Tuesday, so he's never got any money left then until he gets paid again.'

Sailor clucked his tongue against his strong, tobacco-stained teeth. 'But what else can you do but pay for the bugger's drink? If we don't show willing, then we'd soon be out of this job. And it's the same wherever you go to work. Like I said afore, at least the bugger shouts his round when he's got some money.'

At six o'clock that evening the three men walked from the boiler house and made their way to the White Lion. The bar was packed with men and youths, dirty and sweaty from their work. Ned Hands grinned in welcome and pointed to the pint pots lined up on the bar counter.

'Theer you be, I got 'um in ready for you.'

Caleb drank thirstily, the white foaming top of the stout sticking to his upper lip, and Ned Hands chortled.

'That bloody boiler house makes you dry, doon't it, Caleb?'

He distributed the wages, each man receiving a small envelope containing a golden sovereign and some silver and copper coins.

Caleb paid off his slate and called for another round.

The door kept opening and shutting as men came and went, and then a group of building workers entered, ruddy with sunlight, their clothing dusty with lime and sand and mortar dust. Caleb saw that Alfred Payne was among the newly arrived group, and he frowned slightly as he registered the fact that his brother-in-law was already noisily half drunk. They exchanged a nod of greeting and then ignored each other.

Clustered on the pavement outside the bar entrance was a small mob of shabbily clothed, worried-looking women, some carrying babies in their arms, others with tiny children clinging to their long skirts. As men passed them to enter or leave the bar the women begged them:

'Is Robbie Taylor in theer, mister?'

''Ull you tell Billy Walker that his wife is outside?'

'William, 'as you seen my old man?'

The kindlier men would shout into the bar to the erring husbands. Others would shake their heads and grunt, 'No, duck, your old man aren't in theer.'

Caleb could not help but feel sorry for the women, knowing the anxiety that drove them here to try and obtain housekeeping money from their husbands before the men drank and gambled it all away.

After repeated fruitless appeals, one woman, braver or more desperate than the rest, actually put her own head around the door of the bar and shouted, ''Enery Batson, if you'm in 'ere, I wants my housekeeping money.'

Her husband was sitting at a corner table playing dominoes. He had ignored several incoming men shouting for him, but at the sound of his wife's shrill voice he slammed his dominoes on to the table.

The other men in the room began catcalling and jeering.

'Oh, 'Enery, your old 'ooman wants you.'

'Come on, 'Enery, look sharp about it and give her the money.'

'Time to run along 'ome, 'Enery, your missus has come to fetch you.'

The man's unshaven features darkened ominously, and turning, he shouted threateningly at his wife, 'Fuck off 'ome, you.'

'I wants me housekeeping money,' she demanded defiantly. 'The kids aren't had anything to ate today.'

'I aren't telling you again,' he warned.

Other men egged his wife on.

'You tell him, missus.'

'Doon't you let him put you off, my duck.'

'Stand up to him, girl.'

Her face was pale and tense as she stubbornly repeated, 'I wants some housekeeping money.'

The man suddenly jumped to his feet and stormed towards her. 'Gerroff home, you cow,' he shouted.

Although frightened she stood her ground. 'The kids needs some grub.'

Batson reached his wife and his fist thudded into her face. She cried out in pain and fell backwards. Bending, he grabbed her by her straggly hair and dragged her bodily out of the door and into the roadway. The group of women outside scattered, shrieking wildly, and Batson's boot slammed into his wife's body. Again and again he kicked her, while she screamed for mercy and huddled into a foetal position in a vain effort to protect herself.

The other men made no attempt to intervene. Instead, when Batson finally stopped kicking his wife, and allowed the bitterly sobbing woman to scrabble away from him on her hands and knees, the drinkers in the pub applauded his action.

'Serves the cow right for showing him up like that.'

'She deserved all that she got.'

'I'd ha' done the same, only I'd ha' given her more of it.'

Caleb felt angry and disgusted, but he knew better than to interfere between the man and his wife. This was the way of the class he belonged to. The woman had defied and broken a sacrosanct unwritten law by daring to enter a public bar and challenge her husband. She had demeaned him in the eyes of his peers, and if he had allowed her to defy him with impunity then he would have become a figure of contempt, to be mocked and jeered at by other men and their womenfolk. In Caleb's class men were the masters, and their wives were submissive chattels who must obey their husbands in all things and never dare to challenge or defy their rulings.

Henry Batson returned to his game of dominoes, and accepted the congratulations of his fellow players as his rightful due.

Caleb heard Alfred Payne's loud, drunken voice as he boasted to his drinking mates, 'My fuckin' missus 'ud never dare to come into any pub arter me. Or wait outside neither. Her knows what her 'ud get if her did.'

'And what's that, Alfie? What 'ud her get?' one of his mates baited.

Payne shook his meaty clenched fist beneath the baiter's nose. 'Her 'ud get this in her chops. Like her's had it in her chops a good many times.'

Caleb, already angered by witnessing the brutal beating of the woman, felt that anger erupt to a white heat. He turned round and shouted at Payne, 'If you ever lay so much as a finger on my sister again, Payne, I'll settle your hash.'

The noisy hubbub instantly stilled, and all eyes swung to the two men.

Payne scowled, and full of the Dutch courage imparted by drink, snarled, 'If I wants to clout my old 'ooman, then I'll do it. And you wun't stop me. And if you tries to, then I'll give you a taste o' the same as I'll give your fuckin' sister.'

Caleb almost snapped and he lusted to hurl himself at the other man. But then in his mind's eye he saw his sister's face, and heard her begging him, as she had done so many times, not to fight with her husband.

Not trusting himself to retain control, Caleb walked out of the bar without speaking another word to anyone. His anger seethed as he strode towards the town centre, and he drew in great lungfuls of air as his heart pounded from the effects of the adrenalin surging through his body. He decided that he and his daughter would leave Alfred Payne's house that very night, because he realised that if he remained there, a violent clash was inevitable between himself and the man

53

whom he loathed. He was in no doubt about the outcome of any physical confrontation between them. In his youth and early manhood Caleb had been a very skilful boxer, widely considered to have the potential to become a professional champion. But his wife had hated him fighting in the ring, and to please her he had stopped boxing and abandoned his ambition to become a champion. During his years in Canada, though, he had at times been forced by sheer necessity to fight in order to earn money to support his family, and had met and defeated some very good Canadian and American pugilists. He knew that he could master Alfred Payne, big and strong though the man might be. And now it galled him to his very soul to know that by walking out of the White Lion as he had done, he would be thought of as a coward who had been afraid to meet Payne's challenge.

He suddenly slowed his rapid strides as he realised, I've nowhere to take Marie, have I? Where can I find us a place to go at this time on a Saturday? I can sleep rough if needs be, but I can't expect my Marie to sleep in the woods.

His mind full of these distracting worries, he stepped off the pavement to cross the road, completely unconscious of the cantering horseman coming up rapidly behind him.

'Look out!' the rider bawled, and the horse shied and reared in fright. Caleb turned too late, arms lifting to fend off the huge oncoming bulk, and then the horse collided with him and he was smashed down beneath its lashing hooves.

Chapter Six

'Where's my pa got to?' Marie Gurden wondered aloud, and Eva Payne could not help sighing resignedly.

'How many times do I have to tell you, he's more than likely gone for a drink with his friends.'

'But he hasn't got any friends round here,' the child retorted.

'His workmates then.' Her aunt shook her head with sudden impatience. 'Do give over pestering about your dad, will you, and get on with this mending.'

The two of them were sitting in the gas-lit room, patching and darning the pile of clothes on the table between them.

'But it's dark outside,' Marie said plaintively. 'He could have had an accident.'

Eva Payne's impatience left her as she looked at the small, worried features, and a rush of pity filled her for this motherless girl.

'Look, sweetheart, this is Redditch, not the Canadian forests. If your dad had had an accident then somebody would have come to tell us. He's gone for a drink with his workmates. That's sure, that is. All the men round here go and have a drink after they get paid. It's the custom.'

'But Pa wouldn't do that. He'd come and see me first. He always comes home straight from work, and his shift finishes at six o'clock, doesn't it? And it's past eleven now.'

She pointed to the battered old clock standing on the mantelshelf above the fireplace.

'Oh my God, is that the time?' the older woman exclaimed in fright, and blamed the girl. 'There, that's your fault, that is. Pestering me about your dad until I lost track of the time. Quick, clear this lot and take it upstairs out of the way. I'll have to get the table laid for Alf's supper. He'll

55

go mad if he comes in and there's nothing ready for him to eat.'

She bundled the clothing into Marie's arms, and rushed around the small room and adjoining scullery, clattering crockery and pans in her frantic haste to prepare the table for her husband. She tasted the stew that was bubbling in the iron cooking pot over the tiny fire in the grate, and sighed with relief to find it savoury and good to taste, the meat tender and succulent.

'He won't find anything to moan about with that.'

Marie carried the bundle up the narrow stairs and into the bedroom that she shared with the five eldest Payne children. The cramped floorspace was all but filled by the two beds, each sleeping three. The other bedroom was Alfred and Eva's, and the two youngest children slept in a cot in that room. Caleb slept on a coir mattress in the downstairs living room, and when not in use his mattress was stood against the scullery wall.

As Marie carefully pushed the bundle of clothing beneath the nearer bed in her room, she could not help but smile at the peacefully sleeping children, whose faces were bathed by the shaft of moonlight streaming through the cracked panes of the tiny window. The eldest boy was seven years old, the girl twins six, the other boys four and three respectively, while in the neighbouring room were the youngest girl, aged two, and the baby boy of six months.

Despite her youth, Marie was a clever and sensible child, and she could appreciate how hard her aunt worked to keep these children clean, and to feed and clothe and shelter them. It was her aunt's proud boast that those of her children who were at the infants school had never received the dreaded 'green card' from the school nurse, the card that was notification that the child was verminous.

As Marie returned downstairs there came from outside the approaching sounds of men's loud, harsh voices, and she said excitedly, 'I'll bet that's my pa.'

Her aunt smiled at her sadly. 'Well, I know that one of them is my husband, and he's as drunk as a lord by the sound of him. You get on up to bed, my duck.'

'But I want to see Pa,' Marie protested.

Her aunt snapped curtly, 'If it is your dad, I'll come up and tell you. Now go to bed, child.'

With her lips pouting resentfully, the girl reluctantly obeyed. But upstairs she did not undress and join the twins in their bed. Instead she merely took off her shoes, and then sat on the side of the bed, listening intently to the oncoming voices which were growing louder and louder. She heard the slurred, noisy farewells, and the ringing clumping of hobnailed boots echoing hollowly through the covered entry passage of the court. The outside door of the living room crashed open, and with a sickening sense of disappointment she heard her hated uncle snarling aggressively.

'Wheer's me dinner? Gerroff your arse and get me my dinner.'

There was a clattering of boots and a dull thump as the drunken man staggered backwards and collided with the closed door behind him, and he swore loudly.

Marie sat stiff and tense, listening hard for sounds of her father. Anxiety gnawed at her.

Where are you, Pa? Where are you? Why haven't you come back yet?

Below, in the cramped living room, Alfred Payne lurched to slump down upon his chair and sat with his hands resting upon the tabletop, cap pushed on to the back of his dusty mop of hair, cigarette drooping from the corner of his slack wet mouth. He leered triumphantly at his wife as she dutifully laid a plateful of stew in front of him, placed bread to the side of the plate, and filled his mug from the jug of beer she had bought earlier at the off-licence.

The man stared down at the stew, and then glowered at the nervous woman. 'What's this shit?'

She tried to placate him, but fear made her voice tremulous, and her smile faltering. 'It's that stew that you like, Alf. Best mutton.'

Recognising her fear, he grinned contemptuously. 'You aren't so brave when that fuckin' brother o' your'n aren't here, are you?'

'I don't know what you mean, Alf,' she answered submissively.

'Oh yes you does,' he growled menacingly. 'When he's

about you'm really cocky. But I got a bit of news that'll knock all that cockiness out of you.'

He saw the fearful anxiety spring into her worn face, and to prolong the torture he fell silent and began to eat, chewing with open mouth, noisily slurping his beer, wiping his greasy lips on the back of his hand, belching and grunting.

Eva Payne watched him with sick eyes, ever-increasing worry for her brother burgeoning within her, while upstairs the Marie sat rigidly upright on the edge of the bed, eyes wide with fearful dread, ears straining to listen to what was happening in the room below.

Alfred Payne signalled with his hand, and his wife darted forward to refill his mug with beer. After he had cleared his plate he belched loudly and struck a lucifer match to relight the stub of his cigarette, then leaned back and deliberately broke wind. The vile stench filled the air, and the woman's features grimaced in repugnance.

'What's up wi' you?' he demanded aggressively.

'Nothing,' she told him, and would have moved past him to escape into the scullery but he clamped his hand on her thin wrist to stop her.

'Stay wheer you am.'

'But I've got to clear up, Alf,' she argued in a trembling voice. Her fear of him was palpable now. She recognised that he was on the very edge of violent eruption.

Brutally he twisted her wrist until she cried out with pain.

'Doon't you want to know wheer your fuckin' brother is?'

She nodded, but remained silent, and kept her head bent down to avoid his eyes, knowing that he was waiting for some look or gesture or word from her which he would claim was threatening and use as an excuse to launch a vicious assault.

'Your precious brother is in the 'orspital. He might be dead by now,' he informed with brutal glee.

'Oh no!' Eva felt sick and faint, and the shock momentarily overlaid her fear of her husband. She demanded desperately, 'What happened? How bad is he hurt? When did it happen?'

He grinned, happy with the effect his news had had, and released her wrist to pick up his mug of beer and take a drink.

Eva went to take her shawl from the back of the scullery door, and he glowered.

'Wheer does you think you'm going?'

'I'll have to go to the hospital. I'll have to see him.'

His eyes sparked with fury. 'You're going nowheer.'

In her worry for her brother, she defied him. 'I have to go. I can't leave him lying there and not know what's happened to him.'

'You fuckin' cow! Am you disobeying me?' He thrust himself upright, and bodily hurled the table aside to send it crashing against the fireplace. Crockery smashed, and the remains of the jug of beer splashed hissing across the hot coals of the fire, sending up a cloud of steam and fumes.

Terrified, Eva cowered back against the wall as he launched himself at her. His fists thudded into her face and body, and she screamed and crouched low, trying to shield her head with her arms.

Upstairs Marie could hear the crashing of furniture, the bellowed oaths of the man, the screaming of her aunt, and petrified with terror she curled herself into a foetal position on the bed, sobbing bitterly. The other children were woken by the noise and added their frightened wailing cries and sobs to Marie's.

The uproar sounding loudly through the thin brick divides roused the neighbours on each side, and they began hammering on the walls and bawling for quiet.

It was the shouting and hammering of the neighbours that finally caused Alfred Payne to stop beating his wife. He knew that if he provoked them too far they would gang up on him, and fighting drunk though he might be, he did not relish the prospect of having to confront a mob of angry men and women.

He gave Eva a final kick, and then threatened, 'Gerrup stairs and shut them bloody kids up. Or I'll give them a bloody good hiding as well.'

Sobbing, her face bloodied, her body racked with pain, Eva crawled up the stairs, gasping for breath, and began to try and calm her children.

Payne searched for the beer jug, and swore vilely when he found it smashed and empty. Then he recollected something, and grinned blearily to himself. Rooting in his jacket pockets he found a small bottle, and unscrewing its top took a swig of the rum it contained.

He searched the debris on the floor until he found his packet of cigarettes and box of matches. Setting his chair upright he slumped down on it, and sat smoking and taking swigs from the bottle, and grinning inanely with satisfied contentment.

Up in the bedroom Eva gradually quietened and soothed the children, and one by one they drifted again into sleep. But Marie could not sleep, and she whispered frantically to Eva, begging to know what had happened to her father, and where he was.

To comfort the child, Eva lied, telling her that Caleb had had a slight accident and that he would be home tomorrow. She kept on whispering the lies until by sheer force of repetition Marie accepted them as the truth, and at last fell asleep.

Eva remained where she was on top of the bed, cuddling up to the girls, afraid even to move in case she should attract the attention of her husband. She heard him fumbling his way upstairs, and she began to shiver with fear, dreading that he would come and fetch her to their bed, dreading that he would force her to have sex with him, as he had done on so many previous occasions after he had brutally beaten her. But to her abject relief no summons came. Instead she heard him collapse upon the bed in the next room, and within seconds begin to snuffle and snore in piglike slumber. Only then did she relax a trifle, and try to rest her aching body. She could not sleep, her mind was filled with terrible forebodings about Caleb. She longed to go up to the hospital and find out the truth about his condition, and what had happened to him. But she dared not stir. She knew that if she were to sneak out of the house, and her husband should wake and find her gone, then his fury would render him capable of committing any outrage. He might turn on the children, as he had done on occasions in the past, and she feared that if she were not here to take his fury upon herself, they could suffer terrible injuries at his hands.

I'll just have to wait, she accepted sadly. He'll go out to the pub tomorrow, and then I'll be able to sneak up to the hospital.

The chill night air was striking through her thin clothing, and she began to shiver with cold. Her face and body ached from the savage beating, all the miseries of her life overwhelmed her and she wept, cramming her hands against her mouth so that the sounds of grief were muffled; and the long hours of darkness passed with mournful slowness.

Chapter Seven

There were eight beds in the male ward of the Smallwood Hospital. The room was broad, with a high beamed ceiling. In its centre was a columnar chimney stack with two fire grates back to back at its base. The floors were highly polished oak boards, and tall windows lined the walls to admit light and air. The black-painted iron bedsteads were set four on each side of the room, with a locker next to each bedhead for the patient's personal effects. Antiseptic cleanliness and absolute order were the hallmark of both the male and female wards, and noise was absolutely forbidden.

Matron Truslove ruled both staff and patients with an iron hand, and even the doctors were loath to provoke her icy glare.

At seven o'clock on this Sunday morning Matron Truslove walked with a majestic carriage through the length and breadth of the hospital. Mortuary, outhouses, kitchen, scullery, corridors, stairways, offices, bathrooms, operating theatre, wards, every nook and cranny of the building came under her keen scrutiny, and every fault was noted and committed to memory.

The nurses, porters, cleaners and kitchen staff were inspected with equal thoroughness, the youngest nurse reduced to tears by Matron Truslove's withering scorn because her neat white cap was crooked upon her glossy hair. The hall porter was left sulkily grumbling beneath his breath because Matron detected dust on the top ledge of the door, the cook rendered red-faced with ire after being subjected to a tongue-lashing because she had neglected to cover that day's dinner meat with muslin.

In the male ward, where one of the corner beds was surrounded by tall linen screens, Matron Truslove beckoned the nurse to her with an imperiously raised forefinger. The nurse hurried to move one of the screens and allow entrance. Matron Truslove passed into the cordoned area and lifted the noteboard from the end of the bedstead. She read the contents quickly, then stood looking down at the man lying flat on his back in the bed. She did not greet him, and ignored his questioning stare as she pulled the sheet back from his naked body.

Her practised eyes checked the arrangement of weights, pulleys and fracture boards which kept his broken thigh in extension, and she nodded.

'That's well done, Nurse Carter.'

The pretty nurse blushed with pleasure.

The matron checked the strapping of the broken ribs, then with a flick of her hand sent the sheet flapping back to cover his nakedness once more. Turning to the nurse she asked, 'When did he recover consciousness?'

'At ten minutes to five this morning, Matron. He was unconscious when he was brought in, but began coming round while Dr Jardine was examining him. So the doctor ordered sedation.'

'Why haven't you noted the time of recovery of full consciousness, Nurse Carter?' the matron demanded sternly, and the nurse hung her head.

Matron Truslove glanced briefly at the large bruise and swelling on the side of the man's head, and then for the first time directly met his questioning grey eyes.

'What's your name?'

'Gurden. Caleb Gurden,' he answered, and in turn asked, 'What are the extent of my injuries? Have my family been told that I'm here?'

The matron frowned slightly, affronted by the lack of deference in his tone. Deference that she both expected and demanded from her social inferiors.

'You will be informed in due course, my man. If it becomes necessary,' she snapped frostily, and left the screened area with the nurse trailing dutifully behind her.

Caleb grimaced as the dull throbbing aching in his head and thigh suddenly intensified, and he coughed, then groaned, as the involuntary movement of his chest wall caused his broken ribs to pulse with agonising pain.

Jesus! What a state I'm in, he thought despondently, and

acute anxiety for his daughter assailed him. Poor Marie, how will she react to seeing me like this?

He was desperate to find out if his sister and daughter had been informed of his accident and his present whereabouts. He racked his brains trying to recall if he had told anyone who he was and where he lived when he had been brought into the hospital. But all he could recall were blurred images and disjointed, bizarre flashes of remembrance.

Tentatively he moved his hand to explore his swollen head, and accepted ruefully, I don't think I'm ever going to have full recall of what happened. This must have knocked all the sense out of me.

The screen moved and the pretty nurse came to him, smiling.

'Now then, Mr Gurden, I'll take some details from you, shall I?'

'Where's Bismarck gone?' he quipped.

She blushed and giggled, then tried to be stern as she scolded, 'You mustn't be disrespectful of the matron, Mr Gurden.'

'Have my family been told about my accident?' he asked anxiously, and the young woman sighed regretfully.

'I'm sorry, Mr Gurden, I really don't know. Apparently you were too dazed to give any details about yourself last night.'

She saw his worried expression, and smiled sympathetically. 'Never mind, Mr Gurden. You can give me all the details now, and I'll make sure that your family are informed as quickly as possible.'

He smiled with genuine gratitude and thanked her, then began to answer her questions.

In the entrance hallway of the hospital the elderly porter resentfully opened the great doors and with a damp cloth proceeded to wipe and rewipe every surface he could reach.

'Excuse me please, mister,' Marie Gurden asked the man. 'Is my pa here? His name is Caleb Gurden.'

'How the bleedin' 'ell should I know?' the old man growled.

Marie's face was pale and pinched with strain. She had been waiting outside these doors since five o'clock that morning. As soon as she had awoken from her troubled sleep she had insisted that Eva Payne let her come to the hospital to enquire about her father. And the woman, afraid to leave the house herself, had not been able to resist her pleading.

Although the gruff old man had so callously rebuffed her, Marie's anxieties forced her to persist.

'Please, mister, my pa's name is Caleb Gurden. Is he here?'

The old man scowled. 'I'se already told you, aren't I? How the bleedin' 'ell should I know wheer your pa is? Now bugger off, and let me get on wi' me work.'

The child refused to give ground, but stood defiantly facing him. 'I have to know if my pa is here, mister.'

The porter's irascible temper, already sorely tried by the matron's harsh words, now erupted.

'Gerroff out of it, you cheeky little bugger!' He stepped towards her and swiped at her blonde head with the damp cloth.

Marie ducked under the blow, and gathering all her courage, slipped past him and ran into the entrance hall.

'Come back!' he shouted. 'Get back 'ere, you little bleeder!'

Marie flew onwards, calling out, 'Pa? Pa? Where are you? Pa, where are you?'

She ran up a long corridor, her feet clattering on the shining floorboards, her blonde hair streaming, and behind her the old man came bellowing in pursuit.

'Pa? Pa? Where are you, Pa?'

A huge starched white apron abruptly filled her vision, and strong hands gripped and held her.

'What is going on here? What is the meaning of this outrageous behaviour?' Matron Truslove thundered at the small girl wriggling so desperately to break free from her grasp.

The porter came puffing up. 'Her run past me afore I could catch 'old on her, Matron.'

'I'm looking for my pa,' Marie wailed, near to tears. 'I just want to find my pa. He's been hurt. He might be dead even! I just want to find him!'

'You can give her over to me now, Matron.' The hall porter reached out with eager hands. 'I'll soon have the little beggar out in the road again.'

Matron Truslove's face was a granite-like mask, and she snapped at the elderly man, 'You'll do no such thing, Sheldon. Get back to your work. I'll deal with this matter.'

She gave the struggling girl a quick, sharp shake. 'Be still!'

Marie, tears brimming in her eyes, gulping for breath, obeyed and stood trembling from the effects of her overstrung nerves.

'What's your name, you wicked girl?' the matron thundered.

Marie swallowed hard and choked out, 'Marie Gurden, miss.'

'Gurden?' the woman repeated. 'Gurden, you say?'

The child nodded, and her long blonde hair shimmered in glossy waves around her pale, delicate features.

The matron stared down at this small distressed creature, and momentarily her eyes became soft and misty. Then that moment passed, and she coughed and said gruffly, 'Come with me, Marie Gurden. I'll take you to see your father. Don't be alarmed when you see him, because he is going to be recovered and perfectly well again in due course. The attachments to him, and all the plaster and bandages, are only to aid his recovery.'

Hand in hand the small girl and the tall, stately matron walked along the corridor and into the male ward.

The pretty nurse poked her head out from behind the screens when she heard footsteps enter the ward, and her eyes widened in shocked surprise when she saw the small girl holding on to the matron's hand.

'This young lady has come to visit her father Mr Gurden, Nurse Carter. She can remain for half an hour, but not a moment longer.' She frowned sternly down at Marie. 'Do you understand me, girl. Half an hour, and then you must leave immediately.'

Marie nodded solemnly, and again the momentary soft mistiness appeared in the matron's eyes, then she turned abruptly and strode majestically away.

Marie walked nervously behind the screens, and when she saw her father, burst into tears and ran into his outstretched arms.

Nurse Carter smiled sympathetically and quietly withdrew, leaving father and daughter to comfort each other.

When he had soothed his daughter and dried her eyes, Caleb stared anxiously at her pale, worried face. He tried to reassure her.

'It all looks a lot worse than it is, honey. I'll be on my feet and out of here before you know it.'

She tried to smile, but only succeeded in appearing more woebegone.

'How did you know I was in here?' Caleb asked.

'I heard Uncle Alfred tell Auntie Eva last night, when he came back home.' She faltered, and tears again fell from her eyes.

'What is it, honey? What's the matter?' Caleb's inner fears suddenly surfaced. 'Has Uncle Alfred been bad to you, sweetheart? Has he been cruel to you?'

She shook her head, and wept bitterly, her bowed shoulders heaving.

'There now, honey, there now. Don't cry. Tell me what the matter is. Just tell me,' he soothed, cradling her shaking body in his arms, his heart heavy and terrible anxiety gnawing at him.

'I heard Uncle Alf beating Auntie Eva, Pa. He was drunk when he came home, and he started to shout at her and to beat her.'

Caleb's fury exploded, but he tried to keep his voice low and calm. 'Did he hurt you, honey?'

'No. He didn't do anything to me. I was upstairs, and when the kids woke up and started crying, Auntie Eva came and spent the night with us in our room.' She pulled back her head to stare into her father's face, and her expression was puzzled. 'Why does Uncle Alfred hit Auntie Eva, Pa? She had blood on her face when she came upstairs, and this morning when I woke up, her mouth and her eyes were all swollen and cut. She doesn't do anything to deserve that, does she, Pa?'

He sighed raspingly and shook his head. 'No, sweetheart. She doesn't deserve that. No woman does.'

Caleb felt physically sick with worry for his daughter. She was alone now, and virtually unprotected. He knew that his sister would care for Marie to the best of her ability, but he was frightened for his child's safety. Who knew what excesses Alfred Payne was capable of committing when in drink?

I'll kill the bastard! Caleb angrily vowed to himself. I'll kill him if he harms a single hair of my daughter's head.

While the child nestled against him, he cuddled her, and stroked her hair, and his thoughts were bleak.

He hadn't got the money to hire someone to care for her while he was incapacitated. And if he removed her from

Alfred Payne's house, then the only place she could go was the workhouse at Bromsgrove, six miles distant from Redditch. Caleb knew enough about the harsh regime children underwent in that grim place to shrink from having his daughter taken into it. It was not even as if he could be sure of her safety in the workhouse. He knew of children who had been physically and sexually abused by other inmates within its walls. At least if she continued to live with his sister, Marie would be close to him, and would be able to tell him if anything or anyone threatened to harm her.

He began to talk urgently to the child, telling her that if anyone or anything frightened her she was to let him know immediately. She listened intently, her eyes gazing wide and solemn into his.

'Look in the locker and see if my clothes are there. Hand me my trousers,' he instructed on a sudden impulse.

She obeyed, and he took from the pocket of the garment the envelope containing what was left of his wages.

'Here, sweetheart. Take this and keep it hidden. Don't tell anyone that you've got this money. You're to use it if necessary.'

'Necessary, Pa? What do you mean?' She couldn't comprehend why he was doing this.

He couldn't fully understand his instinctive action himself. He only knew that he wanted her to have some money with her that she could use.

'Well, you may find that you need to buy some things before I get out of here,' he answered vaguely. Then he set himself to cheer her spirits, and to reassure her as to their future, and slowly she responded. Colour returned to her pale face, and before the visit had ended he had succeeded in making her laugh once more.

When she had gone, Caleb lay silently cursing his physical helplessness, and willing his broken body to heal quickly. He also did something which he had believed he would never do again. He prayed long and hard, beseeching God to guard over and care for Marie.

But even while he prayed, memories stirred in the recesses of his mind. Memories of how he had so desperately begged God to make his beloved wife well. How he had begged Him not to take her from him. God had not shown him mercy then. Why should He show mercy and grant his pleas now? That was, of course, assuming that God even existed. A reality that Caleb had doubted many, many times.

Chapter Eight

The horse moved restlessly as the man ran his hands down its fetlocks, and the groom holding the animal's bridle crooned softly to allay its fears.

Standing watching the veterinary surgeon making his examination were two men, the younger of whom, a well-built, tall, good-looking man in his early twenties, carried his left arm, which was cased in surgical plaster, in a sling.

The second man was an older version of his companion, and despite the disparity in years their physical likeness was so marked that even a stranger would immediately have identified them as father and son.

The veterinarian completed his examination and straightened his back with an audible groan. He was a short, plump man, balding and red-faced, and now he grunted.

'My back is killing me. I hardly slept a wink last night with the pain.'

The older of the two men, whose grey, short-cropped hair and trim moustache gave him a military air, smiled sarcastically. 'Never mind, Goldman, I expect you'll be able to afford some liniment for it after you've overcharged me, as you normally do.'

Goldman puffed out his cheeks and protested indignantly, 'Come now, Colonel Barton, you're unjust. I have never overcharged you.'

Barton waved aside the protestation with an impatient gesture. 'Never mind that now, Goldman, let me hear your verdict.'

Still pouting, to demonstrate his ruffled feelings, the veterinarian answered offhandedly, 'There's a ligament sprain in the rear offside, and some surface abrasions and bruising on both forelegs. But apart from that the beast is perfectly sound. I'll make some liniment up for your man to rub in three times daily for about a week. You can begin exercising her again, but take it very gently at first. No jumps, only walking and perhaps after the first day some cantering.'

Colonel Barton nodded, 'Very well,' and snapped at the groom, 'Timpson, you'll go with Mr Goldman here to fetch the liniment. Good day to you, Goldman.' He nodded again and stalked away from the stableyard towards the large house.

The younger Barton smiled wryly after his father's ramrod figure, and then jokingly told the veterinarian, 'Please send the bill direct to me personally, Mr Goldman. I don't want Father to have a fit of apoplexy. Your last bill threatened to bring one on when he saw it.'

Goldman chuckled drily. 'There's a good many things other than my bills that upset the Colonel, Anthony.'

Anthony Barton laughed, and agreed ruefully, 'Don't I know it, Mr Goldman.' He tapped the plaster cast on his left arm. 'This will keep him going for a week or more, without any doubt.'

'How bad is it?' Goldman queried.

'Not too bad. Apparently it's a clean break and should heal very quickly.'

'You were lucky you didn't get a broken skull. What happened exactly?'

'I was coming through the town and as I reached the crossroads some fool of a drunk stepped out directly in front of me. Brought the mare down, and sent me over her head. Fortunately I was only cantering. If I'd been coming at a gallop then I might have been much more seriously injured.'

'Will your injury cause you to miss the annual camp?'

'Good Lord, no. It's only a broken arm after all, and fortunately it's my left. I can do most things with my right, and what I can't manage for myself, my batman will do for me.'

'How about the man you knocked over? Is he badly hurt?'

Anthony Barton shrugged carelessly. 'I'm dammed if I know, Mr Goldman. The drunken sot deserves to be for being so criminally careless. Good day.'

He moved away, leaving the other man regarding his back ambiguously.

It was the groom who voiced the thoughts that were in Goldman's head.

'He's a good chap mostly, Mr Anthony is, sir. But there's times when he sounds a bit hard-hearted. But it's only his way.'

Goldman nodded thoughtfully, and murmured, 'Just so.'

As Anthony Barton neared the big half-timbered old house he heard the sound of raised voices coming from the open window of his father's study, and he grinned. Poor Will was getting it in the neck again.

In the study Colonel Barton was berating his elder son, William.

'Goddamn and blast it, you're twenty-seven years old, and I'm still supporting you. You've failed yet again! You persist with nothing. School, university, the army, business, you've stuck at none of them. You're a damned failure! And I'm sick and tired of it! Do you hear me?' He waved a sheet of letter paper in front of his son's eyes. 'And now this! I go to the trouble of finding yet another position for you with yet another firm, and today I receive this! You've failed again, you damned useless lazy wretch . . .'

He held the paper up in front of his own eyes, and voice shaking with temper read out, 'I regret that William is totally unsuited for his situation with this company, and feel it therefore incumbent upon myself to terminate his connection with us forthwith.'

The old man balled up the piece of paper and flung it into his son's face, shouting, 'Goddamn and blast you! What is to become of you? Answer me that, damn you.'

'Really, Father, how can I possibly give you any sensible reply to that question?' William Barton drawled insouciantly. 'Surely only the Lord can know what awaits me in the future. Or what my eventual fate will be.'

The old man's red face darkened to a purplish hue, and shaking both fists at his son he bellowed, 'Get out of my sight! Get out, goddamn and blast you!'

William Barton's thin features lit up with a smile, and he bowed politely. 'But of course, Father. To hear is to obey.'

He sauntered languidly to the door and went through it, leaving his father roaring behind him.

71

Outside the study door William Barton's smile metamorphosed into a grimace of despair, and his shoulders sagged. His fine dark eyes were clouded as he mentally saw again the anger and contempt in his father's face. Then he heard the sound of footsteps and instantly assumed the mask and posture of insouciance.

'Oh, it's you, Tony.' He took his straw boater from the hall stand and would have walked past his younger brother, but Anthony Barton took his arm and accompanied him out of the door.

As their steps crunched over the gravelled drive the younger man asked, 'What was the old man raving about?'

'The usual.' William smiled carelessly. 'My uselessness.'

Anthony clucked his tongue against his teeth, and chided gently, 'Really, Will, it's too bad of you to upset him as you do. He was just coming to terms with my little accident as well.'

William shrugged his narrow shoulders. In comparison with his well-built sibling he was a weedy physical specimen, and his dark ugliness was in sharp contrast to the other's blond good looks.

'Oh, he'll soon recover his customary good humour,' he said sarcastically. 'Don't forget that Empire Day is nearly upon us. He's taking the salute this year, isn't he? That'll cheer him up. He loves playing at being a general.'

The younger man couldn't help but chuckle, amused. His father's rank of colonel was a volunteer commission. Ernest Barton had never served as a regular soldier, and for all his military airs and fire-eating declamations, his nearest experience to war had been the mock fights and field days of the volunteer militia regiment he had for a brief while commanded.

Then Anthony became serious. 'Do you know, Will, I think that's the main reason the old man is so hard on you. When you chucked in the Territorials it nearly broke his heart.'

'Bloody old fool!' William Barton's long, lean features were contemptuous. 'Just because he enjoyed playing at being a soldier, he can't expect me to do so. Patriotic duty, he calls it. Serving the empire! If he loves the empire so much, why in hell's name didn't he join the regular army when he was a young man? God knows there's been enough wars he could have fought in for it.'

Anthony sighed, and retorted wearily, 'Oh, no, please spare me the diatribe against the British Empire, Will. I've heard it all too many times already, and frankly it bores me.'

But William's dark eyes were distant, as though he were lost in his own thoughts, and he carried on speaking with rising passion.

'It's not the empire as such that I'm against. It's the misgovernment of our own people here at home that angers me. Millions of our fellow Britons live in a state of abysmal poverty and degradation. There are slums in our towns and cities and villages that stand comparison with the worst slums in Europe. We rule the mightiest, most far-flung empire the world has ever known, and yet we breed millions of men and women who are fit for nothing but the scrapheap. Do you know how many men were refused enlistment for the South African war because they were physically unfit to serve?'

Anthony nodded resignedly. 'Yes, I do, as a matter of fact. But you'll tell me anyway, won't you?'

'Over eighty-five per cent of those who volunteered in the industrial areas were rejected as unfit,' William continued, seemingly unaware that his brother had spoken at all. 'And that was even after the medical pass standards had been lowered to the standards of 1815. The year of Waterloo.

'It's a disgrace, isn't it? We are possibly the richest nation on earth, and millions of our fellow countrymen live lives of absolute wretchedness. We should be ashamed.'

Now the younger man became impatient. 'No, we personally should not be ashamed, Will. It's no fault of ours that such poverty exists. It's the way life is. There will always be the rich, the poor and the in-betweens. It's a law of nature.'

'No it isn't!' William Barton retorted vehemently. 'It's an injustice that should be put right. And someday it will be. When we have government by the people for the people.'

'Oh damn it all, Will, spare me your socialist claptrap, will you?' Anthony was becoming angry. 'I'm tired of listening to you ranting about social injustice, and government by the people. If you admire the poor so much, why don't you become one of them? Why don't you leave here and go and live and

73

work among them. There are enough slums in Redditch to choose from. Surely you could find one that would satisfy even your demanding taste?'

His brother's dark eyes suddenly filled with shame, and he shook his head and muttered, 'I don't go from here because I haven't the courage to practise what I preach. Father's right when he tells me that I'm useless. Because that's what I am. Completely and utterly useless.'

In Anthony Barton's mind conflicting emotions battled for dominance. Love for his brother, against contempt. Sympathy against scorn. Love and sympathy won the battle, and he grinned wryly and said, 'Oh, pay no attention to what the old man says when he's angry, Will. He blows a lot of hot air at times.'

After a moment or two his brother returned the grin. 'I think that's a family trait that I share.'

The younger man hesitated, then asked, 'What happens now, Will? What are you going to do? Have you thought about finding another job yet?'

William shook his head. 'No, I haven't given another job any thought. I know what I'd like to do, though. But I don't know how to set about doing it.' He was silent as they walked on in a companionable silence for a considerable distance.

Their opulent home was set in the farmland of the broad valley of the River Arrow to the north-east of the town of Redditch, and now as they breasted a sloping hill the town came into their view. From here the red buildings and smoking chimneys spread across the wooded hillsides, with the tall spire of St Stephen's church at the centre, made an attractive picture.

'It looks so pleasant from here, doesn't it?' Anthony remarked casually.

'Well, compared to most industrial towns, it is pleasantly situated. Yet there are slum streets there where the living conditions equal the worst that England can offer.' Will's sense of injustice assailed him with renewed vigour. 'And our family are the owners of some of them, to our shame.' He turned to his brother. 'That's what I'd like to do, Tony. I'd like to make those filthy hovels into places fit for people to live in. I've tried talking to Father about it, but he only

74

rants and raves, and pleads poverty as his excuse for doing nothing.'

Anthony was quick to defend his father. 'The old man has a point, Will. All his available capital is tied up in the Orchard Street development. Until that's completed he's got no money to spare for anything else.'

Will refused to accept that argument, and they squabbled acrimoniously for some minutes, tempers fraying, until the younger man was provoked to jeer, 'Perhaps if our tenants paid their rents on time, then the old man might have some money to spare for cosseting slum rats.'

'I wouldn't call it cosseting to give people decent places to live in,' his brother retorted heatedly. 'I'd call it simple justice. And if I were one of our tenants, I'd be dammed if I'd pay a single penny to live in such vile hovels. Father should be ashamed of himself for charging the rents that he does. It's a disgraceful exploitation of the poor.'

Anthony's good-looking features wore a sneer of contempt. 'People like you make me sick. You keep on preaching about justice, and condemning people like the old man. Yet you live off those rents. Perhaps if you were able to hold a job for any length of time, and begin to support yourself, then Father might have some money to spare with which to improve those vile hovels, as you so indignantly term them.'

He swung on his heel and started to walk away, delivering a parting shot over his shoulder as he did so. 'But you're not capable of supporting yourself, are you, brother? The old man is right when he calls you useless. Because that's what you are, a useless lazy hound, and fit for nothing except living off other people's money. You're a true socialist!'

'I'm proud to be called such!' Will retorted, and in the next moment was sorely regretting that he had once again quarrelled with his brother.

Why must I provoke him so? I know that it will end in a quarrel, and yet I continually force my opinions upon him.

He turned to shout after the other man, wanting to make it up with him, but Anthony had already gone from sight over the brow of the hill.

Will sighed heavily, and walked on towards the distant town. As he neared its hilly streets he began to think about the man

75

whom his brother's horse had collided with. He knew his name, and also that he had been taken into Smallwood Hospital suffering from severe injuries. The police inspector had come himself to the Barton home to take a statement from Anthony concerning the accident. The officer had accepted without question the word of that young gentleman that it had been Gurden who was to blame for what had happened. After all, the Barton family were local gentry, and had wealth and position. He had told the family that Gurden was a labouring man, lately returned from Canada, and that the doctor who had treated his injuries had stated that he had obviously been drinking. This being the case, the Bartons would hear no more concerning what had happened.

Involved in his own troubles, as he had been, Will had given little thought to the injured man. But now he began to wonder about him, and how he was progressing.

I really ought to go and see him, he decided now, and smiled ruefully. After all, I'm always shouting about the injustices done to the lower classes, and how I want to change their lives. It's the least I can do to go and see how the poor fellow is getting on.

The decision lifted his depressed spirits considerably, and he whistled a lilting tune as he lengthened his stride.

At Smallwood Hospital the hall porter, recognising a gentleman, saluted and respectfully enquired how he could be of service.

When Will explained that he wished to see Caleb Gurden, the man openly displayed his surprise.

'Begging your pardon, sir, but Gurden isn't here any longer. He was moved this morning to the workhouse infirmary at Bromsgrove.'

'Why?' Will Barton asked.

'Well, sir, it's the ruling, aren't it. The bloke's a pauper, and he'd got no money to pay for his treatment. And he hadn't got a governor's ticket to stay here, because he aren't been in the town long enough to get on any of the subscribers' charity lists. So the relieving officer had to get him shifted to the workhouse. It'll be months afore he's up and about again, you see, sir. And we needs all the beds 'ere for the respectable people of the town.'

76

'Yes, I see.' Will nodded. 'Does the man have family here in the town?'

The porter tugged on his moustache as he pondered. Then he said, 'Well, a little wench who said her was his daughter come to see him yesterday morning. Cheeky little cow her was, as well. Let's see now, wheer was it her had come from?' The porter made a great show of racking his brains for recollection, and Will took the hint and slipped the man a half-crown coin.

'Oh, thank you very much, sir. Let's see now, wheer was it? That's it. Her come from Edward Street, sir. That's it. He reckoned he was living with his sister down theer. Name of Payne. Wed to Alfie Payne, her is. Gurden's sister, I mean, not his daughter, o' course.'

'Has his sister been informed of his transfer?' Will queried.

'I shouldn't think so, sir. Not yet, at any rate. But I expect the relieving officer 'ull let her know wheer Gurden is in due course.'

'Thank you.' Will Barton walked away. Incipient anger was burgeoning in his mind at how casually Caleb Gurden could be shifted from one place to another, and his family not consulted or even told of the move.

They're treated like dumb cattle, he thought resentfully. 'And people in my class then have the gall to complain about the bad behaviour and ingratitude of the poor.'

He decided that he would go to Edward Street himself and inform Caleb Gurden's sister of her brother's present whereabouts.

Chapter Nine

'Paarraaaddde! Paarraaaddde attennnnshun!'

The massed ranks of children stiffened, arms locked at their sides.

Sergeant Sinclair, pace stick horizontal beneath his arm, strutted along the ranks, his eyes glittering fiercely in his brick-red face, the points of his waxed moustache quivering as he berated some unfortunate morsel of humanity for failing to achieve the correct military posture.

'Attenshun, I said, you fool. You're slumping like a sack of rubbish. Tuck your spotty chin in, boy, and keep your head back.

'You! Yes you, you halfwit! Get those feet in, you look as if you're frightened o' dropping something. Get your heels together, toes at forty-five degrees.

'What do you think you're doing, girlie? No talking on my parade!

'Oh now, what have we here? Beau Brummel, is it? You'll never stop a pig in an entry with them concertina legs, will you? Stand straight!

'You there, that girl with the blue ribbon, push your chest out and keep your shoulders back. Nooo! Not like a moulting pigeon! Like this!'

With a resounding crashing of steel-shod boots he came to attention, and the sun glinted and glistened on his brass buttons and badges as he stood proudly like a rigid khaki-clad statue.

Inspection completed, the sergeant marched back to his position before the ranks. He was a squat-bodied, powerfully built man, with the scarlet sash of his rank crossing his broad chest, which was also decorated with a row of colourful ribbons in testimony to his long and arduous service in his country's wars.

'Paarrraaadde, about turn! By the centre, quuuiiiiccckkk march!'

The serried ranks stepped off in ragged unison and tried to keep in time with the bellowing of the sergeant.

'Lef, ri, lef, ri, lef, ri . . .'

At the side of the school yard the watching teachers exchanged glances and muttered comments, sometimes smiling in amusement at the lack of co-ordination of certain children, sometimes grimacing in sympathy as the stentorian voice of Sergeant Sinclair singled out the offending child for verbal chastisement.

Josie Kitson was standing next to Emily Burgess, and both women were smiling at the section of the infant school who were marching with such solemn intentness, each one sadly out of cadence with its fellows.

'Aren't they sweet, bless them!' Emily exclaimed, and Josie nodded in agreement. She could not help but giggle when one tiny girl veered away from the main body and went striding off by herself, until an older girl ran and caught her to lead her back into file.

The elder woman's bright, birdlike eyes regarded Josie's smiling features, and she remarked, 'It's good to see you looking happy for a change, Josie. You've appeared depressed these last couple of weeks.'

Josie's fresh complexion coloured instantly. 'Oh it's nothing. I've just been feeling a little out of sorts, that's all.' Then in the next instant she demanded, somewhat heatedly, 'Why should you think I've been depressed, Emily?'

The other woman's expression was ambiguous, but she made no further comment, only gave a slight shake of her head and turned her attention back to the children.

Josie stopped herself from pressing her friend for an explanation, and bit at her lower lip in chagrin that she had reacted as she had to Emily's comment. Inwardly she was forced to admit that her friend had only spoken the truth. She was depressed, and what was more, troubled and guilty and ashamed of herself.

When Clement Hulme had come to her house on that Saturday afternoon it was as if a madness had taken possession of her. They had gone to her bedroom and there made passionate love. For the first time in her life Josie had lain naked with a man and had fully experienced the frenzied delights of sexual pleasure. Clement Hulme was a powerful and virile lover, and had brought her to orgasm several times during that afternoon. But those transient ecstasies of the flesh had had a painful aftermath. After he had gone from the house Josie had sat in solitude and wept wretchedly. She felt herself to be depraved and degenerate for having yet again surrendered to her sinful lusts. And terrible guilt racked her when she thought of the man's wife and children. She swore to herself that never, ever again would she allow her flesh to dominate her, and she had continued to avoid going to the chapel, cutting herself off from all social intercourse. But the acute loneliness of her life was beginning to take its inevitable toll on her nerves, and her mother's constant nagging and complaining was at times almost too much to bear.

What was making matters even more difficult was that Clement Hulme had intercepted her on her way to school on three occasions, and each time had threatened to cause a scene in public if she refused to talk with him.

Fearful of the prospect of public shame and scandal, she had allowed him to walk part of the way with her. If he had angrily upbraided her for her fickleness, she could have rebuffed him more easily. But instead he had begged and pleaded with her to see him again. Telling her how much he loved and wanted her, how she was the only good thing in his life, how he was prepared to give up everything, home, family, position, if she would only agree to come away with him. And how without her, his life was no longer of any value to him.

It was his abjectness and humility that troubled Josie, and caused her to scourge herself with guilt. She was now beginning to believe that the entire affair had been her fault, that she was to blame for what had happened between them, that she would be to blame if in his present desperation he was driven to some act which would bring ruin upon himself and his family, and upon her also.

Emily had unwittingly shattered the younger woman's brief respite from torment, and now Josie watched the marching children without pleasure, only longing for the time to pass

81

quickly so that she might escape from people's curious eyes and prying questions.

The drill period ended, and the children were formed in their phalanx in front of the stone steps of the main hall. James Parnell bowed his head briefly to acknowledge Sergeant Sinclair's immaculate salute.

'Thank you very much, Sergeant Sinclair. You've done a superb job. They're marching like guardsmen.'

The soldier's eyes gleamed with contempt for this hyperbole, but he only barked gruffly, 'Thank you, sir. I'll have to be away now.'

He marched briskly around the corner of the building to where his horse was tethered, and mounting the beast, trotted out of the school yard. Many of the boys stared yearningly after the soldier, wishing for the day when they too might present such a resplendent and dashing spectacle in this drab, everyday world.

'Now, children.' The headmaster was in a mellow mood. 'As you know, this coming Sunday is Empire Day. You will be marching in procession through the town, in company with the other schools of this district. I want you to shine in the procession, so that the people who will be watching you will appreciate what a fine school you have the great good fortune to belong to. You will all wear your best clothing. The girls will of course be wearing white dresses. And each girl will also wear a blue sash. The boys will wear collars and ties, and will pin a rosette of red, white and blue ribbons to their coat lapels. All of you will be carrying a small Union flag, which the school managers have very generously agreed to provide free of charge.'

His mellowness abruptly disappeared, and he scowled threateningly. 'If any boy or girl is absent on Sunday morning without very good reason for that absence, I shall personally punish them. And that punishment will be very severe, I promise you that.'

His gaze roamed over the rows of upturned faces for several seconds, then he nodded, as if satisfied with what he saw, and went on, 'We shall now rehearse our song for Empire Day. Begin on the count of three.'

He raised his arms, and counted loudly, 'One, two, three . . .'

then swept his arms downward in signal and the piping childish
voices chorused:

> 'What is the meaning of Empire Day?
> Why do the cannons roar?
> Why does the cry, 'God save the King!'
> Echo from shore to shore?'

William Barton was walking slowly along Edward Street when
he heard the massed voices of the children coming from the
school yard.

> '. . . Why does the flag of Britannia float,
> Proudly o'er fort and bay?
> Why do our kinsmen gladly hail,
> Our glorious Empire Dayyyyy?'

On impulse he quickened his pace and at the end of the long
street crossed over the roadway to stand outside the spiked
railings of the school yard and stare at the scene within. He
smiled bleakly to see the enthusiasm on the faces of the children
as they sang at the tops of their voices.

> 'On our nation's scroll of glory,
> With its deeds of daring told,
> There is written a story,
> Of the heroes bold,
> In the days of old.
> So to keep the deeds before us,
> Every year we homage pay,
> To our banner proud,
> That has never bowed,
> And that's the meaning of Empire Daaayyyyy!'

'That was very good, children,' the tall, bearded man on the
school steps congratulated, and then went on to call for 'Three
cheers for the Red, White and Blue . . . Hip hip hip . . .'

'Hurraayyy! Hurraaayyy! Hurrraaayyy!'

William Barton's gaze travelled along the lines of wildly cheering children, and as on so many occasions in the past, he marvelled at the intense spirit of patriotism that permeated the lower classes of his country. The lower classes, of whom the vast majority knew only poverty and hardship from their births to their deaths.

'Three cheers for Their Most Gracious Majesties,' the bearded man on the steps exhorted, and once more the massed voices roared.

Will's gaze switched to the group of teachers standing around the bearded man on the steps, and he acknowledged that judging from their lusty, full-throated cheers, they too shared that love of country.

And they should know better. They're supposed to be educated and intelligent people, he thought sardonically. Here we are being told every day by the newspapers and pundits that Germany is our enemy, and we're more than likely going to fight her. And there they are all cheering like mad for a monarchy that's German by blood. A King that's cousin to the Kaiser.

Then he turned away from the railings and crossed back into Edward Street.

The day was hot, and outside some of the doors of the mean terraced houses old men and women were sitting, some on stools, some on wooden chairs, yet others on the actual doorsteps. Their worn features turned towards him and their rheumy eyes studied the stranger. There was no welcome or friendliness in their look, only suspicion and wariness concerning this well-dressed man.

He stopped and addressed an old man who was sitting crouched on the doorstep with his head hanging down so low that the top of his huge flat cap hid his face.

'Excuse me, do you know where I might find Mrs Payne?'

The old man coughed wheezily, and spat a great gobbet of phlegm on to the ground by Will Barton's expensive, highly polished boots. But he did not lift his head, or even appear to be aware that he had been spoken to.

'Excuse me . . .' Will began again.

'It aren't no use you askin' the poor old sod anything, mister. He's as deaf as a bloody post, and simple-yedded with it.'

It was a wrinkled, toothless woman who had spoken, and now she came out of her house to stand directly before Will with an aggressively challenging air.

'What's you doin' 'ere, mister?'

He smiled placatingly. 'I'm trying to find a Mrs Payne. Mrs Alfred Payne. Do you know where her house is?'

The woman cocked her hands upon her hips, and with a shock of surprise Will realised that she was much younger than her appearance had led him to believe at first sight.

'I might do,' she announced, then demanded, 'What does you want her for?'

He found himself resenting her attitude, and could not help but snap curtly, 'It's a personal matter.'

'What's you mean by that? Personal?' she questioned suspiciously, then shouted, 'Eric, come on out 'ere, 'ull you?'

In the doorway of her house there appeared a burly, unshaven man with shirtsleeves rolled up to display his massive hairy forearms. 'What's up?'

'This bloke 'ere is askin' for Eva Payne.'

The man's bleary eyes studied Will, and a slight frown of puzzlement creased his narrow forehead.

'You aren't a copper, am you.'

It was a statement rather than a question, and Will, puzzled by the hostile atmosphere which had so suddenly enveloped him, shook his head.

'What does you want wi' Eva Payne then?' the man wanted to know.

By now other men and women were gathering to enlarge the group around Will, and their rough appearances and glowering stares caused a faint tremor of apprehension to shiver through his mind.

'I want to give her a message concerning her brother,' he explained.

'What about him?' the woman demanded.

Annoyance at their attitude suddenly overlaid the apprehension in Will's mind.

'I don't really think that it concerns you, or anyone else other than Mrs Payne and myself,' he snapped curtly.

The answer provoked an angry reaction from the group around him.

'Be you the bleeder that knocked Caleb Gurden down?' another man snarled. 'They says it was a bloody toff who'd done it.'

A collective growl greeted that accusation, and a woman cursed and threatened, 'If it is this bleeder who done it, let's give him what for.'

Other voices joined hers.

'Let's break his fuckin' legs for him.'

'Mad bastard, knocking decent chaps down and nigh on killing 'um.'

Will's instincts suddenly warned him that he was in real danger of receiving some rough handling from these people if he did not take great care in what he said to them.

I can't believe this, he thought incredulously. These people are damned savages!

Aloud he told them hastily, 'No, I didn't knock Mr Gurden down. I only came here from the hospital to tell his sister that he's been moved to the workhouse infirmary at Bromsgrove.'

'Oh, is that all?' the first woman exclaimed. 'Well, why couldn't you come out and tell us that to begin with, instead o' gooing all round the bleedin' houses fust?'

He shrugged. 'I didn't realise . . . I'm sorry.'

'That's all right, mate,' the man with the massive forearms said magnanimously. 'Doon't worry about it.'

The ominously threatening atmosphere changed instantly to rough helpful friendliness.

'Eva Payne 'ull be at work now, mister. But I'll give her the message,' the man offered.

'Thank you very much. That's most kind of you. But I really did need to have a word with her myself.' Will saw the redawning of suspicion this refusal engendered, and hastened to add, 'I just want to reassure her that her brother is all right. She may think the worst about his transfer otherwise.'

The explanation satisfied the man. 'All right, mate, suit yourself. Eva lives in number six court. Over the road theer. But her wun't be home for a few hours yet.'

'Caleb's nipper 'ull be home from school soon though, mister,' a woman told him. 'Her worries terrible about her dad, so you can tell her wheer he's at.'

'Yes, I'll do that. Number six court, you said?'

'Ahr, that's right, mate. Just over the road theer. I'll bring you a chair out, and you can sit and wait 'ere. You'll see the nipper coming home then.'

This kindly offer touched Will, and he hadn't the heart to refuse. So he sat himself down by the side of the bent old man, who was still staring at the ground and periodically coughing up large gobs of phlegm, and waited patiently for Caleb Gurden's daughter to appear.

When school was dismissed, Josie walked through the yard teeming with noisily excited children celebrating their release from bondage, her eyes apprehensively searching the roadway beyond the spiked iron railing. She was fearful that Clement Hulme might be waiting for her, but to her relief there was no sign of him. She saw just in front of her the long blonde hair of Marie Gurden, and on impulse called, 'Marie, how are you?'

The child turned and answered politely, 'I'm very well, thank you, miss.'

Her face was pale and strained-looking, and sensing that something was troubling the girl Josie asked, 'Is everything all right, Marie?'

'Not really, miss.' The girl was tense, and appeared anxious to get away from her questioner.

'What's the matter? Is there anything I can do to help?' Josie's concern was genuine.

The girl hesitated, as if thinking hard, then replied, 'Well, there is something you could do for me, miss. But it would put you out of your way, I think.'

'Tell me, and I'll decide whether or not it will put me out of my way,' Josie instructed firmly.

'It's my pa, miss. He's up in the hospital. He had an accident on Saturday. I want to go up and see him, but I have to look after the little kids for my Auntie Eva until she gets home from work. Old Missus Andrews has them until I get out of school, you see, and then I have to have them. But I'm very worried about my pa, and I want to know how he's getting on. And if my Uncle Alf comes home before my auntie, then he'll forbid me to go up to the hospital . . .'

Josie anticipated what the girl was probably going to ask of her, and she broke in to the rapid recital. 'Do you want me to go to the hospital and enquire about your father, Marie?'

'Oh, could you, miss? And could you tell him why I haven't come up to see him myself? And could you tell him that I'll come just as soon as I can? And could you tell him . . .'

With a smile, Josie held up her hands to halt the flow of requests.

'I've a better idea than that, Marie. How would it be if I were to care for the children while you go to the hospital yourself? I'm sure that your aunt wouldn't object to my doing so, would she? Who is she, by the way?'

'If you please, miss, she's Mrs Payne. Mrs Alfred Payne. Only her name is Eva.'

Recollection instantly came to Josie. 'Of course . . . Mrs Payne. Her boy and twin girls are in the infants school, aren't they? I never realised that she was your aunt.'

Marie Gurden smiled in radiant relief. 'Shall I collect them together now, miss? They're playing over there.'

'Yes, you do that. And then we'll go and fetch the tiny ones from Mrs Andrews. I'll stay in your house and look after them while you go to the hospital to see your father. But you must be as quick as you can, because I have to get home myself.'

The girl thanked her profusely, and her blue eyes were shining with relief.

'There's no need for thanks, Marie.' Josie smiled. 'Collect the children, and let's be on our way.'

Sitting on his chair Will watched the children swarming out from the school gates, and wondered how he was going to recognise Caleb Gurden's daughter.

As if in answer to his thoughts the man with the massive forearms materialised in the doorway behind him and pointed down the street.

'Theer. That little wench wi' fair hair. Her that's walking with the schoolmarm and them little 'uns. That's Caleb's nipper.'

'Thank you very much.' Will voiced genuine gratitude. 'And thank you for the use of your chair.'

'That's all right, mate.' The man disappeared inside the house once more, and Will walked to meet the oncoming group.

His attention fixed on the young woman, and he lifted his hat as he addressed her.

'Do excuse me, ma'am. My name is William Barton. I believe that this young lady with you is Mr Caleb Gurden's daughter.'

He noted the sudden fear in the blonde girl's face, and hastened to reassure her.

'There's nothing to worry about, child. Your father is perfectly well.'

He turned his attention to the young woman once again. 'Apparently Mr Gurden has been transferred to the workhouse infirmary at Bromsgrove. I wanted to make sure that his family knew where he was. That's why I've come here.'

Josie nodded. 'That's very kind of you, Mr Barton.' She paused for a moment, thinking what strikingly beautiful eyes this ugly man possessed, then explained, 'My name is Kitson. Miss Josephine Kitson. I'm a teacher at the school.'

'Oh, indeed.' He smiled, desperately searching for some easy comment which would lead on to further conversation with this young woman, whom he thought to be exceptionally neat and attractive. But he was never completely at ease in the company of young women. He was acutely aware that he was an ugly man, and he believed that his lack of physical attraction had sentenced him to a life bereft of the love of women.

There followed a strained silence, which was eventually broken by Marie's plaintive statement.

'I shan't be able to see my pa today then, shall I, miss?'

Josie smiled sympathetically. 'No, Marie, it seems not. But there'll be other days when you can visit him, won't there?'

The child took no comfort from the words, and her eyes were shadowed.

The adults exchanged a look of sympathy above the bowed blonde head.

'But Bromsgrove's a long way away, isn't it?' Marie seemed to be speaking to herself. 'How can I get there?'

'Oh, it's easy enough to get to, Marie,' Josie said lightly. 'There's the horse bus, or the railway. But to go by rail you would have to change at Barnt Green junction. Some of the carriers' wagons take passengers as well. Or you can walk. It's only six miles . . .' She abruptly realised that she was talking nonsense, and coloured with chagrin. Where would this child be able to get the money for a horse bus or railway ticket? And how could a ten-year-old girl be permitted to walk such a distance along lonely roads?

Josie knew only too well the grinding poverty of the Payne family. There was frequently hardly enough money to buy food with, let alone travel tickets. The young woman's troubled thoughts raced, and she told the despondent girl, 'Let me have a while to think about this, Marie. I'm sure that I'll be able to arrange some mode of transport for you to visit your father.'

Will suddenly saw an opportunity to extend his acquaintance with this young woman. He coughed, and offered diffidently, 'I may be able to be of assistance in this matter. Perhaps we could discuss it further, Miss Kitson?'

She smiled appreciatively. 'Of course, Mr Barton.' She looked down at Marie. 'You get off and take the children from your neighbour now, my dear. I'll discuss the matter with this kind gentleman, and I'll speak to you about it tomorrow.'

The two adults walked side by side up the grimy stretch of Edward Street, and Will's heart was pounding.

It was Josie who broke the silence. 'Are you connected with Smallwood Hospital, Mr Barton?'

'No. I've no connection whatsoever with it.'

She seemed puzzled. 'Oh, I assumed that was the reason for your interest in Caleb Gurden.'

He decided to be frank. 'My interest in the man is because it was my brother who knocked him down, Miss Kitson. I feel a sense of guilt by association, and I want to help the poor fellow if I can.'

Josie glanced sideways at his long, ugly face, and saw the genuine concern in his expression.

What a nice man you must be, she thought warmly, and aloud told him, 'I'm sure that any help you can give to Caleb Gurden will be very much appreciated by him.'

'Do you know him well, Miss Kitson?'

'Why, no, I don't know him at all, Mr Barton. And I've only spoken with his daughter on a couple of occasions. But there is something about the child which I find very appealing. I'm so pleased that you're going to try and help her to visit her father.'

She smiled, and Will felt himself becoming increasingly attracted to her. She radiated a pleasantness of manner, and the fresh neatness of her appearance he thought wholly delightful. To his own wonderment he found that he was now feeling much more confident in her company, and was able to chat easily with her as they walked up the hill to the town centre.

Josie was also enjoying this new acquaintance's company, and as they reached the central crossroads she found herself reluctant to part so soon. She would have liked to talk further with him.

He told her that he was Colonel Barton's eldest son. She knew the colonel by sight. He was one of the town's most prominent citizens. She also knew that the Barton family home lay to the north of the town, and her way homewards was to the east.

'Where do you live, Miss Kitson?' Will enquired, and when she told him he appeared crestfallen. 'I fear then we must travel in different directions.'

'It would seem so, Mr Barton.' She smiled.

He did not want to part from this young woman, and summoning up all his resolution asked tentatively, 'Perhaps I could walk a little further with you towards your home, Miss Kitson? I'm enjoying our conversation.'

She hesitated for a moment, and his fine eyes flinched as if he were expecting a rebuff.

She smiled. 'I'll be glad of your company, Mr Barton.'

He beamed with delight, and they strolled on together, their conversation becoming more animated and mutually engrossing as they continued on their way.

Josie failed to notice the oncoming figure of Clement Hulme on the other side of the road.

He saw her and the man, and fierce jealousy struck through him. His first impulse was to cross over the roadway and accost her, and send her companion packing. But then he realised who that companion was, and did not dare to create a scene. Colonel Barton was a very influential figure and wielded a great deal of local power. A power and influence that his sons would someday inherit. Even now they carried great weight in local society because of their name.

Clement Hulme turned and stared into a shop window,

watching the couple's reflection in the glass as they passed by on the far side of the road. He saw Josie's smiling face and a murderous fury engorged his throat.

'Bitch!' he hissed beneath his breath. 'This is why you've been avoiding me, isn't it? You've found yourself another man. Bitch!'

When they were some distance away, he turned and began to discreetly follow them, and his jealousy intensified as he saw their heads move closely together, and caught the faint echoes of their shared laughter.

He followed them the entire distance to the ford at the bottom of the Beoley Road. At the footbridge they stopped and stood talking, and miserably aware that if he remained where he was it was almost inevitable that they would eventually notice him, he reluctantly turned and retraced his footsteps up the long slope. Jealousy, anger, fear of losing Josie seethed through him, tormenting him almost beyond endurance, creating a raging maelstrom in his mind, and over and over again he gritted between clenched teeth, 'I won't let you go, you bitch! If I can't have you, then nobody else will! I won't let you go, you bitch! I won't let you go!'

Chapter Ten

Ernest Barton took the newspaper from the maidservant, opened it and scowled thunderously as he read the headlines.

Facing her husband across the breakfast table, Madeleine Barton's lips twitched with amusement and she glanced at her sons in turn.

William shook his head resignedly and raised his eyes heavenwards in mock despair.

Anthony, sitting at his mother's left hand, grinned and winked at her, then casually asked his father, 'Anything interesting in the paper this morning, Father?'

The older man snorted in angry disgust and then hurled the newspaper down on to the floor at his side.

'Damn the politicians! Damn Asquith and Churchill! Damn the fools to hell!'

He jumped to his feet and stormed out of the room, and Madeleine Barton smiled and observed placidly, 'Well, we can at least enjoy our breakfasts in peace,' then began to eat her portion of devilled kidneys with every appearance of satisfaction.

The maidservant picked up the discarded newspaper and Anthony held out his hand. 'I'll take that, Milly. Thank you.'

He glanced at the headlines and nodded. 'I thought as much. It's Ireland again. Sir Edward Carson now states he has a hundred thousand armed Ulster Volunteers ready and willing to fight against the imposition of Home Rule, and Winston Churchill has ordered the Third Battle Squadron into Ulster waters.' His lips quirked with contempt. 'I would have thought that after what happened at the Curragh even Churchill would have realised that no true Britisher is ever going to help the Government to force the Ulstermen to accept rule from Dublin.

93

I'm quite sure that the navy will follow the army's example if it is ever ordered to open fire against Carson's men.' He looked towards his mother. 'Oh, that reminds me, Ma, Jack Preseley will be coming to stay with me for a few days. That won't present any difficulties, will it?'

For a moment the woman's features, still fresh and pretty despite the plumpness of her body's advancing years, displayed a trace of doubt as she stole a glance at her other son. Then she smiled and shook her head. 'Of course not, darling. You know that your friends are always more than welcome to visit. Aren't they, William?'

Will's dark eyes remained intent upon the plate of food before him, and he did not reply immediately. His brother looked at him quizzically, and challenged, 'I trust you've no objection to Jack's visit, William?'

William did not meet his brother's stare, only continued to stolidly masticate his bacon and eggs.

A flash of temper showed in Anthony's eyes, and he snapped curtly, 'Of course, you agree with what those cretinous politicians in London are trying to do, don't you, William? You'd like to see Ireland being allowed to leave the empire, wouldn't you?'

William's eyes came up to meet his brother's angry stare, and an answering anger shone from their dark depths.

Madeleine's lips tightened and she spoke sharply to them both.

'That is enough, Anthony. And I don't want to hear your opinion either, William. I'll not have you quarrelling at my table.'

Both men loved their mother too much to willingly cause her any upset, and so they quelled their tempers, and went on with their meal.

In an attempt to dispel the tense atmosphere, Madeleine asked her elder son, 'Have you any plans for today, William?'

He made a conscious effort to relax and told her pleasantly, 'I'm going to Bromsgrove, Mother. To the workhouse infirmary.'

Her eyes widened in surprise, and he smiled and joked mildly, 'There's no need for any concern, Mother. I'm not seeking admittance to the workhouse, much as Father would

94

appreciate that gesture, I'm sure. I'm taking a small girl to visit her father.'

Madeleine looked mystified. 'A small girl? Is it anyone that I know?'

The man hesitated, uncertain as to how his brother would receive what he was going to say. Then he mentally shrugged and informed them, 'It's the daughter of the man that Anthony knocked over. He's been transferred to the workhouse infirmary and the child is very anxious to visit him. I thought that to take her there was the least I could do in the circumstances.'

Anthony's handsome features darkened ominously, and his mother was quick to intervene before a fresh quarrel broke out between her sons.

'Quite right, William. And while you're there, you might see if there's anything that I myself can do to help the poor man.' She turned placatingly to her younger son. 'Yes, Anthony, I know that it was the man's own fault that he was injured, and I do not blame you in any way for what happened. But in all charity I feel that we should at least offer some assistance.'

Anthony nodded. 'If you wish, Ma. But personally I feel that the drunken sot only has himself to blame, and in fact I regard myself as being the injured party.'

He tapped the plaster encasing his arm. 'After all, I did nothing wrong, and have got this for it.'

William laid down his knife and fork. He forced a smile. 'I have to go, Mother. I've several letters I need to write. So if you'll excuse me . . .'

He rose and leaned down to kiss his mother's cheek, and ignoring his brother went from the room.

There was concern in Madeleine's fine dark eyes as she regarded her younger son. 'I do wish that you and William would try to get on together, Anthony. It's not pleasant for me to have this constant discord between you. Brothers should love and respect one another.'

The young man smiled wryly. 'I do love William, Ma. But lately I find that he irritates me.'

She leaned across the table to pat his hand. 'Well, try not to let it bother you so, dear, for my sake.'

'I will,' he promised.

'And what are your plans for the day?' she enquired fondly.

'I'm going up to Birmingham to meet Jack Preseley's train. I thought I'd take the dogcart so that we can bring his luggage back with us. That's if you and Father won't be using it. Only you're going into Redditch with him this morning, aren't you?'

'We can use the trap. It's a lovely morning so I don't think it will come on to rain.'

'Good, that's settled then.' He stood up and kissed her cheek before leaving her.

She beckoned to the maidservant. 'You may clear away now, Milly.'

'But how about the master, ma'm? He's not had anything to ate yet,' she protested nervously.

Madeleine chuckled. 'The master has had his fill from the newspaper, Milly. It's quite taken his appetite away. You may clear the table.'

The sudden spluttering roar of the overtaking motorcycle and sidecar caused the horse to start and veer wildly to one side of the roadway. Ernest Barton exclaimed angrily as he fought to control the frightened beast.

The machine sped rapidly onwards, its rider bent low over the wide handlebars, and disappeared around the curve of the road in a haze of red-brown dust, leaving only the stink of burnt fuel oil and the diminishing echoes of its straining engine to mark its passage.

Beside her husband on the narrow seat of the trap, Madeleine said puzzledly, 'Why, that was William, and he didn't even wave to us.'

'Wave? Damn well wave?' Her husband gritted his teeth. 'Your fool of a son nearly had us into the ditch, and all you can bleat about is that he didn't wave to us? Aren't you bothered about the fact that he could have killed us by riding that devil contraption like a damn madman?'

Madeleine smiled at her husband. 'Now, Ernest, my dear, try to calm yourself. You know that excitement isn't good for your blood pressure. Remember that Dr Protheroe said that you must not allow yourself to become overexcited.'

The man's reddened colour deepened almost to purple as he bellowed, 'Dr Protheroe? Don't you talk to me about that man! It's his fault that William is riding that devil's folly. The fool was perfectly content with horses until Protheroe filled his stupid head with the idea of buying a damn motorcycle.'

Madeleine was not at all perturbed by her husband's ranting rage. She had been wedded to him for nearly thirty years, and had borne him five children, of whom only her two sons had survived infancy. She was the bulwark of her family, and for all his bulk and bombast Ernest was dominated by his wife. Whom at heart he loved dearly, as he loved his sons.

They rounded another curve in the narrow, hedge-lined road, and the town of Redditch came into view, its factories and houses spreading across the plentifully treed hillsides and in the centre of the skyline the tall spire of the parish church pointing like a huge black finger towards the blue heavens.

Madeleine always took pleasure from this familiar view, and now she sighed admiringly and remarked, 'The town always looks so very nice and clean from here, doesn't it, Ernest? And the trees make it very attractive.'

Ernest Barton had been born in Birmingham, and did not share his wife's fondness for Redditch. He chuckled grimly. 'Distance can hide a deal of dirt, my dear.'

She was quick to resent this aspersion on her birthplace. 'It is a clean town, Ernest,' she retorted sharply. 'Compared to Birmingham it's a very clean town.'

'Parts of it, my dear,' he temporised. 'Parts of it.'

By now they had passed over the bridge across the fast-flowing shallow River Arrow and were approaching the environs of the town itself. The road stretched before them in long straightness, only a gentle incline at first, then suddenly steepening up the hill which rose to the central flat plateau of the town centre.

The horse took the gentle slope at a smart trot, passing the tall retort house and huge round holders of the odorous gas works on the right, then abruptly dropped its pace and plodded with painful laborious slowness up the long, steep rise called by the locals Fish Hill.

A group of urchins were playing marbles in the gutter, and as the straining horse plodded past one of them stared at the two passengers and shouted, ''Ere, mister, you and your missus ought to gerrout and let the 'orse 'ave a ride.'

The next instant he let out a yelp of pain as the thonged tip of Ernest Barton's long carriage whip hissed through the air to crack against his naked calves.

The man chortled gleefully. 'That'll teach the little beggar not to be cheeky to his betters.'

Madeleine could not help but smile herself, then, instantly ashamed of being so hard-hearted, she rummaged in her purse for some copper coins. She tossed a handful back towards the gang of urchins, who whooped with delighted excitement as they scrambled for the tinkling, rolling largesse.

'God, but you're a soft touch, Maddy!' Ernest scolded.

On the plateau the horse quickened its pace once more and the trap rolled past the triangular Recreation Garden with its fountain and bandstand, and the adjoining tree-sentinelled graveyard of the chuch of St Stephen. The journey continued past rows of shops, through a couple of streets clangorous with factories and workshops, until at the base of yet another steep hillside Ernest Barton swung the horse's head eastwards into a street of residential terraced houses. But even in this street there was a bustle of industry from small needle workshops and a huge stables.

He turned the horse to the right up another rising hillside street lined on one side with terraced houses. On the opposite side was a row of houses in the process of construction. But there were no bricklayers on the scaffolding, or labourers carrying loaded hods up the ladders, no sounds of carpenters' hammers and saws. The construction site was deserted.

Ernest's ruddy features frowned in puzzlement. 'Where is everybody? It's not meal-break time.'

He handed the reins to his wife and clambered heavily down on to the road, then walked along the length of the half-built houses, bawling, 'Spicer? Spicer? Are you in there, Spicer?'

From one of the houses opposite, a white-aproned woman came hurrying.

'Am you Colonel Barton, sir? Because if you am I'se got a message for you from Charlie Spicer.'

He turned to face her. 'Yes, I'm Colonel Barton.'

'There's bin an accident, sir. One of the lads fell off the scaffold. Charlie Spicer's took him to the 'ospikal. And Charlie Spicer said to tell you that the rest of 'um walked off the job. But he reckons that they'll all turn in to work tomorrow.'

Barton nodded curtly, then swung on his heel and fuming with anger returned to the trap.

'One of the fools fell off the scaffold, and the rest of them have walked off the job. Damn superstitious nonsense! Every time somebody has an accident the rest of the labour force lay down their tools for the day. They say that it's bad luck to continue.'

Madeleine's features showed her concern. 'Oh, the poor man. Has he been badly hurt?'

'How the devil should I know?' her husband snapped impatiently. 'All I know is that he's been taken to the hospital.'

'Then we must go there,' she stated firmly.

He stared at her in genuine puzzlement. 'Why?'

'Because he's one of your workmen, Ernest,' she retorted sharply. 'It's your duty to go and find out how he is.'

'My duty?' he exploded, and flung out his arm towards the deserted construction site. 'My duty is to get these houses built and sold, and that damn fool has already cost me God knows how much in lost production. I'll lay odds he was damn well drunk, and that's why he fell from the scaffold.'

'You don't know that he was drunk.' Madeleine's own combative spirit was now aroused. 'Perhaps the scaffolding was unsafe. The way you drive Mr Spicer to cut corners and rush to get any job done, it could well be that the scaffolding had not been properly erected.'

Ernest glared at her, but underlying his anger was the timidity he always experienced when his normally pleasant-tempered wife became angry, as she was now fast becoming.

'You cannot pass judgement on the scaffolding,' he blustered, and then noticed that the woman who had given him the message from Spicer had drawn near and was standing listening intently to the heated exchange. He jerked his head towards her, and told his wife, 'And you should not be talking about our affairs in front of strangers, should you?'

Madeleine sensed that she was gaining the upper hand, and decided to postpone this dispute temporarily.

'Come, let's go to the hospital.' She held out the reins towards him.

Relieved that for now at least she was offering a truce, he clambered back into the trap and, taking the reins, urged the horse into motion.

Matron Truslove herself came hurrying to the hospital's entrance hallway to answer the imperious summons of Ernest Barton.

'I believe you have one of my workmen here, Matron,' he stated, after returning her respectful greeting. 'My foreman, Spicer, brought the man here.'

She frowned slightly, then told him, 'No, Colonel Barton. There's been no admittance of any patient today. But if you'll be kind enough to wait for a moment I can find out if any casualty has been treated. Won't you sit in my office, you'll be more comfortable there.'

Madeleine gracefully accepted the invitation and the couple were conducted by the matron into her office. The porter was dispatched to fetch tea and biscuits from the kitchen.

He arrived with the laden tray at the same moment that the matron returned with the information she had gone in search of. She hastened to serve her distinguished visitors herself, and while they sipped the tea informed Ernest Barton, 'Apparently your Mr Spicer came here at nine o'clock with a man named Alfred Payne. Dickenson examined Payne and found only minor surface abrasions and slight bruising. The man smelled of drink and was abusive, and the doctor sent him packing.'

Barton scowled ominously. 'And Spicer? What did he have to say?'

The matron shook her head. 'I don't know if he said anything at all, Colonel Barton. I was not present at the time, and the doctor's note in the casualty log makes no mention of Spicer, other than that he accompanied Payne.'

Barton thanked the woman, and told his wife, 'Wait here until I return, please, my dear.'

Scowling thunderously, he strode from the hospital grounds and made his way across the centre of the town. He knew the habits of his workmen, and could make a shrewd guess at where he might find them.

In the public bar of the White Lion Alfred Payne drank deeply from his beer mug, then belched resoundingly and wiped the froth from his moustache with the back of his hand. He grinned blearily at his companions.

'This beats sweating your balls off on that fuckin' scaffold, doon't it, lads?'

They agreed admiringly.

'That was a stroke o' bloody genius you pulled theer, Alfie!'

'Yeah, the best fall I'se ever seen. Like a bleedin' acrobat, you was.'

'You should ha' seen him. Come off the second lift he did, and went straight into the sandheap,' one of the group told the landlord. 'None o' the fuckin' Keystone Cops could ha' done it better.'

'What about Charlie Spicer?' the landlord wanted to know. 'What did he 'ave to say about it? He must have known that Alfie did it on purpose.'

'Charlie Spicer!' Alfred Payne jeered. 'You should have seen his face when I give the fuckin' doctor a mouthful. He looked fritted to death, windy bastard that he is.'

'Charlie Spicer daren't say nothing to Alfie,' another man declared jubilantly. 'He knows what he'd get if he did open his bloody mouth.'

'Alf's fist in it!' a bricklayer chortled, and there was a shout of laughter from his mates.

'I needed a day off,' Payne declared, grinning. 'And so did the rest o' the lads. So theer warn't nothing else for it but to do me party trick, was theer?'

'Three cheers for our Alf,' another man called, and the party roared out hurrahs.

More drinks were called for, and the smiling landlord hastened to fill the quart pots the men were using.

Then the door opened, and a sudden silence ensued as the tall, ramrod figure of Ernest Barton stalked up to the group of men clustered about Alfred Payne.

'I could hear from outside what you men were saying,' he declared grimly. 'You should really try to keep your voices down in future. Your loud mouths have done you a grave disservice.'

Booted feet shuffled uneasily, and eyes flickered from side to side in apprehension.

Only Alfred Payne returned Barton's angry stare.

'We aren't done nothing wrong, gaffer,' he said sullenly. 'I come off the scaffolding and hurt meself. I had to goo to the hospital. You can ask theer if you doon't believe me. And it's the custom that when theer's bin an accident the site closes for the rest o' the day. That's well known, that is.'

'Hold your tongue!' Barton snapped savagely. 'I've just come from the hospital, and have received the report of the staff there concerning your so-called accident.' He spoke to the rest of the group. 'If you lot aren't back working on the site in two minutes flat, then you're sacked. Now move, before I change my mind and sack you anyway.'

Without even finishing their drinks the men began to hurry out.

Barton swung back to the glowering Payne. 'You are sacked, Payne. And I intend to see to it that you'll never work again on any building site in this district.'

Payne's jaw dropped, and his eyes mirrored his shock at what he was hearing. Before he could recover his senses Barton had stalked out of the building, and he was left standing alone at the bar.

'Did you 'ear that?' he demanded of the now unsmiling landlord. 'Did you 'ear what that old bastard said to me?'

The other man nodded.

'I'll fuckin' kill 'im!' Payne bellowed furiously. 'I'll knock his fuckin' yed off his shoulders. The old bastard!'

'Doon't even think about laying hands on him,' the landlord told him bluntly. 'If you so much as lifts a fist to him, you'll be inside for bloody years. He's a bloody magistrate, you fool.'

'I doon't care if he's the soddin' King of England!' Payne blustered. 'I aren't gooing to let the bugger get away wi' blacklisting me in this town.'

'You just leave well alone for the time being, Alfie,' the landlord advised. 'I reckon you should just let the old sod cool down, and not goo aggravating him any more than you 'as already.' He indicated the unfinished drinks left by the departed men. 'Old Barton's done you a favour in one way, Alfie. Look at this lot. They'm all on Paddy Lambert's slate, so you might as well drink 'um down.'

Alfred Payne cheered up considerably at this prospect, and proceeded to do as the landlord had suggested.

Back at the building site Ernest Barton found that his foreman, Charlie Spicer, had also returned. The man faced his employer with visible trepidation, bare head hung low, work-scarred hands nervously turning his battered bowler hat over and over

'I've given Payne the sack, Spicer. And for two pins I'd dismiss you as well.'

'Oh, please, Colonel Barton, sir . . .' Spicer exclaimed in dismay.

Barton interrupted him brusquely. 'Just shut your mouth and listen to me. If you don't do your job properly from now on, I'll see to it that you never work again in this district. You'll make up for the time these men have lost, or you'll be out of a job. Now get on with it.'

Spicer mumbled words of gratitude for his employer's forbearance in not sacking him, and then hurried to obey.

For some minutes Barton remained standing with folded arms, scowling at the now frantically toiling men, who were being bawled at and chivvied by Charlie Spicer to work harder and faster. Then, satisfied that he had reasserted his dominance over his employees, he stalked away.

At the hospital he told his wife what had occurred. Her dark eyes gleamed with a wry amusement, and she chuckled. 'What rascals they are. Poor Mr Spicer, it must be very difficult to control rough men like that.'

Her husband glared at her. 'It's not something to be laughed about, Maddy. It's cost me money.'

Wisely she forbore to answer.

On the journey home Ernest was silent, deep in thought for some time. Then he told his wife, 'I'm going to put William in charge of the site at Orchard Street, Maddy.'

She showed surprise. 'But William knows nothing about building work!'

'He doesn't need to know anything. That's what Spicer is there for. All William has to do is to keep the men hard at it.'

Madeleine looked very doubtful. 'Do you really think that he's able to do that? You know his views on the subject of driving men too hard.'

Ernest smiled mirthlessly. 'Oh yes, my dear. I've heard all his half-baked theories about man-management too many times already. This will prove a good lesson for him. He's got to do something to earn his keep, after all. And God only knows, he hasn't done so up to now.'

She was unconvinced. 'But what if he refuses to do this work?'

Her husband snorted, and stated adamantly, 'He'll do it, and do it to my satisfaction as well. Or he'll leave my house for good. I'll disown him.'

Madeleine knew her husband well enough to realise that once set on a course of action, he would not be easily turned from it, and so accepted that for the time being, at least, there was nothing she could do or say to alter his plans. But inwardly she prayed, 'Dear God, help William to satisfy his father. I don't want to lose my son from my house.'

Chapter Eleven

In the staff rest room at the Bridge Street Council School Howard Billington was once again giving his colleagues the benefit of his worldly experience. Today his chosen subject was the widespread industrial and social unrest throughout the country. One hundred and forty thousand Yorkshire miners were on strike. In London, striking building trade workers' families were facing starvation. Many other groups of workers had also downed tools. On top of this the Suffragette campaign had become increasingly violent, and bombs were now being used by their diehards, while in unhappy Ireland it appeared that civil war could break out at any moment. Even the backbone of the country, the middle and upper classes, was adding its voice to the general discontent after Lloyd George's May budget had increased their tax burden. The Welsh politician had raised the new income tax levels to tenpence halfpenny in the pound on an income of £1,000 per annum, rising to one shilling and fourpence for incomes over £2,500, while the new lower limit for paying supertax had been reduced to £3,000 per annum. The new supertax would add an additional fivepence in the pound at that level, rising to one shilling and fourpence in the pound for those earning more than £7,000 per annum.

'. . . Do you know that in the paper this morning there was a report that even the cricket-ball makers down in Kent have gone on strike for higher wages?'

Howard Billington finished his long-drawn-out declamation indignantly, and his hand moved to an imaginary sword hilt at his side.

'. . . Napoleon Bonaparte had the right idea on how to deal with strikers and riffraff. A whiff of grapeshot! That's what he said they needed. And he was right! I know what the miners and the rest of them would get if I were in command of this country.'

Emily Burgess's bright eyes sparkled, and she asked, 'Would it be cold steel and hot lead that you would give them, Mr Billington?'

He glared suspiciously down at her from his warlike pose before the window. But her face was blandly innocent.

'Yes, that's exactly what I would give them, Miss Burgess. Hot lead and cold steel. That's the only language that agitators and anarchists can appreciate. The miners and the rest of them are bringing this country to ruination with their excessive and greedy demands for more and more money for less and less work. I resent having to pay more taxes while they spend their time in idling and swilling drink.'

The little woman's plump features screwed up in an expression of puzzlement. 'But Mr Billington, how much income tax do you pay at present? None of us earn sufficient to pay it, so you must be receiving more wages than the rest of us. That seems grossly unfair to me. Why should you be paid so much more than us?'

He shook his head, and his smooth pink features were uncomprehending. 'But I don't receive much more than you, Miss Burgess. I'm only paid the normal male stipend for this profession.'

'But you've just stated that your tax demands have been increased to keep those miners in drink and idleness, Mr Billington,' Emily challenged with a touch of asperity, and turned to Josie for support. 'Did he not, Miss Kitson? Did he not state that his present tax was being increased to pay for the miners' idleness and drinking?'

Fighting to hold back her laughter, Josie nodded.

'Mr Mould?' Emily next appealed to their colleague. 'You heard what Mr Billington said, didn't you?'

Thomas Mould buried his features in his capacious handkerchief.

'I'm going to speak with the headmaster about this,' Emily declared forcefully. 'I'm going to demand an explanation.'

'An explanation? For what?' Billington was begining to look concerned.

'An explanation as to why you are being paid so much more

than the rest of us.' The plump little woman was bristling with indignant resentment. 'I have been teaching in this school for twelve years, Mr Billington. Twelve years! And my annual salary and increments do not amount to more than one hundred and eleven pounds per annum. You have been teaching here for less than two years, and already you're being paid a thousand a year, perhaps more than that even. It is grossly unjust, Mr Billington.'

His pink face twisted with dismay. 'But I'm not being paid a thousand pounds a year, Miss Burgess.'

She waggled her fingers at him and scolded, 'Don't deny it! We have all heard you very plainly, Mr Billington. You complained that your tax bill was being made more of a burden than previously. Income tax is to be increased on incomes starting at a thousand per annum. Ergo, Mr Billington, you must be in receipt of an income of more than a thousand per annum.'

She looked sternly at her colleagues, and then told the squirming young man, 'If I do not receive immediate satisfaction from the headmaster, and an increase in salary commensurate with my experience and service to this school, then I shall go on strike. And it will be your fault.'

'But . . . but . . .' he protested weakly, and his arrogant pose crumpled.

Josie's control deserted her and she burst out laughing, and Thomas Mould whooped into his handkerchief. Emily's lips twitched uncontrollably, and then she also began to laugh.

The young man's face darkened with fury. 'Oh, that's very funny, Miss Burgess! Very witty indeed!'

He slammed out of the room, leaving his companions dissolved in helpless mirth.

'Oh, Emily, you'll be the death of me.' Josie wiped her streaming eyes, and tried to catch her breath.

The ringing of the school bell helped her to steady herself, and she sighed.

'Poor Howard. He never learns, does he?'

'And he never will, my dear,' Emily told her. 'Don't feel sorry for the pompous young prig. He deserves all that I give him, and more besides. Don't you agree, Mr Mould?'

The Scotsman was wheezing for breath, but he managed to

nod and pant out in agreement, 'He does that, Miss Burgess. My father was a miner, and having known what his life was like, I can only sympathise with those poor chaps in Yorkshire. It would do young Billington a power of good to go down the mines himself for a spell. He'd not be so ready to criticise the miners then because they go on strike for a living wage.'

Outside in the yard the children were mustering for the afternoon lessons, and the three went out to join the rest of the staff.

As the children were being marshalled into their groups a spluttering roar outside the main gates announced the arrival of William Barton on his motorcycle.

All heads turned towards the newcomer, and the children babbled excitedly to each other, thrilled to see this wonderful machine.

The rider dismounted and came through the gates. On his head he wore a cap with the peak turned to the rear, and a pair of huge goggles half covered his face. His coat was of brown leather and hung down to his boots, while despite the heat of the day a long woollen scarf with its ends dangling loose was wrapped around his throat.

The children stared at him with admiring eyes, the female teachers thought him incredibly dashing, and the male teachers envied his display of modern machismo.

He removed his goggles and lifted his arm to wave at Josie who blushed and dropped her eyes as all attention was immediately focused upon her.

The headmistress, Camelia Blunt, peered at the oncoming man, and then addressed Josie.

'Is this the gentleman you spoke to me about, Miss Kitson?'

'Yes, ma'am. This is Mr William Barton.'

The woman regarded the motorcycle and sidecar doubtfully. 'Am I to take it that he intends to carry Marie Gurden in that machine to visit her father?'

Josie had been expecting the man to arrive in a pony and trap, not on a motorcycle, and she could only shrug in answer to the question and reply, 'Well, ma'am, I can only assume that that is what he does intend.'

William reached the women and greeted them, then asked Josie, 'Is the child ready to go now, Miss Kitson?'

It was Camelia Blunt who answered. 'Yes, Mr Barton, the child has my permission to absent herself from school. But I was of the understanding that you would be taking her in some other type of conveyance. That machine is very dangerous, is it not? It travels at great speed.'

He hastened to reassure her. 'No, ma'am, it isn't dangerous. And the speed is under the control of the rider. I do assure you that I shall travel with caution. The girl will be perfectly safe in the sidecar.'

Camelia Blunt was an exceptionally conscientious woman, who took her self-perceived obligations very seriously. One of these obligations was the safety of the children under her care during the hours of school. She stared unhappily at the motorcycle.

'I cannot help but be of the opinion that the child will be frightened when she is closed into that box, Mr Barton. I'm not sure now that I can allow her to go and visit her father. If some accident were to befall her, I should hold myself entirely responsible.'

'Oh, but ma'am, Marie will be so bitterly disappointed if she's not allowed to go,' Josie protested. 'And Mr Barton has gone to all this trouble to help.'

Camelia Blunt's expression was troubled. 'Yes, I appreciate both those points, Miss Kitson. But I'm unhappy about the girl being enclosed in that box all alone. And one reads such terrible accounts about the accidents that have befallen these machines.'

'Suppose I were to accompany her, ma'am?' Josie offered on sudden impulse. She turned to William. 'Is there room enough for myself and Marie in the box, Mr Barton?'

'Certainly there is,' he informed her, smiling. 'And you'll both be as comfortable and safe as if you were sitting at your own firesides.'

Camelia Blunt pondered for a couple of moments, and then agreed. 'Very well, Miss Kitson. Since I know how much this visit means to the child, I'll allow you to accompany her. But only this one time. I can't have my staff gallivanting about the country in motor machines during school hours.'

While the other children watched with envious eyes, Marie and Josie mounted into the sidecar and the top was strapped down. Then William kicked the engine into life, and to a chorus of cheers and a forest of waving arms, roared away from the gates.

Inside the sidecar Josie hugged the slender body of the excited child, who was sitting between her legs on the cushioned floor, and gloried in this wonderful new experience. She found the rushing, bucketing progress, the roaring power, the hissing of wind breathtaking, and her cheeks glowed and her eyes shone and she exhulted in the passing moments and wished them to last for ever.

The ward stank of creosote, decaying human beings, and death. Along its whitewashed walls, above the beds where the sick paupers lay in their pain and misery, Biblical exhortations to love their God and bless their benefactors had been painted in huge black letters. The atmosphere was heavy with hopeless resignation, and the bleak room was of spartan severity in its furnishings.

The charge nurse of the male ward regarded the couple and the small girl warily as she met them at the emtrance door of the ward. She examined the board of guardians' handwritten permit of entry to the infirmary which the man presented to her and accepted that this gentleman and his companion were obviously people of power and influence. In view of this fact she substituted her usual hectoring, overbearing manner with a grudging courtesy.

'Gurden is over there, sir. The sixth on the left.'

Marie gave a cry and, tugging free from Josie's restraining hand, ran to her father, who held out his arms and enfolded her.

William told the nurse, 'I think it best if Miss Kitson and myself wait outside here and leave the child to talk to her father. But I would like to have a word in private with Mr Gurden before I take his daughter back to Redditch. I'd also like to speak with the doctor who is treating him.'

The woman's curiosity got the better of her. 'Can I ask what your interest is in the man, sir? Only Dr Andrews does not normally discuss his patients' treatments with anyone. I don't think it can be allowed.'

William frowned at this display of obstructive officiousness,

110

and told her curtly, 'If he refuses to discuss Mr Gurden's case with me, Nurse, then I shall go directly to the board of guardians. My family is not without influence in that direction.'

The woman's resentment showed clearly in her expression, but the power of the board of guardians was an absolute in this institution and she dared not appear to challenge it.

'Will you please tell me where I can find this Dr Andrews?' William asked, and it was more command than request.

Sullenly she gave him directions to the doctor's office, and he thanked her gravely, then went on, 'Would you also be kind enough to bring a chair for this lady?'

The woman went silently to do as she was asked.

Josie regarded William searchingly, and he smiled at her and explained apologetically, 'Arrogant bumbledom annoys me intensely, Miss Kitson. Will you wait here for me while I go and find this doctor? I'll be as quick as I can.'

She nodded, and watched his tall figure walking down the long, bare corridor, his boot heels ringing against the grey-stone flags. She found herself admiring the way he had dealt with the nurse. He had displayed a masterfulness that she had not suspected he possessed.

When the nurse returned with the chair Josie thanked her, and enquired tentatively, 'Is Mr Gurden progressing well, Nurse?'

The woman sniffed and replied huffily, 'I'm sure I can't be the judge of that, ma'am. I'm only an underling here.'

With that she turned away and disappeared into the ward.

Josie seated herself and looked at the bed where the child was still enfolded in the man's arms. Even at this distance she could see that Caleb Gurden's face was very pale and drawn and all superfluity of flesh seemed to have been stripped from his frame, leaving only stringy muscles, sinews and bone. There was a thick black stubble upon his cheeks and throat which stood out in startling contrast to the pallid skin, and his eyes were sunk deep in his head.

Concern for the man lanced through Josie's mind, and she hoped desperately for Marie's sake that he was not deteriorating in health, that his sickly appearance was merely due to lack of fresh air and exercise, and not illness.

Marie was also aware of her father's apparent physical deterioration. Alarmed at how quickly his appearance had

111

altered, she pestered him as to how he was feeling. Smiling, he soothed her fears, and eventually she relaxed and began to tell him all that had happened since he had been removed to the workhouse.

'Uncle Alf is drinking a lot, Pa, but he hasn't hit Auntie Eva again. He just comes in late and snores like a pig all night. On Sunday we're having the Empire Day parade. All we girls have to wear white dresses and have a blue sash.'

She gazed beseechingly up into his face. 'Pa, can I use the money you gave me to buy a new white dress, and a blue silk sash? And can I give Auntie Eva what's left so that she can get sashes and rosettes for the kids? Please can I, Pa?'

'Of course you can,' he told her lovingly. 'And you must tell Eva from me that I shall repay her for all her kindness to you while I'm in here. I'll soon be out and about again, honey. You'll see.'

He tapped the plaster encasing the tractioned leg. 'It's mending really well. I can feel that it is.

'Now, tell me how it is that you've found these kind people to bring you here? You mustn't let them go before I thank them for it.'

The child hugged him, and recommenced chattering, and he lay back and listened, and all the love he bore for her shone from his eyes.

William found Dr Andrews in the latter's office.

The man was elderly, grossly overweight, and the smell of whisky hung about him like a miasma. Unlike the nurse, he greeted his visitor warmly, and after perusing the board of guardians' permit was extremely hospitable.

'Will you take a dram with me, Mr Barton?' He opened the cupboard of his desk and took out a half-full bottle of whisky and two greasy-looking glasses. 'I've no soda here unfortunately, but there's water in the jug there.'

William accepted and was pleasantly surprised by the fragrant, peaty flavour of the spirit.

'This is good whisky, Dr Andrews.'

The man's broken-veined complexion glowed, and he chortled, 'It's the very best, Mr Barton. I guard my pennies very carefully, and then indulge myself.'

Indulge yourself to the utmost, judging from the colour

of your complexion and nose, William thought sardonically.

'Now, about this fellow, Gurden,' the doctor continued. 'I must ask you to treat what I'm going to tell you in the strictest confidence, Mr Barton. The strictest confidence.'

'Of course,' William agreed readily.

'Well, of course, he's not been in my care for very long, has he?' Andrews nodded wisely, and swayed in his chair. 'But I think that I can safely say that his leg will heal. He might be left with a slight limp, you understand. But the bone will be just as strong as it ever was.'

William felt a sense of relief as he thought of the child, Marie. 'I'm happy to hear that, Doctor.'

The other man winked owlishly, and William wondered just how many drinks he had taken that day.

'Oh yes, Mr Barton, the leg will heal. But I fear that the man won't.'

William's dark eyes showed his sense of shock, and Andrews continued.

'Since admittance he's had rapid weight loss, night sweats, and loss of appetite. I've seen it happen a hundred times before. Naturally it's still too early to make a positive diagnosis, but I fear that it could be an irreversible decline.'

God help him! William thought with concern. And that poor little daughter of his. What will become of her if he dies?

Another thought sent a shiver of apprehension through him, and he enquired anxiously, 'Doctor, if Gurden has gone into a decline, could that condition have been triggered by his accident?'

The man shrugged. 'Who can say what causes any decline, Mr Barton? Despite all efforts many things about the human physiology are still a mystery to the medical profession. We just do not know why certain conditions occur, and that's the sad fact of the situation.'

He drained his glass and refilled it, offering William another drink also.

William declined politely, sorely troubled by the thought that perhaps the suspected decline had been triggered by Caleb Gurden's collision with his brother's horse.

Andrews regarded him shrewdly, and then offered some comfort. 'Listen, Mr Barton. Medicine is a very inexact science.

113

My diagnosis is only tentative. Gurden's weight loss and other symptoms may not be terminal. As I say, it's very early days yet. I may have seen a hundred cases like his before who have died, but I've also seen many who have displayed similar symptoms and then made a complete recovery to walk out of here healthy and sound-bodied.

'A toast, Mr Barton! To hope! The hope that in this case I'm wrong,' and lifting his glass, he drank with relish.

Deriving what comfort he could from the doctor's final words, William Barton took his leave of him.

He made no mention to Josie of what Andrews suspected, but only told her that the doctor was satisfied with the progress of the healing of the broken thigh.

'That's good.' Josie smiled. 'Marie will be very happy to hear that.'

The allotted half-hour of the visit passed all too quickly for Marie and Caleb, and there were tears in their eyes when the time came to part.

Caleb beckoned William and Josie to his bedside, and thanked them both for their kindness to his daughter.

Josie led the sobbing child away, and William waited by the bedside until the pair were out of easrshot, then told Caleb, 'Mr Gurden, it was my brother who was involved in your accident, and I feel a degree of responsibility towards you because of it.'

Caleb shook his head. 'There's no call for you to feel that, Mr Barton. It was my own fault. I stepped out in front of your brother without looking. He couldn't have avoided me.'

'Nevertheless, my mother and myself would like to help you if you'll allow us to do so,' William persisted.

'You already have helped me,' Caleb assured him warmly. 'By bringing my little girl to visit me. I'm very grateful to you for that, Mr Barton.'

William's dark eyes were troubled as he stared down at the pallid, unshaven features of the other man. 'But surely there is something we could do for you? Help you financially, perhaps?'

Caleb's pride would not permit him to accept any money from this stranger, and his features became a stubborn mask.

'No, Mr Barton. I don't want anything from you, although I

114

do thank you for your kindness in offering. I'll soon be healed and out of this bed and back to work again.'

For a brief moment William was sorely tempted to argue that point, and to tell the man that recovery was not a certain conclusion. But he forced himself to accept Caleb's wishes.

'Very well, Mr Gurden. But please remember that my offer of help remains open, if you should change your mind about it.'

With a feeling of great respect for the injured man, he offered his hand in farewell, and was surprised by the strength of Gurden's grip, which belied his apparent frailty of body.

The school was being dismissed when the party returned to Bridge Street, and crowds of Marie's friends clustered about her as she got out of the sidecar, pestering her to tell them about her adventure.

Before she went off in search of her cousins, she gravely thanked Josie and William, and both were touched by it.

Left alone together, William smiled and asked, 'Will you accept a ride back to your home, Miss Kitson?'

She smiled radiantly at him. 'With pleasure, Mr Barton.'

And within moments she was once more enjoying the breathtaking experience of speed and power.

When Marie had collected her small cousins from the elderly neighbour, she led them home, all chattering excitedly about her ride in the sidecar. Her heart sank as she saw Alfred Payne sprawled upon the broken-backed chair by the rusty fire grate. A quick glance at his bleary eyes and slack wet lips told her that he had been drinking, and she wondered apprehensively what his mood was.

His first words confirmed her dread.

'Be fuckin' quiet, you lot! A man can't 'ear hisself think in this fuckin' 'ouse!'

The frightened children subsided into uneasy silence, staring wide-eyed at their father.

It was Marie's task to give all the children something to eat and drink when they returned from school. This was their last meal of the day, and it meant that they could all be in bed by the time their father returned from work. It also gave their mother time to prepare his food for him upon her own return from work, without being troubled by their demands.

115

Marie signalled to the children to stay quiet and still, and went out into the back scullery to discover what food her Aunt Eva had left there for her use.

She sighed with dismay. The cupboard was all but empty, only the torn scrag end of a loaf and a small portion of margarine remaining on the shelves. Marie realised instantly that her uncle had eaten what his wife had left for the children. Summoning her courage, she went back into the other room and timidly asked, 'Uncle Alfred, did you eat the food for the kids' supper? Only there's nothing hardly left for them to have. Shall I go to the shop and fetch something?'

He glowered at her. 'Am you begrudging me a bit o' grub?'

She stared at him in puzzlement. 'No. Why do you say that?'

He didn't appear to have heard her denial or question, and began ranting.

'A man can't even get a bit o' grub in his own 'ouse, can he, without being blaggarded for it. I work like a fuckin' dog to feed and clothe all you bastards, and to keep a roof over your yeds, and all I gets for it is to be blaggarded!'

As he bawled into Marie's face his foul breath gusted up her nostrils and spittle flecked her face. She flinched back from him, and the smaller children whimpered in fear and cowered in a tight cluster against the wall.

'I'm not blaggarding you, Uncle,' Marie protested nervously. 'I can fetch something else for the kids to eat.'

He stopped bawling, and grinned savagely. 'Oh can you now? And what's you gooing to use for money? Did that fuckin' missus o' mine give you some money?'

Marie shook her head.

'So what am you gooing to do then?' he demanded. 'Am you gooing to put it on the fuckin' slate?'

She hesitated, and he accused fiercely, 'Has you been having stuff on the fuckin' slate from the shop? Has you? Is that what you been spending my housekeeping money on, you thievin' little bastard?'

'No!' she almost wailed. 'No, I've had nothing on the slate.'

'If I finds that you has . . .' He brandished his fist threateningly under her jaw. 'If I finds that you'se run up a slate at the shop, I'll break your fuckin' face for you!'

Fear now gripped the girl, and her voice shook as she said

once more, 'No, Uncle Alfred, I haven't ever had anything on the slate.'

A cunning leer now curved his slack wet mouth. 'Then what was you gooing to use to get the stuff now? Answer me that.'

He suddenly grabbed her long, flowing hair and wrenched her towards him, and she shrieked with pain and fright. His spatulate fingers locked around her slender throat and he squeezed hard until she was choking.

'Answer me, you fuckin' sly bitch! What was you gooing to use to get stuff from the shop?'

He loosened his grip so that she could gasp out, 'I've got some money. My pa gave it to me.'

'You fuckin' liar!' he bellowed, and shook her savagely by her hair, causing her to cry out in agony and terror. 'You fuckin' lying bitch!'

'I'm not lying, I'm not! My pa gave it to me,' she cried out, and began to sob wrenchingly.

He glared closely at her tearful face, and then abruptly pushed her from him. 'Goo and get it, and show it to me.'

In panic she scurried upstairs and from beneath the mattress of her bed pulled out the small envelope containing the coins her father had given her. Choking back her sobs, she hurried to give it to the man.

Payne tore the envelope open and tipped the coins into his hand. His eyes gleamed as he saw the gold sovereign and the scant assortment of silver and copper coins.

'I'll keep this,' he announced, 'until I find out the truth of wheer you got it from.'

Despite her terror of the man, Marie's spirit rebelled at this injustice, and she protested, 'No. You can't keep it. My pa gave it to me. It's mine and his.'

Payne's fury exploded. He lurched to his feet and his clenched fish swung viciously. The brutal blow smashed into the side of the weeping girl's head and sent her flying, to thud against the wall and crumple to the floor. The other children screamed and wailed piteously and Payne bellowed, 'Shut your fuckin' rattle, 'ull you!'

But so distressed were they that not even his bellowing could quieten them, and spewing filthy oaths he pocketed the coins and lurched from the house.

Chapter Twelve

The foreman advanced down the length of the room between the rows of women toiling at the thudding presses, and came to a standstill behind Eva Payne. Above the heads of the women the pulley wheels and belting that powered the presses created a deafening din, and the man was forced to put his lips close to Eva's ear and shout loudly.

'You'm to get off home straight away, my duck. Theer's bin an accident.'

Her thin face stared at him in alarm, and he shrugged his shoulders and bellowed, 'I doon't know what's happened. One of your neighbours come to the gatehouse to give us the message.'

She raised her oily hands to her mouth to hold back a cry of fear, and the man looked with pity at her drawn features, blanched beneath the sweaty patina of working grime.

Other women stared curiously at the couple, and as Eva hurried past them they called out to her.

'What's the marrer?'

'What's happened, my duck?'

'What's up, Evie?'

She was unconscious of their voices, her heart pounding with blind panic.

Oh God, doon't let it be any o' my kids! she begged soundlessly. Let them be all right! Please God! Please God, let my kids be all right!

At the gatehouse she stared wildly about her, searching for the message-bringer, and the gateman came out from his cubicle to tell her, 'It was Daisy Hawkes who come to get you, Eva. Her said you was to get home as quick as you could.'

She nodded, too distraught to thank him, and went running

out from the gates, her shawl gripped in her hand and trailing behind her through the dirt of the roadway.

There was a knot of women gathered about the door of her tenement, and as she came out from the tunnel of the entry they turned. Seeing her terror, one told her quickly, 'Doon't be so feared, duck! It aren't that bad!'

They parted to allow her through. Within the cramped room there were other women, some comforting the crying, wailing children, others bending above the blonde head of Marie Gurden, who was sitting slumped on a chair.

'What's happened? Is it Marie who's been hurt? Is it bad?'

Still in the grip of her terror, Eva bent to stare anxiously into the child's white, bloodless face. 'What is it, darling? What's the matter with you?'

Old Mrs Green champed her toothless gums together in her fury. 'It's your old mon! That's what the bleedin' matter is. That bastard you'm wed to.'

The child's eyes were slightly unfocused, and she seemed dazed, but she tried to smile at Eva, and mumbled, 'I'm all right now, Auntie. I'm all right now.'

Accounts of what had happened dinned into Eva's ears from all directions, each woman seemingly trying to outshout her companions.

'The bad bugger battered the poor little wench!'

'He give her a terrible punch, the rotten bastard did.'

'When I come in her was lay out agen the wall.'

'He knocked all the sense out o' the poor cratur.'

'It was pitiful to see her, so it was.'

'He'd oughter be hung, that bastard you'm married to!'

'He needs his bollocks crushing, he does!'

'He's a fuckin' animal!'

Eva's initial terror was lessening fast, and she was able to think more calmly. She began to carefully examine the child for injuries, and was relieved to find that there was only a large, swollen lump on the side of Marie's head beneath the long blonde hair.

'He only hit her the once, from what I can make of it,' said old Mrs Green, her toothless mouth slurring the words. 'He gid her a wallop on the side of her yed, and it knocked her senseless. But he didn't boot her at all.'

Thank you, God! Eva silently cried.

Now she was able to think clearly.

'Mrs Green, will you watch my kids for me for a bit?' she asked. 'Only I'm going to take Marie up to the hospital. I reckon a doctor should have a look at her.'

The old woman looked doubtful, and Eva could not understand why she did not immediately agree to see to the other children.

'Well, if you can't look after them, will one of you others do it?' Eva asked the rest of the women. 'I won't be long gone.'

None of them replied, and Eva stared in puzzlement.

Then one of them said, 'Listen, Eva, it aren't that we aren't willin' to look arter your kids. But does you think you'm doing right by taking that kid up to the 'ospikal?'

'Of course I'm doing right,' Eva exclaimed, incredulous that anyone should question such a course of action. 'The kid's had a bad knock on her head, and she might have been hurt worse than it looks.'

From the doorway another woman joined in. Her name was Hetty Maries, and she had the reputation in the street of being exceptionally shrewd and intelligent.

'I should think about what you'm doing, Eva,' she advised quietly.

'It don't need any thinking about, does it?' The normally timid and submissive Eva was beginning to lose her temper at this obstructive attitude which the women around her were displaying. 'The kid's had a bad bang on her head, and she still doon't look right to me. She needs the doctor to look at her.'

'Now doon't lose your rag, my duck,' Hetty Maries told her calmly. 'What you'm saying is right, and we all knows it is. But theer's summat you aren't thought on.'

'And what's that?' Eva challenged angrily.

'You aren't thought on what you'm going to do if your old mon is sent to the nick, 'as you?'

This statement caused Eva suddenly to have doubts.

'If the doctor looks at the kid, he's going to want to know how her got that bang on her yed,' Hetty Maries went on in a measured tone. She sounded like a teacher explaining a very simple fact to a particularly dull pupil. 'Now when the doctor 'ears that it was your old mon who gied it to her, he might

121

very well think o' reporting it to the police, or to the cruelty bloke . . .'

The 'cruelty bloke' was the local inspector from the Society for the Prevention of Cruelty to Children.

'. . . That kid aren't one o' yourn, is her, Eva? Alf Payne aren't her dad, is he? Her could lay a charge agen him, if someone like a doctor, or a cruelty bloke was to put her up to it. And then what 'ud happen to you and your kids if the bugger was sent down by the magistrates? You'd all end up in the bloody work'us, 'uddn't you. And that poor little wench 'ud be in theer wi' you as well. Like her dad is.'

Hetty Maries paused to see what effect her words were having on the other woman. Satisfied with what she saw, she went on, 'Now I know that your old mon is a bloody beast when he's on drink. But you tell me a bloody mon around here who aren't? All the buggers am the same when they'm on the drink, aren't they? But bad as they am, we 'em still better off livin' wi' 'um than being in the work'us.'

There was a general chorus of heartfelt agreement from her listeners. Amongst the poorer classes, being sent into the workhouse was the most dreaded fate they could envisage, the most terrible disgrace that could befall them. Men and women alike would suffer any hardship, make any sacrifice, submit to any degradation rather than become workhouse paupers. For many, death was infinitely preferable.

Eva's doubts suddenly multiplied. Her husband was a bad, brutal beast, and she both feared and lately hated him. But no matter how hard she worked in the factory, she was not able to earn enough to support herself and her children, and she relied upon his irregular contributions to the housekeeping budget to keep them all out of the workhouse. If Alfred was sent to prison, she knew that inevitably she and her children would end up being incarcerated in that dreaded place. Once inside its walls she would be forcibly seperated from them, and perhaps might even lose them forever.

Despite feeling sick and dazed, and suffering from the pain in her head, Marie had been listening to all that had passed between the women. Young as she was, she still recognised the truth in what Hetty Maries had been saying. Now she laid her hand on Eva's thin arm, and told her weakly, 'I'm all right,

122

Auntie Eva. I don't need to go to the hospital. If I can just lie down for a while I'll be perfectly well. Really I shall. I don't want to go to the hospital.'

Eva's battle with her conscience continued. She could accept her own hard usage at her husband's hands as being a concomitant of married life. Husbands had the right to treat their wives and children in any way they chose, and legions of women and children endured far harsher treatment than she and hers. But Alfred had no right to ill-treat her brother's child in this manner.

A tense silence descended upon the women surrounding her as they watched the play of emotions upon her face. Even the children's wailing hushed, as if they also understood that their mother was struggling to make a momentous decision which would have far-reaching effects upon their lives.

Eva's heart was pounding, and she was breathing in short, harsh gasps. Deep within her, her cowed spirit was battling to rouse itself, to break free of the chains of fear that had bound it captive for so many years. The choice before her was stark in its simplicity, but terrifying in its possible implications. For long, long moments the inner battle raged, and the women and children stayed silently watching her.

Do it! Do it! her conscience urged.

But . . . but . . . Her fear rattled the chains of servitude.

'Can I go and lie down, Auntie? Please? I feel ever so tired,' Marie begged weakly.

The other women added their urgings.

'Let the poor little cratur have a rest.'

'Bless the poor little mite, her's tired to death!'

'It 'ud be a cruelty to drag her up to the 'ospikal when her's so worn out.'

'You can always take her up arter her's had a rest.'

Uneasily Eva allowed herself to be persuaded. It was Hetty Maries who lifted Marie in her strong arms and bore her upstairs.

A steam whistle sounded shrilly from one of the nearby factories, and old Mrs Green cackled merrily.

'I 'opes you lot got your old mon's grub ready. It's knocking-off time.'

'Oh my God, I aren't even peeled the spuds yet!' another

woman exclaimed in dismay. 'He'll goo fuckin' mad when he comes in.'

Several other women were equally horrified to have forgotten the passage of time during their attendance at this engrossing drama, and there was a hurried general exodus.

'Now doon't fret yourself, my duck,' Hetty told Eva kindly. 'When that little wench wakes up again she'll be as right as rain. You'se done the right thing by staying away from the 'ospikal.'

'O' course you has,' old Mrs Green confirmed positively. 'Anythin' like this is best kept inside the family. You doon't want no bloody cruelty bloke or coppers coming around to your house. They only makes things worse.'

Eva glanced at her own children, who were now playing together quite happily.

'I know I'm doing the right thing,' she agreed. 'I can't risk bringing them into the workhouse, can I? And Marie hasn't been badly hurt. She's only had a thump on the head. Like you say, Hetty, she'll be as right as rain when she's had a lie-down. I'm doing the best thing for all of us by keeping away from the hospital. And I'll warn that bloody rotten husband of mine that if he ever so much as lays a finger on Marie again, then I'll have the police on him.'

But even as she justified what she was doing, and made bold promises to confront her husband, deep in her mind there was the shamed realisation that yet again her courage had failed her. That yet again she would do all that she could to appease the brutal bully who made her life so miserable. And following hard on the heels of that knowledge came an even more unwelcome realisation: that the restraint her brother's presence had kept upon Alfred's violence had gone. He had cast off his own fear of retribution from her brother in the instant he had smashed his fist into the child's head.

Oh, sweet Jesus. A shiver of fear went through Eva. What'll the bugger do next, now that he's not feared of Caleb any more?

Chapter Thirteen

Dorothy Kitson beamed in welcome as she opened the door to her visitor and greeted him fulsomely.

'Why, Mr Hulme, what a pleasant surprise. Do come in!'

The man removed his bowler hat and followed the old woman into her living room.

'Now, you'll take a cup of tea, won't you, Mr Hulme?' she invited.

'You mustn't go to any trouble on my account, dear lady,' he demurred.

'But it's no trouble, Mr Hulme. No trouble at all,' she insisted, and after some further coaxing he graciously accepted.

While she was out in the back kitchen he settled himself more comfortably in the armchair, and used his handkerchief to mop the beads of sweat from his forehead. It was a sweat engendered as much by nervous tension as by the heat of the afternoon. But now that he was inside the house, he felt that he had accomplished the hardest part of his task, and the nervous tension was rapidly easing.

Now remember, he warned himself. Make no mention of Josie. Act as if she's of no importance to you whatsoever.

'Here we are then. That didn't take long, did it?' Dorothy Kitson, moving with an unaccustomed sprightliness, came bustling back into the room carrying a large tray laden with tea and cakes.

He smiled appreciatively. 'My word, Mrs Kitson, they do look tempting. I shall have to take great care that I don't commit the sin of gluttony.'

She gurgled with laughter. 'Oh, Mr Hulme, what a wag you are.'

She poured him a cup of tea, and handed him a plate piled high with the small, round cakes.

'Now you must tuck in, Mr Hulme. A fine big man like you needs a deal of nourishment.'

Now feeling completely at his ease, the man ate heartily, and drank two cups of tea in quick succession.

Dorothy, mindful of her role as hostess, did not question his unexpected visit, but stayed silent while he satisfied his appetite, smiling warmly at him as his jaws chomped stolidly until the cakes were all gone.

He swallowed the last mouthful, took a noisy gulp of tea to wash the final particles down his capacious gullet, and then archly chided the old woman.

'Now, my dear lady, I've a bone to pick with you.'

She assumed an expression of dismay. 'A bone to pick with me, Mr Hulme? Whatever can I have done to cause you any displeasure?'

He regarded her sternly, but allowed a smile to tug at the corners of his thick lips, so that she could see there was no real heat in his gentle scolding. 'You have shamefully neglected me, and the brethren, my dear lady. You haven't been to chapel for ages. That's why I've come here today, to take you to task for abandoning your friends. You've been very naughty, and quite heartless. You know that it deeply hurts us when you do not come to share in our fellowship. We were beginning to think that perhaps we had unwittingly caused you offence in some way or other.'

She threw up her hands and protested, 'Oh, but I haven't abandoned you at all, Mr Hulme. It's not my fault that I haven't been coming to chapel . . .' She went on to complain about Josie making excuses of being unwell. 'She's selfish, Mr Hulme. Heartless and selfish. My flesh and blood she might be, but she has a cruel streak in her which she never got from me, or from her father, God rest his soul! She breaks my heart with her treatment of me . . .'

He broke in smoothly, recognising that if he didn't interrupt, the diatribe would continue indefinitely.

'I'm sure that your daughter truly loves you, my dear lady. She may be selfish, as you say, but young people are invariably guilty of that sin . . . However . . .' He assumed a portentous air and leaned forward, lowering his tone conspiratorially to create an atmosphere of intimacy. '. . . I've something to tell you in confidence, Sister Kitson.'

She glowed inwardly as he used the familial nomenclature, regarding it as a sign that despite her recent backsliding, she was still enfolded within the bosom of the chapel, still numbered among the ranks of the chosen.

She stared raptly into his eyes as he went on in that same intimately low tone.

'. . . Tomorrow I'm taking delivery of a pony and trap. I thought it time that I had my own means of conveyance. After all, a man in my position has a certain standard to maintain, does he not?' He sighed regretfully. 'I have to take the risk that some of the more malicious among my acquaintances might think that to acquire a brand-new trap and fine pony is to pander to earthly vanity . . .'

'Oh no, Mr Hulme!' Dorothy immediately protested vigorously. 'Anyone who has the slightest acquaintance with you knows very well that to pander to earthly vanity, or to seek to satisfy bodily appetites, is totally alien to your nature. It's well known among we Christian people of this town that you are a very spiritual man, and indifferent to things of the flesh.'

'I am but a weak vessel, Sister Kitson, into which the Lord has poured his blessings. Praised be His name,' he intoned unctuously.

'Amen, Mr Hulme. Amen,' Dorothy breathed fervently.

'Now, Sister.' He smiled joyously at her. 'You will not have to worry in future about journeying to the house of the Lord. I shall come and fetch you in my own conveyance.'

'Oh, Mr Hulme!' She breathed out gustily, quite overwhelmed by this prospect.

He held up his hand. 'No, Sister, no. I shall accept no refusal from you. I do not regard the task as being an imposition. I regard it as a wonderful blessing from the Lord. So do not try to refuse me, I beg of you.'

Dorothy had not had the slightest intention of refusing this offer of transport. Already she was fondly anticipating the envy in her neighbours' hearts when they witnessed her being carried in her own personal transport.

'Praise the Lord for His mercies, Mr Hulme!' she exclaimed

excitedly, then demanded with eager greed, 'When will you fetch me, Mr Hulme?'

'This very Sabbath, Sister Kitson.' He smiled fondly at her. 'Morning, afternoon and night, should you so wish it. And of course to our weekday meetings as well. You shall never again be kept apart from your brethren. Not so long as our Blessed Lord allows me the strength to drive my pony and trap.'

'Oh, praise the Lord, Mr Hulme! Praise the Lord!' she uttered with heartfelt thankfulness.

He rose to his feet. 'Will you join me in a prayer, Sister?'

She dutifully closed her eyes and steepled her hands before her face, and he intoned sonorous words of thanks to their God.

As the prayer ended they both heard a rapidly approaching mechanical roaring.

The woman's eyes opened. 'What can that be?'

She struggled to her feet and went to the window, twitching back the corner of the net curtain to peer out. The roaring sound came nearer and grew louder, and then she saw what was emitting it. It was a motorcycle and sidecar. Dorothy hissed in surprise as the machine drew to a halt outside her front garden gate. Her surprise became shocked amazement as the leather-coated rider removed his cap and goggles. He dismounted to open the top of the sidecar, and her own daughter stepped out from the boxlike structure.

'Good Lord!' she gasped aloud, and the man standing in the room behind was instantly solicitous.

'Is anything the matter, Sister Kitson?'

She turned to him and shook her head disbelievingly, causing her pendulous jowls to quiver.

'It's Josie, Mr Hulme! She's just got out of that big box.'

Hulme moved swiftly to her side, and twitched back the opposite corner of the net curtain to stare out at the couple, who were standing close together talking animatedly. He saw the young woman's white teeth gleam as she laughed at something her companion had said, and angry jealousy fired in him.

'Who is that man, Mr Hulme? Do you know him?'

Hulme nodded grimly. 'Yes, Sister. I know him. It's William Barton. One of Colonel Barton's sons.'

The shock of this information caused Dorothy to relapse into the vernacular of her plebeian childhood.

'It never is, is it? Really? Well I never!' she was truly impressed, and now squinted her weak, watery eyes in an effort to see the man's features clearly. 'I didn't know that our Josie knew any gentlemen like that. Well, I'll goo t'Hanover! Who'd a thought it, aye? Our Josie knowing gentry like 'im. And her's ne'er breathed a word to me about it! Sly little cat that her is!'

She exhaled a sigh of satisfaction, and prayed that her neighbours might also be looking out at the couple. To have her daughter seen to be on such friendly terms with one of the Barton family would certainly cause her neighbours to regard her, Dorothy Kitson, with greatly enhanced respect. She would immediately be acknowledged as a 'superior person', a woman of undoubted gentility.

Wildly fanciful ambitions bubbled through her mind, and without thinking she voiced them aloud.

'Wouldn't it be wonderful if Josie were to marry such a gentleman! They certainly appear to be very close friends, don't they? Look at how he's talking, and how she's laughing. I haven't seen her laugh like this since I can't remember. Look at how he's staring at her. And there! Look at that! She's just laid her hand on his arm as familiar as how you please! I'll goo t'Hanover! They does seem like they'm real good friends, doon't they just?'

The woman's running commentary fuelled Hulme's jealous anger almost to exploding point. He struggled to contain himself. As always his sense of self-preservation helped him to maintain outward control.

But inwardly he was vowing, He shan't have you, bitch! He shan't have you! You're mine! You belong to me! He shan't have you!

Normally, Dorothy would have been horrified to see her daughter behaving so familiarly with a man on the public highway, and would have rushed out to put a stop to such a display of shameless hoydenism. But this was different. This man was gentry!

A smile of pure contentment wreathed her lips, and she prayed fervently that the conversation between the couple outside her gate would continue for a long time.

She experienced an acute stab of chagrin when the tall man replaced his cap and goggles, shook her daughter's hand, and remounted his machine. The engine roared, and with a final wave goodbye, the man departed.

But she drew comfort from the lingering manner in which the man had clasped her daughter's hand, and hope was a joyous anthem pulsing through her being.

For some moments Josie remained staring through the clouds of dust trailing behind the speeding motorcycle, a smile wreathing her mouth.

Life had suddenly become sweet and exciting for her. She was strongly attracted towards William Barton, and he was making it very plain that the attraction was mutual. So much so that he had just asked her to accompany him to a party on Saturday evening which was being held at the house of one of the district's leading industrialists, Joshua Morgan, alderman and justice of the peace.

Josie had accepted and now was both thrilled and apprehensive at the prospect. Thrilled because William was so eager to take her. Apprehensive because undoubtedly some of the most important people in the district would be there. Also present would be the local smart set, the aggressively ultramodern young men and women termed knuts and flappers, who slavishly followed the most outrageous trends in fashion and mores, and whose escapades scandalised the staid elders of the town.

Now Josie's smile suddenly faltered. What am I to wear? I've no evening gowns. They'll all be wearing the latest fashion, won't they? I shall look such a terrible frump, William will be ashamed to be seen with me!

'Josephine, my dear.' Her mother had opened the window and was calling to her. 'Are you coming in, dear?'

Josie was surprised at her mother's dulcet tones. She had been expecting her to display her displeasure because her daughter had dared to come home in such a fashion and stand talking to a young man on the public highway.

She turned to see her mother standing at the open window with the net curtain drawn back, and then a sickening shock stiffened her body as she saw the face of Clement Hulme peering at her over the old woman's shoulder.

'Josie, my dear, do come in. We've a visitor.' Her mother smiled sweetly.

Josie nodded, and reluctantly moved towards the house. Anxiety racked her.

What does he want? How dare he come to my home? She tried to think rationally. Mother can't suspect anything, otherwise she'd not be acting so pleasantly towards me. He wouldn't dare say anything to her about what's happened between us anyway, would he? Of course he wouldn't. He'll not say anything now. If I keep calm, then everything will be all right.

But despite her inner urgings to remain calm, Josie could feel the cold dankness of fear stealing over her.

'Mr Hulme is here, Josie,' Dorothy Kitson announced unnecessarily as her daughter entered the room. The older woman's flabby, pallid features were for once glowing with the rosy hue of pleasure. 'He's come especially to enquire why we haven't been attending chapel. Isn't it an honour, for a gentleman of Mr Hulme's standing in the chapel to take the trouble to come personally?'

Josie nodded, and tried to appear suitably impressed. 'Yes, Mother, it certainly is.'

Hulme smiled at her and came to clasp her hand. 'You've been neglecting us quite shamefully lately, Miss Kitson. I was only just now telling your lady mother how the brethren were sorely missing both of you. It must be weeks since you've attended.'

As he talked, he kept his tight grip on Josie's hand, and unable to bring herself to meet his questioning eyes, she kept her gaze focused on his thick lips and discoloured teeth.

'Your mother tells me that you've been unwell, Miss Kitson, and that that's the reason you haven't been to chapel . . .' His fingers tightened their hold until the pressure became very painful. '. . . I do hope that you'll very quickly be recovered from what's ailing you. The brethren are most anxious that you and Mrs Kitson should once again take your rightful place among us.'

Josie hissed sharply as the pain in her hand suddenly intensified, and he grimaced and released her, instantly turning to the older woman to announce archly, 'I have another little surprise for you, Sister Kitson. Tomorrow evening we're having a little social gathering to welcome some new members into our chapel family. Mr Hyde and his wife and children.'

Josie found Hulme's manner intensely irritating, but was relieved that he had turned his attention towards her mother and so granted her a brief respite to marshal her thoughts.

'. . . The occasion will not be complete unless you are there as well, Sister.' Hulme was avuncular now. 'I shall come to fetch you both. And bring you back home here afterwards.'

He smiled towards Josie. 'I've purchased a new trap and pony, Miss Kitson. I do hope that you won't think I'm pandering to earthly vanity.'

'Of course she won't!' Dorothy protested then, told Josie, 'I've already assured Mr Hulme that anyone who has the slightest acquaintance with him knows very well that to pander to earthly vanity is totally alien to his nature. It's well known among we Christians that Mr Hulme is a very spiritual man, and indifferent to things of the flesh.'

Indifferent to things of the flesh? Josie thought sardonically, remembering his ravenous sexual appetite only too well. Jesus Christ, Mother, if only you knew!

'So, it's settled then.' Hulme displayed every appearance of satisfaction. 'I shall call for you both at seven o'clock tomorrow evening.'

Josie thought hard for a moment. She wanted to refuse the invitation, but knowing what her mother's reaction would be to this, she quailed inwardly.

Although her mother was being very sweet to her at this moment, Josie was nervously wondering what would happen when Hulme left. She knew only too well the older woman's ability to wear a false face before the world. Was Dorothy even now masking rage because her daughter had come home with a young man and, worse still, stood talking and laughing with him in public view? Long years of matriarchal tyranny had ingrained a deep-seated fear of her mother within Josie's being, and although she was herself now a woman of mature years, that fear could not be completely quelled.

So now she accepted. 'Yes, seven o'clock tomorrow evening then, Hulme.'

He smiled at Josie, and for a moment his eyes moved up and

down her body, lust coursing through him as he envisaged the firm, warm flesh hidden beneath the neat white blouse and dark skirt. He promised himself that he would enjoy that flesh again, and very soon.

Josie felt a tremor of disquiet. Hulme's expression as he looked at her reminded her of some feral beast, and she wished he would leave. Then she heard her mother inviting, 'Now, Mr Hulme, please have another cup of tea before you go. It'll not take a moment to brew a fresh pot.'

Hungering as he was for Josie, he was sorely tempted to accept, but reluctantly decided that it was best for him to leave now, while things were going so well. He had achieved what he had come for.

He smiled regretfully. 'I really do have to go, Sister Kitson. I have the Lord's business to attend to. If it wasn't for that then I'd be happy to stay and talk with you all night.'

The old woman beamed with gratification, and grudgingly accepted his refusal.

He shook Josie's hand briefly in farewell, and her mother accompanied him to the door.

He grinned happily to himself as he walked up the long, sloping road, his private parts engorging with tumescence as he pictured what he intended to do to Josie at the earliest opportunity. His breathing quickened, and his coated tongue licked his thick lips.

I'll make you squeal, bitch! he vowed. I'll give it to you until you're sore, and begging me to stop. And then I'll give you some more! You aren't going to get rid of me. You're never going to get rid of me . . .'

'There now, it just goes to show how much respect I'm held in, doesn't it?' Dorothy Kitson declared triumphantly as she returned to the living room. 'When a wonderful, saintly man like Clement Hulme comes in person to enquire why I haven't been attending chapel. And then himself makes arrangements to carry me there and back.'

Her fat face glowed with self-satisfaction. This had been a gloriously triumphant afternoon, and there were still more good tidings to come, she was sure.

She seated herself in her favourite chair, gasping with the

effort of settling her billowing flesh comfortably, and then with avid expectation fixed her eyes on her daughter's face and said eagerly, 'And now, my dear, I want to hear all about your friendship with William Barton. How did you come to know him? How friendly are you? What was he saying to you when you were outside with him? Where had you been together?'

The questions poured from her in a ceaseless torrent, and Josie, surprised and greatly relieved by her mother's reaction, at first readily told her all she wanted to know.

The old woman listened with ever-increasing delight, and continually interrupted with exhortations to her daughter to do all she could to deepen the burgeoning friendship.

The torrent of questions began to become repetitive, and Josie found them increasingly wearisome and began to wish wholeheartedly that her mother had not discovered her relationship with William.

When she told Dorothy that the man had invited her to a party at Joshua Morgan's house, her mother shrieked with excitement. Then, after a couple of moments, she frowned, and demanded, 'But what about me? Am I not invited as well?'

Josie shook her head.

'Why not?' Dorothy displayed annoyance.

Josie shrugged uncomfortably. 'Well, perhaps William didn't think the party would be to your taste, Mother.'

The old woman pouted sulkily. 'Well, I think it was very selfish of you to make arrangements to go out without even consulting me. I have to suffer just because you think only of your own pleasures.'

Josie sighed wearily. 'How will you suffer because I'm going out?'

'Of course I'll suffer,' the old woman spat out viciously. 'I'll be staying in this house all alone while you're out enjoying yourself until some ungodly hour. What if something happens to me while you're out?'

'I'm going to arrange with Mrs Harold next door to come in and sit with you while I'm away,' Josie explained patiently.

The old woman continued grumbling and complaining, and her whining, nagging voice seemed to be physically drilling into Josie's skull. She felt the familiar stress clamping within her head, setting up an agonising throbbing behind her eyes. For a brief instant she hated her mother for destroying her sense of joyful anticipation for the coming Saturday night.

'I've a headache,' she muttered dispiritedly. 'I'm going to bed.'

'That's right, go off and leave me to be lonely,' her mother complained. 'If I'd known what my life was going to become, and what a burden you'd regard me, then I would have prayed to the Lord to take me to Him years since. I could be sitting at His right hand now, with your dear father. Loved and wanted, and in the company of saints.'

Josie could only shake her aching head in despair.

As she left the room her mother told her, 'Don't make any selfish arrangement for tomorrow night, my girl, or whine that you're not feeling well enough to go. Because you've got to come with me. Mr Hulme is coming especially to fetch us.'

Josie only nodded silently. It was not until she was in her own room, undressing, that the full import of what had happened this evening came fully home to her.

Clement Hulme has been here in my home, making arrangements with my mother. He's forged a personal relationship with her. Now he's been here once, what's to stop him coming here again and again?

She felt that her inviolate refuge, her fortress walls, had been breached. And that now there would be nowhere safe from Clement Hulme's persecution. She remembered how she had once believed that if she were firm enough in rejection, the man would accept that their relationship was over and done with. Now she jeered bitterly at herself for having been so naïve.

You're a fool! A stupid, blind fool!

Apprehension chilled her as she remembered the feral way he had looked at her body that evening.

He still wants me, doesn't he? He still wants to make love to me.

As she lay in her bed, that realisation caused her initial apprehension to deepen into a foreboding dread, and it was many hours before she fell into unquiet sleep.

Chapter Fourteen

For most of the staff of Bridge Street School, the ringing of the bell at four o'clock on Friday afternoon signalled welcome release from bondage, and they luxuriated in the prospect of the coming weekend's pleasures. Unlike her colleagues, Josie had not welcomed that final bell for several years. All it signalled to her was the commencement of yet another dreary weekend spent mainly in her mother's company.

Now, as she dismissed the children and sat on the high stool behind her tall desk watching them file dutifully from the classroom, a sense of bitter injustice assailed her. This weekend had promised to be the most exciting of her life. For the first time in so many wearisome years she should have been happily anticipating its coming. But instead, a sense of dread foreboding weighed heavily upon her.

The bright birdlike eyes of Emily Burgess twinkled happily as she came through the door.

'My word, but you're slow,' she chuckled. 'I had my hat on and my desk locked before the bell had stopped ringing.'

Josie forced herself to respond lightly. 'It just goes to prove that I'm more conscientious than you.' She opened her desk to take out her straw boater, and used a long pin to secure it upon her glossy piled hair.

'What a weekend you're going to spend, Josie,' the plump little woman said enviously. 'Going to a party with your beau, and then on Sunday we've got the parade. How exciting it's going to be for you.'

Josie thought of this evening's chapel social gathering, and couldn't keep a note of irony out of her voice.

137

'Yes, how exciting it's going to be.'

Her friend peered keenly at her.

'Is everything all right, Josie? You are still going to the party with William Barton, aren't you?'

'Oh yes.' Josie nodded, and made a valiant effort to cast off her dark mood. Forcing a smile, she locked her desk and pocketed the key, then slid from the high stool and took the other woman's arm. 'Come, let's get out of here before Mr Parnell locks the doors on us.'

'What are you going to wear? I expect the gentlemen will all be in evening dress, won't they? Just think of it, Josie, you'll be meeting all the best people in the town, and as their equal. I expect the Milwards will be there, and the Terrys and the Gray-Cheapes. Oh, won't it be grand? All those posh people.' Emily's excitement began to communicate itself to Josie, raising her depressed spirits.

As they came down the steps and into the playground, a pony and trap drew up outside the gates. The bowler-hatted driver clambered out on to the road and came into the playground to greet the two women.

'I was just passing and I saw you both, so I thought that I'd offer you a lift.' Hulme raised his hat to Emily and explained, 'My name is Clement Hulme, ma'am. I'm a friend of Miss Kitson and her lady mother. We are all members of the same chapel.'

Josie was too flustered by his unexpected appearance to make any immediate reply, and without giving her a chance to compose herself Hulme insistently ushered both women towards the brand-new trap, which was gleaming with fresh varnish and glittering brasswork. The pony was groomed and clipped, its harness lustrous, and the whole equipage presented a fine spectacle.

'Oh, it's very smart, Mr Hulme,' Emily congratulated. 'It looks brand new.'

'It is, ma'am, I've only taken delivery of it this after-noon. And I do hope that you'll honour me by being my first passenger?' With laboured gallantry he pressed, 'Two ladies such as yourselves will add the final lustre to its appearance.'

'Oh, Mr Hulme, I fear that you're a shameless flatterer,'

Emily gently mocked, though at the same time she was pleased by his compliment.

Cunningly he concentrated his attention upon the older woman, and before Josie could make any objection to the lift, Emily was perched on the leather-covered seat.

He extended his hand to help Josie up into the trap, and feeling unable to deny him without making herself appear ill-mannered and churlish in her friend's eyes, she reluctantly allowed him to aid her. Then he went around to the other side and climbed in.

Embarrassed and annoyed, Josie sat stiffly upright and kept her face averted from him, even though she was uncomfortably aware that Emily was staring at her curiously.

'Now, ma'am.' Hulme seemed fully at ease. 'Miss Kitson has been very remiss in not introducing us, hasn't she?'

'Indeed she has.' There was a slight trace of doubt in Emily's voice. She was wondering at her friend's stiffness of manner towards this man. 'My name is Burgess, Mr Hulme. Miss Emily Burgess.'

'I'm very happy to make your acquaintance, Miss Burgess. And now, if you'll direct me, I shall carry you to wherever you wish to go.'

Emily lived in a row of houses situated at the bottom of Fish Hill which could be reached without traversing the town centre. Throughout the short journey, Josie remained rigidly upright and gazed fixedly before her, making no attempt at conversation.

Emily was embarrassed by what she perceived to be her friend's deliberate bad manners, and felt impelled to chatter on continuously to the man beside her.

Periodically the little woman glanced at Josie's grim, set features and wondered, What on earth is the matter with her?

Josie herself was burning with resentful anger, and was steeling herself to confront Hulme. She was going to make it entirely plain to him that their relationship was at an end, and that he was in future to stay away from her. She thought of the coming evening, and how he was to call for her mother and herself.

I shan't go to the chapel social, she resolved. I don't care what Mother says. I won't go to chapel ever again.

When they reached Emily's house, Hulme was quick to alight and hand the woman down. She thanked him warmly, and then peered anxiously at Josie.

'I shall see you on Sunday morning, shall I then, Josie? Before the parade.'

Josie nodded to her unsmilingly, and answered shortly, 'Yes, Emily. I'll meet you at the school as arranged.'

Hulme was silent as the pony laboured up the steep hill into the centre of the town, and Josie stayed silent also, inwardly steeling herself to withstand all his abject pleas for the continuation of their relationship.

I don't care how much he moans and whines. It's over. Over and done with, she told herself, and felt strong and sure in her purpose.

As they crossed the central plateau of the town, Hulme broke his silence.

'I have to call into my office. Then I've something to say to you.'

She nodded. 'Very well. There's something I have to say to you also.'

She had no hesitation about accompanying him to the Electric Light Company premises. She felt sure that with people all around, as there would be on that site, he could not cause any sort of scene when she told him her decision.

At the works he got down and offered her his hand, but she shook her head and refused curtly.

'No thank you, I'm well able to manage by myself.'

For a brief instant temper gleamed in his eyes. But he only shrugged and muttered, 'Suit yourself,' then turned away and preceded her into the office building.

A couple of youthful clerks eyed her curiously as she passed through the outer office and followed Hulme down a short corridor into his own private office at its end.

He seated himself behind his desk, and gestured to a chair standing against the wall.

'You can sit there.'

She shook her head. 'I prefer to stand. What I have to say will only take a moment.'

He grinned, and his stained teeth with their oversized canines reminded Josie of a snarling dog.

'Do you want to close the door, Miss Kitson? Those lads out there have got very sharp ears.'

She stepped back and closed the door. When she turned back to him she told him coldly, 'It's over, Clem. Over and done with.'

His head moved very slowly from side to side in negation of her statement.

'I mean it,' she said heatedly. 'It's over between us.'

The snarling grin remained fixed on his face, as his head still slowly moved from side to side.

She emitted a hiss of exasperation at his stubbornness. 'This is the last time that I'll ever speak to you privately like this. I don't care what my mother says, I shan't be coming back to the chapel. Not ever!'

His head stilled, and he asked quietly, 'Is it William Barton? Is he your fancy man now? Is that why you want to finish with me?'

'No, it's not because of William,' she denied hastily. 'I wanted to finish with you before I met him.'

'Why?' he wanted to know. 'Have you fallen out of love with me? Is that it?'

She shook her head in confusion. 'I don't think now that I ever was in love with you, Clem. I don't know what I thought of you. But I do know that what happened between us was wrong. It was a terrible mistake for both of us.'

'You've made a fool of me, haven't you?' he observed bitterly.

Again she shook her head in vehement denial. 'No. I never intended to make a fool of you. I never did.'

His small eyes dwelled on her shapely body, and lust engorged him as he caught the fresh, warm scent of her in his nostrils, and saw the pulse beating beneath the smooth white skin of her throat. His desperate determination to keep her was overwhelming all else in his mind, and he was forced to struggle against the urge to grab her and crush her body against him. To clamp his mouth over her moist, full lips. To tear the clothing from her and ravage the satiny flesh of her breasts and thighs and belly.

He dragged in a long, rasping breath, and his words growled from deep within his chest.

'You'd better listen to me, girl. And listen well.'

'I won't change my mind,' she insisted vehemently. 'It doesn't matter how much you beg and plead with me. I'll not change my mind.'

To her amazement he emitted a gust of laughter. 'I'm not begging or pleading with you, Josie. No.' It was his turn to shake his head. 'I've no need to do that. You've left me no choice now but to tell you what you'll do.'

While she stared at him uncertainly, he took an envelope from his inside pocket and held it up so that she could see it clearly. She gasped in dismay, and he chuckled harshly.

'Yes, I thought you'd recognise it. The one and only love letter you ever sent me. And I've treasured it. Kept it next to my heart.'

'Give it back.' She whispered the words. 'Please, Clem, if you ever have cared for me, then give it back.'

The envelope disappeared once more into his inside pocket, and he nodded.

'Yes, I'll give it back, Josie . . . Some day.'

Now he relaxed and leaned back in his chair. 'Sit down, won't you, my dear. And let's have a little talk about this letter.'

Her brain was a maelstrom of thoughts and fears, and she sank down on to the chair against the wall as she fought to think clearly.

'We'll have a cup of tea,' he said brightly, and lifting the handbell from his desk top he jangled it hard.

Almost instantly there was a clumping of boots along the corridor and the door opened.

'Bring us a pot of tea, and some of those biscuits, will you, Perkes,' Hulme ordered. 'And be quick about it.'

'Very good, sir.' The youth hastened away.

Hulme stretched and yawned expansively, and remarked smilingly to the stricken-faced Josie. 'I don't know about you, my dear, but this warm weather don't half make me feel sleepy at times.'

They sat in silence until the youth returned with the tea and biscuits, and when the door closed again Hulme smiled archly.

'I'll be mother, shall I? Do you want one lump or two?'

Josie was too tense and nervous to respond, and could only sit stiffly as he handed her the cup and saucer.

'Biscuits?' He offered the salver, and she shook her head in refusal.

He noisily slurped his own tea, and crunched biscuits between his strong yellow teeth, all the time keeping his eyes fixed upon her, and there was a triumphant gleam lurking in their bloodshot depths.

He ate all the biscuits, and drained the teapot, before sighing in satisfaction.

'There, that's better. That should sustain me until supper time. Mrs Hulme has got a nice piece of beefsteak for me tonight. I shall have it directly I go home. But I'll have to look a bit sharp about eating it if I'm going to fetch you and your mother at the time we arranged, won't I, Josie?'

There was a jeering, challenging edge to his voice, and he frowned when she made no reply but only stayed staring down at the untouched cup of tea she held on her lap. The sight of the letter had unnerved her completely, and her lifetime's moral conditioning had reaffirmed its power over her. Fear of discovery and scandal was the overwhelming emotion.

'Ah well!' he ejaculated impatiently. 'I've tried to do this in a gentlemanly manner. But maybe I'd better make things a bit clearer to you, girl.'

He steepled his fingers upon his chest and asked casually, 'How many people in this town know about that birthmark you've got on the inside of your thigh? You know the mark I mean. That strawberry-coloured one just a couple of inches from the top . . .'

The cup and saucer fell from her suddenly nerveless fingers and shattered on the floor, and the cold brown liquid splashed across the polished linoleum.

He leaned forward abruptly across the desk, his face pushing aggressivly towards her bowed head, and his voice dropped to a harsh, threatening whisper.

'You've driven me half mad, you little bitch. You've tormented me until I don't care any longer what might happen to me. I'm ready to destroy myself, and to ruin your name. If I tell about what's gone on between me and you, the scandal 'ull kill your mother. And what 'ull it do to William Barton?

143

I've watched him with you. I've seen how he looks at you. He loves you, doon't he? He thinks you'm the purest soul that ever lived. What's it gooing to do to him when I tell him what you and me have done together?'

Josie's eyes were screwed tightly shut, as though by blocking out the sight of Clement Hulme she could wipe out all else that had happened between them. But his harsh whispering penetrated her skull, and reverberated within her brain.

'And it wouldn't be any use you denying it, would it, you bitch? Because I've got the proof, I've got the letter. And I can tell the world what your naked body looks like. I can tell the world how you wriggle and shout out when we make love how much you enjoy it. I can tell the world what sort of whore you really are.'

Her fists were hard-clenched so that her fingernails were digging deep, breaking skin, bringing spots of blood out against the blanched palm. Shuddering gasps tore from her open mouth, and the man suddenly feared that he had driven her too far.

'But I won't tell the world anything, Josie my dear,' he said sharply, repeating the words over and over again until gradually she grew a little calmer. Then he began to talk quietly and kindly to her, telling her how much he loved her, how much he desired her happiness, how he respected her above all other women.

Moving slowly so as not to alarm her, he went to her side. Kneeling down, he gently loosened her rigidly locked hands and with his handkerchief tenderly wiped the blood from the small puncture wounds on her palms.

He collected the shattered pieces of the cup and saucer and replaced them on the tray, then told her huskily, 'Think of all the people who love and care for you, Josie. Your mother and brother. Your friend Emily Burgess. William Barton. And you loved your father dearly, didn't you? As he loved you. Think of his name. You wouldn't want to do anything to bring his name into disrepute, would you now?'

He gently pressed her to reply, and at last, still with her eyes closed, she shook her head.

'No, of course you wouldn't, my dear girl.' He patted her shoulder. 'And it will never happen. Our secret will remain a secret. I love you too much to do anything to hurt or harm you.'

144

Now her eyes opened and she looked up at him beseechingly.

He bent and crushed his lips to hers, his hand hard against
the back of her head to prevent her jerking free. Then he
straightened and caressed her pale cheeks with his spatulate
fingers.

'You only have to be nice to me, Josie,' he murmured
huskily. 'Just be nice to me sometimes, that's all. It's such a
little thing really, isn't it? And our secret can stay our secret
forever. No one will ever know about us. Not your mother. Not
your brother. Not William Barton. No one.'

There came a clumping of footsteps in the corridor and a
knock on the door, and Hulme bit back an angry curse. Moving
to the door he opened it and barked, 'Yes, what is it?'

'The coal delivery's come, Mr Hulme. Only you said that
you wanted to check the quality yourself.'

Hulme nodded brusquely. 'I'll be out directly. Don't let them
start tipping it.'

The inspection of the coal did not take very long, but before
he could return to his office, his father-in-law came into the
yard, insisting that Hulme accompany him immediately to
the council offices to deal with some urgent business there
concerning the Electric Company.

Hulme cursed inwardly, but dared not risk offending by
refusal.

'I'll only be a moment,' he told his father-in-law and hurried
into his office.

'Wait here for me. I'll be back as soon as I can.' It was a
command, rather than a request.

Josie felt utterly helpless. Images formed a vivid kaleido-
scope in her mind, visions of the faces she loved so dearly. Her
brother, her dead father, her mother, Emily Burgess, William
Barton. But none of these could help her to fight against this
man. No one on earth could help her.

Judging her silent, bowed, defeated posture to be proof of his
domination, Hulme smiled in triumphant satisfaction, and went
out into the yard.

Josie remained motionless, head bowed, eyes staring blankly
at her hands lying loosely open upon her lap. As the minutes lengthened and time slowly passed, so the storms of

emotion quietened and receded, leaving her feeling drained and strangely calm. That curious sense of numbed detachment that she had experienced the first time Hulme had made love to her was pervading her once more. Again it was as if she, the spiritual entity, were coolly observing the physical woman whom the world knew as Josie Kitson. Almost dispassionately she considered her own predicament, and sought a way to escape from this entrapment. She knew that she could never subject her relatives to the shameful scandal of discovery of an affair with a married man. She also accepted that the burgeoning dreams of a life with William Barton would be completely destroyed if he were ever to find out about the relationship with Hulme. Of course, there was always that mode of escape taken by many desperately unhappy women unable to tolerate their lives any longer. But Josie would never use that exit. Everything in her being rebelled against taking her own life.

So, it seemed that Clement Hulme would remain in her life like some malignant succubus clinging to her flesh. The Josie Kitson of the past would perhaps have despondently accepted this fact. But the Josie Kitson of the present had found hope during these past weeks. She had finally met a man with whom she could find happiness. A man who appeared to want and need her, as much as she wanted and needed him. A man she was prepared to fight for.

A physical shock jerked through Josie as if the separate entities had suddenly merged to become one. And now she was whole again, united in spirit and flesh.

The resolve to fight pulsed through her. Clement Hulme had the upper hand at present. That was indisputable. She had no doubts that he meant what he threatened about destroying himself to bring ruin on her. She accepted that she could not face the prospect of her ruination, because that ruination would also encompass others within it. Others who were innocent of any wrongdoing in this affair. So, for the present, Hulme was the master. But she knew that she possessed weapons of her own. She knew that she had guile, and cunning. She knew that she had courage. And above all else, she knew that she possessed the capacity of mental endurance. The capacity to endure unhappiness, and torment, and frustration of hopes and dreams. After all, this had been the pattern of her life for many years, and she had endured it. She knew that she could continue to endure, and that knowledge was made doubly certain because now she had the hope of eventually finding happiness with William Barton.

All I have to do is to endure, she told herself now, as she gathered all her stubborn courage like a protective armour about her. To endure. To use cunning and guile. And to watch and wait for my chance to get rid of Clement Hulme once and for always.

For almost an hour Josie sat quietly, waiting for the man to come back. And with each passing minute her resolution fortified and became stronger. But she could still feel her heart begin to thud harder as his footsteps sounded in the corridor and he came through the door and closed it behind him.

He came to stand in front of her, and demanded urgently, 'Well? What's it to be?'

She hesitated for a moment, then rose to face him.

'As you want it,' she said quietly.

He exhaled a gusting sigh of relief and satisfaction. 'You've made me very happy, Josie. More happy than you'll ever know. Come here to me.'

He would have taken her into his arms, but she lifted her own arms to block his embrace.

'No, Clem. Not here. Not now. We must take very great care not to be discovered.'

Victory made him pliable, eager to please her. He nodded. 'Yes, you're right, my darlin'. We must be careful. But when? Where?'

'I'll come to the afternoon Sunday School,' she told him. 'And now let's go. Mother will be wondering where I am.'

He grabbed her to him and kissed her hungrily, and despite the revulsion she felt for his wet mouth and stale breath, she stayed passive for a couple of moments before breaking free.

As they passed through the outer office the two clerks eyed them curiously, and when they had gone one of the youths wondered aloud, 'Is he shagging her?'

His companion laughed in contemptuous dismissal of such an impossibility.

'What, old Clem shagging a young piece like that!' he jeered. 'Pigs 'ull be flying sooner.'

The first youth laughed himself at his own wild notion, and dismissed the matter from his mind.

As the pony trotted briskly down the Beoley Road Hulme asked jealously, 'William Barton? What are you going to do about him?'

Josie pondered for a moment or two, then, as if asking for advice, replied, 'Don't you think it might be best if I were to stay friends with him, Clem? If people see me walking out with him, they're not going to suspect that anything is going on between you and me, are they? Do you think it would be a good cover for us?'

Hulme mulled this over for a few seconds, and found it to his satisfaction.

'That's very good, darlin'. Very neat.' He grinned at her appreciatively. 'You're a sly little cat, aren't you?'

She managed to force a brief smile, then turned her head away and gazed at the road ahead. She experienced a sense of bleak satisfaction at this small victory that her quick thinking had gained.

Yes, I am being sly and deceitful, she thought, and accepted that fact with no pleasure but only grim resolve. And I shall go on being sly and deceitful for as long as I have to.

Chapter Fifteen

'Come on and hear, come on and hear
Alexander's Ragtime Band!
Come on and hear, come on and hear,
It's the best band in the land . . .'

The catchy syncopated rhythm blared out from the horned
trumpet of the phonograph, and the dancers sang in concert with
the tinny-sounding voices of the American Ragtime Octet:

'. . . and if you care to hear the Swanee River
Played in ragtime –
Come on and hear, come on and hear
Alexander's Ragtime Band!'

The highly polished floorboards of the large room creaked
beneath the weight of the couples turkey-trotting backwards
and forwards, dipping low, turning, bending, splitting momentarily to kick out their legs then coming together once more in
close embrace.

Anthony Barton, elegant in evening dress, stood in the 'stag
line' with the other partnerless men and watched the girl he
loved smiling in the arms of another man, and although he knew
that Amy Morgan's dancing partner meant nothing to her, still
jealousy stirred in his heart and caused him to frown dourly.

The tall, dark-haired man standing beside him glanced at
Barton's glowering features and then looked at the couple his
companion was staring at. He smiled appreciatively at the pretty
blonde young woman, fashionably dressed in a flimsy silken
ballgown, with a long osprey feather rising from the jewelled
band around her head.

'The wee girl looks happy, Tony.' His accent bore witness to his Ulster birthplace.

Anthony turned quickly. 'I'm sorry, Jack, what was that?'

The tall man nodded towards the couple. 'I said that your sweetheart looks happy.' He smiled and teased. 'Mind you, judging from the way you're scowling at her, it would be easy to think that you would prefer her to be miserable.'

After a moment Anthony grinned ruefully, and admitted, 'I can't help feeling jealous when I see her enjoying herself with another man.' He indicated his slung arm. 'This stops me turkey-trotting.' Again the scowl appeared momentarily on his face. 'But it doesn't stop Amy doing it.'

'And why should it?' Jack Preseley challenged. 'Sure, she's only young, and needs to enjoy herself while she can. You've no right to spoil her pleasure by glaring at her so.'

Anthony glanced at his sweetheart's smiling features, and retorted wryly, 'It doesn't appear that I'm doing that, does it, Jack?' Then he shrugged, and invited, 'Come on, let's go and get a drink.'

The two men moved into the adjoining room where a buffet and drinks bar had been set up.

The white-jacketed attendant served them with large whisky and sodas, and they carried their glasses out on to the wide stone terrace which overlooked the fertile sweep of the Arrow Valley, now shadowed and wreathed with mists in the dusk. For a while they stood in silence, enjoying the coolness of the evening air.

From the open windows of the ballroom came the sounds of the dancers chorusing a fresh tune:

> 'That Ragtime Suffragette
> Ragging with bombshells
> and ragging with bricks,
> Hagging and nagging in politics –
> That Ragtime Suffragette –
> She's no household pet . . .'

The Ulsterman chuckled and remarked, 'It's a bit different to the last regimental ball I went to in the Curragh. We were doing the veleta and the military two-step. And waltzing, of course.'

Anthony smiled dutifully, but seemed preoccupied. Then he asked very seriously, 'What do you think will happen, Jack? Will it be civil war in Ireland?'

Preseley took a sip from his glass, then stroked his luxuriant moustache with the back of his fingers.

'Well?' the other man urged. 'Will it?'

'Of course it will,' the Ulsterman stated positively. 'That's why I sent in my papers after the Curragh incident. And that's why a good many more of my comrades sent in their papers as well. We want to be free to fight for Ulster when the war comes.'

'But I can't believe that loyal subjects of His Majesty will take up arms against the Crown,' Anthony said.

'We'll be taking up arms to remain loyal subjects of the Crown, my friend. We'll not be forced by Asquith or Churchill or any other damned politician to accept rule from Dublin,' Preseley told him forcefully. 'Home Rule is Rome Rule. I'll not let any dammed Catholic priest tell me how to live my life.'

'But if the Government gives Home Rule to Ireland, how can you fight it?' Anthony argued. 'The Ulster Volunteers aren't really strong enough to stand against the British Army and Navy as well as the Catholics.'

The older man laughed and replied dismissively, 'We won't have to fight the British Army and Navy, Tony. That was proven in the Curragh only weeks ago. The army will never march against us. We're British. And that self-serving bastard Churchill can order as many warships as he pleases into Ulster waters, but when the time comes not one of those ships will send a single shell at us.'

'But what if they did open fire?' Anthony persisted. 'And what if the army did march against you? What then?'

'Why, we'd still fight, of course.' The Ulsterman was adamant. 'And there'll be thousands of good Englishmen, Welshmen and Scotsmen fighting side by side with us.'

Anthony's eyes glowed with hero-worship as he stared at his companion. 'And I'll be one of those men, Jack,' he assured him fervently. 'Ireland's part of the empire, and we must all fight to keep her so.'

'Good man!' Preseley applauded. 'Let's drink to that!'

They lifted their glasses in salute, and tossed the contents down their throats.

From the ballroom windows came the strains of yet another catchy song:

> 'Florrie was a flapper,
> she was dainty,
> she was dapper,
> And her dancing was the limit,
> or the lid.
> When her dainty skirt she'd swish up
> They say she shocked the Bishop.
> I don't believe she did it,
> I don't believe she did it,
> But he told the Missus Bishop
> THAT SHE DID!'

'There you are! I thought I'd find you out here drinking.' There was a scolding note in Amy Morgan's voice as she came to the two men, her flimsy gown moulding against her shapely body and long legs.

Her eyes rested inquisitively on the tall Ulsterman. 'You still haven't introduced me properly to your friend, Tony.'

Anthony made the introduction.

'Amy, I'd like you to meet an old and dear friend of mine, Captain Jack Preseley.'

There was nothing coy or flirtatious in the young girl's manner as she openly appraised the ruggedly handsome features and fine physique of the Ulsterman.

'You're a very good-looking man, Captain Preseley,' she told him forthrightly, as she shook his hand. 'My name is Amy Morgan. Miss Amy Morgan.' She emphasised the 'Miss'.

Anthony was embarrassed by her forward manner, but Jack chuckled delightedly.

'I'm very happy to meet you, Miss Morgan. Are you one of these flappers we keep hearing about nowadays?'

'Really, Jack!' Barton exclaimed huffily, but Amy only laughed, and chided him.

'Don't be so stuffy, Tony. I think that I'm going to like your friend. Particularly if he gives me a cigarette. I've left mine in my purse.'

Anthony frowned unhappily. His sweetheart's seemingly insatiable desire to shock people with her modern manners caused him considerable discomfort.

'Certainly you shall have one of my cigarettes, Miss Morgan.' Preseley took a flat silver case from his inside pocket, and opened it to offer to her.

She took one of the long, slender tubes and examined it curiously.

'It's a Turkish brand, Miss Morgan,' Preseley explained. 'I have them sent to me by a tobacco merchant in Constantinople.'

For all her attempts to be thoroughly modern and sophisticated, Amy was still young and naïve, and she could not help but be impressed by this casual reference to such an exotic city. Momentarily her blue eyes widened, and the astute Ulsterman noted the reaction. He smiled and went on.

'Of course, that's not Constantinople in Turkey, you'll understand. It's Constantinople Street in Belfast.'

Anthony burst out laughing, and the young woman blushed, and for a moment her expression showed resentment. Then she too could not help but laugh at how she had been so good-naturedly teased.

'I deserved that, Captain Preseley,' she admitted. 'I'm not really fast, you know. I only pretend to be to shock the stuffy people in this town.'

Jack experienced a sudden burgeoning of respect for her honesty, and thought that behind this young woman's aggresively modern and very sexually desirable façade, there might also exist a considerable depth of character and intelligence.

He found himself envying his friend for his relationship, and warned himself, Don't go getting any ideas about this wee girl, Jack. She's your best friend's sweetheart.

'What's your regiment, Captain Preseley?' Amy pursed her full lips speculatively. 'I'd say that you were a cavalryman.'

'And why would you say that, Miss Morgan?' The Ulsterman smiled.

'You have a cavalry air about you. My brother Clive is in the army, you see, and he's told me how to distinguish an infantryman from a cavalryman.'

153

Preseley chuckled. 'Well, the easiest way to tell the difference between cavalry and infantry is that the cavalry are normally riding horses, Miss Morgan.'

The young woman was not put out by his teasing. 'You are cavalry, aren't you?' she asserted positively.

The Ulsterman nodded. 'Yes, I'm a cavalryman. At least, I was until a short while ago. I've resigned my commission.'

Again Amy displayed the shrewd intellect that lay behind her frivolous façade. 'You're a Carson man, aren't you.'

It was a statement, not a question, and Preseley nodded. 'Yes I am, and proud of it. Sir Edward Carson is a great man, and a true patriot.'

'Were you at the Curragh when the army refused to march, Captain?'

'Yes, I was. I sent in my papers directly after the incident.'

Her white teeth gleamed as she smiled admiringly at him. 'I think that you've done a fine thing, Captain Preseley. Let's find somewhere to sit and talk. There's so much I want to know about the situation in Ireland.'

In the ballroom a group of musicians now took their places on the small stage and the phonograph was taken away by the servants. The band struck up a waltz and the lilting strains poured from the ballroom windows.

'I see my father has asserted his authority.' Amy giggled. 'He hates ragtime music, Captain Preseley. The phonograph will be locked away for the rest of the night, you'll see, and it will all be old-fashioned rubbish from now on.'

Anthony protested, with a hint of petulance, 'I like to waltz. And you promised to dance a waltz with me, Amy. I can manage that even with this arm.'

She pouted impatiently. 'Oh, Tony, we can dance a waltz at any time. But I shan't have such an opportunity to hear about the Curragh incident at first hand again. You know how interested I am in such matters.'

'Yes, but . . .' the young man began, and Jack smoothly intervened to avoid being the cause of any discord between the couple.

'Forgive me, Miss Morgan, but this dance has already been promised to me.'

The young woman's expressive features mirrored her disappointment. 'Oh, very well, Captain Preseley. But it's still very early. You must talk with me later.'

Her blue eyes were admiring as she watched his tall figure moving away from them, and she remarked, 'He moves like a tiger, doesn't he?'

Jealousy lanced through Anthony, and he retorted stiffly, 'I really couldn't say what his walk resembles, Amy. I've never had any acquaintance with a tiger, so I can't judge.'

There was a hint of cruelty in her smile, as she mockingly chided, 'Now, Tony, stop behaving like a small child who's had his toys taken from him. If you carry on in this way I shall have to reconsider our understanding. I want to marry a man, not a brat!'

A sudden shaft of fear that he might lose this woman with whom he was so besotted caused a tightness in Anthony's throat and chest, and he hastened to apologise for his behaviour. But she spitefully cut his babbled protestations short.

'You're boring me, Tony,' she snapped curtly. 'I'm going to join some livelier company.'

With that she turned and ran back into the house, leaving him staring after her with hurt in his eyes.

In the midst of the swirling dancers Jack Preseley was enjoying himself. He was a good dancer, light on his feet and with an instinctive sense of rhythm. Occasionally he would glance about him, and he caught a brief glimpse of Amy Morgan coming into the ballroom alone. Even in that passing glance Preseley could see the petulant frown on her pretty face, and he felt a sudden sympathy for his young friend Anthony.

'She's a spoiled child, that one.'

'I'm sorry. Did you say something, Captain Preseley?' his partner asked, and he realised that he had unconsciously voiced his thoughts aloud.

He smiled charmingly at her. 'I only remarked at how gracefully you dance, Miss Capes.'

She smiled radiantly at him, and then immersed herself once more in the sheer pleasure of movement.

As he turned again Preseley saw William Barton standing with a young woman at one end of the room. His curiosity was piqued and he sought them out again and again as he circled the floor.

He saw that the young woman was not pretty, yet there was something very appealing about her pleasant features, and her shapely figure showed to advantage in the simple, unadorned dress she wore. He noted also that William could not seem to keep his eyes off her, and wore a doting expression on his long, ugly face. Preseley smiled to himself.

So, you're in love at last, are you, William, you sad stick?

He did not like William Barton. He found the man's social conscience irritatingly oversensitive, and believed that it was hypocritical for any man who lived off the rents of slum properties to continually be bewailing the plight of the poor.

He thought of William as a 'Little Englander', a wishy-washy faint-heart who lacked courage and patriotism. One of a contemptible breed of small-minded, mean-souled cowards who licked the boots of foreign rivals and who would, if they were permitted to, bring the empire down to destruction.

His attention was next caught by a big, burly, middle-aged man with a broad red face, who was surrounded by an attentive coterie of the older guests. Jack smiled warmly at the sight of this individual, Joshua Morgan, alderman and justice of the peace. He was one of the richest and most powerful men in the county, an ardent patriot, and a true believer in his country's manifest destiny to rule its mighty empire.

Jack had a particular reason for appreciating Joshua Morgan's patriotism. The man had been instrumental both locally and further afield in raising funds for the cause of Sir Edward Carson's Ulster Volunteers.

By Morgan's side there now appeared the tall, ramrod figure of Ernest Barton, and Preseley could not help but wonder at the vagaries of heredity. How could a dyed-in-the-wool Tory imperialist like Ernest ever have sired a Little Englander like William?

As Ernest joined the group surrounding his old friend Joshua Morgan, his thoughts also were exercised with the mysteries of parenthood and inherited characteristics. To be precise, he was wondering from which perverse ancestor his elder son had inherited his own perversity.

That morning Ernest had taken William into his study, and

informed him that he was to take charge of the Orchard Street site, and to drive the work to a rapid conclusion. Ernest had expected at the very least a display of reluctance, but to his surprise William had enthusiastically accepted the job. He had also apologised for his slackness and past failures, and had assured his father that he now wanted nothing more than to work hard and make a success of his life.

Then, early that afternoon, Madeleine Barton had coolly informed her husband that William was taking a young lady to that evening's party at Joshua Morgan's house. And that furthermore, William had given his mother to understand that he was very taken with the young lady in question. Considering that his elder son had never to his knowledge shown any romantic interest in young women before in his life, Ernest had received the shock of this news with commendable sang-froid.

'Ahh, Barton, there you are. I was wondering where you'd got to,' Joshua Morgan greeted his old friend. 'Where's your wife?'

'I've left her sitting over there talking to your wife, Morgan.'

'You know these chaps, don't you?' Morgan indicated the group around him, and Barton smiled and nodded in general greeting.

'Yes, we're all well known to each other. I trust I find you well, gentlemen?'

They returned his greeting and for some moments there was a comfortable silence while the newcomer gazed around the ballroom, nodding his head to people he knew, and smiling and lifting his hand to acknowledge Jack Preseley as the latter whirled by.

He saw his elder son and his companion, and studied the young woman closely for some moments.

Joshua followed the direction of his friend's stare, and grinned.

'I see that William has finally found himself a sweetheart, Barton. Who is she?'

Barton frowned and shook his head. 'I'm dammed if I know. In fact I didn't even know that he'd found himself a woman until his mother told me of it this afternoon. She didn't know the girl's name either. My son can be very sly and secretive.'

The other man had lost interest by now, and he merely shrugged. 'Well, you'll find out soon enough, I dare say . . . Now, there's something I wanted to ask you about. What do you know about that new engineering company that's taken the lease of Jolson's old premises down the Hewell Road?'

Although she kept her gaze centred on the dancers, Josie was aware of Ernest Barton's keen scrutiny, just as she was aware of the many other interested stares she had attracted since her arrival here in company with William Barton.

'Are you sure that you don't want to dance, Josie?' William was asking her yet again, his dark eyes tender as he looked down at her.

She smiled and shook her head. 'Perhaps later, William. I'm enjoying watching. There are some very good dancers here, aren't there?'

His long face became rueful. 'There are indeed. I'm afraid that I shall look an awful muff in comparison.' His manner became apologetic. 'I'm not a good dancer, you see, Josie. I've never really been able to get the hang of it. I'm clod-footed.'

She laid her slender hand upon his arm and reassured him, 'I'm sure that you dance perfectly well. And anyway, it doesn't matter to me if you don't. I'm perfectly happy to stand and watch.'

The waltz came to an end, and in the interval before the next dance was to be announced by the master of ceremonies, the dancers and onlookers coalesced into groups, talking and laughing together. William and Josie remained alone. No one came to join them, or invited them into a group.

'I really don't know many of these people very well.' William was fearful that Josie would feel that they were being deliberately snubbed. 'I'm not much of a socialiser.'

He was miserably aware of his lack of popularity and wished now that he had made more effort to form friendships. But during the past years he had offended many of the people around them with his criticisms of their lack of social conscience, and his continual diatribes against the things they valued.

For herself, Josie was not concerned about this present isolation. She had not expected to be welcomed into this festive intercourse of the town's self-considered élite. She lived in a world of intricate and rigid class gradations, and was

158

well aware that from the moment she had entered this house, sharp eyes had been examining and evaluating her clothing and appearance, and allotting to her a place within the social hierarchy. She had no doubt that to some of those present she was already known as being a teacher at the lowliest school in the town, and as such completely beneath their notice. She was truly unconcerned about this, but troubled by William's obvious discomfort.

'Let's go out on the terrace, shall we?' she suggested, in an effort to allay his unease. 'We can have a glass of punch or something.'

He smiled gratefully, and gave her his arm to lead her out of the room.

Mrs Cicily Morgan, large, fat and resplendent in a bright scarlet gown with a daring *décolletage* unsuitable for her advancing years, tapped her friend's arm with her fan and informed her, 'Oh look there, Maddy, William is taking that young woman outside.'

Madeleine refused to rise to the bait. She only nodded casually. 'Oh yes, so he is.'

The third woman sitting with them, a scrawny-bodied, bitter-featured spinster, sniffed disparagingly, and Madeleine asked her with apparent concern, 'Why, Lettice, do you have a cold coming on, I wonder? You really should wear a shawl. At your age the night air can prove treacherous.'

'Who is that young woman, Maddy?' Cicily was avid to know. 'She doesn't appear to be one of us, does she?'

The scrawny woman again sniffed emphatically. 'That young woman is definitely not one of us, Cicily. She's a teacher at the council school.' She sought confirmation. 'Is she not, Madeleine?'

Madeleine hid her irritation at the woman's attitude behind an air of complete indifference. 'I really couldn't say, my dear, I've never seen her before.'

'But surely William has introduced her to you?' Lettice Townsend showed open disbelief.

Madeleine smiled grimly. 'No, William has not introduced the young lady to either myself or his father, or to anyone else as far as I know.' Her tone became edged with acid. 'Of course, Lettice, I can see how it is difficult for a maiden lady such as yourself to understand how thoughtlessly grown men can behave towards their parents. But I do assure you that William's failure to introduce the young lady is not uncommon. There are many similarly thoughtless sons in this town who fail to present their lady friends to their parents.'

Lettice Townsend's shrivelled features twisted with malice, and she spat back, 'Perhaps he hasn't introduced her to you because she isn't a lady. She certainly looks very common.'

'How can you say that without even having met the person?' Cicily chided.

'I can say that because ladies do not work as teachers at council schools,' Lettice retorted sharply. 'In fact, ladies, do not work at all. Except for charity. Only common women work for a living.'

Her lipless mouth snapped shut, and she radiated an air of smug satisfaction, as if that statement was so patently true that no counterargument could be advanced against it.

'Well, anyway, the young woman looks very neat and tidy and wholesome, even if she is low class.' Cicily was not prepared to let the other woman enjoy a complete victory. 'And I'm quite sure that William has brought her here from motives of disinterested kindness.'

At this moment the tall, elegant figure of Jack Preseley loomed above the three women, and he bowed.

'Mrs Barton, may I fetch yourself and your friends some refreshments?'

Madeleine rose to her feet. 'No thank you, Captain Preseley. But you may give me your arm and escort me outside for a breath of fresh air. The atmosphere in here has suddenly become a little too stuffy for my taste.'

She smiled coldly at the other women. 'You will excuse me, won't you, my dears?'

On the shadowed terrace William left Josie while he went to fetch their drinks.

At intervals along the mossy balustrade couples were standing closely together, talking in low voices, while others strolled in the long sweep of garden which stretched away down the hillside.

Josie could not help but contrast the opulence of her present surroundings with her own simple home, and then with the fetid courts and alleys where the poor of the town dragged out their hard lives.

She looked at the strolling couples beneath her, the men's white shirtfronts gleaming in the moonlight, as did the women's ballgowns, of which even the simplest cost more than a working man could earn in many months of back-breaking labour. She could not help but think that her own new dress, which she had been wearing so proudly, was in fact dull and dowdy in comparison with the colourful ballgowns.

How lucky these people are. There was envy in the thought, but no real resentment. Josie knew well that she herself had a comparatively easy and comfortable life compared with the women of the slums. It was all relative.

Her thoughts turned to the happenings of the previous day and night, and she found herself marvelling at how coldly and calmly she could think about Clement Hulme.

Apart from a couple of furtive squeezes of her hand, he had not tried to make any other physical contact with her during the social evening at the chapel. In fact, he had kept his distance most of the time, acting towards her with the respectful politeness he showed the other females present.

Josie had managed to make the necessary small talk, and the evening had passed, as had so many other evenings, with a wearisome slowness.

When Hulme had returned them to their home, he had whispered in parting, 'I can hardly wait for Sunday to come.'

She had made no reply, other than to give him a curt nod.

To her surprise, sleep had come easily to her, and she had awoken feeling refreshed and calm, a calmness that had remained with her all through that day, and was with her now. She could even face with some degree of stoicism the fact that tomorrow afternoon Clement Hulme would undoubtedly demand to have sex with her.

With a flash of bitter humour she thought of the music hall comics' advice to 'lie back and think of England'.

Not if I can help it, she thought defiantly. Then a tiny voice whispered in her mind, 'But what if he gives you no chance to refuse him? What if he forces himself upon you?'

She steeled herself to face that probability. If the worst came

161

to the worst, and she was forced to submit to him, then it would be an ordeal, but it was an ordeal that countless women underwent during their lives.

It seemed that within her head two separate beings now began to fight for domination.

Until I can find some way of getting rid of him, then I suppose there'll be times when I'll have to give in to him.

But why should I have to do that? He has no right to force himself on me.

Because if I don't give in to him, then he will tell the world what has happened between us.

No he won't. He's bluffing.

He's not bluffing, though. Remember how he looked in his office. He was determined to ruin me.

To ruin you, maybe, but he hasn't got the courage to ruin himself as well.

It doesn't need courage. All that it needs is desperation. Love can be a madness, and people will do things when they're in love that they would never do otherwise.

It's not love he feels for me, I'm sure.

No, it's an insane passion. An obsession. It's far more powerful than love. I think he's driven half mad by it . . .

'Forgive my intruding upon you, my dear.'

A woman's voice sounded in Josie's ear, and she turned to find a handsome elderly woman standing next to her, in company with a tall, good-looking man.

'I'm Madeleine Barton, William's mother, and this gentleman is Captain Preseley.'

The woman proffered her hand, and Josie automatically shook it, striving to collect her thoughts.

'William is very careless in the matter of introductions, my dear.' Madeleine smiled expectantly.

Josie, recovering from her initial discomposure, smiled back, and told her, 'I'm Josie Kitson, Mrs Barton.'

'I'm very happy to meet you, Josie. I may call you Josie, mayn't I?'

'Of course, Mrs Barton. I'm pleased that you should do so.'

William came hurrying up to them carrying two glasses of punch. He seemed greatly disconcerted to find them together, and his mother scolded him.

'Since you've neglected to introduce me to this young lady, I've introduced myself.'

'I fully intended to introduce you to each other,' he said flustered. 'Only you were engrossed in talking with your friends, and there was no opportunity.'

She clucked her tongue impatiently, and gestured dismissively with her fan. 'It doesn't matter, William.'

Then she smiled warmly at Josie. 'Now I'm going to be very selfish and keep you all to myself for a while, my dear.' She shooed the two men away. 'Go on, be off with you.' She took the two glasses of punch from her son's hands, and gave one of them to Josie. 'Here you are, my dear.' Then she sipped from her own glass, and pulled a face. 'This is a little too sweet for my taste. But it will serve.'

She regarded the two men with an expression of surprise. 'Are you still here? Go away.'

This time they both retreated, William looking very anxious. His mother fondly reassured him, 'Don't worry about this young lady. She'll be perfectly safe with me, and I shall return her to you eventually.'

When they were alone, Madeleine closely scrutinised this young woman before her, and found herself liking what she saw.

Josie's skin glowed with cleanliness, her hair was glossy from brushing. Her cheap gown was freshly laundered, and her general appearance bore silent witness to her fastidious neatness.

Josie began to feel uncomfortable beneath the searching regard, and noting this, Madeleine smiled and apologised. 'Forgive my staring at you so, my dear, but I'm a very nosy old woman, and I need to satisfy my curiosity.'

She took the punch glass from Josie and placed it with her own upon the stone balustrade. Then she tucked Josie's arm into her own in friendly contact, and invited, 'Come, we'll walk and talk. I want to get to know you. I'm told that you're a teacher. Tell me what it's like to work in a school.'

At first Josie was hesitant, and felt doubtful about the older woman's motivations. But gradually the genuine warmth and friendliness of Madeleine Barton's personality relaxed her, and she found herself liking the older woman. She began to answer readily, and to talk easily about herself.

For her part Madeleine Barton's heart was touched by the younger woman's account of her life. She was shrewd enough to divine the hardships and frustrations of Josie's existence, although the young woman made no mention or complaint of such. She was moved by Josie's stories about the children she taught, and laughed at the anecdotes that the young woman gaily related about her friend Emily Burgess's teasing of Howard Billington.

The two women became so agreeably engrossed in each other's company that they lost all sense of time, and it was not until William came seeking them that they realised just how long they had been walking and talking.

'I suppose we shall have to return to the others, my dear,' Madeleine accepted reluctantly. 'But you must remain with me for a while longer. I want to introduce you to my husband and friends.'

Arm in arm the two women went back into the ballroom, and now sharp eyes noted the obvious friendly intimacy between them. There was an almost instantaneous metamorphosis of attitude. Because of this newly acquired friendship with such a powerful and influential social figure as Madeleine Barton, Josie herself now became someone socially desirable. Cold-eyed stares became warm smiles. Disparaging comments became admiring compliments. Disinterest became interest.

Josie responded with smiling politeness to the welcoming overtures that people were now making. But inwardly she was not at all impressed, or fooled by the sudden transformation in the attitude of her fellow guests. She knew that in their hearts the vast majority of these people surrounding her would always regard her as an inferior being. Although she could believe that there were some people for whom social class had no importance or relevance, she knew only too well that in most of her fellow beings snobbery was too deeply ingrained to ever be completely eradicated from their pysches. And this class snobbery was not confined to the middle and upper orders of society. It permeated every strata of life, from the very highest to the lowest and meanest of her fellow citizens. The clerk considered himself superior to the artisan. The artisan looked down upon the labourer. The publican regarded himself as an aristocrat of the mean streets. The poorest shopkeeper's wife would not be seen dead in the company of washerwomen. The washerwomen despised the rag-sorters. The skilled factory worker would refuse to drink in the same public house bar as the unskilled factory worker . . . And because Josie had been born and bred and raised in this manner of life, she accepted it as perfectly normal, although she tried consciously not to allow class to prejudice her own opinions of the human worth of her fellow creatures.

The party came to an end shortly after midnight, and the guests dispersed in their carriages and phaetons, and a few of the more modern-minded in their motorcars.

William had brought Josie here in the sidecar of his motorcycle, but Madeleine insisted that Josie must ride home with her and her husband in their phaeton.

'I wouldn't be easy in my mind if I let you travel in that wretched machine at this hour of the night, my dear.' She was adamant. 'It's far too dangerous. William can't possibly see the road ahead when he's travelling at such speed. And when he's been drinking he's far too reckless. No, my mind is made up!'

She refused to be gainsaid. 'You shall come back with me. I shall know then that you've been safely brought back to your home.'

William was so pleased that his mother had taken such a liking to Josie that he accepted with only a token argument, while Josie was perfectly content with these new arrangements.

While they were waiting for Ernest and Madeleine to make their farewells to their hosts, William and Josie stood on the gravelled driveway of the large house.

'Have you enjoyed yourself?' he asked her anxiously for at least the twelfth time.

'Yes, I have. Very much. Thank you for bringing me.' Josie smiled at his concerned expression. At this moment she felt very tenderly towards him, and was experiencing a sense of great happiness.

'Look, if you're free tomorrow afternoon, perhaps we could take little Marie to visit her father again?' he suggested eagerly.

Unthinkingly she was about to accept his invitation, then

recollection flooded through her, and her bubble of happiness burst.

He saw her smile disappear, and dismayed, he questioned, 'What is it, Josie? Have I said something to offend you?'

She shook her head. 'No . . . no, of course you haven't. I would have liked to come with you tomorrow. But I can't. I've promised to take a class at Sunday School.'

'Oh, I see.' Disappointment sobered him momentarily. But almost immediately he cheered up, and suggested, 'Perhaps we can take her on Monday, then?'

Josie frowned doubtfully. 'I doubt that Mrs Blunt will give Marie permission to absent herself from school, William . . . And anyway, didn't you say earlier that you were going to be working on Monday?'

He had momentarily forgotten that fact, and now he grinned ruefully and admitted, 'Yes, of course I am.'

Then he proposed, 'Perhaps we can arrange something for a later date? Perhaps I could call at your home one evening to discuss it? Monday evening, maybe?'

She considered for a brief instant, then smiled and nodded. 'Yes, all right then.'

His parents and their hosts came out from the house, and the coachman brought the phaeton round.

William took Josie's hand and pressed it gently between his own. 'Until Monday then.'

'Yes, until Monday.' She returned his smile, and then took her seat in the phaeton beside Madeleine.

Ernest and Anthony sat facing the women, and the phaeton's iron-rimmed wheels crunched over the gravel while the Morgans waved their goodbyes from the top of the steps.

Ernest, who had drunk a great deal of whisky, began to relate a very long and involved story about some incident that had happened whilst he was commanding his regiment of militia, and Madeleine smiled at Josie and once more slipped her arm through that of the younger woman.

She frowned slightly at the sight of Anthony's depressed expression, surmising correctly that he had yet again had high words with his sweetheart. Then she mentally shrugged. Young love was always difficult and painful. But even if Amy Morgan did eventually break his heart for him . . . well . . . broken hearts mended, didn't they? She could feel the warmth of Josie's body close against her side, and she sighed contentedly. This young woman had proven a delightful surprise to her. And she found herself hoping that William might someday make her his bride. She would be the daughter that Madeleine had always longed for.

She remained in silent contentment during the journey back to Redditch, and when they reached Josie's home, and the young lady thanked them and dismounted, she leaned across and told her, 'I do hope that we shall meet again.' She patted Josie's cheek. 'Goodnight, my dear. Sleep tight.'

Josie waved goodbye as the carriage moved on, and then went into the house. She expected to find her mother and their neighbour, Mrs Harold, waiting for her return. But no one was there. Then, from the upstairs landing, she heard Mrs Harold call.

'I'm coming down, Josie.'

The woman clumped heavily down the narrow wooden stairs

'Where's my mother? Has she gone to bed?' Josie asked. 'Was she too tired to wait up for me?'

Mrs Harold's gaunt features were pallid beneath the flaring light, the deep lines on her face etched black.

'Yes, your mam's in bed, Josie. She's had a queer turn.'

'Oh no!' Josie gasped in fear and shock. 'How bad was it?'

'It was bad,' the woman told her bluntly. 'The doctor's been. He said he'd call back tomorrow morning. I reckon your mam's had a stroke, meself. But the doctor 'udn't say nothing about it to me. He said he'd have to talk to you first.'

'Oh my God.' Josie's heart was pounding, and her stomach knotted in apprehension. Although she and her mother were not affectionate towards each other, still in her heart Josie loved the old woman. There was a bond between them which could not be denied.

She hurried up the stairs and into her mother's bedroom, and Mrs Harold followed her more slowly.

The gas light had been turned low so that only a weak glow illuminated the face of the woman lying in the bed. Dorothy Kitson's eyes were closed, but one side of her mouth sagged open and a trickle of saliva ran down from it and across the

167

bulging jowls beneath her jawbone. Her stertorous breathing was laboured, and phlegm gurgled in her throat.

'The doctor give her summat to send her to sleep,' Mrs Harold whispered hoarsely. 'It was the young 'un who came. Dr Sinclair. Mrs Thompson's boy run and fetched him.'

Josie nodded. 'I'll thank him tomorrow, and give him something for going.'

With sudden concern she told the other woman, 'And you, Mrs Harold. I'm very grateful to you. But you must be feeling tired. I can manage here all right now, thank you. I'll sit with my mother until the doctor comes again.'

The woman stretched and yawned. 'Well, I am feeling I could do with a bit o' sleep, my duck. I'll tell you what. I'll goo and lay down for a whiles, and then when I wakes up I'll come back and let you have a lay-down.'

Although Josie protested that she would be all right, and was not feeling at all sleepy, Mrs Harold was adamant.

'I'll not take no for an answer, my wench. I'll be back in a couple of hours or so.'

Gratefully Josie accepted the kindness. Then, when Mrs Harold had gone, she settled herself to watch over the comatose woman in the bed.

She used a small towel to wipe away the saliva from her mother's lips and chin and throat, but as fast as she dried the dank skin, more saliva trickled from the slack mouth, and eventually Josie admitted defeat and let it flow free, contenting herself with arranging the towel to protect the pillow and sheet.

The night outside was still and very quiet. No wind moaned, no nocturnally marauding animals disturbed the silence with their cries. Only the hissing of the gas and the harsh breathing of Dorothy Kitson sounded within the cramped, stuffy bedroom.

Josie sat slumped in tiredness upon the plain wooden chair, and gazed with troubled eyes at the sleeping woman. Long-buried memories rose to populate her thoughts. Forgotten images of childhood came vividly back. Memories of her mother as a young and laughing woman, playing with Josie and her brother. Memories of Dorothy walking proudly arm in arm with her husband, Josie's long-dead father, a stern yet kindly man, who had dearly loved his small family, and had been dearly loved by them in return.

Unshed tears stung Josie's eyes and blurred her vision as she remembered her grief when her father had died, still a comparatively young man. His death had radically altered his children's lives. Dorothy, made wretched by her own grief for her husband, and forced into penurious existence by the loss of the wage-earner, had changed from the fond, laughing mother she had been into a shrewish, querulous tyrant, who ruled over her two children with a harsh rigidity. The passing years did nothing to mellow Dorothy's changed character, but only served to deepen her self-pity and sharpen her nagging tongue. Habitual hypochondria had been overtaken by a genuine deterioration of her health, and her self-pity had become a strident martyrdom.

Josie's brother Phillip had, as he became older, rebelled against his mother's harsh strictures, and had quarrelled repeatedly with her until, driven beyond endurance, he had enlisted in the Royal Navy to escape her.

Josie's tears brimmed over and fell freely now, as she relived that awful day when Phillip had left the house carrying his toilet gear in a newspaper parcel.

'As soon as I can, I'll send you the money so that you can get a room for yourself and leave this house,' he had promised fervently, fighting to hold back his tears, his immature, boyish features twisted with the grief of parting.

Then he had set off along the road, turning frequently to wave back at Josie, who stood watching him from the gate, until finally he had disappeared from her view.

But despite her grief at parting from her brother, Josie's life had become a little more bearable. Shocked by her son's departure, Dorothy had tried to curb her cruellest excesses towards her daughter, and to control her querulous temper and soften her acid tongue.

And so the years had passed, and mother and daughter stayed locked in their unhappy bonding, and imperceptibly Josie had become resigned to her dull, bleak life. Her youthful dreams and hopes of love and romance had remained only dreams and hopes. The dashing prince on the white horse had never come galloping to set her free from the emotional fetters which bound her to her mother.

The image of William Barton's long, lean features suddenly rose up in Josie's mind. Now, miraculously, the love she had dreamed and hoped for during so many lonely, empty years and had all but abandoned hope of ever finding had finally been proffered to her.

A wrenching sob tore from Josie's throat. She had been prepared to lie and cheat and degrade herself still further if that was the price she must pay for one day having William Barton as her husband. If doing all these things made her a sinner, then she was ready to accept that burden upon her soul. But now a fearful dread struck her to the heart. Was God punishing her for being ready to behave so badly? Had He struck the mother down to punish the sins of the daughter?

She suddenly felt totally helpless, powerless to struggle against an inexorable fate. Her sobs became a constant moaning outpouring of despair, and she buried her face in her hands and her body heaved and shook as that despair overwhelmed her.

Chapter Sixteen

This Empire Day was going to be commemorated with the longest procession ever to be seen in Redditch, and even before dawn, the preparations were underway. On the Church Green workmen were erecting the platform which was to serve as the saluting dais, and festooning it with massive Union flags surrounded by wreaths of laurels, and the smaller flags of the empire's dominions and colonies. Along the route of the procession more workmen were stretching streams of brightly coloured bunting across the fronts of the buildings, and between the trunks of trees and gaslamps and telephone poles.

As dawn paled the cloudless skies, men, women and children throughout the town and its satellite villages were rising from their beds to make ready. Hurried breakfasts were gulped down, and everyone put on their Sunday best finery and left their homes to gather at prearranged meeting points. From these they set out to march towards the procession's mustering area, which was the Victoria Recreation Ground lying to the east of the town's Church Green.

In the narrow back scullery of her home, Eva Payne was washing the face and hands of her seven-year-old son, while in the living room Marie Gurden combed the tangles from the long hair of one of the six-year-old twins.

'Owww!' The girl wailed in protest as the comb snagged in a knot of hair.

Marie whispered, 'Shush now,' and pointed a finger at the cracked, stained ceiling in warning. 'Don't wake your father up.'

Alfred Payne's snores could be heard clearly through the thin flooring, and the small girl pulled a face and clapped her hand across her mouth, causing her sister to giggle.

171

Marie smiled and kissed the child's head where the hair had been tugged by the comb. 'There now, I've kissed it better, haven't I?'

She herself had risen before the rest to make her own toilet, and was a picture of neat freshness, despite the shabbiness of her threadbare clothing.

Eva came into the living room and touched Marie on her cheek.

'Now, are you sure that you feel all right, Marie?' she whispered, afraid to speak in a normal tone for fear of disturbing her husband.

Marie had remained in bed for the previous two days, recovering from the effects of the injury Payne had inflicted upon her.

'Yes, thank you,' she whispered. 'I'm fine now. Really I am.'

Eva stared anxiously into the clear blue eyes gazing up at her, and was relieved to see how focused they were. She gently felt the large lump beneath the blonde hair, and found it softer to the touch than before.

'Does it still hurt as much, sweetheart?'

'No.' Marie smiled reassuringly. 'It doesn't hurt at all now. I'm fine, really I am.'

Eva was still racked by guilt over what had happened, and she still inwardly castigated herself for not having had the courage to report her husband to the authorities for what he had done.

Marie, for her part, although bitterly resentful towards Alfred Payne and fearful of his violence, had decided with a wisdom beyond her years that she would say nothing to anyone about what had happened. Particularly not to her father. She knew how he would react, and she would not add to his present heavy burden of pain and worry.

Eva and Marie finished readying the excited children for their outing. Eva had gone to the local scrapyard, and had begged some pieces of material from the rag collectors. These she had sewn into sashes and rosettes, and now the small boy and girls stood straight and proud as they were adorned with these home-made decorative emblems.

'My word, but you look smart! Real mashers!' Eva smiled, and tears stung her eyes as she saw the thrilled pride and

172

pleasure with which her children surveyed themselves in the broken piece of mirror.

'Come on, kids.' Marie gathered the children to her, and asked Eva as she led them out, 'Are you going up town to watch the parade?'

Eva shook her head.

'No, I can't do that, my duck. He wouldn't like me going out. But I'll pop down and watch you all marching from the school yard.'

Out on the street there were other groups of children walking towards the school, and Marie joined them in happy anticipation. She was eager to see Miss Kitson again, and to find out from her when they would be going to visit her father once more. She thought Miss Kitson and her gentleman friend were wonderful people, and was hoping fervently that they would get married and invite her to their wedding.

But when she reached the school yard she searched through the throngs of children and adults and could see no sign of the teacher anywhere. Disappointment struck sharply through her, and momentarily clouded her happy anticipation for the day. But then she comforted herself.

'Perhaps Miss Kitson has been delayed. She'll come later. I'm sure she will . . .'

Emily Burgess hurried along the lines of chattering, excited children, distributing small paper Union Jacks from the large hamper being carried by the two boys accompanying her. Even as she handed out the flags Emily continually peered around her, searching for a glimpse of her absent friend.

'Miss Burgess? Miss Burgess?'

It was James Parnell who called to her, and she went to him.

'Have you had news from Miss Kitson?' he questioned, and she shook her head.

He clucked his tongue in exasperation. 'Really, it's too bad of her. She knows how much we are all needed here today.'

Emily immediately bridled and sprang to her friend's defence. 'I'm sure that it is something of importance which is delaying her, Mr Parnell. Miss Kitson is very conscientious in her duties.'

'Yes, yes, Miss Burgess, I appreciate that fact,' he retorted

173

testily. 'However, she is not here, where she is sorely needed, is she?'

'If she isn't here then there must be a very good reason,' Emily argued.

The man wasn't listening to her. His eyes were ranging along the lines of his pupils, and he scowled as if what he could see was unpleasing to him.

'Those girls there, and those boys, do you see them, Miss Burgess?'

His pointing finger moved along the ranks. 'There, and there . . . that one . . . the fat boy there . . . that girl . . . the small boy . . . those two girls . . .'

He shook his head. 'Just look at them. After hearing my strict instructions, they still have not done as I told them.'

He turned to scowl fiercely down at the small, plump woman beside him. 'Did I, or did I not, distinctly tell every pupil of my school that they were to dress in a certain manner for this parade, Miss Burgess?'

She was uncertain if he was making a statement or asking a question. So to be on the safe side she nodded.

'Exactly so!' he declared with an air of satisfied vindication. 'Exactly so, Miss Burgess . . . And I have been disobeyed!'

'Disobeyed, Mr Parnell?' She was still not sure what he was talking about. 'How have you been disobeyed?'

His prominent blue eyes bulged, and he exclaimed, as if in amazement at her obtuseness, 'Can you not see what is in front of your very eyes, Miss Burgess?' He flung out his arm and waved it along the lines of children. 'Look at them! I told the girls to wear white dresses and blue sashes, did I not? I told the boys to wear clean shirts and stiff collars and rosettes of red, white and blue, did I not? And look at them, Miss Burgess. Just look at them.'

She stared along the lines of the pupils. Out of the combined total of girls and boys, she judged roughly that perhaps a third had made some attempt to dress as the headmaster had ordered. The remainder were in their normal everyday clothing, which varied from shabby to ragged. The woman smiled wryly as she noted how some of the children had made an effort to fashion rosettes and sashes from whatever scraps of old paper and rags they could beg, borrow or

174

steal. She felt driven to remonstrate with the man beside her.

'Mr Parnell, surely you didn't really expect that our children would be able to appear in new dresses and shirts and clean white collars, did you? Good Lord above! I doubt if most of them have ever worn an article of new clothing in their lives.'

He was reluctant to accept that his chagrin at their appearance could not be morally justified. So he attempted to bluster.

'Even if they could not afford new clothing, they could at least have made some attempt to clean their bodies and faces, and to brush and comb their hair, could they not? They could have tried to achieve some small degree of neatness and order in their appearances. They resemble nothing more than a gang of ragamuffins.'

Emily Burgess's normally placid temper erupted. 'They resemble ragamuffins because that is precisely what they are, Mr Parnell. But that is no fault of their own, is it? Or has poverty now become a wilful crime?'

He stared in surprise at the furious flushed face of the little woman. And after a moment's reflection accepted that he was at fault in the matter.

'You are right in what you say, Miss Burgess,' he told her in a quiet and apologetic tone. 'I should not blame the children for their poverty. It was very wrong of me to say what I have said, and I'm sorry for it.'

Her temper subsided as quickly as it had arisen, and she told him, 'I think the stress of this occasion is adversely affecting all our tempers, Mr Parnell.'

'Exactly so,' he murmured, then regarded the children with troubled eyes, and said uneasily, 'Nevertheless, Miss Burgess, we have a duty to our school to present the best appearance we can make of it to those who will be watching us this morning. So, we shall form the ranks with the best-dressed and the neatest children on the outer files, and the worst-looking in the centre files.'

She made no answer, and to forestall any possible fresh outbreak from her, he went on to explain.

'You and I both know how cruel people can be, Miss Burgess. I fear that some of the most ragged of our children will be mocked and jeered at by certain of the hooligan elements

175

among the spectators. By placing them in the centre files we shall be shielding them from any close or direct contact with the crowd, shall we not?'

Although Emily was inwardly sceptical about the purity of the man's motives in this matter, nevertheless she recognised that there was truth in what he was saying. She knew that the sight of some of these pathetically ragged and misshapen children trying to march smartly in step would run the risk of provoking mockery and taunting jeers from certain of the town's more unpleasant elements. Similar incidents had occurred during other occasions when the school had formed a procession.

'Very well, Mr Parnell,' she assented reluctantly.

'Good, I'm glad we agree on that point, at least,' he said briskly. 'I shall pass on those intructions to the other staff members.'

With that he walked away.

Emily went on with the distribution of the flags, and was engrossed in this task when one of the elder children told her, 'Look, miss, theer's Miss Kitson over theer.'

Emily sighed in relief, and telling the girl, 'Carry on with giving these flags out, will you please?' she turned to meet the oncoming figure of her friend.

As she neared Josie, Emily gasped in concern.

'Whatever's the matter, Josie? You look awful!'

The young woman's face was white and desperately weary-looking, and huge dark shadows ringed her eyes.

'It's my mother. She had a stroke last night.' Josie seemed very tense and overstressed. 'My neighbour's looking after her now. I've just come to tell Mr Parnell why I shan't be at work for a while. I'll have to stay at home and care for her.'

'Is there anything I can do to help?' Emily offered immediately, but Josie shook her head.

'What happened? Were you at home when your mother was taken ill?' Emily began to fire questions at her friend, and Josie answered as best she could.

While the two women were talking, the rest of the staff completed the formation of the children into their ranks, and with Mr Parnell at their head, the first contingent marched out from the school gates and up the long stretch of Edward Street.

Women came out of their houses to watch and wave at them passing.

'Oh look, he's gone before I could have a word,' Josie exclaimed in dismay, and told her friend hurriedly, 'I'll run after him and explain what's happened. Goodbye now.'

As she half ran towards the gate, Marie Gurden called to her from the ranks of one of the contingents waiting to be marched away.

'Miss Kitson? Miss Kitson? Can I speak to you, please?'

Josie slowed her pace and stared about her, and then saw Marie. Her own troubles were weighing so heavily upon her that at this particular moment she forgot the child's difficulties, and her physical weariness and worried mind caused her to frown and to snap irritably, 'Not now, I haven't time.'

She hurried on in pursuit of Mr Parnell, and behind her the child's expression mirrored her hurt and shock.

Why is she so angry with me? Marie asked herself in helpless puzzlement. What have I done to make her speak to me like that?

Marie felt suddenly near to tears. Her shining heroine had spoken to her as if she were an unpleasant nuisance.

She bit her lip, and rallied her stubborn courage.

'All right then. If she thinks I'm a nuisance, I shan't trouble her ever again.'

By mid-morning purposeful groups of marchers were thronging every road leading towards the central plateau of Redditch town. On reaching the plateau the groups converged towards the northern apex of the Church Green, and from there were funnelled down Easemore Lane to debouch upon the flat grass and cinders of the Victoria Recreation Ground.

The harassed parade marshals rushed around shouting and sweating and frantically chivvying the new arrivals into their various march echelons. Here the white-dressed, blue-sashed schoolgirls, and the eton-collared, knickerbockered, rosette-wearing boys. There the Boy Scouts shouldering their long wooden staffs like rifles. Next to them the diminutive, green-jerseyed Wolf Cubs. Then the sportsmen and athletes forming colourful phalanxes in the various jerseys and caps of the many

177

different football, cricket, cycling, swimming and athletic clubs of the district.

In more sombre garb of dark serge suits and bowler hats were the banner-carrying groups from the multitude of clubs and societies that existed in the district. The Temperance Society, the Loyal Fidelity Lodge for Females, the Provident Sick Society, the Union Club, the Loyal Brunswick Lodge, the Loyal Excelsior Lodge, the Liberal Club, the Church Men's Club, the Women's Suffrage Society, the United Patriots National Benefit Society, and a score of others. Each church and chapel had also sent its representatives, and for this day at least Anglicans, Methodists, Baptists, Rechabites, Roman Catholics, Congregationalists all mingled in cordial fellowship and with common purpose.

The fire brigade's brass helmets glittered in the sunlight as they lounged around their steam tender and fly. The blue-uniformed Territorial Artillerymen soothed their horses and gave a final polish to their gleaming field guns and limbers, while their brothers-in-arms of the Territorial Infantry Company preened themselves in their newly issued khaki uniforms and peaked caps.

Standing between these two sets of weekend warriors was a sizeable party of men, almost two hundred strong. Some of them were shabby, some well dressed, some were worn and gaunt, others fat and rosy, their only uniformity the rows of medals pinned to the chests of their coats. These were the members of the National Reserve. Time-expired old soldiers, sailors and marines, veterans of battles fought in South Africa, Egypt, the Sudan, India, Burma, East Africa, China, West Africa. They smiled with a genial contempt at the smartly uniformed Territorials who flanked them, and exchanged reminiscences of old campaigns, reliving the days of their youth.

One corner of the field was reserved for the town's musicians, and the warm air was rent by the discordant cacophony of their instruments being tested and tuned, the scarlet-jacketed Redditch Town Band trying to outblast the green-coated Imperial Band, while the bands of the Salvation Army and the civilian-suited Holyoake's Field Brotherhood sturdily drummed and trumpeted and brayed to the greater glory of the Lord. And as the hour of the parade drew nearer, so crowds of spectators began to gather along the processional route, and the carriages of the dignitaries rolled up and deposited their important passengers by the saluting platform and the stands of benches flanking it, which were the reserved seating for the town's élite.

Lieutenant Anthony Barton, smartly uniformed in the blue patrol jacket and breeches of the Territorial Artillery was subject to a mental dichotomy. He was disappointed because a shortage of draught horses meant that his two-gun section of the six-gun battery would not be taking part in the procession, so he would not be able to march past at the head of his own men and guns. On the other hand, he was now free until the advent of the parade to ride his charger continuously up and down the processional route, looking as if he were carrying important dispatches, and creating a frisson in the hearts of many of the young lady spectators with his gallant martial air. He particularly savoured the opportunities to dashingly caracole and turn his mount in front of the stand where Amy Morgan was sitting, looking ravishing in pastel silk gown and broad-brimmed feathered hat, with a dainty parasol shielding her delicate complexion from the sun.

He had not been able to resist discarding his sling, and he carried his plastered arm ostentatiously hanging down by his side, holding his reins with a single hand and drawing sighs of admiration from the more susceptible ladies. Anthony found that he loved playing the role of the wounded warrior.

The stands were now full, and the saluting party was in position upon the platform. The Redditch Town Band were to lead the parade, and now from the distance the sounds of their music could be heard advancing up Easemore Lane towards the town centre.

Anthony wheeled his mount to a standstill in front of the platform, and bowed his head in salute to his father.

'Do I have your permission to rejoin my battery, sir?'

His ringing request brought sighs of admiration from the ladies. It was as if this handsome young officer were asking permission to return to the terrible dangers of the battle front. Ernest Barton, clad for this occasion in the scarlet and gold full dress uniform of a colonel of militia, nodded sternly, and his son again bowed his head in salute,

179

wheeled his horse and galloped away to the applause of the onlookers.

William Barton, who was standing alone in the midst of the ordinary spectators, smiled as he watched his brother's performance.

You should have been an actor, Tony, he thought with amusement. But at the same time he could not help envying his brother's dashing display, and for a brief moment found himself wishing that he could have shown off in front of Josie Kitson in such a gallant manner.

He smiled fondly now as he pictured Josie's gentle face, and waited impatiently for her to come into view among the ranks of the schoolchildren.

'Excuse me, is this seat taken?'

Amy Morgan looked up into the face of Jack Preseley, and felt a fluttering of her heart as she told him flirtatiously, 'Well, I was saving it for my friend, but it doesn't look as if she will come. Please do sit down, Captain Preseley. If she comes we can all squeeze closer together, can't we?'

He smiled, but forbore from making the obvious complimentary rejoinder, and seated himself beside her, keeping a decorous distance between their bodies.

'Did you see Tony showing off?' There was a sneer of disparagement in her voice. 'Really, he's very immature at times. He still behaves like a silly callow youth. I wonder sometimes why I bother with him.'

Her tone invited Jack to add his own critical comment, but again he forbore, and only replied simply, 'Tony's an excellent horseman. If I could ride as well as he I'd doubtless be tempted to show off a little myself in front of all these pretty women.'

There was a hint of petulance now in Amy's expression. She had given the man two obvious openings to begin to flirt with her, and he had quite deliberately ignored them. 'But surely, Captain Preseley, you're a better rider than Tony. He says that you are counted as one of the finest horsemen in the entire cavalry.'

He smiled. 'Tony is a very good friend of mine, Miss Morgan. But his friendship sometimes causes him to overpraise my abilities, and fail to do justice to his own.' He paused and stared at her meaningfully. 'He's a fine man, and I honour and respect him.'

Amy was not accustomed to having her veiled invitations to a flirtation rejected in this manner, and felt quite mortified. She turned away abruptly, and twirled her parasol, and covered a delicate yawn with her gloved hand, as if she were extremely bored with her present company.

Jack sat smiling pleasantly, occasionally nodding in answer to the greeting of passing acquaintances, and ignoring her completely.

His apparent unconcern initially deepened her sense of pique, and in her mind she berated him in very unladylike words that her parents would have been utterly shocked and horrified to find out were known and used by their beloved daughter.

But Amy's volatile temperament could not long sustain inaction. She glanced from the corner of her eye at the man beside her, and as if sensing her covert regard he turned and smiled.

'Come now, Miss Morgan, let's you and I be friends. It's too nice a day to spoil with disagreement.'

She was not to be coaxed so easily, however, and she lifted her pert nose in the air and snapped, 'I'm sure I don't understand what you mean, Captain Preseley, with your talk of disagreement. I haven't been disagreeable.'

Despite his reluctance to flirt with the sweetheart of his friend, Jack was finding it increasingly difficult to resist the temptation. Amy Morgan was an extremely delectable young woman, and he had always been very susceptible to such.

For her part Amy was now determined that she would entrap this man. Justifiably she was confident that she could make almost any man fall in love with her. Now, her vanity irresistibly impelled her to make a conquest of the man beside her.

She smiled mischievously at him, and confessed artlessly, 'All right, so I am behaving disagreeably. But I won't behave so any longer.' She held out her hand. 'Let's be friends.'

Even though he found her wiles blatantly obvious, Jack was still utterly charmed by her, and he took her hand and held it for far longer than was necessary.

'Oh look, here's the band coming.' She gently disengaged her fingers to point to the northern apex of the Church Green

181

where the scarlet jackets and white crossbelts of the town band had now appeared.

'Don't they look fine!' she exclaimed, and smiled happily in the realisation that she was already beginning to draw this man into her web.

The procession passed along its route, the bands playing, the flags waving, the marchers stepping in concert to the thudding of the drums, and the spectators sang the words of the tunes of glory that the bands were playing . . . 'Rule Britannia', 'Hearts of Oak', 'Soldiers of the Queen', 'The Bulldog Breed', 'The British Grenadiers'. Chests swelled and bodies stood straighter, and men, women and children were proud in the knowledge that they were the rulers of the greatest empire that history had ever known, that they were an invincible race, God's Englishmen, the captains of the earth.

And so for this hour on this Sunday morning, the people of Redditch town were united in their pride for country and race, even the poorest and meanest among them feeling that they shared in the glory of an imperial dominance that raised them above the lesser breeds of the earth. At this moment it seemed to them that their ordered, secure, unchanging world would endure forever.

Chapter Seventeen

Clement Hulme was humming happily to himself as he took his seat at the head of the table and waited for his wife to serve him with his Sunday dinner. Ranged on either side of the table, his children were seated in descending order of age, from his sixteen-year-old son to his three-year-old daughter. There were another seven children in between, three boys and four girls. A further three children had died in infancy.

Hulme was proud of his large family, regarding their numbers as proof of his manly virility, and paradoxically, although he was a bully to his wife and his underlings, he was not unkind to his children. His favourite among them was Bernard, his eldest son, who was presently a pupil at the privately owned Redditch Grammar School. He was a tall, well-built, personable boy, with a pleasant disposition, and the local wags would laughingly surmise about his parentage, jokingly refusing to accept the fact that such an unpleasant man as Clement Hulme could have fathered a son who was so different to him in appearance and personality. The other children all physically resembled their father.

Gladys Hulme now brought in the roasted joint of beef, and while her husband carved it, she fetched in the dishes of vegetables. When all had been served she did not sit down with them to eat, but remained standing like a dutiful servant, ready to anticipate any needs of her husband and children.

As a small child Bernard Hulme had accepted this aspect of his mother's behaviour as being perfectly natural. But now it increasingly troubled him, as did many other aspects of his family life, such as the contrast between Clement Hulme's manner towards his children, and that towards his wife. Bernard resented hearing his father speak to his mother as if she were a stupid, inferior being. He resented the way his father constantly criticised whatever she did and berated her for her failings. Clement seemed to take an actual delight in nagging her for any minor fault of omission or commission, and appeared to be on a constant lookout for such. He would blame her for any misbehaviour by the children, but at the same time would not allow her to chastise them. He demanded obedience from them, and was quick to enforce it, but would protect them from their mother's justifiable anger when they were naughty. Like all children they were quick to recognise how powerless their mother was, and took full advantage of that fact.

Bernard suffered pangs of remorse as he remembered how he had behaved exactly like them, before he grew old enough to understand. Now, at sixteen years of age, he was greatly disturbed by his confusion of feelings about his parents. Despite his father's indulgence towards him, Bernard realised that at heart he disliked the man. Over the years he had come to know that there were many of the townsfolk who hated and despised his father. Once Bernard had fiercely resented them for this hostility. Now he unhappily conceded that they had good reason for it. But at the same time he felt guilt for his own lack of filial affection towards a man who had in fairness not been a bad father to him.

In relation to his mother the boy suffered an equal dichotomy. He loved her, yet despised her for her abject surrender to her husband's tyranny. Her servile acceptance of inferiority infuriated him. He was convinced that she deliberately acted as if she were a dull, stupid woman because she hadn't got the courage to assert herself. That she was an appeaser, without spirit or pride. Yet even in the moments that Bernard was feeling angriest with her, he still loved her, and pitied her.

'You'll be taking the little ones to the church Sunday School this afternoon, I expect. And then to visit your parents.' Clement Hulme sought confirmation from his wife, who nodded dutifully.

'Humphh!' Hulme snorted indignantly. 'I hope your father is satisfied that I'm keeping to the terms of our agreement.'

'I'm sure he is, Clement.' Gladys Hulme fluttered nervously. 'And he honours you for it.'

'Humphh! So he should do.'

Gladys's father, Charles Dolphin, was a staunch adherent of the Church of England. When Clement had asked him for his daughter's hand in marriage, Dolphin had been reluctant to accept a Nonconformist as son-in-law. But eventually he had agreed to the match on the condition that any children of the union were to be raised in the Anglican faith, and not to follow the Methodist persuasion like their father. Consequently, while Clement continued to worship at the Methodist chapel, his wife and children attended the parish church of St Stephen.

Secretly Hulme was more than happy with this arrangement. He did not want his wife or children with him at chapel gatherings, where they would be a hindrance to his socialising with the female members of the brethren. And since the affair with Josie had begun he'd inwardly poured blessings on Charles Dolphin's head for having insisted on the agreement. But he still enjoyed tormenting his wife about it, and she lived in constant fear that he would one day break the agreement and stop her and the children attending the parish church.

Of course, quite apart from his affair with Josie, for as long as Charles Dolphin remained chairman of the Electric Light Committee of the council, there was no likelihood whatsoever of Clement breaking the agreement, no matter how much he might want to torment and spite his wife.

There was pride in Hulme's eyes as he turned his attention towards his eldest son.

'No Sunday School for you, I take it, Bernie? Morning service is more than enough, isn't it?'

'Yes, Father.' The boy kept his eyes fixed upon his plate, and busied himself in cutting his meat.

'What will you be doing with yourself this afternoon then?' Hulme's manner was heavily jocular as he winked broadly. 'Playing tennis? Is that what you'll be doing? Playing tennis at the club?'

It was a source of immense gratification to Clement Hulme that his son was a member of the Cricket, Hockey and Tennis Club. This was the venue of the social élite among the youth of the town, and to actually belong to it carried tremendous social cachet, because membership was only by invitation of the club committee. Hulme frequently bragged about the fact that his son was a member, and would lead his listeners to understand that it was his own prestige that had gained the entrée for him. The fact that Bernard's membership was due solely to the boy's own personal popularity with the sons and daughters of the local élite was something Hulme totally disregarded. He had by now convinced himself that his own version was the correct one.

'I expect I will be playing, Father,' Bernard said quietly, and Hulme chortled happily and rubbed his hands together.

'I did you a bit of good when I got you into that club, my lad. It was a good move on my part. They're the people you have to get well in with in this town, if you want to get on in life, like I've got on . . .'

The boy groaned inwardly. Oh no! Here we go again.

'. . . Yes, you don't know how lucky you are to have a father like me, my lad.' Hulme's self-satisfaction radiated an almost tangible aura. 'I had to pull myself up by my own bootstraps, I did. I never had anyone to help me through life. My father was a sick man, and my mother took in washing to earn a crust. I never knew what it was to have a full stomach when I was a boy . . . Do you know, when I first started school . . .'

The familiar recital of Hulme's early hardships, and his almost superhuman struggles to rise in the world, continued on and on and on, and the elder children exchanged sly glances, and nudged each other under cover of the table. His wife stood with dulled eyes, and drooping shoulders, waiting patiently for her lord and master to finish his meal so that she could clear the table and wash up, and then make the younger children ready for Sunday School.

Chapter Eighteen

'Well played, Bernie!'

'Fine shot!'

'Game, set and match, I think.'

The plaudits of the spectators sounded in Bernard's ears as he went to the net to shake hands with his defeated opponent, then moved off the grass court.

The shaded veranda of the clubhouse was a welcome haven from the blazing heat of the sun, and the youth used a towel to wipe the sweat from his face as he mounted the wooden steps to join the young men and women congregated there.

'Bernie, come over here.' Anthony Barton, elegant in a colourfully striped blazer and white duck trousers, a cravat knotted around his muscular throat, beckoned the youth to join the group sitting around a table on which were placed jugs of iced lemonade.

Barton handed the youth a glass. 'You look as if you need this.'

Bernard drank thirstily, enjoying the fresh tartness of the cold liquid.

The group at the table was mixed: Amy Morgan, accompanied by some of her girlfriends; Anthony Barton, Jack Preseley and some other young men. All wore sports clothes, the young women in long white dresses with coloured scarves around their slender waists, the men in white ducks, white shirts, striped blazers and cravats.

'Come and sit by me, Bernie,' Amy invited, and ordered the young man next to her, 'Get up and let Bernie sit down. The poor boy must be exhausted.'

With a mock grumble the young man obeyed, and patted the youth's shoulder as he seated himself.

'You played really well, Bernie.'

Other compliments on his playing were directed at the youth, and he was both pleased and embarrassed, and murmured words of thanks.

'This young man is the club champion, Jack,' Anthony informed his friend, and leaned over to ruffle Bernard's tousled brown hair. 'And I think he's good enough to enter for the national championships.'

The Ulsterman smiled and nodded. 'You could well be right.'

He liked the diffident modesty with which the youngster accepted the praise being showered upon him.

Bernard sat surrounded by the gaiety of his companions and a feeling of utter contentment pervaded him. He hero-worshipped Anthony Barton, and nurtured a romantic secret love for Amy Morgan. To be here now, sitting beside her, having Anthony smiling warmly upon him, was absolute happiness.

The conversation and badinage became general once more, and Preseley leaned comfortably back in his chair and covertly studied the people around him. He was a few years older than most of them, and now, listening to their light-hearted, nonsensical chattering and laughter, he suddenly felt immeasurably older.

A line of Shakespeare's entered his mind . . . 'Golden lads and girls all must, As chimneysweepers come to dust . . .'

A weird sensation suddenly engulfed him. The day became dark, the sounds of talk and laughter grew faint and muffled. A conviction of impending doom invaded his mind, along with nightmarish images of the happy, laughing, youthful faces around him metamorphosing into the rotting masks of death.

'Why, Captain Preseley, what's the matter? You look as if you've seen a ghost.'

Preseley shuddered, and the terrible images abruptly dissolved. The day lightened, voices and laughter were loud and clear, and he was looking into the concerned face of Amy Morgan.

He forced a smile and tried to collect his disordered thoughts. 'Oh, it's nothing.' He waved away her concern. 'A momentary headache, that's all.' His smile firmed. 'I had rather too much to drink last night, I'm afraid.'

Their exchange attracted Anthony's attention, and he advised jocularly, 'You'd better have a hair of the dog that bit you, then, Jack. That's the only cure.'

'Yes, I think you're right, Tony.' Preseley could laugh easily now, and assure Amy, 'I'm really perfectly well, Miss Morgan.'

Another of her friends spoke to her, and she turned away and within moments was chattering gaily once again.

Preseley curiously sought within himself to find some explanation for that unaccountable feeling that had so suddenly oppressed him. It must be because of the situation back home, he decided. It's because I'm expecting there to be civil war there . . .

But this answer did not entirely satisfy him.

The troubles at home, even if it comes to civil war, won't threaten these people here. So why should I suddenly visualise their destruction?

He pondered for some time, and then, realising that he would not find any rational explanation for what had happened, tried to put the disturbing incident from his mind. But he could not. He became restless, and decided that he would walk for a while. Excusing himself to the company, he stepped down from the veranda and strolled away from the clubhouse.

Amy's eyes followed his tall figure. Anthony noted the direction of her pensive gaze, and jealousy stirred within his mind.

Bernard Hulme, sensitive to the moods of the two people he worshipped, was puzzled by their sudden silence, and experienced a disturbing unease. A vague, fearful instinct that all was not well between his idols.

On the central cricket pitch of the club's extensive grounds a match was in progress, and Jack wandered across to stand and watch. The match was between the club first eleven and a team from one of the local factories, Works Sporting Clubs. The Ulsterman smiled grimly to himself as he noted the physical and sartorial disparities between the opposing sides. The cricket club's team were batting, the two batsmen immaculate in white flannels, coloured caps and white boots. Their teammates lounging around the pavilion were similarly clad, and presented a fine spectacle of tall, ruddy-cheeked middle-class manhood.

In contrast the factory workers of the opposing side were noticeably shorter in height, and less robust in physique, their complexions sallow from spending their long working hours shut away from sunlight and fresh air. And instead of a uniformity of white sports clothes, they wore a wide variety of shabby everyday trousers, shirts and footwear.

Jack's gaze shifted to the wooded hillsides west and south of the club grounds, and the rolling farmland to the north. Half a mile behind him to the east was the town centre, hidden from his view by yet another high spur of ground. Although he was not a native son of this small corner of Worcestershire, Preseley loved it and felt at home here. His primary loyalty was to his birthplace, the province of Ulster, but his secondary loyalty was given to this district, with its ancient woodlands and steep hills, its half-timbered villages and hamlets secluded in fecund farmland, and not least the town of Redditch itself.

Built from bricks made from the red marl clay which had first given the original monastic settlement its name, Redditch was a town that possessed a distinct individuality. Although distant from the country's main trading routes, and situated deep within the agricultural region of the Warwickshire/Worcestershire borders, it was a thriving industrial complex, and the world centre for the manufacture of needles and fishing tackle. For centuries it had dominated the international markets for those two commodities. During the last couple of decades its hard-headed businessmen and entrepreneurs had also diversified into other fields of manufacture. Motorcycles, bicycles, springs, batteries, even motor cars were now being produced in the grimy, noisy factories and workshops which were to be found in every nook and cranny of the district. Over the centuries the townspeople had also developed a certain corporate identity. Their accent was harsher than that of the people of the immediately surrounding agricultural areas, and their speech patterns differed. They were clannish and unwelcoming to the stranger, with a tendency towards quick aggression, yet paradoxically they had absorbed and assimilated many waves of immigrants from other parts of Great Britain and Ireland, and a large assortment of individual foreigners, most of whom, within the space of a generation or even less, had acquired the parochial patriotism and attributes of the native townsfolk.

190

Jack's maternal bachelor uncle had come to live and work in the town several years previously, and it was during visits to him that Preseley had come to know the area and to make friends with Anthony Barton. His uncle had died several years since, but Jack had kept up his friendship with Anthony, and made regular visits when his army service permitted. The Ulsterman had often toyed with the idea of leaving the army and going into business in the town himself. Many fortunes had been made, and were still being made here.

A mirthless smile hovered on his lips. Well, now I've left the army, there's nothing to stop me coming here. That's providing I survive the civil war, of course.

'I'd offer you a penny for your thoughts, Captain Preseley. But you're looking so dour, perhaps I'd not enjoy hearing them.'

Amy had come up silently behind him, and now he experienced a mixed reaction upon hearing her voice.

The rapidly growing strength of the attraction he felt towards her troubled him greatly. He was a man who fully believed in the old-fashioned concept of a gentleman's honour, and the increasingly strong desire he had to possess this beautiful young woman was to him dishonourable. Anthony was his dear friend, Amy his friend's intended wife. She was forbidden territory in Jack Preseley's morality.

But now, as she moved very close, her blue eyes dancing with mischievous invitation, her small white teeth gleaming, her soft red lips moistly tempting, the peachlike skin of her face and throat glowing in the sunlight, the warm fragrance of her scent enveloping him, Jack's morality, his sense of honour, his loyalty to his friend, were all stretched perilously near to breaking point.

He looked beyond her in the direction of the tennis courts, and saw that she had come alone. A mingling of pleasure and dismay coursed through him, and unconsciously those feelings were displayed upon his face.

Amy felt an inner glow of satisfaction as she correctly judged his unguarded expression. Her vanity-impelled determination to emotionally enslave this man had hardened to something near obsession. Now she let her instincts guide her.

'I deliberately came to find you, Captain Preseley,' she said without any trace of flirtatiousness in her voice or manner. 'Because I want you to tell me about the Curragh incident, and about the situation in Ireland.'

He regarded her doubtfully, and she went on.

'I told Tony I was coming to find you, and I've promised him that I shall bring you back with me. But first you must tell me all that I want to know. It's no use me trying to hold a serious conversation with you when we're with the others. They're too full of nonsense.'

She slipped her free arm through his and exerted a gentle pressure to draw him into walking with her.

'Now we haven't a deal of time, Captain Preseley. So please begin.'

Jack's doubts about what he was doing had been somewhat soothed by Amy telling him that Anthony knew she had come in search of him. And he was relieved at the absence of flirtatiousness.

They strolled slowly arm in arm, and she asked questions, and he answered. They discussed points, and stated opinions. His enthusiasm for what he had to say was kindled by her obvious interest, and he spoke at length and fluently. He found himself impressed by her intelligence and was utterly charmed by her gravity of manner. The depth of character that he had thought she possessed she now displayed in full measure and beyond, and his respect for her qualities of shrewdness and understanding burgeoned immeasurably.

By the time they rejoined the group at the clubhouse, Amy's objective of enslaving Jack Preseley was all but gained. She sensed that she had almost succeeded, and savoured her triumph.

She noted the jealous frown on Anthony's face when he saw her coming back arm in arm with Preseley, and this increased her pleasure. She suddenly felt an all-encompassing scorn for the male sex.

How stupid they all are. They pride themselves on their physical and mental superiority to we women, and yet they are really only overgrown babies.

She glanced at the other men in the party, and was secretly thrilled to know that she held the two most attractive men present in emotional thrall. She felt immeasurably strong and confident, and with malicious glee promised herself that she would make both of her lovers become even more subjugated to her imperious will.

Chapter Nineteen

Clement Hulme's sense of happy anticipation of what the afternoon was to bring was rudely shattered when Josie did not come to the Sunday School. His first impulse was to rush down to her home and find out why she was not here at the chapel. But he knew that if he deviated so dramatically from his usual routine by cancelling the class, then the children would go home and tell their parents, and their parents would wonder what the matter was, and tongues would wag. So he led the children through their prayers and hymns and Bible readings, and grimly restrained his ever-increasing impatience. He was continually tormented by his own imagination picturing Josie and William Barton together, walking arm in arm through the meadows that surrounded the town. He pictured them talking and laughing, kissing and caressing, lying locked in each other's embrace, their naked bodies writhing in sexual passion. The vivid images caused him to scowl fiercely, and he began to sweat heavily. With a sickening shock he realised that the children were staring at him with wide eyes, made nervous by his strange manner.

He pulled out his voluminous handkerchief and mopped his streaming forehead, then forced a sickly grin as he reassured them, 'It's this heat. It's making me feel quite giddy.'

They appeared to accept his explanation, but as the afternoon went on he continually sensed their covert, wondering glances.

Time passed with a grinding slowness, and when the moment came to dismiss the class he breathed a sigh of heartfelt relief.

He locked the door behind him, and stood for a moment mentally debating whether to go back to his home and collect his pony and trap to make the journey to Josie's house. He decided against that course of action. He would draw less attention to himself from any passers-by if he were on foot.

The heat of the afternoon was intense, the pitiless rays of the sun melting the tarmac of the recently gravelled road and blasting against the red-brick walls of the buildings. The streets were strangely quiet and deserted, and the only living thing Hulme could see was a stray dog lying panting in a shadowed corner. Before he had walked many yards his body was wet with sweat, and he could feel his stiffly starched high collar becoming soggy and wilting. He was tempted to take off his thick serge jacket, but immediately dismissed that fleeting temptation. A man in his position could not risk being seen walking along the public highway in his shirtsleeves.

At the bottom of Beoley Road some boys were playing in the river, jumping from the footbridge into the water, shouting and splashing each other.

Hulme wished that he too could dive into the water, and let its cool flow lave the sweat from his body. A memory surfaced in his mind of how when he was a boy he had enjoyed such carefree sport. Sad regret momentarily overwhelmed him as he tried to remember, and failed to recall, the last occasion he had laughed as joyfully as these naked urchins were laughing.

He was surprised when a stranger opened the door of the Kitson house.

'Yes?' Mrs Harold peered questioningly at him.

'I, errr . . . I called to see Mrs Kitson,' He fumbled for an explanation. 'I'm an elder of her chapel.'

'You aren't heard then,' the woman stated, and there was a note of indignation in her voice, as if he was somehow at fault.

'Heard what?' he asked.

'Mrs Kitson's been took badly. Her's had a stroke.'

'Oh!' He could think of nothing to say in immediate response.

'Josie's sleeping. The poor wench has bin up all night with her mam. I doon't want to wake her. You'd best call some other time.'

The woman made as if to close the door.

'No, wait!' Hulme's dismay at being balked from seeing Josie caused him to cry out and press his hand against the door

196

to prevent it closing. 'Perhaps I should see Mrs Kitson. Comfort her with a prayer,' he improvised desperately. 'Or read her the word of God.'

'The doctor says that her's not to be disturbed.' Mrs Harold's expression brooked no argument. 'Not by nobody.'

'But I'm an elder of her chapel,' Hulme protested, 'and it's . . .'

'Look, mister, whoever you am it doon't make any difference. The doctor says her's not to be disturbed. Now I'se got to goo back and sit with her. I can't stay here arguing wi' you.'

By sheer force she pushed the door against his restraining hand until it was nearly closed.

Hulme reluctantly accepted defeat, knowing that he could not afford to create a scene. 'Very well then. But will you tell Miss Kitson that I called?'

Mrs Harold nodded brusquely, and the door snapped shut.

Hulme realised that the woman had not asked him his name, and he bent to push open the letterbox and call through its elongated slot.

'Tell her Clement Hulme called. Tell her Clement Hulme was here.'

His only answer was the hollow clumping of the woman's feet mounting the staircase.

'God damn and blast you, you ignorant, miserable bitch!' he snarled in fury, and reluctantly turned and trudged back along the way he had come.

From behind the net curtain of her bedroom Josie watched him go, and sighed with heartfelt relief.

Mrs Harold poked her head around the bedroom door and whispered hoarsely, 'Theer, I soon sent him packing, didn't I just?'

She radiated satisfaction. Mrs Harold didn't like men.

'Thank you, Mrs Harold.' Josie was truly grateful. 'I just couldn't receive any visitors now, not the way I'm feeling.'

'Nor you shan't have to, my duck. Not while I'm here at any rate,' Mrs Harold promised, and then went back to sit at the bedside of the sick woman.

Josie remained motionless, and thought sombrely that at least some good had come of her mother's stroke. It had served to shield her from Clement Hulme, for this day at least.

Chapter Twenty

William Barton arrived at the Orchard Street building site at half past six on Monday morning. The roaring of his motorcycle brought a couple of curious faces to the windows of the houses opposite the site, but there were no other signs of life in the street.

William took off his goggles and leather riding coat and laid them in the sidecar, then turned his peaked cap the correct way around on his head and walked slowly along the length of the half-built row of houses. The sun had already risen above the eastern horizon and its rays were striking diamond glints from the dew which covered the bricks and scaffolding. William breathed in the smells of damp clay and wood and experienced a keen sense of anticipation for the coming day. He felt fresh and alert, and very happy.

Now he smiled to himself as he thought of the reason for his happiness, and pictured Josie lying asleep in her bed, or rising with tousled hair and sleep-flushed cheeks. His smile broadened and he felt like singing. He had often wondered what it was like to be in love, and now he knew. It was the most marvellous feeling he had ever known. He felt like a youth again, and was ready to slay dragons for the woman he loved. He was determined to make her proud of him. This job his father had given him was to be the stepping stone to greater things. No matter that he knew nothing about the building trade, and had never had the slightest interest in it. Things were different now. He had found a purpose in life, and all his previous failures were to be put behind him. This was the new beginning which would lead to success. He sighed with contentment as he visualised Josie's features, and murmured her name aloud.

There was movement further down the street, and William

saw the stocky, bowler-hatted figure of Charlie Spicer hurrying towards him.

'Is anything the matter, Mr Barton?' the man asked anxiously as he panted to a standstill.

'No, Spicer, not as far as I know.' William smiled. Such was his mood that he found even the weatherbeaten ugliness of the man before him appealing. 'I'm to take charge of the site.'

Charlie Spicer caught his breath in sudden fear, and blurted, 'Am I getting the sack then?'

'No, of course not.' William felt the impulse to make a friend of this man, and explained, 'My father wants me to learn this business, and who better to teach me than you, Spicer? So, until I know enough to take charge, you'll still oversee the job.' He chuckled wryly. 'I shall be in the position of your apprentice.'

Spicer assimilated what he was hearing, and his expression was stolid and unrevealing. But inwardly he was fiercely resentful, and told himself, Oh yes. That's the way the land lies, is it? I'm to teach this bugger enough to run this site, and then I'll be sent up the fuckin' road when he's got no more use for me.

He was strongly tempted to tell William Barton exactly what he could do with this new apprenticeship arrangement. But that moment of rebellion passed in a flash. Harsh necessity dictated his acceptance. He forced a grudging smile, and though sullenly cursing in his mind, told Barton, 'I'm sure I'm honoured to have you being my apprentice, Mr Barton.'

'Good man.' William clapped the other's shoulder. 'Well then, let's begin my education, shall we?'

Spicer led the way to the shed which served as the site office and unlocked it. Inside he took out the ledgers in which were entered all deliveries, hours worked and other details appertaining to the site, and began to explain their contents to William Barton.

Just before seven o'clock the workmen began to arrive: bricklayers, carpenters, plumbers, plasterers, labourers and youthful trainees and apprentices. William told Spicer to gather all of the work force in a group in front of the site office shed, and when the foreman had done so he addressed them himself.

He felt no diffidence or uncertainty as he faced them.

Despite his genuine sympathy and concern for the poorer classes, William could never have accepted any one of them as an equal. After all, he had been born and bred to be a gentleman, and it was a gentleman's place to command, and the lower classes' place to obey.

His eyes moved across the faces of the men and youths before him. Some were unshaven and grimy, others bleary-eyed from drink, others clear-eyed and clean. All stared at him with undisguised curiosity.

He spoke with immense confidence and surety. 'I'm known to you all, I believe. From now on I am taking charge of this site. I shall say nothing about the disgraceful happenings of the other day. You have all been granted a fresh start, so to speak. But I expect you to work hard and well. If I am not satisfied with any man or boy here, then he will be immediately given the sack. Any problems that may arise or any queries you may have will be directed in the first place to Mr Spicer. Now, is there anyone who wishes to ask me anything?'

Blank faces and silence greeted his question, and after a pause he dismissed them.

'Very well, get on with your work.'

He spoke directly to the foreman. 'Spicer, as soon as the work is underway, you will return here to me.'

The men dispersed, and only when they had moved some distance from the shed did they begin to talk excitedly among themselves.

William returned inside the shed, and seating himself on the tall stool at the high desk, bent his head over the ledgers once more. He felt elated, and wished that Josie could have seen him asserting his command over the men. For perhaps the hundredth time he wondered at her absence from yesterday's parade. He had searched eagerly for her in the passing ranks of schoolchildren, and had been bitterly disappointed at not seeing her. But now he smiled to himself. He would be seeing her this very evening, and in his case her absence yesterday had definitely made his heart grow fonder.

Out on the site some of the older tradesmen were jeering at Charlie Spicer, the younger workers, the labourers and the youths listening with immense enjoyment.

'That's it then, is it, Charlie, you'm gooing up the road shortly?'

'No I'm not,' he asserted furiously. 'I'm just showing him the ropes, that's all.'

'It's because you was fritted of Alfie Payne, you know, Charlie. That's why you'm getting your sack.'

'I'm fritted o' no fucker!' Spicer's weathered features were purpling with suppressed rage which he dared not give vent to.

The older tradesmen were the aristocrats of the site, and in such a transient industry as building, where most men moved continuously from site to site, being employed for the length of the contract only, many of them had also been site foremen in their time, and would very likely be foremen again in the future. Charlie Spicer knew that if he ever lost his present job he would undoubtedly be dependent on the goodwill of one or another of these men to find work at his own trade of bricklayer. So although he could bully and browbeat the less experienced tradesmen and the labourers and youths, he could not afford to antagonise these older, highly experienced men.

'You'm fritted o' Colonel Barton, Charlie, and that's plain to see. You'd tell him to fuck off else.'

'Why should I tell him that?' Spicer demanded.

'Well, he's making a right idiot out o' you, aren't he? Putting his bloody son in charge here. Willie Barton doon't know his arse from his elbow, does he? He's never worked on the buildings in his fuckin' life.'

'Neither has his old man, come to that,' put in a grizzle-headed carpenter, wearing the huge-pocketed brown apron of his trade. 'The old man's only a bloody speculator. This is his fust contract, aren't it?'

'Well, Len, it don't really matter how many contracts the old sod's done, does it?' one of the bricklayers chuckled grimly. 'He's the bugger whose paying the wages on this 'un, aren't he? And there aren't a deal o' work hereabouts. Look at all the good tradesmen in this town who'm out o' work.'

Charlie Spicer was quick to seize upon this timely reminder of how much unemployment currently existed in the building industry.

'You'm right theer, Tom. Theer's a good many blokes who're just itching to jump into our shoes on this job. So

let's get to work, shall us? Afore that bastard comes out o'
the bloody office and sends some of us up the bloody road.'

The group of men separated, and within scant minutes work
was in progress all along the site.

Chapter Twenty-One

During the course of Sunday and Monday, Dorothy Kitson remained comatose, her laboured breathing slow and stertorous, her cheeks puffing out with each expiration. The doctor, Eamon Sinclair, came at three o'clock on the Monday afternoon. He was youthful in appearance, clean-shaven, and wearing small, round-rimmed spectacles. His manner was aggressively abrupt. When he entered the stuffy bedroom he frowned and told Josie, 'You must open the window, Miss Kitson. Fresh air is always beneficial.'

His frown deepened as he pulled back the bedclothes from the sick woman and found the hot water bottle which Mrs Harold had placed at Dorothy's feet.

With an angry exclamation he removed the rag-swathed earthenware bottle and challenged, 'Who put this here?'

'My neighbour.' Josie was flustered. 'She says it's necessary when someone has had a stroke to keep their feet warm.'

'It's an old wives' tale. A complete nonsense! Only fools give it any credence,' he snapped contemptuously.

His rudeness roused Josie's resentment, but she accepted that he must know better than she, and made no protest.

'Has your mother regained consciousness at all?' he wanted to know.

She shook her head, and then qualified, 'At least not while I've been watching her. But my neighbour thought that Mother almost woke while she was sitting with her.'

'Was that today or yesterday?'

Josie could only shrug helplessly in reply. 'It was today. But I'm not sure of the hour. I presume it was during the late morning.'

'To presume is not good enough, Miss Kitson,' he snorted

205

in disgust. 'In medicine we need facts, not presumptions.'

Bending over Dorothy Kitson he pulled up her closed eyelids, then ran his hands down her arms and legs. Turning again to Josie, he asked, 'There has been incontinence of faeces and urine, I take it?'

'Yes. We washed and changed her an hour since. But she's only passing urine now, and not a great deal.'

He nodded, and then instructed, 'I'll need your assistance to turn her on her side for a moment.'

Together they levered the heavy, flaccid body over, and Sinclair lifted the long white nightdress to briefly stare at the massive buttocks. The skin was badly discoloured in one area, and indicating this, the doctor told Josie, 'Acute decubitus. It would be best if she were admitted to hospital.'

When Josie made no immediate answer he stared quizzically at her, and after they had laid Dorothy back into her original position questioned, 'Do you understand the term "acute decubitus", Miss Kitson?'

Josie nodded. 'Yes. It means bedsores, I believe.'

'Exactly so. And those bedsores can break out within hours, as can other serious trophic changes in the condition of the skin. Are you a subscriber to Smallwood Hospital, Miss Kitson?'

'No.'

He pursed his lips judiciously. 'That's unfortunate. It means that you'll have to pay for your mother's admittance and treatment.'

Josie felt a burgeoning embarrassment as she was forced to admit, 'I haven't the money to pay for hospitalisation, Doctor.'

He gestured as if in dismissal. 'It's no matter, Miss Kitson. As a schoolteacher you must surely know a subscriber who can issue you with a governor's ticket for admittance.' He paused, and, as if recognising that people such as the Kitson family would regard using a governor's ticket as being branded as paupers, went on in a kindlier tone. 'To make use of a governor's ticket is no cause for shame, Miss Kitson. There are a great many worthy and respectable families in this town whose names are on the subscribers' charity lists.'

Behind her impassive mask Josie was being racked by an inner conflict. On the one hand she wanted her mother to

206

have the professional care and attention she would receive in hospital. On the other hand, if her mother were to be removed from this house, then Josie's protective shield would go with her. While she had her mother here to be cared for, then she possessed the means to keep Clement Hulme at bay. If her mother was in the hospital, how would she be able to fend off Hulme without precipitating a confrontation between herself and the man which might end in a terrible denouement.

Coming to a decision, she drew a deep breath and informed Sinclair, 'I shall care for my mother myself, Doctor. She would want to remain here in her own home.'

He stared at her incredulously. 'She should go into the hospital, Miss Kitson. You have obviously no conception of how she must be cared for, or what that care entails. Otherwise you would obtain a governor's ticket.'

For the first time since his arrival Josie allowed her resentful irritation to show itself. She shook her head and snapped curtly, 'Thank you, Doctor, but my mother will remain here in her own home, and I shall care for her. So would you please have the courtesy to stop addressing me as if I were the village idiot. If you will have the goodness to explain what I must do for my mother, then I shall carry out that treatment. If you are not prepared to explain these matters to me, then I shall buy a handbook of nursing and find out from that what it is I must do.'

For an instant he seemed about to explode with anger, his eyes firing behind the rounded lenses of his spectacles. Then, to her surprise, he sighed heavily, and his whole demeanour altered radically. Now he spoke to her in gentle, apologetic tones.

'Please forgive me, Miss Kitson. I've been behaving towards you with unpardonable rudeness, haven't I?'

'Yes, you have indeed,' she told him forthrightly.

His thin face suddenly appeared to be that of a chastened boy, and with a shock Josie realised how young he actually was. Curiously she asked, 'How long have you been in practice, Dr Sinclair?'

He grinned shamefacedly. 'Six months, Miss Kitson. I joined Dr Protheroe six months ago.'

She could not help being sarcastic. 'I suppose six months is little enough time to acquire a pleasant bedside manner.'

He actually blushed, and she felt an instant remorse, and in her turn apologised.

'I'm sorry, Doctor, I shouldn't have said that.'

'No, don't apologise, Miss Kitson, I deserved it.'

Josie could think of nothing else to say but 'Perhaps you'd care for a cup of tea, Doctor?'

He eagerly seized the proffered olive branch.

'Yes, Miss Kitson. I'd like that very much. Very much indeed.'

He looked again at Dorothy, and said, 'She'll be all right to be left for a little while.'

Downstairs he sat at the table in the living room, writing with a stub of pencil upon a sheet of foolscap paper while Josie brewed a pot of tea, and arranged some biscuits on a plate.

When Josie rejoined him they sat sipping their cups of tea, and he ate some biscuits with every appearance of gusto. Then he handed the sheet of paper to her.

'Do you have a thermometer, Miss Kitson?'

'Yes.'

'Very well.' His manner became sombre. 'I am going to be completely honest with you. It is my diagnosis that your mother has suffered a severe intracerebral haemorrhage. In the old days it was known as apoplexy.' He paused, as if reluctant to continue, and she urged him to go on.

'Please, Doctor, I want to know the worst. I assure you that I shan't faint or have an attack of hysteria.'

A bleak smile touched his lips, and he nodded. 'Very well, Miss Kitson. On that sheet of paper I have noted my diagnosis and prognosis of your mother's case. If there is any marked deviance from that prognosis then you must send for me immediately, is that understood?'

He waited for her agreement to this, which she readily gave him. Then he went on, 'I have diagnosed that she has suffered a right-sided cerebral lesion. This means that her left side is paralysed. To be precise, the lower left part of her face, left arm and leg. The muscles of the upper part of her trunk and face may also be greatly weakened. If she recovers consciousness then she will very probably also have aphasia, difficulty in formulating speech. It's possible that she will have her head turned to her paralysed side, and also be suffering conjugate deviation . . .'

Josie frowned in puzzlement at this last, and Sinclair smiled sympathetically and explained, 'Her eyes will also be turned in that direction.'

He paused again, as if to give emphasis to his next words. 'Now you must listen very carefully, Miss Kitson. Your mother's temperature is subnormal at this moment. If the effusion of blood into her brain from the lesion continues, then her coma will deepen, her temperature will remain subnormal, and death will supervene in a matter of days. But I do not expect that will be the case. I am confident that your mother will survive. I expect that within two or three days there will occur inflammatory changes around the lesion, her temperature will rise and her pulse beat will accelerate. She may well become delirious at this stage. Following this a gradual recovery will ensue.'

Josie was completely engrossed, her eyes fixed upon his face, and he found himself thinking that although plain, she possessed a certain feminine appeal. Then, castigating himself for this momentary lapse from professional detachment, he went on rapidly.

'I've also noted the nursing treatment, as you see, Miss Kitson. It's very straightforward really. You must keep her in bed in the recumbent position with her head raised. Absolute quiet is necessary, and she should be moved as little as possible until the acute symptoms have subsided. I've recommended that she be given a calomel purge every thirty-six hours. And if her temperature drops you may apply a hot water bottle to her feet.'

At this juncture he had the grace to look shamefaced, and to admit, 'I know, I know, Miss Kitson. I said it was an old wives' tale, did I not? But it is only to be used if her temperature drops sharply.

'No stimulants must be administered. Sponge her mouth with fresh water at frequent intervals, and try to get her to sip water also. When her temperature rises, you may apply ice bags to her head to cool her. And while she remains comatose you must keep a careful watch on her incontinence. If there is any sign of urine retention, then you must send for me immediately. I may well have to perform catheterisation. As recovery begins I shall instruct you about the further treatment you must give her.'

He laid his hands palms downwards on the table and pushed himself to his feet.

'Very well, Miss Kitson. I shall leave you to the discharge of your duties. I'll call again later in the week.'

She saw him to the front door, and before leaving he shook her hand and told her, 'Look, Miss Kitson, if you should change your mind about having your mother admitted to the hospital, then I myself will arrange for a governor's ticket to be issued to you.'

'Thank you very much, Doctor, but I really do prefer to care for my mother here,' she answered.

When he had gone, she closed the door behind him, and leaned back against it. Already doubts as to the wisdom of what she was doing were clamouring in her mind. Guilt assailed her.

Perhaps I should get her admitted to hospital. What if she dies because I've kept her here?

She experienced an overwhelming urge to fling open the door and run shouting after Dr Sinclair. She turned and took hold of the doorknob. Then an image of Clement Hulme's face entered her mind, and stayed her hand. She heard the back door opening and the voice of Mrs Harold calling, and she let her hand fall to her side, and went to greet the woman.

It was half past six in the evening when William Barton parked his motorcycle and sidecar outside the gate of the Kitson home. All day long he had been eagerly anticipating seeing Josie, and now, after depositing his leather coat, cap and goggles in the sidecar, he hurried up the front path.

When she opened the door to him he was shocked to see how pale and drawn her features were, and he demanded anxiously, 'What's the matter, Josie? Are you ill?'

She took his hand and drew him into the house, explaining rapidly what had happened to her mother.

He pondered for a short while on what she had told him, then suggested tentatively, 'Perhaps it might be best for your mother to go into hospital, Josie.'

She shook her head and her expression was stubborn. 'No,

210

William. I know my mother's character. She would hate having to be under the care of strangers. I shall look after her here, in her own home.'

His fine eyes became troubled, and he said diffidently, 'Forgive me if I seem to be prying, Josie. I do not intend any offence by it. But how will you manage for money if you are not able to go to your work? You'll need to buy medicines, and also you'll need someone to help you nurse your mother. You can't do it all by yourself.'

The same thought had already occurred to Josie, and she had made a decision about that point.

'I've a little money put by,' she told him quietly. 'And my mother has some savings of her own, which I shall make use of if it becomes necessary.'

'Let me help you,' he requested eagerly. 'I can well afford it.'

She frowned and shook her head in emphatic refusal. 'Many thanks for your kindness, William, but that is out of the question. I can manage perfectly well.'

He misunderstood her motivation for refusing, and said hurriedly, 'But it wouldn't be charity, Josie. If you wish we can call it a loan.'

'No! No matter what term is used, it would still be charity, and I'll never accept that.' She spoke more sharply than she intended, and chided herself when she saw the hurt in his dark eyes. She reached out and took his hand between hers, and went on in a gentle tone, 'Please don't think that I'm not truly grateful for your offer, William. I am grateful for it, but I must manage this trouble by myself.'

He experienced a surge of loving admiration for her courage and pride, and impelled by an irresistable urge he bent forward and kissed her mouth.

The tender touch of his lips, so different from the brutal greed of Clement Hulme's kisses, sent a shivering delight through Josie's body, and she responded, moving close against him, her fingers caressing his shoulders and neck and running through his hair.

They stood entwined for long, long minutes, and as their kisses lengthened Josie felt her sexual passion exploding. The need for physical loving that Clement Hulme had awakened

211

within her had now become focused on this man who held her tightly in his arms, and she moulded her body to his, pressing her breasts and belly hard against him. The warm, clean, masculine scent of his flesh, the hot, sweet taste of his mouth, the feel of his lean, hard body overwhelmed her senses, and from deep in her throat there sounded the yearning moaning of her hungry need. Mindlessly her hands roamed down over his shoulders and back and cupped his taut buttocks. Lost in a private world of sexual hungering she rubbed herself against him.

Then, abruptly, she felt herself pushed back.

William Barton was a virgin who had never had any sexual contact with any woman. He was a romantic, whose dreams of love were poetical. The woman he had longed for, the idealised creature whom he had prayed he would one day find, was a creation of his own fancy, pictured in the poems he had read, fashioned from his own lack of actual physical experience with women. Of course he had experienced sexual desires throughout his youth and manhood. But the crudities and obscenities of other men's stories about their sexual conquests he had always found repellent. For him love was to be a spiritual, almost chaste relationship. Romantic kisses, entwined hands, a purity of thought and feeling. The thought of a woman possessing sexual desires and needs revulsed him. He envisaged the sexual relationship between man and wife as being ordained primarily for procreation, and secondarily to serve a man's need for release, which the woman endured because it was her ordained duty towards her husband. William Barton was a celibate prude.

Now he was shocked by Josie's reaction to his kisses.

Josie seemed dazed as she opened her eyes, and she stared at him in puzzlement.

'What is it, darling?' Her feverish need for his loving drove her to try and embrace him once more, and misunderstanding his reaction, she smiled and whispered huskily, 'You don't have to worry, darling. I want you to make love to me.'

He shook his head as if in bewilderment. 'But's it's wrong!'

'No,' she protested. 'It's not wrong, because we love each other.'

'But we're not yet married.' Now unbidden thoughts were

swarming to torment him, and he stared at her with suspicion, as the unthinkable forced itself into his mind. 'Have you?' he blurted out, then abruptly shook his head and closed his mouth, not daring to ask the question.

Her eyes were wide and uncertainty flickered in their depths. A sudden crushing sense of fearful guilt assailed her as she sensed what he was suspecting. For some moments she stayed silent as inner conflict raged. Then she summoned all her resolution, drew a long quavering breath, and told him, 'I'm not a virgin, William. I've known a man's body.'

His mouth dropped open in shock, and seeing his reaction she reached out to him. He cried out as if in distress, and roughly struck her hands aside, then thrust her away so hard that she almost lost her balance.

She shook her head in utter dismay, and begged him, 'Please, William, I've only ever known one man, and then only for a short while. I never loved him. I love you. I love you.'

He was staring at her in horrified disgust.

Alarm widened her eyes. 'Forgive me. Please forgive me!' she pleaded.

His features twitched in erratic spasms, and he blurted, 'You're nothing but a prostitute!' Then turned and without another word blundered from the house.

Josie remained motionless as the motorcycle's roar diminished and died away.

She felt stunned.

She seemed to hear his words repeating over and over in her brain: You're nothing but a prostitute! You're nothing but a prostitute! A prostitute, a prostitute, a prostitute . . .

She clapped her hands over her ears, as if by doing so she could shut out that accusing voice, but still it reverberated inside her head: . . . a prostitute, prostitute, prostitute, prostitute, prostitute . . .

Her stunned mortification was being rapidly overwhelmed by a terrible sense of shame and self-disgust. She felt degraded, soiled beyond all measure. She remained standing motionless in the quiet room and all awareness of time and place deserted her. Unable to move, unable to think, silent tears trickled down her cheeks as she was held entrapped in a mental prison of misery.

The minutes passed and lengthened into hours, and still she stood motionless, and then strange sounds began to penetrate her consciousness. Guttural moaning cries that sounded like an animal suffering the agonies of hell.

Josie shuddered, and the guttural cries suddenly dinned deafeningly into her ears, as the invisible bondage that had enveloped her senses abruptly dissolved and set her free. Fear struck through her as she realised that it was her mother who was venting the terrible moans, and she rushed up the stairs and into the bedroom.

Dorothy Kitson's eyes were bulging with terror, her right arm waving desperately in the air, her distorted mouth gaping, streaming with saliva which glistened upon her chin and the folds of her fat neck. Her body was jerking and heaving as she tried to lift herself upright, and all the time the dreadful sounds of anguished horror gouted from deep in her throat.

At first the sight of her mother filled Josie with fear and repulsion. But then she saw the terror in her mother's eyes, and pity filled her. A pity so intense, so all-encompassing that it overwhelmed her own anguish and drove her pain back from the forefront of her mind. She moved forward and wrapped her arms around the other woman, and crooned soothingly to her.

'There now, Mam . . . there now . . . Don't be afraid . . . don't be afraid . . . I'll look after you . . . Don't be afraid, Mam, I'll take care of you . . . Don't be afraid . . . Please don't be afraid . . .'

Very gradually the terrible moaning quietened and ceased, and the frantic heavings of the crippled body lessened and stilled.

Still cradling her mother in her arms, Josie talked gently to her, reassuring her over and over again that she would care for her. That she would nurse her back to health. That she would not leave her, or allow her to be taken away from her own home. And as Josie comforted the old woman, so her own tearing anguish became somehow easier to bear, and she could feel deep within herself the first faint stirrings of a stubborn determination to face whatever the future might hold for her.

Chapter Twenty-Two

After two weeks of caring single-handedly for her mother, Josie Kitson was feeling both mentally and physically exhausted. She had not anticipated the sheer muscular strength needed to move the old woman's partially paralysed body when she needed to change her bedding, to wash her, to dress her in clean nightclothes.

Since Dorothy had not yet regained control of her bladder and bowel movements, Josie used a rubber covering to shield the flock mattress, but it was still necessary to change the soiled sheets and blankets every day. The ceaseless laundering became a nightmarish slavery. The wash house at the rear of the kitchen was always filled with steam from the constantly boiling copper, its floors awash and its walls and ceiling dripping with condensation. The damp penetrated into the main rooms of the house, creating a musty, moist atmosphere.

The old woman was a terrible patient. When Josie had to move her for any reason, she would slaver like a rabid animal and strike at her daughter with her usable hand. She was not able to speak clearly, but she could screech, and throughout the days and nights, at frequent intervals, she would begin caterwauling until Josie came to her bedside. Josie had not been able to get a single unbroken night's sleep, and every waking hour it seemed that she must attend to her mother's ceaseless demands.

During the first few days Mrs Harold had sometimes come in to help Josie, but at her advanced age the effort was too much for her, and now she rarely appeared. Josie had employed a nurse, who had only lasted one night. She had left telling Josie bluntly that her mother was an impossible patient to care for, and should be put into a special hospital as quickly as possible.

Josie struggled on alone, stubbornly determined that she

215

would not surrender and take the advice of others by having her mother committed to the care of strangers. But the strain was cumulative and now she was having to force her exhausted body and brain to continue, and was fast nearing the limits of her endurance.

It was Sunday afternoon, and she was in the wash house using a wooden dolly to pound the soiled bedding in the boiling, bubbling copper. Sweat dripped from her face and chin and ran into her eyes, causing them to sting sharply. The pain heightened her sense of depression and she was filled with a consciousness of bitter injustice. All the miserable events of her life seemed to pass in procession through her mind, and it seemed that only an eternity of gloom stretched before her. She stepped back from the steaming copper to wipe her eyes, blinking to clear her blurred sight, and was completely unaware of the man standing in the doorway behind her. When he spoke her name she cried out in startled fright and turned to confront Clement Hulme.

'What are you doing here? How did you get in?' she demanded.

'I knocked on the front door for a long time.' He gave her a placatory smile. 'And then I came round to the back here. I'm sorry if I frightened you, I didn't mean to.'

The memory of how he had added to her miseries now goaded her into sudden anger.

'I don't want you here,' she told him sharply.

She paused as if inviting his departure, but when he made no reply, only stared at her beseechingly, she snapped, 'It's all over between us. I mean it, Clem. You can threaten to tell everyone about us if you like, but it makes no difference to me any more. I don't care what you do, or who you tell. I just want you gone from my house.'

An unfamiliar emotion was insidiously invading Clement Hulme as he stood staring at her drawn face. She looked utterly spent, huge black shadows ringed her eyes, and her clothing was disarranged and bedraggled, in stark contrast to her normal pristine neatness.

He had spent the previous weeks in a fever of sexual desire, thinking about her constantly, unable to sleep at night because of his intense frustrations, and suffering torments of jealousy

216

as he imagined her to be with William Barton. Driven beyond endurance, he had come here today determined to possess her once more. Yet now, finding her so harassed and tired and unhappy, his sexual longing was in retreat as a sincere concern for her advanced to replace it.

Pity was a rare emotion for him to feel, and at first he could not fully understand what it was that was happening within him. So he stood silent, trying to comprehend this new sensation.

Josie's sudden anger passed as quickly as it had arisen to be overlaid by self-disgust that she could have behaved so squalidly with this man before her.

It's all my own fault, she admitted to herself. It's my shame, not his.

Then, from upstairs, the summons of her mother screeching like a frantic beast acted as the final goad to Josie's overwrought nerves, and she burst into tears of despair.

Seeing her break down like this impelled Clement Hulme to step towards her with outstretched arms.

'No! Don't touch me!' she shouted at him, and violently struck out at his seeking hands.

'You don't understand!' he said desperately. 'I only want to help you.' A pleading note entered his voice. 'Let me help you, Josie. Please . . .'

Dorothy Kitson's screeching seemed to grow louder and louder, and Josie's brain whirled dizzyingly so that she feared she was going insane.

Clement suddenly gripped her arm and by sheer force pulled her out into the garden at the rear of the house. Here the screeching that was so unbearable indoors lost its piercing, nerve-lacerating edge.

'You stay out here,' the man instructed firmly. 'I'll go up and see to your mother.'

Before she could make any protest he had disappeared indoors, and brief moments later the screeching halted abruptly.

The sensation of relief was so acute that Josie experienced intense gratitude towards the man who had brought about the cessation of that terrible noise.

After some time he came out to her once more, and smiled.

'Your mother was so shocked to see me that she shut up as I came through the door of her bedroom. There was nothing the

217

matter with her, as far as I could see. I've been talking to her and she's much calmer now.'

Josie's strained nerves still kept her tense and on edge.

Hulme studied her briefly, then instructed, 'You sit yourself down on that bench beneath the tree there. I'm going to make you a cup of tea, and then I'm going to finish the washing for you. When I've done that I shall go upstairs and sit with your mother. Why don't you try to have a nap, you look worn out.'

Her eyes widened in disbelief that she was hearing these words. She could not accept this sudden transformation of personality.

Once more he took her arm, and this time she did not fight against him but allowed herself to be led to the crude wooden bench beneath the old apple tree.

He stood before her and said in a low voice, without any trace of his normal bombast, 'You need a true friend, Josie. So please give me the chance to be that friend to you.'

She stared at him with doubt in her eyes and in her heart. But at this moment she felt so utterly weary in body and spirit that she could not bring herself to make any protest. All she wanted was to be left to sit here in this shaded spot, and find healing solace in the warm, sunlit peace of the garden.

He brewed a pot of tea, and carried a cup out to her, then once more left her alone.

He removed his jacket, rolled up his shirtsleeves, and went into the wash house, where he began to plunge the dolly into the mass of bedding in the copper.

Later he carried the bedding out to the garden and hung it on the clothes line.

Josie was lying back against the curved trunk of the tree, her eyes closed, sleeping peacefully.

He stood staring at her and the pulsing lust for her began to engulf him once again. But now there was a different quality intermingled with that fierce sexual wanting. He felt stirrings of tenderness towards her which he had never previously experienced.

Am I properly in love with her? he asked himself wonderingly. Is this how it feels when you love a woman, apart from just wanting to have sex with her?

Hulme had never really known what it was to love any

woman. Certainly he had never romantically loved his wife. Nor any of the other women he had felt sexually attracted towards in his past.

He thought jealously about William Barton, and burned with the need to know how that man's relationship with Josie now stood. Above all else, one determination was paramount in his mind. He intended to have Josie solely for himself. He could no longer tolerate the thought of any other man being in her life, and he was ready to do anything that he must to achieve that goal.

In his agile mind he had already perceived how he could bind her to him. How he could win her trust and draw her into a dependency upon him.

She stirred and muttered in her sleep, and he quickly moved away from her and back into the house, his instincts warning him that if she was to wake up and find him standing watching her, then this present precarious and very uncertain re-establishment in her life would be irretrievably lost.

He pulled on his jacket and went upstairs.

Propped up on pillows Dorothy Kitson's grotesquely misshapen face turned jerkily towards him as he entered her bedroom, tears leaking from her left eye and a string of saliva running from the twisted corner of her mouth.

He smiled unctuously and seated himself on the chair at her bedside. Using his handkerchief he gently wiped dry her flaccid cheek and hanging jowls. Then, taking her paralysed hand in his he said softly, 'Now, Sister Dorothy, let you and I seek the guidance and help of the Lord . . . Let us pray . . .'

Down in the garden Josie again stirred and muttered, as if a dream were making her uneasy.

Chapter Twenty-Three

Alfred Payne came reluctantly awake, his head throbbing, his mouth painfully dry, his eyes bloodshot and sore. He groaned aloud and shifted to lie on his back, then levered himself upright on his elbows. The throbbing in his head became a pounding, and his sight swam giddily. He dropped back and lifted both hands to press hard against the sides of his skull.

Slowly the pounding impacts eased, and when he opened his tight-screwed eyes he was able to focus his sight upon the cracks of the stained ceiling plaster. He listened hard, and from the room below there came the faint sounds of whispering voices, and the rustle of cautious movement.

'Bring us a drink,' he shouted. His tongue felt stiff and thick and the words were all but unintelligible.

There came a sudden exclamation of alarm from below, and a louder rustling of movement. Then Marie called nervously up the stairs.

'Are you awake, Uncle Alfred?'

'O' course I bleedin' well am,' he grunted. 'Bring us a drink, 'ull you.'

Within seconds the girl was offering him a cracked mug filled with water. 'There's no tea made, Uncle Alfred. And I couldn't find any beer,' she explained hastily.

Cautiously he once more levered himself upright, scowling as the pains in his head momentarily intensified. Then he took the mug from her outstretched hands and greedily swallowed the musty-tasting liquid. He drained the mug with quick, slobbering gulps, water running from the corners of his mouth and down his thickly stubbled chin and throat, and the girl's eyes filled with repulsion as she watched.

He held the empty mug towards her, and grunted, 'Fetch us another.'

When she reappeared he drank this one more slowly, and while he drank his bloodshot, red-rimmed eyes stared at her from over the rim of the mug, and there was something in his stare that made her feel very uneasy.

'What time is it?' he wanted to know.

'It's just gone eight o'clock, Uncle. I was getting the kids ready for school.'

His unblinking gaze moved up and down her body, and she shuffled her feet nervously.

He was dressed in a dirty, evil-smelling long-sleeved vest and long underpants. His shirt, trousers and jacket were lying in a heap beside the bed.

'Hand us me trousers,' he ordered gruffly, and when she gave them to him he rummaged in the pockets. To his relief he found some coins and counted them out.

They totalled nearly a shilling. All that was left of the money he had forced his wife to give him from her scant wages.

'Here.' He handed her a sixpence. 'Run down to the corner and fetch me a jug o' beer. And tell Billy Crow I wants it drawn fresh from the barrel. And tell him as well that if he tries to palm me off with any o' them fuckin' stale slops he tries to get rid of, he'll feel the weight o' my fist in his chops.' He growled threateningly into the girl's nervous face. 'You make sure that you tells that humpity-backed bugger exactly what I'se said, does you hear?'

Marie made no answer, only nodded, took the money and fled.

At the beershop the dwarfish, crooked-backed proprietor listened impassively to the message sent to him by Alfred Payne. Then he grinned and winked at the girl.

'Now doon't you moither, my duck, I'll give you the freshest drink I'se got. I 'udn't want that nasty bastard getting riled up with me.'

He served her with a foaming jug of brown beer, and handed her the change from the sixpence. Then he joked, 'I 'ope you wunt drink too much o' that afore you gives it to him, my duck. Else he'll be thinkin' I'se given you short measure.'

She smiled back, grateful for his friendly kindness to her.

As Marie left the shop Billy Crow's blowsy wife came out to join him at the counter, and he jerked his head after the blonde-haired girl, and said feelingly, 'Poor little soul. I 'ope her dad gets out o' the work 'us before there's any harm comes to her from that bastard Payne. I'se heard a couple o' stories about him and young girls.'

The woman frowned and nodded in grim agreement.

When Marie got back to the house the children were still clustered together in the living room, and she placed her finger to her lips for them to stay quiet and avoid provoking their father's anger. Then she took the jug of beer upstairs.

Alfred Payne was sitting up in the bed now, smoking a cigarette. He held out the mug which had contained the water, and she filled it with beer. She would have placed the jug on the floor by the bed, but he frowned and gestured to her to remain standing holding it.

He sucked the beer greedily down his throat, the noise of swallowing clearly audible, and nodded to her to refill the mug. Then, as he took mouthfuls from this fresh drink, and long draws of the cigarette, his eyes once more moved continuously up and down her body and face. There was something in his expression which made her feel nervously embarrassed, and she felt her pale cheeks become hot and flushed.

'You'm a fine big girl for your age, aren't you?' he told her, and his coated tongue curled out from his wet lips to noisily suck the beer froth from his thick, ragged moustache.

Unable to meet his eyes, she bent her head and stared down at the floor, and he grinned wolfishly. He took a long final draw from the stub of his cigarette and tossed it on to the floor at her feet.

'Tread on that!' he ordered, and her foot moved and crunched down upon the glowing stub. His hand slid beneath the bed-clothes and his fingers cupped his testicles and then moved to squeeze and rub his rapidly swelling manhood.

Marie's eyes were still downcast, gazing at the floor, but she could hear his breathing quickening and becoming heavier.

Then she started and cried out in shocked alarm as his hand snaked out to clasp her wrist, and she looked up into his red, sweating face. His mouth was wet and loose, and his eyes were strangely glazed.

'Doon't be feared,' he whispered hoarsely. 'I aren't gooing to hurt you. You be a good girl and do what I wants you to, and I'll give you some sweets.'

She jerked back from him, terror giving her strength, and all but broke free of his grasp.

'Be a good girl,' he whispered urgently, and began to draw her back towards him as she struggled to pull her wrist free.

'It's only me! I'se come for the little 'uns!' Old Mrs Green's cracked voice sounded loudly from below, and Alfred Payne jerked in surprise, and the mug of beer that he was holding in his other hand spilled on to the bed.

'Fuck it!' he swore, then glared warningly at Marie. 'Doon't you move.'

There came the sound of a footstep on the bottom of the staircase, and the old woman called loudly, 'Am you up theer, Marie? I'se come for the little 'uns.'

Again the man swore sibilantly, and then bellowed, 'Her's up here talking to me, Mrs Green. Her 'ull be down in just a tick.'

'Oh, I didn't know you was in, Mr Payne.' The old woman sounded alarmed. 'I didn't mean to give you any shock.'

'That's all right, doon't you worry about it.' Payne sounded almost pleasant. Then he jerked his head at Marie and said loudly, 'Get them kids to school then, my duck.'

He let go of her wrist, and she rubbed the soreness his brutal grip had left on her soft skin.

With a sensation of relief so strong she felt light-headed, Marie rushed down the narrow stairs, and with a frantic haste bustled the elder children out of the house, telling the old woman, 'You see to the little ones then, Mrs Green. I'll collect them from you at the usual time.'

'You'm in a powerful rush, aren't you, girl?' The old woman was quite affronted at Marie's unseemly hurry to leave.

'We're late for school,' Marie shouted over her shoulder as she dragged the children at a run up the tunnelled entry.

The old woman's toothless mouth quivered in protest. 'The school bell aren't even started ringing yet, you silly little bugger.'

But the children had already gone out into the street.

As she gathered the smallest children to her skirts Mrs Green called upstairs to ask, 'Is theer anything I can do for you, Mr Payne, afore I takes the childer away?'

Alfred Payne grunted sourly, and muttered, 'Only if you was fifty years younger, you fuckin' old bat!'

When she received no reply from the man, the old woman jerked two forked fingers at the ceiling in silent insult, and went from the house.

In the school yard Marie's cousins went running to join some other early arrivals who were playing a noisy game of tag. She had no inclination to play. Instead she went to a quiet corner, and leaning against the railings thought about what had happened between herself and her uncle. She was greatly troubled by Alfred Payne's behaviour, and her fear of him had been intensified. Like the vast majority of the children who lived in the poorer quarters of the town, Marie knew some of the basic facts of life. When children shared bedrooms and even beds with parents, they sometimes inadvertently witnessed sexual acts. Some of Marie's classmates had related to her highly coloured accounts of what they had seen taking place between their parents. One girl had told of seeing her elder brother and sister having sex, and another had claimed that her father was doing things to her personally. Marie had not believed this last girl's stories. Because of the strong love between her own father and herself, she just could not accept that any father would behave so towards his daughter. All these tales had both repulsed and yet somehow thrilled and fascinated her. It was as if she were being allowed to enter a mysteriously secret and forbidden world.

Since living in Edward Street Marie had frequently heard noises coming from Alfred and Eva's bedroom, which, as a result of her schoolfriends' stories, she had guessed were the sounds of sexual intercourse. Now, fearfully, she wondered if that was what her uncle had intended to do to her that morning. To have sexual intercourse with her. While she was not completely conversant with all the physical mechanics of sexual congress, she had been told by her schoolfriends that the man's penis became very long and hard before he stuck it into the woman's body. That morning she had glimpsed her uncle's penis when the bed coverings had slipped back during their brief tugging match, and it had appeared to her terrified eyes to be very long and thick. Now a sensation of utter panic overwhelmed her, leaving her feeling sick and shaken as it slowly ebbed away.

The loud ringing of the big school bell jerked her back to reality, and still feeling shaken she walked with bowed head to join the forming lines of children. She felt that she should tell someone about what had happened that morning, but then remembered how she herself had not believed the girl who had claimed that she was being sexually abused by her own father.

Who would believe me? Marie asked herself, with a fast-mounting sensation of helplessness. My pa would. He'd believe me.

But her father was lying helpless in a hospital bed miles from here.

Miss Kitson. That hope died as quickly as it had been born. Miss Kitson had rejected her. And besides, Miss Kitson wasn't in school this morning, and had not been in school for weeks.

Miss Jones, her class mistress? Marie miserably pictured the mean, pinched features of the bespectacled woman, and knew that her story would be instantly dismissed as lies. Miss Jones frequently proclaimed her belief that all children were wicked, untrustworthy, worthless creatures, fit only to be berated and beaten.

Auntie Eva? Marie became near to tears. Auntie Eva was too afraid of her husband to do anything. Even to try to protect her own children from his drunken violence.

'Gurden! I'll teach you to be so insolent!' It was Miss Jones striding down the files of girls, her thin lips compressed in a spiteful line.

'I've called your name three times, you wicked girl. And you've deliberately ignored me.'

Before Marie could even open her mouth to reply the woman's bony hand whiplashed backwards and forwards across her cheeks.

Although the painful slashes rocked her head and brought tears to her eyes, Marie refused to give the woman the satisfaction of seeing how much she had hurt her. Instead she stubbornly held her head high, and drew courage from her own anger at this injustice.

'Let that be a lesson to you. We want none of your colonial

insolence and bad manners here. I for one will not stand for it, even if there are those among the teachers who will.'

Miss Jones frequently sneered at Marie's Canadian accent, and was infuriated by the fact that several of her fellow members of the teaching staff made something of a favourite of this pretty blonde-haired girl.

The woman stamped away, and in Marie's mind there solidified the frightening realisation that there was no one here she could turn to in her present troubles. That with her father lying helpless in the workhouse infirmary there was no one else to help or to support her. She was alone. She was completely and utterly alone.

Chapter Twenty-Four

Jack Preseley reined in his mount to a walking pace as he entered the bridleway which led through the Muskats Wood. Great oaks and elms spread their mighty branches above his head, creating a green umbrella to shade him from the hot sunlight. Birds sang and squirrels darted through the thick foliage, while from the undergrowth furtive rustlings betrayed the presence of a myriad other more secretive creatures.

The man breathed in the warm, moist, fecund scents of the woodland, and for brief moments his troubled thoughts were soothed by the peaceful beauty of this ancient place. The horse plodded slowly onwards, and its rider's body swayed gently in relaxed motion. The bridleway curved sharply and broadened into a long, straight stretch of greensward plentifully dotted with wild flowers, their varied colours glowing in the bright sunlight.

Jack halted his mount on the edge of the open space. He felt a tension building within him created by his mingled feelings of eager anticipation and guilt. Sharp disappointment swept through him when he saw no sign of the woman he had come to meet, and he urged his mount onwards out from the shadows and into the sunlight, his eyes searching among the trees and shrubs which edged the greensward. At the end of the long open space he wheeled his horse and retraced his path. His feelings of guilt had by now been vanquished by his intense disappointment, and fleeting shafts of irritation.

She's just been toying with me. Amusing herself. And I'm a dammed fool to allow her to have done so.

Then, through the thickly clustering leaves and branches of the undergrowth, he glimpsed a white moving figure, and instantly all his irritated disappointment was submerged by joyful happiness. He heard her laughter, and he laughed himself and slid from his saddle and plunged headlong into the undergrowth, disregarding the clinging, sharp-thorned tentacles that obstructed him, crashing through them until he stood face to face with Amy Morgan.

'There now, Captain Preseley, wouldn't I make a fine ambusher? You rode right past me and couldn't see me, could you? If I had had a gun I could easily have shot you. And you're supposed to be such an experienced soldier.'

She was teasing him, laughing with delight at her own triumph in evading his sharp eyes.

'Never mind that. I've got you now, haven't I?' He smiled, and before she could move he had encircled her slender body with eager arms and pulled her to him. His lips sought her mouth, and she giggled and jerked her head to avoid his kisses, then allowed her mouth to be captured by his, and returned his passionate kiss with an equal passion.

For long, long moments they remained locked in a close embrace, then she gently pushed his head back. Her blue eyes were soft and loving.

'I thought you'd never come,' she told him huskily. 'I've been waiting here for hours.'

'Hours?' He grinned happily, and chided tenderly, 'I do believe that you're exaggerating a litle when you say hours.'

She giggled. 'Well, I've been waiting for some time anyway. It seemed like hours.' She sobered suddenly. 'I can't stay for very long, Jack. My mother is expecting me to meet her in town. I'm supposed to be calling at my friend's house at this time. So I'll have to go there before I meet my mother, just in case she checks up on me.' Her pretty face hardened momentarily with resentful petulance. 'My parents still try to treat me as if I were a child. There are times when I feel that I'm a prisoner. They don't allow me to have any freedom to lead my own life.'

Preseley could not help but smile with a fond indulgence. He knew that this young lady was allowed a great deal of freedom by her doting parents. Far more then the vast majority of other young ladies in her social class.

She saw his smile and mock-scolded, 'Oh you, you're just as bad as they are. If I were your wife you'd give me no freedom either, would you? Let me go.'

She broke free of his restraining arms and walked away and out into the greensward, where she turned to see if he were following.

He stood where she had left him, and his heart seemed to swell with love and longing as he gazed at her. She wore a simple white dress, with a beribboned boater hat on her high-piled hair, and he thought that he had never seen anyone so beautiful.

He moved to join her as she strolled slowly on, and when he caught up with her their hands touched and clasped.

The horse was cropping the grass and Amy stared at the animal briefly.

'You're very honoured, Jack,' she remarked lightly. 'That's Tony's favourite mare. He's absolutely besotted with the beast. I'm surprised that he's allowed you to ride her like this. He must trust you absolutely.'

Her careless words caused guilt to strike the man like a physical blow, and brought him to an abrupt standstill. She stared at him in surprise, and asked with concern, 'What on earth is the matter? Why are you scowling so?'

'I'm sorry,' he mumbled, and tried to explain. 'It's just that the thought of Tony has made me feel very badly about what I'm doing here.'

'What you're doing here?' She seemed puzzled. 'I don't see why you should feel badly about that.'

He stared miserably at her, and fumblingly tried to clarify what he meant. 'Well, I feel that I'm betraying Tony's trust. He's my dearest friend, and here I am with you.'

She instantly showed pique. 'Tony doesn't own me.'

'Yes, but you and he are engaged to be married, aren't you?'

'We are not engaged to be married,' she retorted heatedly.

'But I thought that . . .'

She would not allow him to finish the sentence.

'I don't care what you thought. I am not engaged to Tony. Not officially anyhow,' she qualified, and went on in a more reasoned tone. 'We have a sort of understanding that perhaps one day we might get wed. But that is all it is. An understanding, nothing more.'

'And now?' he interjected.

She stared at him with speculation in her eyes, then replied quietly, 'Well, Jack, I really think that that depends on you, doesn't it?'

She waited expectantly for his answer, but he stood silent while turmoil raged in his brain.

All his own selfish instincts were urging him to accept what she appeared to be offering. To ask her there and then to marry him. But ranged against his selfish instincts were all those other deeply ingrained mores which dominated his life. His sense of honour and decency. His belief in the code of a gentleman. His bitter shame that he had allowed his own desires to drive him into a betrayal of his closest friend's trust and confidence.

She hissed audibly with a mounting impatience, and haltingly he told her, 'It's not easy for me, Amy. Tony loves you so much, it will destroy him if he loses you. I feel bitterly ashamed for betraying his trust in me.'

Her impatience flared into anger. 'It's a pity you didn't think of that before you made love to me!'

'I haven't made love to you,' he protested, misunderstanding her meaning.

'Well, what else can you call it?' she stormed. 'You've pursued me for weeks. Begging me to meet you. Snatching kisses from me at every opportunity. That's making love to me, isn't it?'

The truth of her accusing words caused him to feel an even deeper shame, and he could make no defence.

Their hands were still clasped, and now she tugged her fingers free, and told him scathingly, 'It's a little late for you to feel ashamed, isn't it? You betrayed Tony's trust the very first time you asked me to meet you.'

He nodded in miserable acknowledgement. 'I know, Amy. But that only makes me feel worse about it.'

'Phoo!' She expelled a noisy gust of contempt. 'You're the same as all the rest of the men, aren't you? You regard women as playthings. We're only here to pander to your vanities. And then, when we fall in love with you, you turn from us and bleat about honour and shame, and the sanctity of trust between men. What about trust between men and women? Doesn't that have any importance for you? You say that Tony trusts you. Well, what about me? I trusted you also. And now you're betraying my trust, aren't you?'

She hurled the words at him, her voice shrill with fury. And each word was a whiplash to his raw conscience. When at last she halted to draw breath, he blurted, 'Very well. I shall tell Tony what's happened between you and me. And I shall tell him that we're going to be married.'

Her eyes widened, and a glint of alarm hovered briefly in their blue depths.

Highly intelligent, yet emotionally shallow, Amy Morgan was a wilful, self-centred, spoilt young woman, who enjoyed taking centre stage in what she regarded as the ongoing drama of her life. Although she wanted this man to be her emotional slave, she had not really thought through the possible consequences of her flirtation with him. As always in her overindulged life, she had merely sought to gratify her own immediate desires. She had thoroughly enjoyed having this relationship with Jack Preseley, finding an intense excitement in its secrecy and intrigue. But now the unwelcome realisation was rapidly burgeoning that this was no longer merely a game, a theatrical play in which she could indulge her need for self-dramatisation, but instead had become a real-life situation which was dangerously near to getting completely out of control.

As her thoughts raced, Jack was still talking urgently to her, adding constantly to her dismay.

'I love you, Amy. And I want you to be my wife. Please say that you'll marry me. I know that I've behaved dishonourably towards Tony, but somehow I'll make amends to him for it. He'll understand that we could not help our feelings in this matter, that we couldn't stop ourselves from falling in love with each other. As soon as I've seen Tony, I shall come and speak with your father. But even if he forbids our marriage, we'll still marry. We'll go away from this town if necessary, and marry elsewhere. You're going to meet your mother in town, aren't you? Let me come with you. Perhaps we should let her know first how we feel about each other, before I speak with your father. It won't come as such a shock to her then, will it?' Jack's tone was becoming increasingly charged with anxiety as Amy's expression remained ambiguous.

At last he stopped speaking, and gestured beseechingly.

'Well, Amy? What do you say? Will you marry me straight away?'

She found herself in a quandary. She did not want to marry anyone yet. She certainly did not want to be the object of scandal, which she would undoubtedly become if Jack Preseley did as he proposed to do. At the same time she did not want to release either of the two men who professed to love her and set them free to fall in love with another woman. For Amy, the two were valued prizes, tokens of her ability to ensnare men, the constant satisfactions of her vanity. At this moment Amy wanted things to stay exactly as they were. She as the mistress, and the two men as her puppets and playthings. She as queen, and they as supplicant courtiers.

Unable to formulate any immediate plan, she took refuge in the safe haven of tears.

Jack instantly blamed himself as he saw her begin to weep, and he cradled her against his chest and tried to soothe her.

'Please don't cry, sweetheart. I'm sorry. I'm truly sorry.'

The fact that he could not really think what it was in this particular instance that he must be sorry for he disregarded.

Amy kept her face pressed against the soft tweed of his jacket until she had managed to think out her next move.

Then she pleaded with him in a soft, tearful voice not to tell Anthony about their love affair. In fact, not to tell anyone of it. She lied fluently and convincingly about her mother's weak heart and parlous state of health, and about how she alone must gradually make her parents aware of how their daughter's love had been given to him, Jack Preseley. She lied tremulously about the financial dealings between her own father and Ernest Barton, and how her understanding with Anthony was the underpinning for these financial dealings. Any rift at present between herself and Anthony would undoubtedly cause a rift between their elders, and such a rift would inevitably entail her father's financial ruination. Finally she pleaded with Jack to be patient, and to leave matters as they lay for the time being, and assured him that this continued secrecy and subterfuge would someday end in their being able to be married with the full blessings of her parents.

Jack listened intently and, made a fool by love, believed

234

all that she told him and fervently promised to obey her wishes.

Then he reluctantly broke the news to her that he was going back to Ireland for a short time. He did not explain the reason for that return.

'It's to do with the Ulster Volunteers, isn't it?' Amy guessed instantly. 'That's why you have to go back there.'

After a momentary hesitation he admitted, 'Yes. I've completed my business here, and now I have to report back to my commanders.'

Amy was thrilled. 'Are you going back to fight, Jack? Is there really going to be civil war in Ireland?'

His expression was bleak. 'It looks likely at this moment in time. I pray to God that it doesn't come to that. But if it does, then yes, I shall fight.'

He forced himself to smile at her excited face. 'But whatever happens, you can be sure of one thing. I shall come back to you, just as soon as I can.'

With tender kisses, and on his part a genuine sadness, they parted shortly afterwards.

As Amy walked slowly to her friend's house she dwelt enjoyably on the events of the past hour, and smiled with immense satisfaction.

It's all really exciting, isn't it? she concluded happily. I do hope that Jack comes back soon, though. Otherwise I shall have to find someone else to bring some excitement into my life.

Chapter Twenty-Five

At breakfast on Tuesday Ernest Barton read the *Times* report of the assassination of the heir to the Austro-Hungarian throne, the Archduke Franz Ferdinand, and his morganatic wife, the Duchess of Hohenburg, and commented sourly, 'I see there's trouble in the Balkans again. The heir to the Austrian throne and his wife have been assassinated. It seems the Serbians are implicated.' He brushed his long moustache with the back of his hand, and his eyes sparked fiercely. 'I know what I'd do if I were the Austrian Emperor. I'm march my armies into Serbia and teach it a lesson that it would never forget.'

'Oh yes, dear,' his wife responded absently, not having listened to a word her husband had said. Her thoughts were engrossed with other matters. Namely the depressed mood of her elder son, William, who for the past three weeks had been acting as if he had suffered a bereavement.

'What do you think, Jack? Do you agree with me?' Ernest asked the house guest, Jack Preseley, who was the only other person present at the table.

He also was preoccupied with his own thoughts, and seemed unaware that he had been spoken to. Ernest Barton was forced to repeat his question.

'Jack? I asked you what you thought?'

The Ulsterman started slightly. 'Oh, I'm sorry, Colonel. I was daydreaming. What was it you were saying?'

Barton showed him the newspaper report. 'It's my opinion that the Austrian armies should march into Serbia and teach those dammed barbarians a lesson. What do you think?'

Preseley pondered for a moment, then offered doubtfully, 'I'm not convinced that it would be the wisest course of action, Colonel.'

'Why not?' Barton challenged aggressively, as if indignant that his judgement should be doubted.

Again the Ulsterman pondered briefly before explaining.

'I was present at the Austrian grand manoeuvres three years ago, and I thought then that their army was badly led, and lacked the capability to launch swift offensive operations. Their cavalry are poorly horsed, and appeared unable to co-ordinate efficiently with the other arms.'

'But surely the Austrian Army is able to deal with a tinpot nation like Serbia?' Barton argued forcefully.

'If it were to remain purely a conflict between Austria and Serbia, then you might well be correct in that assumption,' Preseley agreed. 'But I fear that that will not be the case. In the event of Austria attacking Serbia, I believe that Russia might well intervene on the side of the Serbs.'

Barton waved that argument aside. 'The Tsar would never do that, Jack.'

'Why not?' Preseley was now warming to the argument. 'Traditionally the Russians have always supported their fellow Slavs against outside aggressors.'

'Yes, but in this case the aggression would be justified. And don't forget that the Tsar is unlikely to accept without protest the assassination of a brother monarch's heir. Remember he has a son of his own.' Barton shook his head and asserted emphatically, 'No, Russia will not intervene to protect Serbia.'

Before Preseley could reply, Anthony came into the room.

'Good morning, Ma.' He kissed his mother's cheek. 'Morning, Father, morning, Jack.'

He went to the long sideboard and helped himself to devilled kidneys, bacon, and sausage from the bain-maries.

His mother poured him a cup of coffee, and he ate and drank with great gusto, wielding his knife and fork easily now that his almost healed arm was only strapped instead of being encased in plaster.

'What time does your train leave from Birmingham, Jack?' the young man asked his friend.

'Two o'clock,' the Ulsterman told him.

'Then we've time to go and have another look at that stallion Simpson is selling before we set off from here.' Anthony spoke directly to his father. 'It's a fine animal, Father, I think we should buy if the price is right.'

Ernest frowned forbiddingly. 'Anthony, we already have fourteen beasts in the stables, eating their heads off and practically bankrupting me with vet's bills. Not to mention the grooms' wages. I can't afford another beast.'

The young man blithely disregarded his parent's protest. 'I tried him out yesterday over the jumps, and he took them superbly. He's a bargain at any price. Jack was with me, weren't you, Jack? Tell Father what a beauty he is.'

The Ulsterman was loath to be drawn into any wrangle between father and son, but he was obliged to confirm that the horse in question was an exceptional animal.

Despite himself, Ernest Barton's interest was aroused. He was as fanatical an enthusiast for horseflesh as his younger son.

He began to question Anthony more closely about the stallion, and Jack Preseley was able to retreat into his own thoughts.

He felt a great relief that he was leaving this house. His guilt was an ever-present torment, and several times during the previous evening he had been tempted to draw Anthony aside and confess his love for Amy Morgan. Now he glanced covertly at his companions. At Madeleine's gentle face, which was sombre and withdrawn. At Ernest, animated and combative as he argued the points of horseflesh with his son. At Anthony, so handsome and open-featured, his eyes shining as he forcefully put his case.

These people are my dearest friends, Jack thought miserably. And I've behaved so shabbily towards them.

The sudden urge to rise and hurry from the room swept over him, but he kept his seat. He could only pray that while he was in Ireland Anthony might meet another girl and fall in love with her, and so be saved from the pain of losing Amy. Meanwhile, he himself must try to act as normally as he could during the few hours that he was to remain a guest beneath this roof.

Madeleine was reliving a heated exchange she had had with her elder son, William, two days previously. His morose air of depression had increasingly troubled her during the last three weeks. He spent his days at the Orchard Street site, and his evenings either walking alone through the fields or secluded in his room. He ate hardly anything, and his thin face and body had now become positively gaunt. Madeleine was convinced that her son's problem was to do with the young woman, Josie Kitson, and she had tried to delicately question him concerning this. He had remained glumly silent, refusing to be drawn, and Madeleine's anxiety for him had finally driven her two days ago to demand point-blank what it was that was causing his present depression. Was it Josie Kitson?

William had reacted with an outburst of angry resentment that Madeleine had never seen him display before. He had told her very rudely to mind her own business, and to stop prying into his personal affairs. Shocked and hurt by his attitude, Madeleine could not help but brood, but she accepted that she could not shield him from the troubles and heartaches that life brought. She could only pray that he might soon recover from whatever it was that was hurting him so badly.

Her eyes went to her younger son's handsome, animated features, and she smiled sadly. He also was heading for heartbreak, of that Madeleine was convinced. She considered Amy Morgan to be a selfish, heartless flirt, who was only toying with Anthony's affections. Madeleine could only hope fervently that the girl would reveal her her true colours before much more time elapsed. The younger the heart that was broken, the quicker it would heal. Once the break was made Anthony would soon find a salve for the pain. There were any number of pretty young girls who would be more than happy to set their caps at him.

Madeleine covertly studied Jack Preseley, noting how in unguarded moments his face looked tense and strained. She had noticed how Amy looked at Preseley, and had shrewdly guessed that that young woman was eager to ensnare him also in her web. Now she wondered if Amy had already succeeded in her aim. The man's often abstracted air and the tense strain she saw in him now surely could not be caused solely by the situation in Ireland.

Madeleine mentally pictured the girl's pretty face, and silently scolded her for being a young hussy.

But some day you will reap what you have sown, Amy Morgan, she promised grimly. And I for one will most definitely not feel any sympathy for you whatsoever!

240

Chapter Twenty-Six

As June became July the gloriously fine weather continued. Day after day the sun shone in cloudless skies, and corn and fruit ripened in the fields and orchards, giving promise of a bounteous harvest to come.

But as a consequence of the assassination of the heir to the Austrian throne, political storm clouds were rapidly gathering.

On the fifth of July Kaiser Wilhelm reaffirmed Germany's alliance with Austria.

On the fifteenth the French President, Raymond Poincaré, arrived in St Petersburg on a state visit to the Tsar of all the Russias, reaffirming the alliance between their two countries.

On the twenty-third the Austrian Government presented Serbia with an ultimatum, making a series of drastic and humiliating demands which Serbia could not accept without gravely impairing her sovereignty. Serbia rejected the ultimatum two days later and Austria immediately broke off diplomatic relations and began a series of extensive troop movements towards the Serbian frontier.

On the twenty-sixth Serbia ordered full mobilisation of its armed forces. On that same day from St Petersburg the Tsar warned Germany that he could not remain indifferent if Serbian territory were to be invaded. The following dawn the Austrian army began the invasion of Serbia, and Austria made a formal declaration of war on the day after her soldiers had crossed the frontier.

The Russians immediately mobilised 1,200,000 troops. The German Kaiser reacted by warning the Tsar that unless Russia ceased mobilising within twenty-four hours, Germany would also mobilise.

In France the first steps towards full mobilisation were taken, and reservists were recalled to their regimental depots.

From the Admiralty in London coded signals were sent out to the far-flung fleets of the British Empire, and the Royal Navy began to put itself on a war footing. Tourists going abroad were advised to take their holidays in Switzerland rather than the famous German spas of Marienbad and Carlsbad. Apart from this there was in England little or no sign of this sudden international crisis having any effect on the nation's daily life. The quarrels of foreigners were of little interest to a people that knew themselves to be made inviolate by their invincible navy.

Certainly the international crisis made no impression on Josie Kitson. She was too involved in dealing with her own personal problems. Her mother's physical condition had seemed to improve as the July days passed. She had begun to speak a little more clearly, and had regained some slight movement in her paralysed leg. Dr Sinclair had expressed his satisfaction with this improvement, and had even suggested a course of electrical treatment to be commenced shortly to help in restoring mobility to the old woman's limbs. The improvement in her mother's condition coincided with changes for the better in Josie's own life. Clement Hulme had proven to be a tower of strength to her. He was tireless in his aid, coming to the house almost every evening, helping Josie with every aspect of caring for the sick woman. He had also enlisted other helpers from the chapel brethren who would take turns to come and sit with the old woman for a few hours, and so enable Josie to go shopping, or even to attend a chapel service or function on occasion. Her mother still made ceaseless demands, but with the help she was now receiving Josie was able to cope much more easily, and, viewing the undoubted improvement in the old woman's physical condition, to look forward to a future in which she could soon return to her teaching position at Bridge Street School.

Because she was now able to rest and sleep more easily Josie's own physical condition was better, and she had regained her vitality. The return of that vitality was however something of a mixed blessing. For with it had returned her sexual hungers, and faced constantly as she was with the evidence of human deterioration and decay Josie could only feel her own physical frustrations more intensely, bitterly conscious of the fact that these were her prime years, and she was spending them deprived of the solace and pleasures of physical union and love.

She thought often and yearningly of William Barton, but accepted that there was no possibility of ever rebuilding any relationship with him. Sometimes, during the dark hours of the night, she would sit gazing out of her window, drawing pleasure from the beauty of the peaceful moonlit countryside. On a couple such occasions she had imagined that she glimpsed William Barton's tall figure standing shrouded in the shadows, staring up at the window. She had rejected these momentary glimpses as figments of her imagination. But then on one shopping expedition into the town she had actually encountered William. He had come to a shocked standstill, and stared at her, his face pale and his expression a bizarre mingling of sorrow and uncertainty and regret. Josie had the strong impression that he was trying to summon the courage to accost her. Instinctively she had slowed her own pace, and turned towards him. But then the shaming, humiliating memories of the last time she had been in his arms had flooded through her, and with her cheeks scarlet with embarrassment she had walked on past him, keeping her eyes averted from his tormented gaze.

Towards Clement Hulme Josie entertained curiously mixed feelings. During the many hours he spent with her, he had never once attempted to make any physical advance. Sometimes she would be aware that he was staring at her hungrily, but always when she resentfully met his eyes he merely smiled apologetically, and said gently, 'Forgive me, Josie. I can't help the way I feel about you.'

Then he would turn away and busy himself with some task or other, and her resentment would quickly pass, to be replaced by feelings of gratitude for all the kindness he had shown towards her during these days of her greatest need.

Lately she had found herself feeling actual momentary pulses of affection for him. Not love in any sense, but an emotional warmth nonetheless. There were other moments when in unguarded mood she found herself remembering how virile a lover he had been, and how she had known such lustful physical ecstasies in his arms. She would feel the hot liquidity of desire suffusing her, and despite all her shame and regrets would be unable to resist the terrible need to give herself furtive, hurried relief, mentally reliving the physical passions of their lovemaking as her hands tried to satiate her all-consuming hungers.

After each such occasion she would go down on her knees and beg God to forgive her for her sinful lusts. These fervent prayers would ease her troubled mind, but it was becoming dismayingly apparent to her that her own efforts to satisfy her lusts were not enough. She hungered for a man's loving, and at times would weep with frustration and despair that she, who had so much to give to a marriage, seemed doomed to remain forever a spinster.

And during these passing weeks of July, Clement Hulme patiently watched and waited, and worked tirelessly towards the attainment of his goal. The binding to himself of Josie Kitson.

Chapter Twenty-Seven

At the building site in Orchard Street William Barton was sitting in the office shed, staring glumly through the open door, his mind filled with bitter thoughts of Josie Kitson. From this vantage point he could see along the front length of the half-built terrace and hear the voices and laughter of the workmen nearest to him.

In his present mood he found their light-hearted banter unbearably irritating to his frayed nerves, and after one loud outburst of laughter he jumped to his feet and stormed out of the shed to cross the intervening space.

One of the bricklayers saw him coming, and warned his workmates, 'Watch it, here's Misery Guts on the warpath agen.'

'Look at the bastard's face, 'ull you?' a second man hissed. 'It 'ud curdle the fuckin' milk.'

'I'm sick and tired of his bloody bad temper.' The first man hawked and spat gloweringly. 'He's bin treating us like dogs ever since he took over the site.'

'And I'm sick of it as well,' his workmate agreed. 'I aren't going to put up wi' much more of it neither.'

William halted beneath the scaffolding where the men were working and shouted up at them, 'Get on with your job, you two. I'm paying you to lay bricks, not spend your time lazing about and chattering like old women.'

The two bricklayers exchanged resentful looks, and the other men along the terrace halted their toil to stare curiously.

Ted Aston, the elder of the two bricklayers, straightened and came to the edge of the planking to stare down at Barton's upturned features.

'We am working, gaffer.' He gestured towards the courses

245

of new-laid bricks. 'Just measure this lot if you thinks that we 'em slackin' on the job.'

William scowled. 'Don't give me any of your cheek, Aston. I've just told you to get on with your work, haven't I? Now do it, or I'll have you off this site. I'm not paying good money to useless chattering idlers.'

The bricklayer's weather-beaten face hardened, and without another word he turned away, collected his tools together and deposited them into a small sack. Then he shouted loudly, so that all the watching men could hear, 'I doon't know about you lot. But I'se just about had enough of this lanky bastard treating me like I was a piece o' bloody shit. He doon't know a brick from a turd. He ought never to be in charge of this site.

'Theer's a new job starting up this week in Headless Cross, and they'm wanting tradesmen and labourers. So that's wheer I'm going, and if you lot has got any balls, you'll be coming up theer wi' me.'

He began to descend the ladder, and his mate shouted, 'Hold on a minnit, Ted. I'm coming wi' you.'

He hurriedly collected his tools into a sack and followed Aston.

William's temper flared as he confronted the pair at the foot of the ladder.

'If you want to leave this job, then you'll work a proper notice. I won't pay you what's due to you unless you work a full notice.'

The burly Aston grinned contemptuously. 'Oh yes you 'ull pay me me dues, gaffer. I'll be down for 'um on Saturday morning, and if you aren't got 'um ready, then I'll goo direct to the police. Your old dad 'ull love that, wun't he? Folks in this town 'ull really have summat to talk about then, wun't they? Colonel Barton's son robbing honest working chaps of the money they'se sweated for. I'll see you on Saturday morning, or you can give my dues to Charlie Spicer to give to me if you'd sooner not see me!'

He slung his heavy sack across his broad shoulders and began to walk away.

William lost his head completely. 'You come back here, you two, or I'll see to it that you won't find work any-where else.'

The two men exchanged a look and halted. Then Aston came walking back to stand face to face with William.

'You just lissen to me, gaffer,' he growled threateningly. 'You might be able to frit these other bleeders, but it doon't work wi' me. I'm the best trowel in this town, and that's well known, that is. Any gaffer is glad to gi' me the start. You can't stop me getting work, you nor twenty fuckers like you. And I'll tell you summat else as well. You'se proved a bad 'un to work for. The worst gaffer I'se known in many a day's march. You knows sweet fuck all about the building, and you'm a miserable, sour-faced bastard with it.'

With that parting sneer he swung round and rejoined his friend.

As they passed along the terrace other men came to the edges of the scaffolding, and one shouted down, 'Am you sure that we can get the start up at the Cross, Ted?'

'O' course I'm sure,' he answered positively. 'They wants brickies, navvies and hod carriers.'

Several other bricklayers and labourers came down the ladders and followed in Aston's wake, shouting and laughing excitedly.

Charlie Spicer came puffing up to William, his broad face showing real fright, words tumbling frantically from his mouth.

'Christ Almighty, Mister William, what's your dad going to say about this? He'll goo bloody mad, he 'ull. Stark staring raving mad! We'em never going to get finished to time now. Your dad 'ull goo mad. Bloody raving mad!'

William's temper subsided abruptly and dismay engulfed him. The work progress on site was already behind schedule and this abrupt withdrawal of labour threatened to be disastrous.

Charlie Spicer was almost moaning in distress.

'This 'ull be the finish of me with your dad. He'll blame me for it, I knows he 'ull. He'll blame me!'

The man's whining voice grated on William's nerves, and he snapped impatiently, 'You won't be blamed for this, Spicer. I shall tell my father what happened here.'

He fell silent for a few moments as he considered the situation, then said, 'We'll take on replacements. We needn't lose that much production if we find men straight away.

And there are plenty of building workers looking for jobs, aren't there?'

The other man did not share William's confidence.

'There aren't so many since last week, Mister William. Don't forget that the Enfield factory started its new extension last Monday, and a lot of men got jobs there. Then there's this new site up at Headless Cross. It's a big contract and they'll be starting on a lot of hands.'

'There are still plenty left who need work.' William became impatient with Spicer's apparent obstructiveness, and suddenly shouted angrily, 'For God's sake, stop whining, man, and get up into the town and find me some new labour.'

Spicer bitterly resented his employer's attitude, and his expression became mulish.

'There's men looking for work, right enough, Mister William. But they'll mostly be the ones that nobody else wants.'

'What do you mean?' William demanded.

'I mean that the only ones we'll get to come on this site now 'ull be the lazy bastards, and the bad tradesmen, and the drunks and troublemakers.'

Spicer's servile demeanour now disappeared, as if he had suddenly acquired courage and pride from hidden depths within himself, and he stood straighter and faced his employer squarely, matching William's scowl with his own.

'I'm going to spake straight and true to you now, Mister William. And you can give me the sack for doing so, if you want. But tell you straight I'm going to. Since you'se took over the charge of the job, this site has gained a rotten name for itself. None of the good tradesmen wants to work here under you, because of the way you'se bin treating the men already here. Skilled men doon't like being spoke to as if they'm shit. Neither does the labourers. I knew that as soon as other sites opened up we'd be losing men from here. And it's all your bloody fault.' He nodded his head several times. 'Oh yes. I can get men here today, right enough. But they'll only be the bloody dregs. Blokes like Alfie Payne and Shanto Evans. And them two has already been sacked by your dad, so even if they agrees to start back here, we'll have to keep 'um a secret from your dad, won't we?'

He stopped speaking, and waited for William's reaction, steeled to take the consequences of his blunt speaking.

All William's temper drained from him, leaving him feeling deflated and despondent. He accepted the truth in Spicer's words. He knew that he had treated the men badly, and that this situation was entirely of his own making. Inwardly he bitterly derided himself.

I'm pathetic. It's true what my father says about me. I'm useless. Unemployable. A living, breathing joke of a man. Because a woman causes me grief, I take it out on others. I make them suffer for my own troubles.

His shoulders slumped, and he felt utterly defeated. Shaking his head helplessly, he mumbled, 'Well, do whatever you can to find some men, will you, Spicer? Just set on anyone who you think might be able to do the work. Take on anybody who'll come.'

He turned away and walked with bowed head back into the office shed and closed its door behind him.

Charlie Spicer watched with contemptuous eyes, and muttered scornfully, 'That's right. You just fuck off like a yellow-bellied coward and leave it all to me to put right. You useless, gutless bastard!'

He swung round to face the watching men, and saw from their expressions that they shared his contempt for William Barton.

He called up to the eldest tradesman, 'Tommy, you'm in charge until I gets back. Come on now, lads, get back to work. I'll not be long gone.'

With that he left the site to go in search of fresh labour to replace the men who had left.

It was many hours before he returned, and glumly informed William Barton, 'I can find plenty of labourers and navvies, Mister William, but no brickies. All the best tradesmen have been given the start on the new sites.'

William grimaced with disappointment, then ordered, 'Well, just keep on searching, Spicer. I must have more bricklayers.'

The foreman nodded. 'All right, Mister William.'

As he walked away he thought sullenly, We'd do a sight better if we was to start looking for a new bloody gaffer for this job.

Chapter Twenty-Eight

Caleb Gurden lay listening to the thready, spasmodic wheezing of the old man in the next bed, and knew that death was very near. In the distance the great clock of the workhouse chimed three times, and as if he had been waiting for that cue the old man cried out, and then the breath rattled from his throat in final exhalation. From the other sleeping men there sounded a sudden outburst of coughing and snorting and uneasy mutterings, as if they sensed that death had come to claim one of their companions.

Caleb peered through the darkness at the dead man, but could only distinguish the pale, featureless outline of face and neck. He felt no sorrow, other than a sense of pity that the old man had died friendless and alone, without a kindly human touch to ease his passing. Caleb murmured a brief prayer for the departed soul, then grimaced bleakly. In the weeks he had spent in this ward, he had repeated this prayer with a disturbing frequency and sometimes felt that he was dwelling in Death's antechamber.

As always, during these dark, sleepless hours of early morning, his thoughts turned to his daughter. He had neither seen nor heard from Marie since her single visit and worried constantly about her welfare, drawing scant comfort from the fact that if something had happened to her then undoubtedly his sister would have made sure he was informed of it. Now he sibilantly cursed the ill fortune that had rendered him helpless to care for and protect his daughter, and felt that he could not bear yet another day of this enforced idleness. He would lie for hours impatiently willing his broken bone to heal and grow strong, and he truly believed that by sheer force of his will he was in some way speeding the healing process.

Now, waiting for the dawn, he began to work through the repertoire of strengthening exercises that he had devised for himself, pitting the force of his muscles against one another, and stretching tendons and ligaments. He interspersed these exercises with breathing techniques to work his heart and lungs. He followed this regime every day, and was confident that the self-imposed discipline was combating the inevitable physical deterioration that this forced confinement to bed had wrought upon his physique. Caleb was well aware of the drunken Dr Andrews' belief that he, Caleb, was in a condition of sharp decline, and he grimly looked forward to the day when he would walk out of this ward and prove the medical man to be wrong in his diagnosis.

By the time he had completed his programme dawn had come and the orderly was shuffling into the ward. The man was singing softly to himself in a cracked, wavering voice.

> 'Oh where would I be when me froat was dry?
> Oh where would I be when the bullets fly?
> Oh where would I be when I come to die?
> Whyyyeeee . . . somewhere's anigh my chum.'

His rheumy eyes fixed on Caleb's face and he grinned, displaying long snags of blackened teeth.

'Well now, my old china, you aren't died yet then. The Doc 'ull be very disappointed. You'm proving him wrong by staying alive like this.'

Caleb returned the grin. He liked this disreputable old soldier, Jack Tilly, whose only reward for fighting his country's battles was to be here in the workhouse, spending his final years as a pauper inmate.

'I intend to prove him wrong, Jack.' He indicated the dead man in the next bed. 'Old Pearce died at three o'clock.'

Tilly looked quickly about him at the rest of the sleeping figures and then moved with surprising speed to the dead man. He grinned into the sightless, staring eyes and shook his forefinger at the waxen face as if in admonishment.

'You avaricious old bastard, you. I told you that you couldn't take it wi' you, didn't I?'

252

Caleb stared in astonishment as Tilly's fingers disappeared into the dead man's gaping mouth.

The old soldier winked at Caleb, and chortled happily. 'This old bastard thought that he'd get the better of me, Caleb. But I'm too fly to be had like that.'

His fingers reappeared, and clutched between their black-nailed tips was a gold coin. He cackled with hoarse laughter at Caleb's shocked expression, then explained, 'The old bastard's kept this under his bloody tongue for years. He found it laying on the road outside the gates one day when he was doing gate porter. The tight bleeder that he is, he's hoarded it all this time. He's so mean that he 'udn't give a blind man the time o'clock even if he was wearing two watches. He'd sell it to the poor blind bugger. Many's the time I'se begged him to lend me a couple o' coppers to buy a bit o' baccy wi', and he's always told me that he hadn't got a penny piece to bless hisself with. And all the time he knowed that I knowed that he was keeping this bloody sovereign under his lying tongue.'

He laughed into the dead man's face. 'I 'opes you knows what's going on, Pearce, you bloody Jew you. I 'opes you'm cursing and swearing at me from wherever you might be now. Because I'm going to spend this on grog and baccy just as soon as I can.'

He flourished the coin before the sightless eyes and jeered, 'Take a good look at it, you tight bastard, because it's the last you'll be seeing of it.'

The man in the bed beyond the dead man's stirred and grumbled in uneasy sleep, and the gold coin instantly disappeared. Jack Tilly came to whisper into Caleb's ear.

'Say nothin', Caleb, and half o' this is yourn. I reckon Ashwin might know that Pearce was holding on to this sovereign. So if her wants to know what I'se bin doing, just tell her that I only pulled the sheet over him, and didn't touch him at all.'

Caleb was a realist. He knew that if the ward nurse or any other of the workhouse staff had found this coin then they would have pocketed it without scruple, and without giving any share of it to any pauper. He nodded agreement, and the old soldier grinned and winked slyly, then covered the dead man with the bed sheet, and went away to fetch the wheeled trolley which was used to convey corpses to the workhouse mortuary, a small dark room known by staff and inmates as the slabs.

A brief while later the heavily built Nurse Ashwin came bustling into the ward, shouting loudly.

'Come now, rouse yourselves! Rouse yourselves! Rouse yourselves!'

The paupers stirred and scratching, farting, coughing, moaning, groaning, reluctantly came awake to face another pointless, empty, miserable day. The trapped stenches of their bodies were expelled from beneath displaced bedclothes, and the cold, dank air became charged with foulness.

'I said rouse yourselves!' The nurse's stentorian bellowing grew angry at the lack of movement from Pearce's bed, and she came pounding down the length of the ward to chastise the offender. Then, seeing that he was dead, she smiled with satisfaction. She turned the sheet back from his face and briefly glanced at him, then pulled open his jaw, and with her forefinger explored the insides of his mouth. She hissed in chagrin as she removed her finger and snapped the slack jaws shut. She stared balefully at Caleb.

'Was you awake when he went?'

Caleb was hard put to keep from laughter. She obviously had known of the secretly hoarded treasure.

He nodded. 'Yes. He died at three o'clock. I heard the clock striking the hour as he went.'

Her hard eyes dwelt speculatively on Caleb's tractioned leg, and then appeared to measure the distance separating him from the dead man.

'Did Jack Tilly mess about with him?' was her next question.

Caleb could not resist baiting her a little. 'What do you mean by that, ma'am? Mess about with him?'

She snicked her tongue against her teeth with irritation. 'Did Jack Tilly look into his mouth, or anywhere else on his body?'

Caleb shook his head solemnly. 'No, ma'am. He only pulled the sheet over him. That's all.'

The woman did not seem totally convinced by his answer, and stayed frowning doubtfully at him.

Jack Tilly shuffled back into the ward pushing the trolley. He grinned ingratiatingly at the woman.

'I'm just going to take poor old Pearce down to the slabs, ma'am. Does you want the doctor to have a look at him afore I clanes him up and lays him out proper?'

She pursed her lips and folded her meaty arms, and her booted foot tapped in staccato rhythm. Glaring suspiciously, she questioned, 'Have you found anything, Tilly?'

The old soldier stared with exaggerated puzzlement, and scratched his greasy, tousled mop of grey hair.

'Has I found anything, ma'am?' he repeated bemusedly several times. 'Has I found anything? Has I found anything?'

The tapping of her foot became a hammering, and her scowl deepened. Then he grinned delightedly, and said artlessly, 'Well, I'se found a deal of hardships since I'se bin in here, ma'am.'

She snorted in disgust, and ordered, 'Go and fetch your bucket and scrubbing brush, and clean this floor. It's a disgrace.'

He pointed to the dead man. 'But what about him, ma'am? Doon't you want him to goo to the slabs?'

She muttered furiously beneath her breath, then jerked her head at the dead man.

'Get him on the trolley. I'll take him to the slabs myself. And when I come back I want to find you on hands and knees scrubbing this floor. Do you hear me?'

'Certainly, ma'am, whatever you say. I'm here to obey your orders, ma'am, like a good soldier.'

Tilly was humbly obsequious, and hastened to do as she had bidden. Then, as she wheeled away the trolley with its sheet-covered burden, he winked at Caleb, and whispered, 'Just watch now what her gets from the store cupboard.'

Caleb watched Nurse Ashwin stop at the tall cupboard and from its interior bring out a pair of rubber gloves, which she placed on top of the shrouded corpse before going on her way.

As she disappeared Jack Tilly cackled with glee, and told Caleb, 'Her's took them gloves so that her can have a feel up old Pearce's arsehole. Her thinks that the old bugger's most likely hid his money up his arse.'

He roared with hoarse laughter, then with contemptuous derision hissed, 'Aren't her a daft fat cow!'

Caleb chuckled with grim amusement and the old soldier

whispered, 'I'll get this sovereign changed down the town, and I'll give you your half of it tonight.'

Then, with a final cackle of glee and a sly wink, he went shuffling away.

Caleb experienced a sense of eager anticipation for the coming of the night. He had been completely penniless since being here. With the money he could now buy a pen, envelope, paper and stamps and write to his daughter. He frowned thoughtfully. All these articles would have to be obtained surreptitiously and kept hidden, otherwise Nurse Ashwin would want to know how he was able to afford them. He grinned happily. Perhaps he might also buy a clay pipe and some tobacco. He was finding his poverty-enforced withdrawal from tobacco extremely difficult to bear. The pipe and tobacco would also have to be kept hidden away from Nurse Ashwin, and he would only be able to enjoy them during the dark hours of night when she was absent from the ward.

When Jack Tilly came back with a bucket and cleansing implements Caleb beckoned him to the bedside and told him what he wanted to do with his share of the money.

The old soldier grinned and winked. 'You leave it to me, my old china. You'll 'ave everything you needs tonight, and your letter can be in the post fust thing in the morning. No need to worry about the fat cow finding anything. I was playing the grifty-wallah out in the shiny afore her was born. Why, I can remember one time when we was marching up to Peshawar that I . . .'

'Tilly! If you don't get this floor scrubbed I'll have you in front of the board this very day!'

The old soldier's reminiscences of India were cut short by the angry bellowing of the returning Nurse Ashwin.

He stamped to attention and saluted in a grotesque parody of military smartness.

'Very good, ma'am. At your orders, ma'am. I'm an old soldier, and I knows me duty. I'm a disciplined man, I am, ma'am.'

Caleb hid a grin as the nurse almost shrieked with fury.

'Just get on with it, will you, and let's have no more of your nonsense, you old fool!'

With a final sly, grinning wink at Caleb, the old man knelt

and began to scrub the floor, splashing the cold water plentifully across the flagstones, and singing to himself.

> 'Jane 'Arding was a sarjint's wife.
> A sarjint's wife was she.
> She married him in Aldershot,
> And comed across the sea.
> 'Ave you never 'eard tell o' Jane 'Arding?
> 'Ave you never 'eard tell o' Jane 'Arding?
> 'Ave you never 'eard tell o' Jane 'Arding?
> The pride o' the Companeeee . . .'

Caleb lay back against the hard, rough-textured pillow and resigned himself to waiting patiently through the long hours for the coming of night.

Chapter Twenty-Nine

The postman frowned doubtfully at the name and address on the letter, and rapped the double knock of his calling on Alfred Payne's door.

Payne, bleary-eyed and unshaven, peered questioningly at the blue uniform and peaked cap of this rare caller, then growled, 'What the 'ell does you want, Billy?'

'I'se got a letter addressed to your number, Alfie.' The postman was an acquaintance, but not a friend. 'It's for a Miss Marie Gurden. Only I doon't know anybody o' that name living here.'

'Give it here.' Payne thrust out his dirty hand.

The postman looked doubtful. 'Who is her then, this Marie Gurden? Does her live here?'

'O' course her does, you silly bastard!' Payne swore irritably. 'It's me niece, aren't it?'

The postman still hesitated. 'Well, by the feel of it there's some money in the letter. I really should ought to give it to her direct.'

'Doon't talk so sarft! Her's in bloody school, aren't her?' Before the postman could react, Alfred Payne's hand shot out and snatched the envelope. 'I'll see that her gets it the minute her gets home. Now just fuck off, 'ull you, and let a man get a bit o' peace and quiet!'

The postman reluctantly accepted the *fait accompli* and went away down the entry, leaving Payne staring at the neat handwriting on the envelope.

It's from that bastard! he decided, and grinned as he felt the rounded outline of a coin through the paper. He ripped the envelope open and tipped the silver florin out into the palm of his hand, chuckling with satisfaction.

'That's me entrance fee for today.'

Then he extracted the double sheet of notepaper and began to read. Being a poor scholar, he could only read slowly and with difficulty, but fortunately for him, Caleb Gurden's handwriting was clear and well formed, and so Payne was able to understand the content of the letter.

It was a loving father's testament to his concern and yearning for his daughter, and would have touched the hearts of the vast majority of people who read it. But it left Payne unmoved. Caring nothing for his own children, he could not comprehend how deeply and unselfishly a man could love a child, and the tender warmth of the sentiments and the deep devotion that Gurden expressed for his daughter merely brought scoffing jeers of laughter from Payne.

He replaced the letter in the envelope and stuffed it into his jacket pocket. Then he pulled his flat cap on to his tousled mop of hair and went whistling from the house towards the town centre.

As he walked up the steep Unicorn Hill he pleasurably anticipated the taste of the beer he was going to swill down him. The florin should serve to get him drunk, and also leave enough money for a couple of days' supply of tobacco.

A pert-looking young girl passed him, and he stared lustfully at her slender body. Payne's sexual appetites contained elements of both sadism and paedophilia. He enjoyed hurting women while he used their bodies, and thrilled to the powerlessness of a naked woman crushed beneath him. But as he grew older he lusted more and more after very young girls. The vulnerability of their immature bodies aroused him to a pitch of greater sexual excitement than any older woman had ever made him feel.

He had on several occasions during the past couple of years slyly interfered with a neighbour's small daughter, but had managed to retain sufficient self-control not to cause her physical injury, or to terrify her so that she raised the alarm by shrieking. On one occasion the girl had prattled about what had happened to her, and had aroused the suspicions of her mother. But Payne had been able to allay the woman's suspicions, and had taken care to keep well away from the child in question since then. But despite that fright of near-discovery, his perverted urges

260

had intensified, and now had become centred on his niece, Marie Gurden. Since that one occasion in his bedroom when he had tried to make her hold his penis, she had taken care to avoid being alone with him. Cunningly, he had made no effort to force her, to be alone with him. Instead he had slyly fondled her in passing. Squeezing her small, firm buttocks, and when opportunity presented pressing and rubbing himself momentarily against her body. But he wanted more; and now, in his degenerate brain, there was the thought that somehow or other he might be able to use her father's letter to further that aim.

His lust engorged now as he visualised how Marie Gurden would look with her long blonde hair spread across the pillow, her pretty face showing terror, her slender body flinching from his ravaging hands. He imagined how it would feel as he thrust into her virgin flesh, and then how he would terrorise her until she became his slave, fearfully prepared to obey his every whim, and satisfy his every cruel and twisted perversion.

'How bist, Alfie, wheer you gooing?'

Payne grimaced as he heard the voice. It was Shanto Evans, one of his many drinking cronies, a ragged, unshaven, filthy-bodied man with a throat that was perennially dry. Payne knew that Evans would have no money in his pockets. If he had cash then he would be in the public house, not lounging here on the corner of the main crossroads. Although Payne was a gregarious drinker and normally would have welcomed Evans' company, now he mentally subdivided his florin into two, and decided that he lacked sufficient funds to treat his crony to a drink. So he returned the greeting with a noncommittal grunt and would have walked on, but the other man caught hold of his jacket sleeve and detained him.

'Has you got the price of a pint on you, Alfie? Me throat's that dry I'm spitting sand.'

Payne shook his head. 'No, mate. I'm flat broke.'

'You bloody liar!' Shanto Evans grinned knowingly. 'If you was flat broke then you 'udn't be up and about so early.' His tone became wheedling. 'Come on, Alfie, just get me a pint in. I'd do it for you, 'udn't I?'

Payne sighed heavily in surrender. 'All right then. But I'se only got a couple o' bob. So you'm only getting the one pint.'

The other man laughed happily. 'That's all right, mate. Once I'm in the White Lion theer's bound to be somebody else come in who owes me a pint, aren't there?'

Side by side the two men swaggered through the town centre and made their way to their favourite public house, the White Lion.

The landlord's face brightened as he heard the arrival of customers, and he came hurrying from his rear room to serve them. Then he saw who it was and his smile faltered.

'Your slates are full,' he announced grimly. 'There's no more tick for either of you until you'se paid summat on account.'

Alfred Payne produced the florin with a flourish. 'What does you thnk this is, Kenny, Scotch mist?'

He tossed the coin on to the tall counter and the landlord snatched it up then asked Shanto Evans, 'Wheer's your entrance fee, Shanto?'

Evans' swarthy features twisted in aggrieved protest. 'That two bob is from both of us.'

'Oh no it aren't, Shanto,' Payne denied indignantly.

'But you said you'd get me a pint in!' his friend challenged.

'Give him a pint out of that 'ull you, Ken,' Payne requested.

The landlord grudgingly agreed, but warned, 'This is the only one you'll get, Shanto, until you puts some money across the bar.'

He served them with two glasses of foaming beer and they drank greedily. Payne drained his glass to the dregs and pushed it across the bar for a refill. He belched noisily before taking a long pull from a fresh drink, while his friend stared at him enviously, and nursed the remains of his own beer.

The door opened and the weathered features of Charlie Spicer appeared around its edge. He looked quickly about the room, and frowned with disappointment when he saw the bar's only occupants, then sighed resignedly and came fully into the room.

The two friends regarded him sourly as he ordered a half-pint of stout, which he stood sipping reflectively, ignoring them both.

The landlord leaned across the counter. 'What's this then, Charlie? Taking the morning off, are you?'

Spicer shook his head. 'No, mate. I got too much to do to take any time off. I'm just putting the word around that I wants to set on some more brickies and labourers.'

'Why's that then?' The landlord was interested. 'I thought you had plenty.'

'I have. But I wants to get this job finished a bit quick. We'se got another contract to start soon, you see.'

Alfie and Shanto exchanged a meaningful look. Although neither of them were ever eager to work, weeks of idleness had left them in a parlous financial state. Their credit in all the town's pubs had dried up, and they had tried without success to find work. Unfortunately for them, their bad reputations were widely known, and they had been turned away from the sites currently in progress.

'Well, you shouldn't have any trouble finding more men,' the landlord said, then qualified, 'Mind you, there's not so many blokes looking for the start as there was last week. There's bin a couple of new contracts started, aren't there?'

Spicer nodded, but shrugged. 'It makes no matter, Ken. I can always find some hands.'

In actual fact he had been trying for several days to find skilled bricklayers and had failed to do so. His coming here was a last resort. He had been sure that Payne and Evans would be in the White Lion, and had reluctantly accepted that he would have to employ them once more. But he had no intention of immediately offering them work. If he did that, they would realise that he was desperate for hands, and that would place him in a weak position regarding enforcing work discipline on the site.

It was Shanto Evans who made the approach.

'How about giving me and Alfie the start then, Charlie?'

Spicer frowned doubtfully. 'Alfie's already been sacked once, and you was sacked the last time you worked for me.'

'But that was then, waren't it, Charlie?' Shanto was magnanimous. 'I aren't a chap to bear malice. Let bygones be bygones, that's what I always says. And Alfie's the same, aren't you, Alf?'

Payne nodded. 'That's right, Charlie. I doon't bear you any grudge for what happened between me and old Barton.'

Spicer expelled his breath in a noisy gust as he shook his

head. 'I dunno, Alfie. If the Colonel was to come on site and find you theer, he'd goo bloody mad.'

Payne winked slyly. 'He needn't see me theer, need he? I can always hide if he comes on site. Besides, he doon't come up very much, does he, now that his son's running it.'

'But how about the wages book?' Spicer demurred. 'He checks that, and he'd see your name there, 'udn't he?'

'You can book us in under different names, Charlie.' Spicer's prevarications were making Alfred Payne more eager to be given a job. 'Now come on, Charlie, be a sport. You knows that me and Shanto are bloody good trowels when we puts our minds to it.'

The foreman was forced to acknowledge the truth of this claim. Both men were capable of turning out good-quality work when they cared to.

'Yes, Charlie, be a sport.' Shanto added his urgings. 'I promise you on me kids' lives that we'll do a good job for you. We can work as a gang on piecework. That'll make sure that we lays plenty, won't it?'

Spicer remained silent while the two men continued to cajole him. He truly was reluctant to give them jobs. But on the other hand, he was desperate for tradesmen. And if they would only behave, these two bricklayers might ensure that the lost production was made up. They were fast trowels.

Eventually he feigned a grudging acceptance, and told them, 'All right then. I'll give you the start. You can be on piecework. Bring your own hod carrier, and be on site in an hour.'

The two men exchanged a glance of pure alarm. Now that they had found work their credit would be restored, and they had both envisaged a pleasant day spent drinking.

It was Shanto who smoothly evaded the necessity of working that day. Feigning disappointment, he told the foreman, 'Young Simmy James 'ull be carrying the hod for us, Charlie. But he's just this morning gone off to Brummagem, and he won't get back until tonight. It's no use our starting back using another kid. By the time we'se got him into our way o' working, it'll be time to goo home. So we shan't really get anything done, shall we? It's best if we starts tomorrow with Simmy.'

Spicer reflected on this for a couple of moments. He knew that Simmy James was a good worker, and was usually employed with these two men. And it was true what Shanto was saying. A good team could not be created in a matter of hours. He nodded acceptance.

'All right then. Start tomorrow with young Simmy.'

He finished his stout and left the bar.

Shanto grinned at the landlord. 'Now you heard all that, didn't you, Ken? We starts tomorrow.' He lifted his empty glass. 'Is me slate open?'

The landlord wordlessly took the glass and filled it from the pump, and Shanto chortled happily.

'Right then, Alfie. Let's have a good day, shall us?'

Chapter Thirty

The factory steam hooter wailed and the pulleys and driving belts slapped to a halt. Machines came to a standstill, and weary men and women breathed sighs of relief and thankfully stopped work.

Eva Payne wiped her oily hands on a piece of cotton waste and took her shawl from the hanging nail. She settled the threadbare cloth around her thin shoulders and slowly limped down the length of the workshop.

One of the women she passed stared at her sympathetically and nudged her friend.

'Evie Payne's man has bin up to his old tricks agen.'

The other woman peered at the limping Eva and clicked her tongue against her teeth.

'Bin giving her a kicking, has he?'

'It sounded as if he nigh on killed the poor cow last night. I could hear her screeching and I lives across the yard from her. Brought half the folks out to find out what was happening.'

'If he was mine I'd bloody well swing for him,' the second woman declared forcefully. 'I 'udn't let any man serve me bad like that. I'd wait till he was asleep and then I'd shove a bloody knife into his guts.'

The first woman looked at her friend's blackened eye, and asked drily, 'Is that what you'm going to do to your old man then, Ivy?'

Eva Payne was well aware that her awkward gait was the subject of comment among her workmates. The fact of her husband's ill treatment of her was hard enough to bear, and knowing that it was talked about by the other women was an added shame and embarrassment to her.

She thought about the events of the previous night and felt

267

like weeping. Alfred Payne had had no money for beer, and she had had no money to give him. He had lost his temper and had brutally kicked her on the shins. The agony had been so intense that she had feared he had broken her legs. Now she was dreading returning to her home, fearful of what his mood would be. If it had not been for her children she would have run away rather than go back to face her husband. With a heavy heart she passed under the big archway and out into the street with the swarms of other workers.

As she hobbled along the pavement Eva was making a mental inventory of her few remaining possessions, wondering what she could pawn to get enough money to buy food for the children's supper and her husband's evening meal. Since he had been unemployed Alfred had been forcing her to give him the major part of her scanty wages and wasting the money on drink and tobacco, and she had had to pawn nearly everything in the house to survive. She had already applied several times to the relieving officer for help. But he had refused to give her any outdoor relief, and had only offered to accept her and her children into the Bromsgrove workhouse as paupers. His reason for this refusal was that her husband had lost his employment through misconduct, and consequently was not eligible for any monetary payments or credit vouchers from the board of guardians. Eva was now desperate and at her wits' end for means to support her family. Increasingly she was having to face the terrible prospect that she and her children would eventually suffer the ultimate degradation and shame of entering the workhouse as pauper inmates.

The early evening air was warm and sultry, the stored heat of the day radiating back from the red-brick walls of the tenements. The street was lively and noisy with children playing and adults lounging outside their houses, talking, arguing, laughing, happy to be released for a few precious hours from their grinding labours. But there was no laughter in Eva's heart. Only bitter sadness and foreboding.

> 'Rat a tat tat, who is that?
> Only Grandma's pussy cat.
> What do you want?
> A pint of milk . . .'

The rhythmic chanting came from a group of pinafored girls skipping in the centre of the roadway. Two of the tallest girls held the long stretch of rope, sending it hissing and whirling in huge circles, and other girls continually succeeded each other within the hissing circle, their feet jumping rapidly as their friends chanted in loud rhyming cadence:

> 'Where's your money.
> In my pocket.
> Where's your pocket?
> I forgot it . . .'

The chorusing voices rose to a loud shrilling.

> 'Oh you silly pussy cat.
> Walk out! Walk out! Walk out!'

The skipping girl would duck agilely out from the whirling rope to be replaced instantly by another, and the chant would begin again.

> 'Rat a tat tat, who is that?
> Only Grandma's pussy cat . . .'

Eva's eyes filled with tears as the memories flooded through her of how she had once been a young, light-hearted girl, skipping with her friends, chanting the self-same rhyme . . .

Hurriedly she wiped away the tears, and blinked rapidly to clear her blurred sight.

Further along the street, outside the entry to her home, she saw her children huddled around the taller, blonde-haired figure of Marie Gurden.

Her heart jumped sickeningly. Oh my God! Has Alfie chucked them all out of the house? Has he done something bad to them?

She broke into a painful run, every lurching step sending agony shafting through her badly bruised shin bones.

The children saw her coming, and ran to meet her.

269

'Can we have our tea, Mam?'

'I'm ever so hungry, Mam!'

'I wants a piece, Mam!'

Eva's anxious eyes swept over the small upturned faces, and relief coursed through her when she found no signs of injuries or distress.

Marie came to Eva's side. 'Have you brought any food, Auntie? Only there was nothing in the cupboard that I could give to the kids.'

'Where's your uncle?' Eva questioned apprehensively.

Marie shrugged. 'I don't know. Mrs Green said he went out this morning, and he hasn't come back yet. She said that the postman brought a letter to our house. And Mrs Warner from across the road told me that the postman had told her that the letter was addressed to me. But I've searched all over the house and I can't find it anywhere.'

'A letter? For you?' Eva smiled. 'It must be from your dad.'

Marie's pretty face was troubled. 'Mrs Warner said that the postman told her he wanted to give the letter to me in person because there was some money in it. But Uncle Alfred took it off him.'

Eva instantly realised why her husband was not at home. She knew without any doubt that he had taken the money for drink.

'I expect your uncle's kept the letter with him for safe-keeping, my duck.'

Marie's expression was cynical beyond her years.

'Do you really think that, Auntie Eva?' she asked.

Tears once more stung Eva's eyes, and sadly she shook her head.

Marie was hesitant to ask her aunt to question her uncle concerning the letter. She had been awoken by her aunt's screams the previous night, and had herself lain terrified and sleepless for many hours after that. But finally her overwhelming need drove her to plead nervously, 'Will you ask him for my letter when he comes back?'

Eva swallowed hard and screwed up her courage. 'Yes, I will.'

'You won't forget, will you?' the girl pressed anxiously.

'No. I promise I won't forget.' Eva spoke with a weary

resignation. Certain that her husband would have spent the money and destroyed the letter, she expected that his reaction to her question would be another violent outburst of temper.

With an effort she assumed an air of spurious gaiety. 'Now then, kids. Let's go into the house and see what we can take up to Uncle's. Because as soon as we can get a few pence from him, then we can have something to eat.'

Too young to be aware that to pawn was to be desperate, the smallest children applauded and happily skipped behind their mother as she hobbled down the dark entry. The older children shared Marie's knowledge of their family's poverty, and they followed more glumly.

The pawnshop was situated halfway down the Unicorn Hill, and beneath the three hanging golden balls a queue of women were already waiting, carrying bundles of clothing and bedding and other assorted articles.

When Eva and her children joined the queue she asked one of the women, 'Why is he closed?'

The careworn, shabby woman tossed her head and with an air of righteous condemnation told her, 'Because the dirty old bastard has got one of his bloody fancy tarts in theer with him. As soon as the cow walked into the shop the bloody door was locked and the blinds come down like lightning. She waren't even carrying any bundle, the hard-faced whore!'

'Ahr, and the blinds waren't the only things that come down like lightning, I'll bet,' another woman joked harshly, and her sally was greeted with roars of raucous laughter.

'What's they all laughing for, Mam?' Eva's eldest boy asked curiously.

She blushed and told him sharply, 'Never you mind! Just be quiet!'

Marie stood silently, her expression troubled as though her thoughts were disturbing her.

'Are you all right, Marie?' Eva asked, and the girl forced a smile.

'Yes, Auntie.'

But she immediately fell silent once more, and in scant seconds her features again wore a troubled expression.

Eva studied the girl's face, and noticed with concern how pale and peaky she was looking. For some time now the child's

271

normal happy disposition had been absent, and at first Eva had assumed it was because she was pining for her father. But lately she had begun to doubt that Caleb's absence was the only reason for Marie's obvious unhappiness. She had tried to casually question Marie, to find out what exactly was troubling her so. But the girl had merely returned evasive answers, and when Eva had pressed she had seemed to become more distressed. Unwilling to upset her further, Eva had let the matter drop. But inwardly she was becoming increasingly worried. Terrible suspicions were gnawing at her, suspicions which she shrank from examining more closely, in case they turned out to be facts. Although she castigated herself for this cowardice, she still could not find the courage to voice her suspicions openly and force the child to give her a full answer to them.

Now those suspicions returned in full strength to torment her.

Surely he wouldn't dare? She tried to soothe her torment. Marie's only a little kid. Surely he wouldn't try to do anything to her. Why should he need to anyway? I've never refused him. I do everything he wants me to. Even when it turns my stomach to do some of the filthy things he likes so much I still do them, don't I? He doesn't need to look for it anywhere else. I give him everything he wants.

But the more desperately Eva tried to allay her fears about her husband's sexual proclivities, the more naggingly insistent her suspicions became.

She was distracted from her unhappy reverie by a sudden outburst of clapping and cheering from the front of the queue.

The pawnshop blinds had been lifted, and as the door opened a woman scurried out. She kept her head bent low and had wrapped her shawl to conceal her face, but the keen eyes of the waiting women recognised her, and their jeers and catcalls filled the air.

'How was it today, Flossie?'

'Did he give you a bloody good screwing?'

'How many times did the old bleeder come?'

'That's your rent paid for this week, girl.'

The shawled woman ran away up the hill, and the jeering voices followed her mercilessly.

'I'm surprised you can run arter what you bin doing, you dirty cat!'

'Wait till your husband finds out, Flossie Smith. He'll give you a bloody sight more than this old bugger could.'

The elderly pawnbroker came to stand in the doorway and glowered at the shouting women. He was a tall, stoop-shouldered, cadaverous man who wore an ancient tasselled smoking cap on his bald head, and a greasy velvet jacket.

'The next 'un to shoot her mouth off can take her custom elsewhere,' he shouted in threat, and singled out one particularly vociferous woman. 'And you can sod off right now, Nellie Atkins, because you aren't going to pledge anything wi' me.'

'Why not?' the woman demanded aggressively. She was a formidable figure, with massive bare forearms, meaty shoulders and a tough, brawl-scarred face.

The pawnbroker was not deterred by her menacing appearance, however. 'Because your mouth is too big. And you lets it run away wi' you! Now just piss off, or I'll have the law on you.'

'I doon't give a bugger for the bleedin' law,' Nellie Atkins proclaimed defiantly.

'Doon't you now?' the pawnbroker sneered openly. 'All right then. You just stay theer.' He turned and shouted into the shop.

'Elly, get on up to the police station and tell Sergeant Jefferson that I wants him to come here immediate. Tell him there's an 'ooman causing an upset.'

After a brief pause the pawnbroker's diminutive wife came out of the shop door, and pinning her flowered bonnet upon her stringy, bunned hair, readied herself for her journey.

'You rotten, filthy old bastard!' Nellie Atkins hissed furiously, and shook her fist in the old man's face.

He stepped towards her with a sneering grin, and invited, 'Yes, cummon then. Give me a smack in the chops, why doon't you? Do it now in front of all these witnesses. Cummon then. Do it. Give me a smack in the chops.'

She growled in sheer frustration, then let her raised fist drop, and turned and trudged away, shouting back over her shoulder as she did so, 'You'll get what's coming to you one day, Vincent, you filthy old devil. You'll get yourn.'

He chuckled triumphantly and challenged the remaining women, 'Right then, does any o' you lot want to goo wi' that big fat cow?'

Although there were many glowering looks directed at him, nobody spoke, and satisfied with his victory he jerked his head to his waiting wife to return inside the shop, then told the women, 'Right, I'm open for business. Form an orderly queue when you gets inside. And I doon't want a lot o' noise and pestering. I'se got an headache.'

'And I bet you'se got a ballsache as well,' a voice shouted from the queue, and the old man grinned delightedly and lewdly cupped his groin with his hands. His action provoked laughter from the women, and he disappeared back inside his shop to be instantly followed by an eager crowd, shoving and pushing and loudly disputing their positions in the queue.

Marie watched and listened to the adults surrounding her and wished with all her heart that she was far away from this place, and these noisy, foul-mouthed, bad-smelling women. Most of all she wished that she were far away from Alfred Payne. She hated and feared him, and his sly fondlings and the feeling of his body pressing and rubbing against her own filled her with a terrified repulsion. She was tense and afraid whenever he was anywhere near her, or even in the vicinity of the house. The nervous strain was affecting her badly, her sleep was fitful and constantly broken, and her schoolwork had deteriorated. Time and time again she felt the urge to tell her Aunt Eva what was happening, but always when on the verge of telling she was held back by the knowledge that her aunt's burdens were already too heavy to bear, and she could not bring herself to add to them. Every day she prayed fervently to God to make her father well enough so that he could come back to her. She wanted to write to him, but had no money to buy paper, pen and ink, envelopes or postage stamps, and even if she had had the money she had no idea of where to send the letter. When she had asked her aunt to tell her the address Eva Payne had become very agitated, and had told her that her uncle had forbidden anyone in the family to write to her father, and that if Marie was to write, then she, Eva, would be punished. Marie sadly accepted the prohibition for her aunt's sake.

The pawnshop was divided into two sections by a long

counter surmounted by a metal grille which reached to the ceiling. The clients' section was simply an empty space. Vincent's section was tiered with shelves piled high with pawned goods and bundles. He sat on a high stool behind a small hatchway through which the articles for pledging were passed.

After a long wait Eva finally reached the hatchway and pushed the small bundle she carried towards the old man. He scowled and unwrapped the bundle, which consisted of the last few spare articles of clothing that she, her children and Marie possessed.

The old man clucked his tongue in disparagement.

'What are you expecting to get for these bits o' rag, missus?'

Eva's face flamed with shame. 'They're not rags,' she protested. She pointed to Marie's remaining spare dress. 'Look at that. It's hardly been worn. It's as good as new. And the boy's boots were resoled only a month ago.'

The old man snorted in disbelief, and his filthy fingers flicked through the other pieces of children's clothing and Eva's only blouse.

'How much am you expecting to get, missus?'

'Eighteen pence,' Eva stated.

The old man blew out a gusty breath of rejection, then offered, 'I'll give you a tanner.'

Eva shook her head. 'I'll take a shilling and threepence.'

Vincent shrugged. 'I'll goo to a shilling, and not a farthing more. Take it or leave it.'

Realising that she would get no increase on that offer, Eva nodded despondently, and the old man tossed the silver coin across to her and signalled his wife to place the bundle on a shelf. He scribbled on a ticket and thrust it towards Eva, then shouted, 'Next . . . Cummon, damm you, I aren't got all the bleedin' night to waste waiting for the likes o' you.'

Eva led her small party back down the hill. She went into a shop and bought bread, cheese, potatoes and onions, and then stopped at a butcher's to buy a piece of liver, which took the last of the money.

While her aunt was in the butcher's shop, Marie stood with the children on the pavement outside. She looked up the hill and dismay filled her as she saw the figure of her uncle lurching down towards them.

His face was red and sweaty, and as he loomed above her the acrid stench of his unwashed body filled her nostrils, and his foul, beer-laden breath gusted into her face as he bent low to growl, 'What's you doing here?'

'We're waiting for Aunt Eva. She's in the shop,' Marie informed him nervously.

At that instant Eva came out to join them.

'I've just been buying a nice bit of liver for your supper, Alfie. I thought you'd like liver and onions tonight.' Uncertain and apprehensive as to her husband's mood, she spoke as nervously as Marie had done.

To her relief he grinned, and said jocularly, 'Yes, I'd like some liver and onions tonight.'

Then her heart chilled within her as he leered at Marie and went on, 'That aren't all I'd like, though. I'd like a bit o' summat else as well.'

Waving to them to follow, he went on lurching down the hill, and they dutifully trailed behind him, the children now silent, and Marie enduring an ever-increasing sense of apprehension.

Inside the house Alfred brusquely ordered his wife, 'Get this lot up to bed.'

'But they haven't had anything to eat yet,' she pointed out meekly. 'I was going to give them some bread and cheese.'

'They can take it upstairs with 'um,' he growled.

The children began to troop upstairs, but he told Marie, 'No, not you. You can take the jug down to Crows and fetch me some beer.'

Eva looked frightened as she told the man, 'I've got no money left, Alfie. It all went on food.'

He ignored her, and instructed Marie, 'Tell Billy Crow to put it on the slate. Tell him that I'm starting work tomorrow.' He turned to his wife and snarled threateningly, 'If you doon't look sharp and get my grub cooked, I'll give you summat to quicken you.'

The dwarfish, humpbacked Billy Crow grimaced sourly when Marie gave him the message from Alfred Payne. But he took the jug and filled it with beer. When he handed it back to her he asked, 'How's your feyther getting on, my duck? He must be well on the mend by now. He'll be home soon, won't he?'

The child's clear eyes clouded as she whispered huskily, 'Oh, I hope so, Mr Crow. I do hope so that my father will come home soon.'

She ran from the shop before he could say anything more. He stared after her with concern, and said to his wife, 'That kid is being pulled down. It 'udn't surprise me if that bastard Payne is treating her badly. For two pins I'd call the cruelty bloke in to have a look at her.'

'You'll do no such thing, Billy Crow.' His wife rounded on him furiously. 'You'll mind your own bloody business. I doon't want bloody Alfie Payne to come down here blaggardin' me.'

The man rolled his eyes resignedly upwards, and knowing that where his marriage was concerned discretion was definitely the better part of valour, held his tongue.

Marie placed the jug of beer on the table in front of her uncle and started to go upstairs. But once again he stopped her, and pointing to the empty chair across the table from himself, told her, 'You sit theer. You can have a bit o' my liver and onions for being a good girl.'

Eva was bending over the fire grate cooking the meat and vegetables in a cast-iron frying pan. She gnawed her lips anxiously as she heard her husband offer the girl, 'Here you are, kid, have a drink of beer. It'll do you the power o' good.'

Marie took a sip of the liquid from her uncle's pot, and then sat slumped with her head dropped, her eyes fixed on the fingers which she twisted together upon her lap. She was being ravaged by a terrible sensation of foreboding, which dried her mouth and brought a lump to her throat.

Eva served her husband with the cooked food and he began to eat noisily, smacking his lips and grunting audibly with satisfaction. She then stood by the fireside in readiness to obey any further orders he might issue.

At intervals he sliced tiny portions of the liver and offered them to Marie on the end of his fork.

Initially she refused the offerings, but he scowled warningly, and afraid of his temper, she took the meat into her mouth and chewed and swallowed it with difficulty, wanting only to spit it out and run from this house.

277

Marie's gaze flickered imploringly to Eva, and the woman plucked up her courage and asked, 'Did a letter come for Marie this morning, Alfie?'

To her relief he didn't explode into a tirade, merely grinned and nodded his head, but vouchsafed nothing further.

Marie again silently implored her aunt, and Eva nerved herself to ask tentatively, 'Where's the letter then, Alfie? Only Marie wants to read it. She's been very worried about her dad.'

He scowled at his wife, and she quailed inwardly. Then he poured the last dregs from the jug and ordered Marie, 'Run and get this filled up agen.'

While she was away he finished his meal, and leant back in his chair. He grinned savagely at his wife, and taking the letter from his jacket pocket, waved it in front of her face.

'Here it is, you nosy cow. I'll let her read it when her gets back.'

Eva nodded and forced a grateful smile. 'Thank you, Alfie. It'll put the poor little soul's mind at rest to know that her dad's all right. She misses him really badly.'

Alfred stretched his arms wide, yawned hugely and belched resoundingly, then grinned at Eva and told her, 'Goo to Sammy Watkins' house and fetch me that pointing trowel that he's got o' mine. I'll be needing it tomorrow.'

Weary from her long day's toil, and feeling almost sick with hunger because she had not eaten since having two thin slices of bread and margarine for breakfast, Eva heard him with dismay.

'I'll just have a bite to eat first, shall I, Alfie?'

He mimicked her cruelly, 'I'll just have a bite to ate fust, shall I?' then slammed his clenched fist down upon the table with enough force to make the crockery rattle. 'I needs that trowel for tomorrow,' he shouted. 'So goo and get it.'

'But Sammy Watkins' house is at Crabbs Cross, isn't it?' she pointed out plaintively. 'It'll take ever so long to walk there and back. I'm really hungry, Alfie. I'll have to have something to eat before I walk as far as that.'

'Take the fuckin' grub wi' you then,' he snarled. 'Now sod off, before I loses me temper.'

Knowing that further argument would only worsen the

278

situation, Eva snatched up a piece of bread and cheese, and taking her shawl, left the house.

Payne settled himself comfortably, and lit a cigarette, then pulled a small flagon of rum from his pocket. He grinned with satisfaction as he looked at the dark spirit. His new job had once again reopened his slate at the White Lion, and he felt that luck was running well for him. He tapped the pocket which held the letter, and his grin became a lascivious leer.

Yes, me luck is definitely running well, aren't it?

He was impatient for Marie's return.

Marie came into the house, and instantly her eyes searched for her aunt. She listened hard for Eva's voice, hoping that she was upstairs with the children. She placed the jug on the table and went to go upstairs, but yet again her uncle stopped her.

'Wheer's you off to, my duck? I thought that you wanted to read your dad's letter.'

He pulled the torn envelope from his pocket and held it invitingly towards her.

She reached out to take it, but as her outstretched fingers touched the paper he jerked it back out of reach.

Marie felt tears brimming in her eyes. She hungered desperately with every atom of her being to read her father's words.

Payne chuckled cruelly at her expression of hurt disappointment, then told her breathily, 'I'm only having a bit o' fun wi' you, my duck. O' course you shall have your dad's letter.'

His eyes were beginning to glaze over, and he could feel his excitement mounting unbearably and his manhood becoming tumescent.

Again he proffered the letter, and again jerked it back from her seeking fingers.

He laughed wildly, and now Marie suddenly became terribly frightened.

He saw her fright and his mouth became dry and sticky as his breathing quickened.

'Here, take it,' he ordered hoarsely. Only this time he kept the letter close to his chest. 'Cummon! You'll have to come and get it.'

Fear, doubt and desire all battled for domination in Marie's mind. But the overwhelming hunger to read her father's letter enabled her to screw up her courage sufficiently to move around the table and approach the man.

'Lets have a bit o' fun, shall us?' He vented a high-pitched giggle, and stuffed the letter down the low neck of his waistcoat. 'You have to take it from here.'

She halted and stared at him with a look of distress upon her thin face.

'Take it from here.' His voice hardened and he scowled. 'Does you hear me, girl? Take it from here!'

His thick, black-nailed fingers tapped the envelope edge protruding from the top of his waistcoat.

Marie emitted a whimper of fear, but the irresistible need to have the letter impelled her to step close into the man's seated body and reach for the envelope. Her fingers locked on the paper and withdrew it.

'Got you!' Payne's arms clamped around her slender body, and even as she screamed, his mouth crushed smotheringly around her lips. She was helplessly trapped between his thighs, and his hand cruelly mauled her buttocks and pressed her hard into his groin.

Mindless terror engulfed her, and she fought desperately, but she was powerless against his brute strength.

He was grunting deep in his throat like some savage beast and she felt as if she were suffocating. She wriggled and struggled, sobbing with fear and anguish, as his hand reached under her skirt and his fingers dug brutally between her thighs and into her naked flesh.

Waves of blackness began to sweep across her sight as her senses reeled. He drew back his head and his hand clamped hard over her mouth, then he snarled into her ear, 'You be a good girl and do what I wants you to. Does you hear me, you little bitch? Keep still and do what I wants you to, and then I'll let you go. Does you hear me?'

His fingers pressed upon and parted her lips and she felt the roughness of hard skin between her teeth. In blind instinct she bit hard upon his flesh.

'Fuckin' 'ell!' he bellowed in shocked pain, and his grip slackened momentarily. With a sudden surge of terror-engendered strength, she pulled free of his grasp, and screaming at the top of her voice ran to the door and into the yard. Even as he came blundering after her, she was through the entry and out on the street. She ran with her blonde hair streaming behind her, and her shrieks brought men and women to doors and windows, and halted children at their play.

In blind fury Payne pursued her, but before many yards his wind gave out and he came to a gasping standstill. Dragging in strangled wheezes of breath, he stood bent over, his hands on his knees.

In his mind he spewed a torrent of filthy curses after her as her fleeing figure disappeared around the street corner. Slowly the strangled whooping of his breathing quietened, and his rapidly thudding heart slowed. He straightened and looked about and became aware of the suspicious faces staring at him from along the entire length of the street. He suddenly realised that he could face dire consequences for what he had done, and his cunning brain sought desperately for an explanation that would satisfy the watchers and allay their suspicions.

He started to walk slowly back towards his house and as he passed the staring faces he grinned ruefully.

'I copped the little cow pinchin' money from me pocket. I was going to give her a belting, but she runs faster than me. I'll tan the bloody hide off her when her comes back.'

As he constantly repeated this lie he became increasingly fluent and confident in his delivery. So much so that by the time he reached the entry to his own court he was satisfied that his listeners were accepting the truth of what he told them.

The vast majority of them did in fact believe him. It was a very common occurrence in the street to see shrieking children running to escape the punishment of enraged parents.

Billy Crow had been drawn out on to the pavement by the uproar and had walked up the street to see what was happening. He stood with a group of his neighbours near the entry to Payne's court, and as the man neared them Crow heard him relating what had happened.

The hunchbacked man was genuinely concerned about Marie Gurden. And now all his suspicions concerning Payne's treatment of her came clamouring at him with renewed vigour. Billy Crow possessed a great deal of physical courage, despite his bodily weakness and afflictions. He scowled as he heard Payne's explanation, and spoke out loudly.

'How could the poor little wench be pinching money from your pockets, Alf Payne, when you aren't got a copper to bless yourself with?'

Payne came to a standstill, and stared at the litle man as if he could not credit his boldness.

'And how does you know what I got in my pockets, Crowie?'

'I knows that I'se got a slate of yourn that needs clearing, Alf Payne.' The little man appeared unafraid. 'And I knows that I'se had to put two jugs o' beer on it in the last hour. So how could that little wench be pinching money from you, when you aren't got none?'

His reasoning did not impress those who heard it. It was standard practice to run up a slate, even if a man had money in his pocket. The slate could be cleared at a future date, and ready money was always desirable for more immediate, pressing needs.

Payne's initial impulse was to smash his stunted tormentor into a quivering, bloody pulp. But he was too cunning to fall into such a trap. If he reacted violently to this challenge, then although it might strike fear into those who saw it, it would also fuel suspicion as to why he had acted so. Tongues would wag, and people would say that he must have something to hide. So he merely forced a jeering laugh, and scoffed, 'Listen, Crowie, I hardly knows how to break this news to you, but theer's a lot of us in this street who runs up a slate wi' you, even though we might have a couple o' bob in our pockets.'

Heads nodded in agreement, and emboldened by this show of support, Payne shook his own head in mocking commiseration. 'As a matter o' fact, Crowie, I was going to put the money that little cow has stole from me into clearing my slate wi' you. But now you'll have to wait a bit longer for it, wun't you, my old cock? Unless you can run a sight faster than I can, and then you might catch the thieving little bitch afore her's spent it.'

This final sally evoked appreciative laughter from his audience, and he grinned cockily and swaggered down the entry of the court.

Out of view of the people in the street, his grin instantly metamorphosed into a grimace of mingled rage and apprehension.

I hope the fuckin' little bitch aren't gone running to the

police, he thought worriedly. Or I might have a lot more explaining to do. And they might not be so ready to believe me as these buggers here am.

Back in his house he slumped down on to the chair, and sat drumming his fingers against the table top as he tried to reassure himself that all would be well. Then he remembered his small flagon of rum, and drawing out the cork with his teeth, he spat it aside and greedily sucked the fiery spirit down his throat.

The fierce heat spread through his stomach and chest, and brought with it a renewal of his nerve.

Well, even if her does get the police on to me, all I'se got to do is to stick to me story about her pinching money. It's her word against mine, aren't it? And they always believes an honest working man before a bloody rotten pauper's kid, doon't they?

Cheered somewhat by this assumption, he lit a cigarette and inhaled its fragrant smoke with satisfaction.

I aren't got a thing to worry about, he told himself. Not a bloody thing. Then he frowned doubtfully . . . I hope!

Marie ran and ran, terror fuelling her flight. Instinctively she headed up the steep Red Lane towards the broad woodlands whose twisting paths and hidden glades she had come to know well. As soon as she reached the first outlying clumps of trees and undergrowth, she left the road and plunged into the shadowy green haven. As she moved deeper into the thickets, her terror lessened and she became aware of the fiercely aching muscles of her legs and the painful strainings of her overtaxed lungs as she gasped for breath. She slowed her headlong pace and then turned and ducked into a hugely spreading clump of blackberry bushes, burrowing like a frightened animal beneath the thorny branches.

She lay face down, drawing in long, shuddering breaths of earthy, decay-scented air, her ears tuned for any sounds of pursuit. Long minutes passed and imperceptibly the gentle soughing of the soft breezes rustling the leaves soothed her terrors. She knew that she could not remain here, that she must find help. But she felt completely drained of all energy, her limbs seeming to have lost all strength. She slowly curled into a foetal position, and began to suck her thumb.

* * *

'She's done what?' Eva Payne stared in stupefaction at her husband.

'Her's run off!' he growled, and stayed slumped in his chair, staring aggrievedley at the empty flagon of rum on the table before him. 'I couldn't half do with a drink. Me throat's as dry as a bone. Am you sure that you aren't got any money?'

The shock of what she had just been told momentarily overlaid Eva's fear of her husband, and she retorted angrily, 'Money for drink? You tell me that Marie has run off, and then ask me for money for drink? Where's she run off to? And why has she run off? Never mind asking me for drinking money! You tell me what's happened to that poor little soul.'

Payne glowered sullenly at his wife. Normally he would have ruthlessly crushed her show of temper and battered her into her usual state of submission. But this situation was too fraught with danger for him to resort to violence to quell her. While waiting for his wife to return Alfred Payne had had time to cool his temper, and to think with increasing trepidation about what he had done.

Keep cool! he warned himself now. Doon't let this cow rile you into acting foolish. Keep cool.

Almost beside herself with worry, Eva stood over him with her hands on her hips, and demanded, 'Tell me what's happened, Alfie. Tell me right now. If you've done anything to harm that poor little wench I'm going to go and fetch the police to you!'

As he heard her threat a murderous fury swept through him, and he lusted to smash her to the ground and kick her senseless. But his cunning instincts clamoured at him to restrain himself. This was not a problem that he could resolve in his usual way of violent assault. But his instincts also brought the realisation that he must not retreat, only attack.

'Oh, doon't you worry, I'm gooing to tell you all about what's happened all right!' he snarled aggressively. 'I should never have let you bring that fuckin' dosser of a brother o' yourn and his thievin' little bitch into my home in the fust bloody place. They aren't fit to live wi' decent folk.' He suddenly raised his clenched fists and shook them in her face, and despite her own anger she could not help but flinch back from him as her fear of his violence reasserted its customary hold.

'If I gets my hands on that thievin' little bastard, I'll break her fuckin' neck!' he bellowed.

'What do you mean? Why do you call Marie a thief?' Eva's anger was faltering now in the face of his outburst of rage, and she was struggling to maintain her brave front.

Once again Payne allowed his instincts to guide him. Shaking his head slowly, he scowled accusingly at her. 'Oh no . . . oh no . . . Doon't you try and tell me that you doon't know about her thievin' ways. Her's your blood kin, aren't her? You'm bound to be knowing what her's really like behind that bloody innocent act her puts on. Her's got to have got it from your side o' the bloody family, aren't her? All my family has always been as straight as a die. Good, honest, hard-working people each and every one on 'um. We'se never had a bloody thief in the Payne family, and that's a well-known fact, that is. We'em all honest folk.'

It was Eva's turn to shake her head in bafflement. 'I don't know what you're talking about, Alfie. Why are you keeping on about thieves like this?'

He now spoke coldly and contemptuously. 'I'm keeping on about thieves because that's what that little bitch is. A dirty thief!'

'Oh no!' Eva burst out in vehement denial. 'Oh no! Not Marie. She's not a thief. She's a good, sweet girl.'

'That's right!' he exclaimed in disgust. 'That's right! You stick up for the little cow, wun't you? Well, I'se had enough of it.' He got to his feet. 'I'm going to the police station right now, and I'm going to lay charges against that thievin' little cow. And I've a good mind to lay charges against that dossing brother o' yourn as well. Because it's him that's put her up to it, if I'm any judge. He's sponged off me ever since he come back from Canada, and if that waren't enough, he's more than likely put his bloody daughter up to thievin' from me as well.'

All Eva's anger had died away, and she was shaking her head in frantic, fearful denial of what she was hearing.

'But why are you calling her a thief, Alfie?'

'Because I caught her stealing me last bloody shillin', that's why,' he declared indignantly.

'When?' Eva pleaded to know.

'Just after her come back wi' that jug o' beer I sent her for.'

'But what's she stolen from you?' Eva couldn't believe what she was hearing.

'Me last shillin', that's what.'

Payne stared hard at his wife and saw the doubt and pain in her face, then went on more quietly, 'Her come back with the beer, and I went across to the privy to have a shit. I'd left me jacket hanging on the nail theer. Well, theer was somebody in the privy so I turned round and come straight back. And I saw the little cow gooing through me jacket pockets. When she saw me looking, she cried out and jumped back looking really guilty.'

'No, no, she wouldn't do that. Not Marie.' Eva's protest was virtually a moan of despair.

'I asked her what her was doing, and her told me that her was looking for a bit o' rag to blow her nose on.'

Alfred Payne could not help feeling a warm glow of self-approbation as he improvised so fluently and confidently.

'I just told her all right, and then I asked her what her'd got so tight-clenched in her hand. She went bright red, and I guessed then what her'd done. This aren't the fust time I'se missed money from me pockets since her and her bloody dossin' feyther come to stay.'

For a moment he stopped speaking, and then, assuming the expression of a grievously wronged victim, went on in an aggrieved tone.

'Well, I wanted to give her the benefit o' the doubt, so I didn't accuse her of anything. But I went and I searched through me pockets meself, and I couldn't find the shillin' piece that I'd left in 'um. So I asked her real quiet if she'd took it. She 'udn't answer. And I'se got to be honest wi' you now, I lost me temper, and I shouted at her that if her didn't tell me the truth, I'd give her a bloody leathering. I went to take me belt off, just to frighten her a bit, and her started skrawking like a bloody mad 'ooman and run hell for leather out o' the door. I went after her to try and catch her, but her was too fast for me.'

He drew breath, and then played what he considered to be a master stroke. 'As God is my judge, Eva, I swear on my kids' lives that I never so much as laid a finger on the thievin' little

286

bitch. Though I'll tell you straight, I was going to make her arse sore wi' me belt. But her was too quick for me.'

He lifted his flat cap from its hanging nail and pulled it on to his mop of greasy hair.

'But she wun't be too quick for the police to catch her, I'll be bound.'

He moved towards the door. 'I shan't be very long. I'm only gooing up to the police station to lay charges agen her, and then I'll come straight back here.'

'No, Alfie!' Eva cried out, and threw herself against his body to clutch at him and beg, 'Please don't do that, Alfie! Please don't go to the police! Please don't!'

He made as if to push her away, but there was no real force in his attempt, and she continued to cling desperately to him, begging and pleading with him.

Alfred Payne now found himself in a quandary. If the girl had run to the police and made accusations against, him he would be put in the position of defendant. On the other hand, if he were to go to the police and lay charges against her of pilfering from his pockets, he would become a figure of derision and contempt in his immediate community, jeered at as a man who could not keep a mere child under control. Despised as a man who had betrayed a member of his own family to the hated tyrannical authorities.

Quickly he considered these alternatives, and thought back over what had happened. He decided that it would be best to leave matters as they stood, for the present at least. He knew that his story about the girl's thieving had been widely believed among his neighbours; and it was obvious from the way she was now behaving that Eva believed his account also.

Feigning a reluctance he was far from feeling, he allowed his pleading, tearful wife to persuade him against going to the police. He was even gracious enough to give her permission to go in search of the missing child.

Slavish in her gratitude for her husband's magnanimity, Eva took the jug to the beer shop and persuaded Billy Crow to fill it on credit. Then, leaving Payne drinking at the fireside, she went anxiously out into the approaching darkness.

She went from one to another of her neighbours' houses, asking if Marie was with them. Each succeeding negative reply increased her anxiety for the child. Most of the people she questioned were sympathetic, yet at the same time dismissive of her concern.

'Doon't you moither your yed, my wench. The little bugger 'ull come back when her's hungry enough.'

'But she's never done this before,' Eva would protest. 'She's never run off like this.'

'All kids runs off sooner or later, my duck. Especially when they's bin getting up to their tricks, and they knows they'm gooing to get their arses tanned.'

Eventually Eva had exhausted all possible neighbourly refuges for Marie except one. Finally she went back to Billy Crow's beer shop.

The little man was serving a customer when Eva called, and as soon as he saw her worried face again he knew why she was there.

'That poor little cratur aren't come back then?' It was both statement and question.

'No.' Eva shook her head. 'I don't suppose she's with you, is she?'

'No.' He frowned angrily. 'More's the pity. It 'ud have been a sight better for the poor little soul if her had been left wi' me in the fust place, arter her dad was hurt.'

The scathing words lacerated Eva's tight-strung nerves, and she was uncomfortably aware of the interested gaze of the female customer.

'What do you mean by that, Billy Crow?' she demanded indignantly.

'Just what I said, missus.' His voice dripped contempt. 'The poor little cratur 'ud have been safe wi' me. And well cared for, as well.'

'She has been well cared for.' Eva's cowed spirit for once took fire at this imputation. 'I treated Marie as if she was one of my own kids. I've loved her like a mother.'

The dwarfish man's own temper took fire. 'Ahr, that's maybe so, missus. But I'll bet your fuckin' man never loved her like a feyther, did he? He had another sort o' loving in mind.'

'What do you mean by that?' Eva shrilled furiously. 'Speak plain and tell me what you mean.'

Drawn by the heated voices, Billy Crow's wife had come

288

from the back room to hear the last exchanges. Now she told her husband warningly, 'You just keep your big mouth shut, Billy.'

But the man was too irate to heed his wife.

'No, I wun't keep my mouth shut. So you just keep out o' this,' he shouted at her, and swung back to Eva. 'I'll tell you plain what a good many folks am thinking, but they'm too fritted o' that fuckin' animal you'm married to to spake out. Well, I aren't fritted of Alfie Payne, and I'll spake out. I reckon that little wench has run off because your husband had been getting up to no good wi' her. And I'll tell you summat else, missus. If her don't come back safe and sound I'll goo straight to the police and tell 'um what I reckons, as well. And neither your husband nor twenty fuckers like him 'ull stop me doing that. I'll get bleedin' Alf Payne put away for twenty years.'

As Eva heard this threat, actual fear shuddered through her, and for a brief instant all her own suspicions of her husband surfaced from the depths of her mind. But once again she ruthlessly suppressed them. For the sake of her own children, to save them from being forced into the workhouse, she would not, and could not, accept that what Billy Crow was saying was the truth.

White-faced, her eyes wild and glaring, she told him, 'God ought to strike you down dead for saying such filthy, wicked lies about my husband. He's never so much as laid a finger on that girl. She's run off because he caught her stealing money from his pockets.' Driven by a madness of utter desperation, Eva now voiced her own lies in an effort to convince her listeners. 'And it's not the first time she's done that, neither. I've caught her stealing from my purse, as well. And more than once. So you just watch what you say, Billy Crow. Or it'll be you that ends in the police station for telling such terrible lies about my husband.'

She ran from the shop without waiting for any reaction, already bitterly regretting what she had said about Marie.

Behind her, Billy Crow scoffed jeeringly, 'She's as big a liar as Tom Pepper, that cow is.'

But the female customer and his own wife had been convinced by Eva's impassioned declaration that she was speaking the truth about the girl's stealing, and they simultaneously turned on the man and told him so.

289

An acrimonious three-sided dispute then commenced between them, which continued for a long time and was joined in by a second and then a third customer upon their entering the shop.

Eva walked distractedly along the street. Darkness had now fallen and she saw the lamplighter using his long pole to ignite the gas lamp which stood near the junction with Red Lane. She hurried to the man and questioned him anxiously.

'Have you see a blonde-haired girl anywhere around here, mister?'

He shook his head, 'No, missus,' then, noticing how drawn and worried she looked, added reassuringly, 'Now don't you fret yourself, missus. I'm sure your girl 'ull be home directly now it's got dark.'

Despite the lateness of the hour, like moths drawn to a lighted candle children now came running towards the hissing, flaring lamp, and commenced their games within the pale circle it cast.

As the lamplighter walked away, Eva called after him, 'Please, mister, if you should see a blonde-haired girl, could you ask her if her name's Marie. And if it is will you tell her that I'm looking for her, and that she's to come home directly.'

He waved acknowledgement, and went on.

One of the ragged boys playing at the lamp asked Eva, 'Aren't Marie come back yet then, Mrs Payne?'

She shook her head. 'No, my duck. I don't suppose you've seen her anywhere, have you?'

'I saw her when her went running off and Mr Payne was chasing after her,' he informed with a cheeky grin. 'He couldn't catch her though. He was puffing and blowing like a bloody railway engine.'

The other urchins clustered around Eva, faces eager and excited.

'Does you want us to help you to look for her, Mrs Payne?' one offered, and Eva nodded gratefully.

'Yes please, if you would I'd be ever so grateful. I'm getting very worried about her.'

'I knows wheer her 'ull be.' It was a girl who spoke this time. 'She's got a camp up in the woods. She showed me wheer it is. It's a secret camp.'

Sudden hope burgeoned in Eva's heart, and she pleaded, 'Could you take me there, my duck?'

The child looked doubtful. 'It's too dark, Mrs Payne. I'm scared o' the woods when it's dark.'

'But I'll be with you,' Eva urged eagerly. 'You'll be safe with me.'

'But how 'ull we be able to see in the dark?' the girl asked reasonably enough.

'I'll get a lantern.' Eva could hardly restrain herself from grabbing the child and bodily carrying her towards the woods.

'Yeah, we'll all come wi' you, Lettie.'

'Goo and get the lantern, Mrs Payne.'

'Come on, let's all goo up to the woods.'

The excited children were clamouring to take part in this adventure.

'Can I come?'

'Can I come as well?'

'Come on, everybody, we'em gooing up to the woods to look for Marie Gurden.'

'Yeah, let's goo.'

'Let's goo now.'

'Come on, we'em gooing to the woods.'

'All right then. I'll show you wheer the camp is,' Lettie agreed, and Eva could have shouted out with relief.

She ran to borrow a lantern, and then, with the crowd of shouting, laughing, excited children gambolling around her, hurried up Red Lane towards the dense black masses of the woodland.

Marie heard her name being shrilled out by childish voices long before she caught sight of the bobbing, swinging light of the lantern. She was crouched within the depths of the blackberry thicket, shivering with cold, hungry and thirsty, and mortally afraid of the darkness and the weird, unearthly night noises that continually sounded around her.

At first the shouts struck terror through her as she imagined that it was Alfred Payne come to hunt her down. But then she realised that these were children's voices, and she thought that she recognised some of her friends' and playmates' distinctive shrills. Next, a stronger, fuller-toned shout echoed through the trees, and the child knew that it was her Aunt Eva.

She thankfully shouted back, but her dry throat and mouth could only emit a wavering, croaking call which did not reach the ears of the searchers.

Their cries came louder, and now Marie saw the lancing beam of the lantern nearing her, and she sobbed with relief that she was to be rescued from her frightening ordeal. Crawling out from beneath the shelter of the bushes, she began to stumble towards the oncoming light.

'Look theer, it's her!' a boy shrieked in wild excitement, and Marie was clasped in the eager embrace of her Aunt Eva. She could feel the woman's tears of relief wet against her cold cheeks, while all about her the children cheered and voiced their admiration for her daring escapade, and fired questions at her.

'You bad girl! You've worried me near to death! You bad, wicked girl, you,' Eva scolded, but the kisses she rained on the child's face and the loving hugs she gave her belied the scolding.

Marie tried to tell her aunt why she had run away, but Eva shushed her to silence.

'Not now, darling. Let's get you home and in the warm first. You're freezing cold, and you must be starving for something to eat.'

Marie, half dazed and full of relief to be in the company of friends and loved ones, docilely allowed herself to be led from the woods. But as the noisy group entered Edward Street, the thought of her uncle waiting in the house filled her with dread, and in the pale light of the gas lamp she tugged back against the pull of her aunt's hand.

'Do we have to go back now, Aunt Eva? Can't we go somewhere else?'

Eva recognised the real fear the girl was in, and with a sinking heart realised that she herself must now face up to what she dreaded to accept as the truth.

She thanked the children for their help and with some difficulty persuaded them to leave her and Marie alone beneath the gas lamp.

When the last lingering child had grudgingly left them, she cradled the trembling girl close, and gently tilted her face so that she could look down into her eyes.

'Now, sweetheart, I want to ask you something, and you must tell me the truth, no matter what that truth is,' she coaxed softly,

292

and her own heart was thudding in apprehension of what she might now hear. 'What happened to cause you to run away like you did?'

Marie swallowed hard in a fruitless attempt to dispel the painful lump in her throat. Tears brimmed and fell from her eyes, and in a choked voice she said simply, 'Uncle Alf grabbed hold of me. He tried to do nasty things to me.'

Eva moaned in distress. 'What things, sweetheart? You must tell me.'

Now the child was sobbing heartbrokenly, and Eva was hard put to understand her gasping words. 'He pushed his hand inside my knickers. He scared me, Auntie. He really, really scared me. He hurt me, and he told me that if I was a good girl and did what he wanted me to, then he'd let me go . . . He's always grabbing hold of me and doing dirty things to me . . .'

She broke off as her grief overwhelmed her, and Eva's tears fell also as she cuddled the slender, shaking body close and felt her own miseries remorselessly engulfing her. With a terrible despair she finally accepted the truth of her own suspicions, but like a sufferer driven to probe an agonising ache, she pressed the child to repeat her story again.

'Don't make me stay in the house with Uncle Alf, Auntie. Please don't make me stay with him,' Marie finally begged piteously. 'Don't make me stay with him, please, Auntie. Please.'

'Hush now, I won't, I won't,' Eva soothed, and slowly her horror and despair metamorphosed into a white heat of rage against her husband. But as the moments passed that rage became pervaded with a sense of helplessness.

What can I do? What'll happen to my own kids if I go to the police? And even if I bring charges against him, it'll still be his word against Marie's, won't it? And he'll just say that she's lying to cover up her stealing from him. A terrible guilty remorse shook her, as she suddenly recalled, And I've made sure that the police will believe him, haven't I? Because I've told lies about Marie stealing as well.

The realisation of the damage she had done filled her with bleak despair, and all she could do was to stand cuddling the sobbing child, and stare in silent misery at the bowed blonde head beneath her.

*   *   *

293

'You wants me to keep her here?' The old woman seemed hard put to understand.

'Please, Mrs Green, talk quietly. I don't want anyone to hear us.' Eva spoke in low-pitched tones, nervous that she might attract attention from the neighbouring tenements. 'It's only for tonight I want you to have her. I'll pay you for it.'

The old woman peered at Marie's woebegone, tear-stained face and demanded, 'What's bin done to the poor litle cratur, Mrs Payne? Her looks pitiful.'

'She's upset, that's all. She'll be all right. It's a private matter,' Eva answered sharply, unable to bring herself to tell the other woman what had happened. 'Will you take her in for the night? I can pay you next Saturday when I get my wages.'

'O' course I can take her in.' The old woman bared her toothless gums in a smile of welcome. 'The poor little morsel can stay wi' me as long as she wants. And I doon't want paying for it, neither. She's a good child.'

She reached out and drew Marie into her malodorous home, and closed the door without another word to Eva.

Thankful that for tonight at least Marie would be safe, Eva turned away and walked across the court to her own home. She peeped cautiously through the window and saw that the gaslit room beyond was empty.

The wicked bugger must be asleep upstairs. She felt a rush of relief. She had decided that she would confront her husband with Marie's revelations, and since taking that decision had been trying to steel her courage to carry it through. Now, even while castigating herself for her own cowardice, she still felt thankful that that dreaded confrontation could be avoided for a few hours more.

Moving slowly, and as quietly as she could, she crept into the house, and heard Alfred's loud snoring coming from the room above. Not daring to risk waking him by climbing the stairs and lying down beside him, Eva turned out the gas light, seated herself on the wooden chair and using her arms as a pillow laid her head down on the table top and tried to sleep.

Across the yard Marie Gurden lay fully clothed beside the

old woman in the narrow, stale-smelling bed, and silently and tearfully prayed that by some miracle her father might come back to her by morning.

Chapter Thirty-One

'Get your arse off that chair, you lazy, useless cow!'

Alfred Payne roughly shook his sleeping wife and bellowed furiously into her bemused face.

'Why aren't you brewed the tea? Wheer's my grub? Why aren't it ready? You knew I was starting back to work today, didn't you?'

Still half dazed, Eva hurried to obey, raking the dead ashes from the damped-down fire and feeding the still-glowing embers with scraps of wood and paper until the flames leapt and she was able to place the filled kettle on top to boil. Then she hastened to wrap slices of bread and cheese in a clean rag for her husband to take with him.

Cursing sullenly to himself, Alfred Payne laced up his heavy boots, and then sorted out his tools.

Once this task was done he demanded, 'Wheer's that thievin' little bastard? Did you find her?'

Now that the moment for confrontation had come, Eva's courage failed her. All her determination to challenge her husband about what he had done to the child suddenly evaporated, leaving her feeling sickened and helpless as she stared at his irate face.

'Well? Did you find her?' he reiterated angrily.

Eva nodded, and blurted defensively, 'I've left her at Mrs Green's. I didn't think that you'd want her back here.'

This information caused Payne to pause for thought. Now that he was sober, the possible repercussions of what he had done to the child struck fully home to him. He realised that he must act cautiously and cunningly. In the circumstances it would perhaps be better for the girl to stay away for a while.

He nodded, and grunted, 'You thought right. If you'd fetched her back here I'd have kicked both your arses out of the door. Old Ma Green can have the thievin' little cow and welcome.'

The kettle bubbled out steam and Eva brewed a pot of tea. There was no milk in the house, and she offered, 'Shall I go and borrow a cup of milk, Alf? I'll only be a minute.'

He shook his head. 'No, I'll have it as it comes.'

She poured him a cup of black tea and he drank it without milk or sugar. Then he picked up his bag of tools, and the rag-wrapped bread and cheese, and went out of the door without another word to Eva.

Since it was Friday the children had to be got ready for school, but before Eva roused them from their beds she went to Mrs Green's to fetch Marie.

The girl had not slept well, and her eyes were puffy and her face pale and drawn. Eva sent her ahead and then asked the old woman, 'Do you think you could have Marie staying here with you for a while longer? I'll pay you for it.'

Mrs Green appeared offended. 'Aren't I already told you that the poor little morsel can stop wi' me as long as she wants. And that I doon't want paying for it. Now fetch your little 'uns round, and goo to your work.'

Eva thanked her fervently and hurried back to her own house, to find that Marie had already brought the rest of the children downstairs and was getting them ready for the day ahead.

Eva told Marie about the arrangement for her to continue staying with Mrs Green, and the girl voiced her relief.

'Yes, you can stay with her until your dad comes back.' Eva felt thoroughly ashamed of her own cowardice as she went on, 'But listen now, Marie, I want you to promise me something. I want you to promise that you won't tell anybody else what you told me last night. I want it to be a secret between you and me.'

Marie stared doubtfully. 'But how can it be a secret between us, Auntie Eva, when Uncle Alf knows it as well? And what if he does it again?'

The woman's own sense of guilt and shame caused her to react irritably to the simple logic of the questions.

'It won't happen again!' she snapped curtly. 'So you just do what I tell you, and keep quiet about it. You're not to tell anybody, least of all your father. Do you understand?'

Marie nodded obediently, but her aunt's words seared her mind with a sense of betrayal, and she knew that never again would she ever be able to fully trust this woman.

The distant sounds of factory steam whistles shrilly summoning the workers to their labour carried clearly on the still air, and Eva sighed wearily.

'I'll have to go or I'll be late.' She stared worriedly at Marie, and in tentative apology offered, 'I didn't mean to snap at you, my dear. But when you're older you'll understand why what happened has to be kept a secret.'

Marie made no answer, but there was reproach in her eyes. Eva bent and kissed the clustering children goodbye. She moved to kiss Marie also, but the girl drew back from her and Eva's lips encountered only empty air. The rebuff deeply hurt her and when she left the house there were tears of sorrow and remorse in her eyes. But she was still convinced that the course of action she had taken was the only one open to her, and that she was acting in the best interests of everyone, including Marie herself.

Chapter Thirty-Two

On that Friday, the thirty-first of July 1914, Marie Gurden was not the only one who was suffering from a sense of betrayal. Irish Nationalists and the British Liberal and Labour politicians who supported the cause of Home Rule for Ireland shared that feeling. The Government in London had announced on the previous night that because of the crisis in Europe the Home Rule question would be shelved indefinitely, and the supporters of Home Rule felt that their objective, which had seemed so tantalisingly near achievement, had been snatched from them. In Northern Ireland the leaders of the armed Ulster Volunteers grimly accepted that the threat of civil war had been set in temporary abeyance, and quickly determined that they would give their whole-hearted support to King and Country should the British Empire be drawn into a general European war.

In accordance with this, Jack Preseley and the majority of those other Ulstermen who had resigned their commissions in the British Army immediately took steps to rejoin their regiments.

Jack telegraphed the commanding officer of his old regiment, and upon receiving a favourable promise of support in his application to the War Office, sailed on the earliest available ferry back to the mainland.

He intended to go first to Redditch to see Amy Morgan before continuing on to London.

By the time he reached Redditch, early on Saturday evening, the German Kaiser had already declared war on Russia and the German Army was flooding across the frontiers of Russian Poland.

Redditch town centre presented a festive appearance in the balmy evening. The August Bank Holiday had commenced,

301

and happy crowds of young men and boys, young women and girls, dressed in all their fineries, paraded around and around the Church Green and the Recreation Garden, in the bandstand of which the Redditch Town Band were playing a selection of rousing tunes.

The stalls along the marketplace were thronged with shoppers, and the public houses were filled with men and women enjoying surcease from their grinding weekday toil. Long queues had formed outside the public hall and Treadgolds Picture House and the Palace Theatre, while on the road leading eastwards from the town centre streams of people headed towards Beoley Road Recreation Ground, where the August pleasure fair was ablaze with electric lights, and the steam organ blared over Pat Collins Scenic Motor Railway, the Animated Teddy Bears, the Electric Galloping and Waltzing Horses, the Circus Menagerie and a host of other sideshows and amusements, presided over by hoarsely bellowing, tough-looking, colourfully dressed showmen and their equally tough, garishly clad womenfolk.

Now that he had reached the town, Jack found himself in a quandary. Because of the secrecy of his relationship with Amy he could not go openly to her house and ask to see her. Equally he did not feel able to go to the house of Anthony Barton. The Ulsterman's feelings of guilt towards his friend had intensified during his sojourn in Northern Ireland, but he knew that no matter how greatly his conscience troubled him, he was not strong enough to break free of Amy's ensnarement. He wanted her so badly that no demands of honour or ties of friendship could deter his pursuit of her.

He had his baggage delivered to the Royal Hotel in the marketplace, where he had engaged a room. Then he bathed and changed his travel-stained clothing for something more suited to the holiday, a lightweight grey suit and dashing broad-brimmed slouch hat. Twirling a gold-headed cane between his fingers he once more rejoined the clamorous crowds in the streets, and for a time wandered aimlessly among them, his eyes constantly seeking for some sight of a familiar face. He hoped that he might meet Amy Morgan amid the thronging pleasure-seekers. Surely she would be somewhere among them, celebrating the holiday with her friends, he told

302

himself, remembering how she had talked of previous Bank Holiday weekends she had spent in the town, listening to the band and visiting the funfair, enjoying herself hugely with her group of friends.

Of course! That's where she'll most likely be at this time, he decided. She'll be at the funfair now while it's early. Before the drunks and the roughs go there from the pubs.

The fact that if Amy were to be at the funfair, then undoubtedly Anthony would be there also, caused Preseley a momentary disquiet. Then he shrugged. If that was the case, then so be it. He would just have to face it out as best he could.

With a new impetus to his steps he turned and strode eastwards in the direction of Beoley Road Recreation Ground.

The swingboat dipped deep and soared high, and Amy Morgan closed her eyes and gripped the safety bar tightly, and gloried in the thrilling sensations of swooping flight. Bernard Hulme gazed adoringly at the young woman's beautiful face and pulled down on the hanging rope with all the strength of his muscular arms, building a rhythm, swinging the boat like a huge pendulum higher and higher and higher.

Below them Anthony Barton stood with frowning eyes, watching jealously and inwardly fiercely resenting the young interloper whom he considered was in his, Anthony Barton's, rightful place.

Other members of the group were in the row of swingboats, laughing and calling to each other as they hauled on the ropes, competing to see who could reach the highest pinnacle of flight, and Anthony felt that he was being deliberately excluded from their gaiety.

His resentment encompassed Amy Morgan, and he seethed as he thought of how she had been acting towards him that afternoon and evening. Flirting outrageously with the youthful Bernie Hulme, a mere callow schoolboy. Ignoring Anthony himself, and when he sought to establish the innocent intimacy of a sweetheart's possession, cruelly rebuffing him, and spitefully refusing to let him take her hand or even to accompany her on the carousels and motor railway.

'Hello, Tony, what's the matter? You look as if you've lost a pound and found a penny.'

303

Anthony turned to find that Charlie Parker, his fellow lieutenant in the battery, had come to stand next to him.

He forced a smile. 'Oh, hello, Charlie. I'm all right. I've a bit of a headache, that's all.'

'I'm not surprised. That steam organ would give anyone a migraine.' The newcomer grinned wryly and, as if to confirm his statement, the wailing steam organ suddenly emitted an ear-splitting squeal. Then, as the music resumed once more, Charlie exclaimed excitedly, 'It's great news, isn't it? Major Tunbridge phoned me about it an hour ago.' A peevish note entered his tone. 'Of course, as always I expect that I was the last one to be informed. You were the first he told, I'll wager.'

Anthony shook his head in puzzlement. 'I don't know what you mean, Charlie. Told of what?'

The other man raised his eyebrows in surprise. 'You mean to say that you haven't heard?'

'I've heard nothing,' Anthony asserted irritably. 'I've not been home since this morning.'

'It's the Kaiser! He declared war on Russia this morning. Major Tunbridge had a phone message from the War Office. The battery is to immediately prepare to bring itself up to full war establishment.'

Anthony could only stare in blank shock. 'But we're not at war.'

'No, not yet. But there's a chance we soon might be.' The young man grinned with delight. 'Won't it be a lark, Tony? We could well be commanding our sections in a real battle before the end of the year. I hope our dammed windy politicians won't miss this chance. We can give the Kaiser what he's been asking for for years, can't we? A damned good thrashing!'

Anthony was still having difficulty in coming to terms with what he was hearing.

'But how are we involved in this, Charlie?'

His companion hissed with exasperation. 'Are you really such a blockhead, man? We're involved because of the Treaty of London.'

Anthony shook his head in bafflement. 'I've never heard of it.'

Charlie laughed good-naturedly, and confessed, 'Neither had

304

I until Major Tunbridge explained it all to me. Apparently we signed a treaty in 1839 in which we guaranteed to protect the neutrality of Belgium, and also to guard the French coastal ports against occupation by an aggressor who was hostile to our own country. Major Tunbridge thinks that France will go to war in aid of its ally, which is Russia. The French have already ordered full mobilisation and war footing. Now we all know that in the event of war with France the Germans have the Von Schlieffen Plan, which involves their troops sweeping through Belgium . . .'

He went on at some length, explaining all the connotations, but Anthony was no longer listening. He was visualising himself in a myriad of heroic roles against a background of thunderous battle. Eventually he shook free of these inspiring daydreams to interrupt his friend's recital.

'So what does the Major want us to do, Charlie? If we're to bring the battery up to full war establishment shouldn't we be doing something right now, instead of wasting our time here?'

The question seemed to abruptly deflate the other man's bubble of excitement. He grimaced, and shook his head disappointedly. 'Well actually, Tony, when I asked the Major what he wanted me to do, all he said was nothing at present.'

'Nothing?' Anthony's own heroic visions disappeared completely. 'We're to do nothing?'

'No.' Charlie was now quite despondent. 'He said that after the recruits' drill on Wednesday night, we officers would have a chat about the situation.'

He sighed. 'Ah well, we'll just have to be patient, won't we, Tony? I have to meet a friend, so I'll say cheeribye.'

He wandered away, leaving Anthony deep in thought.

The showman pulled the lever which lifted the braking board up against the bottom of the swingboat, and wood clattered jarringly against metal as the boat was brought to a juddering halt.

Bernie Hulme leapt agilely out and reached up to help Amy dismount. Laughing gaily, she jumped down in a froth of skirt and petticoat, and leaning forward kissed the youth resoundingly on his mouth.

'That's to say thank you for being my beau today,' she told

him, and giggled as he blushed bright scarlet and stammered in delighted confusion.

Amy stared at the handsome youth with extreme pleasure. She found him utterly and delightfully charming, and drew a sweetness of satisfaction from his obvious adoration of her, which she had never experienced before. There was a purity and innocence in him that evoked an unaccustomed tenderness of response in her. In her present mood she found herself regarding older, more mature men with a faint distaste. Compared with this sweet boy they were somehow coarse and stale. She was still a virgin in the flesh, if not in the mind, and although she had enjoyed the fervent kisses and caresses of her other admirers and lovers, there was mingled with that sexual excitement a definite fear of the latent brutality in their sexual overtures. She had always been nervously aware of the fact that should they lose control, they were physically strong enough to overcome whatever resistance she might make. With this handsome, blushing, stammering adorer she felt none of these nervous fears. She felt that she would always be the one who would be in control, should she ever choose to permit him to kiss and caress her.

She looked about her and met Anthony's frowning stare. She pouted petulantly at him. He had lately become a frightful bore, always grouchy, always trying to maul her about, always demanding that she set a date for their wedding. That, of course, was out of the question. She knew now that her relationship with him had been a mistake. She could never marry him. Or any other man who was older than herself, for that matter. A sly smile briefly wreathed her full, moist lips. How could she even consider marrying some brutal, demanding, domineering older man when there were so many sweet, innocent, malleable youths such as Bernie Hulme to worship her with such humble, undemanding adoration?

In quick succession the other swingboats were brought to a standstill, and the group coalesced around Amy and Bernie, laughing and jokingly disputing who had reached the highest point of flight.

Anthony pushed through the close-packed bodies and took Amy's arm. She reacted with a frown, but resentful of her treatment of him, Anthony disregarded her reaction and spoke urgently to her.

'Amy, I must talk to you alone. Charlie Parker has just given me some very important news.'

'Not now, Tony, please. I want to go on the Electric Gallopers.' She tried to free her arm, but he tightened his grasp.

'No,' he told her loudly, fighting to restrain his urge to physically drag her from the midst of the group. 'I want to talk to you first. It's very important. The Kaiser has declared war against Russia.'

Although a couple of his listeners displayed expressions of concern at hearing this information, the remainder were sublimely indifferent, and Amy herself assumed an attitude of sarcastic mockery.

'Well, Tony, what do you expect me to do about that? Am I to declare war against the Kaiser?'

This sally brought a roar of laughter from her friends, and his face burned with embarrassment.

'No, of course not. But we could be drawn into it also, so we should be ready,' he blurted miserably, and his answer evoked a further roar of laughter, but this was of a jeering quality, as though they were mocking a fool.

Although she smiled, there was cruelty gleaming in Amy's eyes as she saw the misery in his expression, and to compound his torment she suddenly produced from her skirt pocket a 'teaser', a short leaden tube filled with water, and aimed it at his face.

'Then I hereby declare war on you, Anthony Barton.' She was in the grip of manic excitement by now, and she squeezed the tube hard, bursting the thin seal and spraying a stream of water into his eyes.

He gasped in shock as the liquid struck his eyeballs, and released her arm so that he could wipe his eyes and clear his sight.

'Come on everybody,' she shouted, and her laughter was tinged with hysteria. 'Let's escape. I can't bear to spend another moment in this man's company.'

She gathered up her flowing white skirt and ran swiftly away, followed by her laughing, shouting friends.

Feeling crushed by shame, Anthony finished wiping the

water from his face, and blinked his sight clear once more to find young Bernie Hulme standing looking at him. The youth's expression mirrored uncertainty and concern, and a trace of apprehension.

'Are you all right, Tony?' he asked anxiously. 'I'm sure she only means it as a joke.' He hesitated, then forced a grin. 'Will you come on the Electric Gallopers with the rest of us? I'm sure it'll be tremendous fun.'

All the angry resentment that had been festering for hours in Anthony's mind against this youth suddenly dissolved and disappeared as he recognised the genuine concern in the fresh, boyish features before him.

It's not your fault that Amy is as she is, Bernie, he thought, and a sensation of sad, weary resignation suffused his mind as he realised that he had lost his love. But that that love had never been truly his anyway.

He tried to smile, but it was only a rictus-like grimace that contorted his face, and he patted Bernie on the shoulder and told him gently, 'No, I don't think that I'll be joining you on the Gallopers, Bernie. I'm going home. But you go and enjoy yourself. You're a good lad. Try not to let her break your heart.'

As Anthony turned and walked away, he felt as if he might burst into tears at any moment.

Bernie stood with a troubled expression, watching the other man until he was swallowed up in the crowds.

'Bernie! You're to come immediately, Amy says. She's waiting to ride on the Gallopers with you.'

One of the group came hurrying up to fetch him. Bernie saw Amy waving to him, and the surging emotion of besotted adoration thrust all other thoughts and emotions from his mind.

He waved back and ran eagerly towards her.

On the other side of the fairground, Jack Preseley was also eager as he sought the woman he loved. Some deep-seated instinct made him confident that she was here, somewhere among these sideshows and stalls, swirling crowds and strident music, and he walked quickly, his gaze flicking from face to face to face.

Then, before he could properly see who it was, Anthony Barton had come up at his side and greeted him.

308

'Jack, I thought you were still in Ireland.'

Shocked by this unexpected sudden encounter, the Ulsterman could only force a smile and stay silent while he groped for words. Then he noticed the dampness of his friend's collar and shirtfront, and saw the strain and distress in Anthony's face.

'What's the matter, Tony? Has something happened to upset you? Have you been in a row?' He was truly anxious, and for a brief moment all thought of Amy Morgan was banished. 'You don't look yourself, man. What's up?'

Anthony smiled bitterly. 'I've just discovered what a bloody fool I've been, Jack. That's what's up.'

Preseley instantly feared that Amy was involved in this matter, and he asked hesitantly, 'Have you quarrelled with someone, Tony? With Amy?'

Now he was uneasy as the familiar sense of guilt invaded him. But he was also uncertain, and his thoughts raced.

Has she told him about us? But if she has, surely he'd be furious with me? What has she told him?

Anthony's cheeks reddened with shame as the tears he had fought to hold back now brimmed in his eyes. Brokenly he blurted out, 'Amy and I are finished, Jack. She's in love with someone else now.' A gust of anger erupted. 'It's not even another man, Jack. It's a bloody boy! A bloody snot-nosed schoolboy.' He glared furiously and gritted out, 'Can you believe it? She's throwing herself at a bloody schoolboy. A schoolboy not turned eighteen yet! And she's a grown woman! It's bloody well unbelievable, isn't it?'

For Jack Preseley it was incredibly, absolutely, totally unbelievable.

He shook his head, and said forcefully, 'No, Tony. That can't be! It really cannot be!'

'Oh, but it can, and it is!' Anthony asserted fiercely, and grabbing Jack's upper arm physically dragged him along. 'Come on, I'll bloody well show you!'

Jack allowed himself to be pulled to a position from where they could clearly see the Electric Gallopers carousel.

'Look!' Anthony flung out his arm and pointed with his forefinger. 'Look there, and then tell me again if it can't be.'

Preseley's throat felt tight, and his breath came in short, rapid pants. He felt the urge to break free and to turn away from what he was seeing. Shock, sickening despair, hot anger all boiled like a maelstrom in his brain as he saw Amy come into view, perched side-saddle on the gaudily painted, flaring eyed wooden horse, her full white skirts trailing gracefully, her beautiful face glowing with radiant happiness and excitement. Her hand stretched out to clasp the hand of the good-looking youth who was gazing at her adoringly.

Still Jack could not accept the truth of Anthony's words, until he saw Amy lean across and plant a kiss on the youth's cheek, and then draw back laughing, and again lean across and this time kiss the youth fleetingly on the lips.

'Look at her!' Anthony exclaimed furiously. 'She's behaving like a bloody factory girl. Like a common tart. It disgusts me! It bloody well disgusts me!'

Jack was also feeling anger and disgust. But these emotions were not directed against Amy Morgan, but against himself.

What a bloody idiot I've been, he derided himself silently. What a stupid, conceited fool! I thought that I'd only to snap my fingers at any woman I fancied, and she would immediately fall madly in love with me. Obviously I was wrong, and there's the proof of it.

The slowly bobbing wooden horses continued to circle and Amy was borne away to the far side of the carousel, and Jack Preseley's gaze followed her.

Unlike the young man at his side Preseley had experienced many brief infatuations, and it was the recognition of this fact, plus his own fatalism, which enabled him now that the initial shock was passing to accept Amy's fickleness with a measure of sardonic humour.

It seems that I've been hoisted with my own petard, he accepted, and after watching the beautiful girl pass around the circle once more, he took Anthony's arm and gently urged the young man to come away.

Angry and miserable, Anthony snarled, 'She's just a common tart, isn't she, Jack? A cheap little tart!'

A mirthless smile briefly curved the Ulsterman's lips, and he shook his head and murmured, 'No, Tony, she isn't. She's just a silly, immature little girl, that's all . . . You're well rid of her, boy. I don't think she'll ever bring lasting happiness to any man.'

He was honest enough to admit silently to himself, though I'll be grieving for what might have been, I don't doubt.

Aloud he said, 'Come on, Tony, we'll go and take Paddy's cure. When you've a few whiskies down you, the world will look a whole lot better, you'll see.'

Anthony offered no objection, and side by side the two men walked away from the funfair, and the happy crowds, and the stridently blaring steam organ.

Chapter Thirty-Three

The Sunday newspapers carried the reports of the German Kaiser's declaration of war against his cousin, Tsar Nicholas of Russia, and the news provoked a heated debate at the breakfast table of the Barton family. As on so many other topics William and his father held sharply diverse opinions.

'Russia can never be defeated by Germany and Austria. The country is simply too big. Just remember what happened to Napoleon.' Ernest Barton pointed his knife and fork at the various plates and dishes upon the table to explain his strategic insight. 'There are the Germans advancing through Poland. There are the Austrians crossing the Galician frontiers. Here are the Russian frontier garrisons. The frontier fortresses must fight to the last man, and the last round, to give the Tsar time to complete the mobilisation of his army.'

Ernest suddenly broke off his explanation to ask his wife sharply, 'Are you paying attention to me, Madeleine? I'm explaining something of great importance here.'

'Yes, dear,' Madeleine answered soothingly. 'I know I was cutting up this slice of bacon, but I was listening to you with full attention.'

Ernest scowled at William, who was slumped in his chair, toying with his breakfast. 'I hope that you're listening to me as well, William. You might learn something useful for a change.'

William stared coldly at the older man, but made no answer, and Ernest went on, 'Now then, the strategy I suggest that the Tsar must follow is extremely simple. But like all supremely simple plans, there is an element of genius in it. He must apply the scorched earth tactic. He must use a small part of his army to entice the Germans and Austrians further and further into

Russia, retreating and destroying everything as they go, so as to leave nothing to aid the invaders. It's August now. If he carries out my plan successfully it would be winter before the Germans could arrive in Moscow. Now!' Ernest leaned back in his chair, beaming with self-satisfaction. 'Here is the crux of my plan. While enticing the Germans further and further into Russia, the Tsar will be forming his fully mobilised armies behind the Moscow line. Just imagine, there are the Germans and Austrians, starving because of the scorched earth tactics, freezing in the bitter cold. And here are the Russians. Well fed, warmly clothed, fresh and strong. The fully mobilised Russian army is like a steamroller. It will simply crush all opposition by sheer weight of numbers.' Ernest spoke with absolute conviction. 'The Tsar will lead them forwards and destroy every German and Austrian soldier on Russia's soil. That's what happened to Napoleon, and that's what will happen to the Kaiser and his horde.'

The old man swung to ask Anthony, 'Well, Anthony. What do you think to my plan? Will it work?'

Anthony, miserably depressed by Amy's behaviour of the previous evening, nodded listlessly.

'Yes, Father. I'm sure it will.' Then a thought struck him which seemed to perk his low spirits up a little. 'Do you think the French will shortly declare war on Germany, Father? Jack Preseley thinks it a certainty that they will. He also thinks that we shall be drawn into the war if the French do so.'

'I sincerely hope that we shan't stand back and let the damn French do our fighting for us.' Ernest twirled his military moustache and looked very fierce and warlike.

'I hope with all my heart that there will be a British army marching side by side with the French. What a lark it will be . . . God! How I wish I were young enough to go! And you'll need to look pretty sharp if you're to see any of the action, my boy. If full-scale war comes, it will all be over within a few months. Germany and Austria will be beaten into the dust by then, and Berlin will be occupied by the allied armies.'

William's ugly features twisted with scornful contempt. 'What rubbish you do talk at times, Father . . . Russian steamroller!' he jeered. 'How can you call hordes of badly armed, untrained, primitive peasants a military steamroller?

The German Army is the best-equipped, the most highly trained, the best-disciplined mass army that the world has ever seen. And behind them is the industrial might of Germany.'

Ernest flushed with temper, but he answered coolly enough. 'That was Napoleon's opinion of his own army, and look what the Cossacks did to them.'

'The Cossacks were not facing machine-guns and barbed wire then, were they?' William retorted. 'Napoleon had short-range cannons, not high-precision, rapid-firing artillery pieces. His supplies had to come by ox-drawn wagons. The Germans have the most highly developed railway network in the world.'

'That won't help them when they're deep into Russia, will it?' the old man riposted triumphantly.

'And how long will it take the German engineers to construct temporary railway lines behind their advance?' his son retorted. 'I don't think that you have any conception of what modern warfare is. You still seem to believe it's a matter of cavalry charges and infantry squares.'

At this the old man erupted. 'And how would you know what warfare is? Any sort of warfare. You couldn't even make a success in the Territorials, could you? It was too hard for you. Don't you talk to me about warfare, you useless hound!'

'That's enough! Now stop this, both of you! I will not have my table turned into a brawling tap room! Stop it, this instant!' Madeleine's gentle face was set hard with anger, and this rare occurrence caused both protagonists to hesitate.

Then William said, 'Please excuse me, Mother. I didn't mean to upset you.'

He got up from the table and walked to the door. As he opened it, however, he could not stop himself from firing one parting shot.

'If there is a general European war, it won't be over within months, Father. It will drag on for years, and every country that gets drawn into it will be ruined.'

Before Ernest could reply, the door shut behind his elder son. With a thunderous scowl the old man shook his fist at the closed door, and muttered furiously beneath his breath.

'Now, dear, calm yourself, do. Remember that Dr Protheroe said you weren't to excite yourself unduly. It's bad for your blood pressure.' Madeleine's customary gentle good humour

315

had replaced her momentary anger, and she smiled placidly at her irate husband. Then she asked her younger son, 'Why didn't you bring Jack Preseley back here to stay?'

'He couldn't remain in Redditch any longer, Ma. He has to go to the War Office to arrange his recommissioning into his old regiment.' The young man's initial depression was being overlaid by the excitement of possible war. 'Jack seems convinced that we shall go to war with Germany, you know. And I met Charlie Parker last night as well, and he told me that Major Tunbridge had received a phone call from the War Office instructing him to be ready to bring the battery up to full war strength. Just think what an adventure it will be, a full-scale European war.'

His mother frowned worriedly. 'I hope and pray that there won't be a war.'

'But there already is a war, Mother,' her son pointed out. 'Between Russia and Serbia, and Germany and Austria-Hungary.'

'They're all a long way away from England, Anthony,' Madeleine pointed out. 'And if they choose to fight among each other, I really can't see how that is any concern of ours. Or of the French, for that matter.'

'It will do the youth of today a bit of good to experience what war is,' Ernest put in forcefully. 'They've had it too damm easy all their lives. It'll harden them into men.'

'Will it now?' Once again Madeleine's temper rose, and she spoke harshly. 'Did the South African war harden Clarence Jephcott's son?' She immediately answered her own question. 'No, it did not. The poor boy died of enteric fever three weeks after landing at Cape Town.'

'Clarence Jephcott's son was one of the unlucky ones.' Her husband dismissed her argument with a wave of his hand. 'All the young fellows I knew who went out to South Africa came back as better men. They told me many times that the experience had been the making of them.'

He smiled towards his son. 'I'll be a proud man when Anthony leads his men off to fight, and I make no bones about that. I'll be a proud man.'

Madeleine's patience was exhausted. 'Well, I won't be feeling any pride if that should happen,' she snapped heatedly.

316

'I'll only be feeling grief and anguish, and worried half to death.'

With that she also left the table and swept out of the room.

'Phooo! Women!' Ernest ejaculated in disgust. 'What do they know about how real men feel about war?'

For once Anthony found himself in complete and whole-hearted agreement with his father. He remembered how Amy had been behaving with young Bernie Hulme, and his despair metamorphosed into an angry scorn.

Just wait until I march off to war. She'll be sorry then that she behaved so. She'll realise then that she has lost a real man, and instead gained a mere boy.

His heart lifted as he visualised himself returning from war, covered in glory, the very epitome of a hardened warrior. Amy would beg him to take her back, and he would contemptuously reject her, and tell her to go back to chasing boys.

He became aware that his father was talking again, volubly explaining how the French generals should commence their attack, and he eagerly began to expostulate his own views on that subject.

Outside in the sunlit garden Madeleine wandered slowly among the flowerbeds and shrubberies, but could find none of the usual pleasure she took from the colourful profusion of blossoms, and the heady, delightful scents that permeated the warm air.

She saw William standing with his back to her at the edge of the garden, staring out across the rolling fields beyond.

Since his rebuff of her questionings she had never again broached the subject of Josie Kitson with him. But she had silently observed and worried about his continued depression, and had become convinced that the reason for it was to do with that young woman.

She stood and watched her son, and her heart wept to see how solitary and miserable he appeared. Impelled by the need to comfort him, she went to his side and touched his arm. He turned and smiled bleakly at her, and began to apologise once more for the scene at the breakfast table. She laid her finger against his lips and shook her head, telling him gently, 'No, there's no need to apologise to me, Will. As it happens I'm in full agreement with you about this awful war. I pray with all my heart and soul that our country does not become involved in it.'

He fell silent, and again stared out across the fields to where in the distance could be seen the spire of St Stephen's church.

Madeleine could not help herself. 'You still think about her, don't you, William?'

She waited apprehensively for him to rebuff her angrily. But this time he only sighed heavily, and replied, 'Yes, Mother, I do.'

Emboldened, Madeleine pressed. 'What happened between you, Will? I'm not prying, but I love you, and it upsets me to see you so depressed and low-spirited.'

He shook his head, but there was no anger in the gesture, only sad resignation.

'I'm sorry, Mother. But I really do not want to discuss it.'

'It might help you if we did discuss it, my dear,' she told him gently. 'Sometimes it's better to bring problems out into the light, rather than brood over them in the darkness.'

He looked fully at her, and said frankly, 'I've thought of nothing else for weeks now, Mother. I've wanted to talk about it, but I know that it will serve no purpose. I don't blame Josie for what has happened. In all honesty I've slowly arrived at the conclusion that the problem lies more with me than it does with her. But it's something that I must resolve myself, and in my own time. No one else can help me with this. The answer must come from within myself. Can you understand that?'

Madeleine nodded, and reached to touch his thin, pale face. 'Yes, my dear. I can understand that. I would only ask you to remember that I'm here whenever you need me.'

He smiled in gratitude, and then, making a visible effort to lighten their shared mood, invited, 'Come, let's walk down to the river. I want to see if that kingfisher is still there by the old footbridge.'

Together mother and son walked slowly across the fields, and above them the larks fluttered and gaily sang, but their joyous song evoked no answering echoes within the hearts of William Barton, or his mother. Both of them were too heavy with care to respond with gladness.

Chapter Thirty-Four

It was the early afternoon of August Bank Holiday Monday, and through the open window of her bedroom Josie Kitson could hear the far-off echoes of the funfair's steam organ. Drawn by these sounds of distant gaiety, she leaned out over the sill and gazed across the sunlit hedgerows and fields to where the land rose and the buildings of the town spread over the hillsides.

Her neighbours' houses appeared still and deserted and she knew that the occupants had mostly gone out to enjoy the holiday. Intense yearning burgeoned within her for the sights and sounds of laughter and congenial company, and her loneliness was a cold, dark, cheerless void in her heart and soul.

She sighed heavily and drew her head back inside the room. From the adjoining bedroom she heard the snuffles and snortings of her mother's stertorous breathing and drew a bleak satisfaction from the fact that Dorothy was sleeping after her noontime meal. At least she, Josie, was not having to sit with the old woman, who constantly demanded her enforced company.

Josie went downstairs and into the front room. She seated herself on the window seat and tried to read a book, but could not find any interest in the turgid prose, and let the book fall from her hand. Only the frantic buzzing of a large fly trapped behind the net curtains broke the silence.

It's like being entombed, she thought unhappily, and the prospect of the long, empty hours stretching ahead until bedtime suddenly became unbearable to her. 'Oh God, how I wish . . .' she muttered aloud. Then realised that she must not allow herself to wish for anything more than she had already. She must count as a blessing the fact that her mother was asleep, and with any good fortune at all would not wake up until it was time for her evening meal.

At least I'm not having to sit and listen to her grunting at me, and watching her dribbling all down herself.

Now Josie felt ashamed at her own cruelty. It's not Mother's fault that she's like she is. She's suffering, and I shouldn't feel this way about caring for her.

She jumped to her feet and paced restlessly up and down the room.

There came an outburst of noisy voices and laughter from the road outside, and Josie hastened to peep out.

She saw a group of young men and women dressed in shabby clothing, walking arm in arm in a human chain, obviously hurrying up into the town in search of pleasure and excitement. She stared enviously at the girls' laughing faces, one in particular catching her eye. A short, fat girl who was dressed in a cheap blouse and skirt and wore a flowered hat on her high-piled frizzed hair. She was laughing up into the face of the tall young man at her side. He looked like a rustic, with his red cheeks, great clumping boots, rough jacket and trousers and collarless shirt. But the girl was looking at him as if he were a Greek god, and he was gazing down at her homely features with patent adoration. Josie felt a sudden rush of resentment and jealousy.

Why should they find such happiness with each other, and I'm alone, with no one to love or be loved by?

She stayed staring at the group until they passed from her view, and her sense of loneliness intensified until she could have wept with self-pity.

In an effort to escape her own thoughts she went out into the kitchen to begin preparing the meat broth for her mother's next meal. While she was there she heard a knocking on the front door, and with thankfulness that for a moment or two at least she would have some human intercourse she hurried to answer it.

Clement Hulme smiled at her, and she felt glad to see him. But before she could ask him why he had come, because he had made no previous arrangements to call on this day, he told her, 'Now be quick and get ready. There's no time to lose.'

She stared at him blankly, and he demanded in mock puzzlement, 'Don't you want to go to the fair, then?'

'Oh, Clem, you know that I can't leave Mother alone,' she replied irritably, thinking that he was being unkind to mock her so.

He gestured for her to step out of the door. 'Come here, there's someone I want you to see. She's waiting for you.'

Still puzzled and uncertain, Josie stepped out on to the path and saw Emily Burgess sitting with Bernard Hulme on the seat of Clement's pony trap.

Emily smiled and waved, calling out, 'Do be quick, Josie.'

'No arguing now,' Clement smilingly instructed. 'I'm going to stay with your mother, and my son is going to deliver you and your friend to wherever you wish to be taken. You're to go off and enjoy yourself, young lady. And I will not accept any refusal.'

Still she attempted to argue, but he would not listen.

He lifted the brown paper parcel he was carrying and showed it to her.

'I've brought my own holiday refreshment with me, Josie. So I shall be perfectly happy while you're out enjoying yourself.'

Then he chivvied her through the house until she had put on her hat and was outside once more.

'But how did you arrange this?' she asked him, the excitement of this almost miraculous deliverance now pulsing through her. 'What about your wife and children? I thought that you would be spending today with them.'

'My wife's father insisted on having all of them to tea with him today. So I suddenly thought that here was an opportunity not to be missed. You really deserve this holiday outing, my dear. And you need it.' Clement was more light-hearted than she had ever seen him. He was almost boyish in his laughing enthusiasm. 'Now get off with you,' he urged, and handed her up on to the trap seat. 'Now, Bernard, you drive carefully, and take these ladies to wherever they want to go. Then you're to wait for them.'

'Oh no, he mustn't wait. We can walk back home.' Josie and Emily Burgess were both adamant on this point.

'Then can I use the trap for the rest of the day and for this evening, Father?' the youth asked eagerly, and grinned with delight when his father gave his permission.

Bernard Hulme had his own plans for that evening. And he

was looking forward with eager expectation to seeing Amy Morgan's face when he drove up in this spanking vehicle and invited her for an outing.

'Well, what shall we do?' Emily Burgess was in high spirits. 'This is a treat for me, Josie. I'd resigned myself to a solitary walk around the town because all my family have gone off to the seaside. And then Mr Hulme knocked on my door and asked me if I'd like to spend some time with you. I was delighted. He's proved to be a wonderful friend to you and your mother, hasn't he?'

Josie readily agreed. 'Indeed he has. Do you know, Emily, there are times when I wonder how I could have got through all this trouble without his help. He's been a true friend to me.' Then she slipped her arm around her friend and hugged her. 'I'll bet that you're not half as delighted about this as I am, my dear. It's so good to see you again.'

'Where would you like me to take you, ladies?' Bernard Hulme smiled warmly. 'The funfair? Or the town centre?'

'I don't mind where we go,' Josie said truthfully. She was just content to be out in the fresh air and sunlight, and to have these hours of unexpected freedom to spend with congenial company. 'You decide, Emily. I'll be equally happy wherever.'

The plump little woman's bright, birdlike eyes twinkled. 'Do you know what I'd really like to do, Josie? I'd like to go to the Palace. There are two drama pictures showing, and the Keystone Cops, and there's a bill of artistes as well.'

'That's it then,' Josie agreed readily, and told the youth jokingly, 'Take us to the Palace Theatre, driver.'

Standing concealed behind the net curtains of the sick woman's bedroom, Clement Hulme watched the trio drive away. A sheen of perspiration glistened on his forehead, and he felt both excitement and a vague apprehension as his fingers touched the small glass bottle that lay in his jacket pocket.

He turned and studied the sleeping woman.

I'll have to time it carefully, he thought. I don't want you waking up and setting up your bloody screeching at the wrong time, do I?

Then he grinned, and fondled the small bottle. This will do the business.

He went downstairs and unwrapped the brown paper parcel

322

to disclose two bottles of strong sherry wine. Taking one of them into the kitchen, he left it there and returned with a glass tumbler. He uncorked the remaining bottle and poured himself a large measure of the wine, then sat down and settled himself comfortably.

He drank slowly from his glass, sipping the rich, heady liquid, savouring the slight biting undertaste as it went down his throat. Mentally he savoured also the anticipation of what he intended to happen that night, when Josie returned.

He took the small glass bottle from his pocket and held it up, grinning at it, speaking to it as if it were an old and dear friend.

'You'll do the business for me, won't you, matey? A good slug of you will keep the old cow snoring for hours. And another little drop or two mixed in with a couple of glasses of sherry, and Josie won't know what's hit her, will she? She'll be all over the shop. I'll be able to do whatever I want to her. And then tomorrow, when she wakes up, she'll think it was all her own idea, won't she? Especially when I tell her how after she'd taken a couple of glasses of wine she was all over me, and I just couldn't stop meself. Naturally I'll be really remorseful about it.'

His manhood engorged and stiffened as he visualised how Josie's naked body would look and feel to him after his long abstinence.

'It's been a long, hard wait, but it will all have been worth it,' he said with immense satisfaction, and repeated the old saw, 'Everything comes to him who waits, don't it . . . Don't it just . . .'

Throwing caution to the winds in celebration of this unexpected treat, Josie and Emily bought seats in the best part of the theatre, the dress circle. Josie could hardly believe her own recklessness in paying one whole shilling just for entertainment, but assuaged her sense of guilt by telling herself that such extravagance was only once in a lifetime, and she deserved it after the hard times she had recently experienced.

The house was packed, every box was taken, and down in the pit the semi-intoxicated roughs and scruffs of the town, although uproarious in their applause, for once did not start brawling among themselves, or torment the various artistes with too severe a heckling.

Josie sat in the malodorous, overheated darkness, and enjoyed herself thoroughly, thrilling to the drama of *The Man in the White Cloak*, weeping tears of pity for the plight of the orphaned child in *The Red Club*, helpless with laughter at the antics of the Keystone Kops. She enthusiastically applauded the vocal, musical and speciality act of Jubb and Jerome, laughed at the drolleries of comedian Jack Crew, and marvelled at the physical feats, strength and contortions of the world's classical celebrated gymnasts, Petro and Leon. She even experienced a secret frisson of sexual excitement at the sight of these latter two handsome young men, their oiled bodies so taut and muscular in their leotards and tights.

After the performance was ended she parted from Emily outside the theatre with mutual protestations of devotion, and then began the long walk back to her home.

As she walked through the warm night she hummed a gay tune beneath her breath, and took pleasure in recollecting the performances she had just seen. There were many people on the road, and sometimes she crossed from one pavement to the other to avoid passing closely by the noisy, obstreperous groups of drunken men and women. At this hour most of the respectable family parties had returned to their own homes, and although Josie would have liked to round off her night out by taking a stroll around the funfair, which she must pass on her way home, she knew better than to do so. No respectable woman would visit the funfair alone at this hour, when all the rowdy elements of the town's population were taking their pleasures there.

Inevitably she passed pairs of lovers walking arm in arm in the dusk, the more shameless entwined closely, sharing hugs and kisses. Sadness threatened to overshadow her mood as she compared their shared affection with her own solitary state. But she refused to allow any sombreness or regret to spoil the delightful night she had spent, and so ruthlessly put aside all dreams of what might have been with William Barton.

She thought of Clement Hulme with a warm sense of gratitude.

I really misjudged that man, didn't I? she thought with some degree of remorse. Isn't it strange that I can now accept him as a true friend. I don't know how I would have managed without all his help these past weeks. As soon as Mother is well enough I'll do what he wants and return to the chapel. That will please him and show him how much I appreciate what he's done for Mother and me.

She reached the bottom of the long hill and crossed over the footbridge. She saw that the lights were lit in some of her neighbours' houses, and frowned in surprise to see that her own home was in darkness. Instant anxiety seized her. Could her mother have suffered another stroke and had to be rushed to the hospital? Her heart beat rapidly as she unlocked the front door and stepped into the tiny hallway.

'Is that you, Josie?' Clement Hulme's voice sounded quietly from the front room.

'Yes, Clem, it's me. Has anything happened?' She moved to stand in the room doorway, and peering through the gloom she saw his dark bulk sitting by the partially opened window.

'No, everything is fine,' he reassured her. 'I was just sitting here enjoying the peace and quiet.'

'Has Mother been any trouble?' She came to stand looking down at him, and now that her eyes were accustoming themselves to the gloom she could see that on the small table by his side there was a bottle and two glasses.

'No, she's been as good as gold. She's sound asleep. I gave her her supper and then we sat and talked and prayed together. She was really pleased that you had gone out for the evening.'

Josie smiled wryly, finding this last statement hard to believe.

'Now, you sit down there, my dear.' He indicated the facing chair. 'And take a glass of sherry wine. It's the best quality.'

Her first impulse was to refuse. She drank only rarely, and then abstemiously.

'I insist,' he urged jocularly. 'I know that I preach against the evils of drink, but I also remember that our blessed Lord enjoyed a glass of wine on occasion, and this is a special occasion, isn't it? You've had a real holiday for once.'

'All right then.' Josie could not be churlish and continue to refuse. She accepted the glass of sherry from him and drank from it. The liquid left a slightly cloying aftertaste in her mouth, but it didn't impair her pleasure in it.

'This is really nice, Clem,' she told him, and as he chuckled she glimpsed the paleness of teeth in the shadowy outline of his face.

'I told you, Josie, this is the best quality sherry. It's produced especially for the royal family and the aristocracy.'

'You should be ashamed to know so much about it,' she teased happily. 'As a preacher you're not supposed to know such things.'

He chuckled again, and then urged her, 'Now tell me about your evening out. And I want to hear every detail.'

His warm encouragement heightened her sense of what an adventure the evening had been, and she began to relate to him all that she had heard and witnessed. She became animated as she relived the excitement of the films she had seen, and he pressed her to drink another glass of wine, and then another, and another, and she drank without thought, so totally engrossed had she become in her recital.

She lost all track of time, and Clement waited and watched and judged. Eventually he told her, 'I'll have to be thinking of getting home, my dear. It's late.'

She giggled as she apologised, 'I'm sorry, Clem, I was carried away.' She suddenly became aware of how giddy and strange she felt. Yet the giddiness and strangeness were not unpleasant. She giggled again as she told him, 'Do you know, Clem, I think this sherry has gone to my head.'

'No, I'm sure it hasn't,' he told her gently, and stood up. 'You're only tired from all the excitement, that's all.'

'I'll see you out, Clem.' She giggled again, without conscious volition, and went to stand up. The instant intensification of dizziness caused her head to whirl, and she felt his hands on her shoulders.

'I think I'd better help you to lie down, my dear,' he whispered softly.

'No, I'll be all right in a moment.' She drew a deep breath, and her head whirled sickeningly, and she would have fallen if he had not pulled her hard against his body and kept her upright.

'Come on now, no more argument. I'm going to see you

safely to your room.' He could not keep a harsh edge from creeping into his tone. The feel of her breasts and belly pressing against him was exciting him almost beyond control, and he lusted to crush his mouth to hers.

Trying to speak more lightly, he told her, 'You'd better be really quiet, or you'll wake your mother up.'

By now Josie's brain was a maelstrom, and she felt that she had no control over her limbs. She was thankful for his strong arms supporting her as they moved slowly up the stairs and into her bedroom. The darkness seemed to undulate around her, black and purple waves advancing and receding. Her legs felt like jelly, and she was hardly aware of being laid down on the coverlet. She felt the coolness of the night air upon her heated skin as her clothes were stripped away from her, and then the heaving weight of his naked body was on top of her, and her thighs were pressed apart and his manhood was suddenly deep inside her.

She tried to struggle, tried to push him off, and she opened her mouth to scream at him to stop. But all that emerged from her lips was a long-drawn-out moaning, and the long-denied urgent hungerings overpowered her, and mindlessly she clutched, and gasped, and writhed, as the man thrust ever harder, ever deeper into her.

Chapter Thirty-Five

While people in Redditch were celebrating Bank Holiday Monday, events elsewhere moved with frightening speed. Germany declared war on France, and immediately began to put the notorious plan of Count Von Schlieffen into effect. While minimal reinforcements were dispatched eastwards to hold off the expected Russian offensive, the bulk of the German Army was marshalled for the invasion of Belgium and France.

The mobilisation of the British Royal Navy had been completed, and now the British Government issued an ultimatum to Germany, calling on her to respect the neutrality of Belgium, guaranteed by the 1839 tripartite Treaty of London, signed by Britain, France and Prussia. The German Kaiser dismissed the treaty as a 'mere scrap of paper'. The British Government, led by the Prime Minister, Herbert Asquith, steeled themselves for war against Germany.

Early on Tuesday, the fourth of August, German troops invaded Belgium, and later that day Asquith told the House of Commons that the British Empire was now at war with Germany. The War Office and the Admiralty immediately put prearranged plans into motion. The battle fleets went to war stations, and the army prepared for the dispatch of the Expeditionary Force to Belgium and France.

In Redditch police station, Constable Tom Lamb answered the ringing telephone, and grimaced at the crackling line which made it difficult for him to understand what the caller was saying. Tom Lamb was in a bad mood. He had been on duty until the early hours of the morning, coping with brawling drunks, and his aching, badly swollen jaw was a constant reminder of the punches he had received.

'Listen, will you speak up,' he irritably interrupted the garbled voice on the line. 'I can't make out a word you're saying.'

The line crackled angrily with unintelligible speech, and the constable slammed the receiver back on its hook.

'Bollocks to it!'

He tenderly fingered his jaw, and wished fervently to go off duty. The phone rang again, and again he put the receiver to his ear. This time the voice was clearer, but when Tom Lamb heard the message he grunted sullenly.

'Look, mate, I aren't in any mood to have jokes played on me today. So just pack it in, will you?'

The tinny-sounding voice of the caller poured out a furious tirade, to which the constable listened with fast-escalating dismay. The very instant the voice paused, Lamb, flustered, said, 'I'll fetch the Superintendent, sir. I'll fetch him right this minute, sir.'

He ran to the office of Superintendent Davis and without bothering to knock burst through the door.

'What the hell?' Davis was an irascible Welshman who terrorised his subordinates, but at this moment Tom Lamb was too excited to care about that fact.

'Sir, we're at war! There's a colonel from the War Office wants to speak to you. We're at war, sir. We're at war.'

'War?' Davis's black eyes bulged.

'Yes, sir, war!' The constable was hopping from one foot to the other in his excitement. 'There's a colonel on the phone now, sir. We're at war.'

Davis went to the phone himself. After a brief exchange of conversation, he replaced the receiver and pursed his lips thoughtfully, then recalled the operator and asked to be put through to the Royal Enfield factory.

'I want to speak to Captain Smith . . . Oh, it's yourself, is it, Frank? Good. It's Geraint Davis here . . . Look now, can you loan me the use of one of your motorcycles and sidecars. We're at war with Germany . . . Yes, that's right . . . We're at war with Germany . . . Oh, I don't rightly know exactly. Not too many hours ago, I should think . . . Anyway, the War Office has just phoned me, and I've got to post the notices to call up the reservists . . .'

Within scant minutes following his phone call, Superintendent Davis was seated on the pillion of a six-horsepower

Enfield motorcycle, driven by the manager of the Royal Enfield factory himself, Captain F.W. Smith. Its sidecar was loaded with hammer, nails and the recall-of-reservists posters which had been kept in the station since the Boer War.

The machine roared around the district, bucketing over the rough-surfaced roads, and the policeman was forced to clamp his hand down hard on to his peaked cap to keep it from being blown away. Each time the motorcycle came to a halt, its noisy, spluttering roar attracted curious onlookers. When the policeman nailed up the posters these onlookers clustered to read them, and the news invoked strangely mixed reactions. Some cheered, some looked grave, others laughed as if it were a huge joke. Several of the women who were married to reservists seemed near to tears, and bemoaned the recall of their men to the colours. Other women grinned happily, and expressed their pleasure at the imminent removal of their husbands.

The news of the outbreak of war spread like wildfire throughout the entire district and even before the Superintendent had completed his task, men and women were leaving their workplaces and an excited crowd was gathering on the Church Green.

On the building site in Orchard Street, Alfred Payne and Shanto Evans were sweating out their holiday hangovers, bent almost double as they laid the initial courses of brickwork for a new foundation. Their labourer, Simmy James, had loaded their line of work with a plentiful supply of mortar and bricks, and had gone to fetch them a jug of ale from the nearest beer shop to slake their thirsts.

Alfred Payne groaned as he straightened his back and stared down the site to see if the hod carrier was returning.

'Wheer's that bastard got to?' he growled ferociously. 'If he's drunk the beer hisself I'll cut his fuckin' throat.'

Shanto Evans lifted his peaked cap and rubbed his shirtsleeve across his sweating face, frowning as he also peered down the site. Then he grinned with relief.

'Here's the bugger coming now, Alf. I'll tell you summat, mate, that bloody drink won't even touch the sides o' my throat. It'll goo up in steam in me mouth.'

'Hold on a minute.' Payne raised both hands to shield his eyes against the glare of the sun. 'Just look, Shanto. The way he's waving that bloody jug about, it looks as if it's bloody well empty.'

He suddenly hurled his trowel down, and stepped away from the brickwork. 'I'll kill the young bastard if he aren't got the drink!'

The youthful labourer was running up the slope, shouting wildly to the other men as he passed by them.

'We'em at war! We'em at war! We'em at war!'

He reached the waiting Alfred Payne still bawling.

'We'em at war, Alf! We'em at war, Shanto! We'em at war!'

'Never mind that, wheer's the fuckin' beer?' Payne roared furiously, and raised his clenched fist. 'I'm gooing to knock your fuckin' yed off!'

'We'em at war!' The youth seemed unaware of the threat. 'We'em at war. All the reservists am being sent for.'

It was Shanto Evans who first fully realised what the lad was bawling.

'Hold on a minute, Alf.' He interposed himself between the irate Payne, who was about to put his threat into action, and the excited youth.

'Just calm down a bit, will you, Simmy. Now tell me what's up.'

The panting boy steadied himself, and gasped out, 'The coppers have bin putting the posters up, Shanto. All reservists has got to goo to the police station and get rail passes to goo back to their regiments. We 'em at war wi' Germany.'

'Is this a fuckin' joke?' Alfred Payne demanded furiously. 'Am you trying to take the piss out of us? Because if you am I'll fuckin' well cripple you!'

'No!' Simmy James shook his head wildly. 'No! It aren't a joke! I'se seen the posters meself. They'm all over the place. And there a stack o' folks up on the Church Green, all shouting and cheering. We 'em at war with Germany, and all the reservists has got to goo back to the army and navy straight away.'

'God fuck me!' Evans swore disgustedly.

Payne knew the reason for his friend's disgust. 'O' course, you'm an old sweat yourself, aren't you, Shanto? You'm on the reserve!'

'God damn and blast the fucker!' Shanto Evans shook both

his fists at the clear blue sky. 'I hated the fuckin' army, I did. And now I'se got to goo back to it. God fuck me!'

By now the other workmen had come down from the scaffolding and up out of the trenches and had gathered in a crowd around the trio.

William Barton and Charlie Spicer came out from the office shed, shouting angrily at the men to get back to their work, demanding to know why they had stopped.

When told by half a dozen simultaneous voices the reason for the stoppage, both Barton and Spicer appeared to be momentarily dumbstruck.

'Well, that's it then, gaffer. You'd better give me me hours. I'll have to be leaving straight away,' Evans informed William. But it was Charlie Spicer who answered.

'You can stay and finish the day out, can't you, man?'

By now Evans had recovered from the first shock of the unexpected news, and was remembering that he had had some good times with good comrades in the army. It hadn't all been bad. He was also determined that he would not spend whatever hours of freedom he had left to him in hard, sweaty work.

'You heard what Simmy said, didn't you, Charlie? All reservists am to go straight to the police station and collect their rail passes to goo back to their regiments.' Evans stood erect and puffed out his chest. 'Well, that means me, 7983201 Private Evans, of the old Vein Openers, the Twenty-Ninth o' Foot, the First Battalion, Worcestershire Regiment.'

Some of the younger men and youths were staring enviously at Shanto Evans.

'Cripes, I wish I was gooing wi' you, Shanto,' one youthful labourer announced, and Evans looked at him and sneered.

'It's men they wants to lick the bloody Germans, not snottynosed kids like you.' Then he demanded of William Barton, 'Well, gaffer, am I gooing to get me hours, or what? You can't refuse to pay me, can you? I'm under the orders of the War Office, aren't I?'

With a bad grace William agreed, and jerked his head as he walked away. 'Come to the office, and I'll work out what you're due.'

Alfred was now regarding his crony with a burgeoning envy. 'You'm gooing straight on the piss, aren't you, Shanto?' he challenged, and the other man winked broadly and grinned.

'Too right I am, me old cock. I'll be thinking o' you in about five minutes when I'm sitting in the White Lion tipping the fust pint down me throat.' He slapped young Simmy James on the shoulder. 'You can borrow me tools, Simmy. I shan't be needing 'um wheer I'm gooing. But doon't lose 'um, because I'll be wanting 'um back after I'se give the bleedin' Germans a good tanning.'

He swaggered away and Charlie Spicer bawled at the rest of the men to return to their work.

Alfred Payne sullenly picked up his trowel and once again bent to the gruelling labour.

Young Simmy James was still excited and kept on talking volubly. 'Does you reckon the war 'ull last a long time, Alf? I 'udn't mind gooing meself, you know. I reckon I'd look good in uniform. All the girls likes a chap in uniform, doon't they? Does you wish you'd been a soldier, Alf?'

Payne's head throbbed. Sweat dripped from his face to fall on the bricks he was laying. The thought of his crony by now undoubtedly sitting at his ease in the White Lion, drinking a cool pint of beer, was maddening him. And Simmy James' voice drilled in his ears.

'. . . One of the chaps who was reading the poster said that he'd heard that they was gooing to be taking a lot more new recruits for the army.'

'And who the fuck did he hear that from?' Payne jeered. 'The bleedin' war's only just started, aren't it? Who the bloody hell told him that? Was it the bloody Prime Minister?'

'He said it stood to reason, didn't it,' the youth rejoined. 'He said look at the South African war. Look at how they'd had to take thousands o' new recruits before it was over. He said it was bound certain sure to be the same this time. I'll tell you what, Alf. If they does take new recruits for this war, I'm gooing to be one of 'um.'

Payne straightened his back, and kneaded the stiff and painful muscles along his spine. He pondered hard for a few moments, and then said thoughtfully, 'And me as well, Simmy. I'm sick o' this bleedin' work. And I'm sick o' my bleedin' missus. Yeah, I reckon the army 'ull suit me down to the ground, and that's a fact, that is.'

Chapter Thirty-Six

The staff and pupils of Bridge Street School were summoned to a special assembly in the large vaulted main hall at half past three on Tuesday afternoon.

On this occasion the teachers stood with their classes and the headmaster, James Parnell, mounted the low platform alone. His bulging blue eyes were gleaming with excitement, and his body was proudly erect.

'Ladies and gentlemen, boys and girls, today our country has declared war against Germany. Side by side with our gallant allies, France and Russia, brave little Serbia, and Belgium, we are going into battle against Kaiser Wilhelm and his hordes of barbaric Huns, and the decadent empire of Austria-Hungary.

'I am proud to announce that a member of our staff, Mr Howard Billington, will be leaving us this very afternoon to go on full-time service with the Redditch battery of the Territorial Royal Field Artillery. The unit, together with the Redditch Territorial company of the Worcestershire Regiment, are both being embodied this week, and will be travelling to join their respective parent units.

'Now, School, let us give three cheers for Mr Billington.'

The cheers shrilled out, and Howard Billington blushed, and stroked his military moustache, and tried to look very fierce and warlike.

Emily Burgess did not join in the cheering. Instead she fumbled for her handkerchief, and blew her nose very hard to keep herself from bursting into tears of dismay. She had already known the bereavement brought by war, and feared that this present conflict would bring fresh grief upon herself and millions of others.

James Parnell carried on in his familiar theme of glory and

empire, duty and patriotism, and those children who were old enough to understand felt themselves being whipped into enthusiasm for the great adventure that they had now become a part of.

One child, however, paid little or no attention to the impassioned words of the man on the platform. Marie Gurden, pale-faced, her once pristine appearance now shabby and neglected, her hair straggly and uncombed, remained staring at the floor, and in her mind prayed that her father would soon come back to her.

Mrs Green was kind to her, and she felt much safer now that she was living in the old woman's house, but she yearned with all her being for her father, and during the long, dark hours of the night she would lie awake, stifling her sobs for fear of waking the woman sleeping beside her.

The headmaster's oration ended with more cheering for King, Country and Empire, and when they were dismissed the children excitedly began to play a brand-new game, 'British against Germans', and ran wild through the surrounding streets in noisy mock battles.

Marie collected her cousins together and led them to Mrs Green's house. The door was shut and bolted and Marie anxiously hammered the warped panels and shouted, 'Mrs Green? Mrs Green? Are you in there?'

The bolts were drawn, the door creaked partially open and the old woman peered out and grinned a toothless smile at the girl.

'We'se got a new lodger come to live with us, my duck. I 'ope you doon't mind.'

Marie shrugged listlessly, and the old woman laughed and flung the door wide.

'You'd best come in and say hello then.'

Marie saw the man sitting facing her on the wooden chair by the rusty fire grate. Her breath burst from her in a mighty whoop, and crying with joy she flung herself into her father's loving arms.

Chapter Thirty-Seven

'What's that you say, Goldman?'

Ernest Barton seemed completely taken aback, and the veterinary surgeon hid a smile, and repeated, 'I've had a telegraph to inform me that remount officers will be calling on me later this week for my assistance in examining the horses they're going to requisition.' The short, plump man waved his arm along the line of stables, where several horses' heads were poking out over the half-doors. 'You'll be sorry to lose these fine beasts, I don't doubt, Colonel.'

'What makes you think that I shall be losing them?' Ernest scowled ominously. 'I've no intention of selling any of my horses to the army.'

The vet chuckled inwardly, hugely relishing this chance to repay some of the bullying hectoring and insults the other man had subjected him to through the years.

'You'll have no choice in the matter, Colonel. All suitable beasts are to be requisitioned. It's compulsory. If I declare that the horse is fit for service, then for service it goes. No one is exempt.'

Ernest silently digested this unpalatable information. Then he asked with an assumed casualness, 'But how can the horses be requisitioned if the owner does not come forward voluntarily to offer them? After all, horses can easily be moved and hidden, can they not?'

Again the vet was forced to hide his smile. He had for long years lusted to deflate the pompous arrogance of the man in front of him, and now he was savouring doing so.

'Certainly horses can be moved and kept hidden, Colonel Barton. That is why the authorities are enlisting the aid of people who are in a position to know exactly who possesses

337

suitable beasts. Local knowledge is what the authorities require, Colonel, and that is why they are calling upon my services. I have an encyclopaedic knowledge of the horseflesh in this district, and any owner who attempts to hide his animals will find himself in very serious trouble indeed.'

Barton was near to losing his temper, and he exerted all his willpower to refrain from a violent outburst. He was shrewd enough to realise that this plump, balding little man was baiting him, and shrewd enough too to recognise that this same man held all the power in this situation. He tried to smile bluffly.

'But surely, in the case of an old friend, you wouldn't be so heartless as to take all his finest beasts from him?' He paused. 'Would you, Goldman?'

The vet offered fervent thanks to his God for giving him this opportunity to take such sweet revenge. He drew himself up to his full height, and with icy scorn announced, 'If it were my own father I would take his last animal from him. I am a patriot. Our country has need of horseflesh. I shall do my very utmost to supply that need, without fear or favour. I would suggest, Colonel Barton, that you take a last farewell of all your beasts, because these are the first stables I shall be bringing the remount officers to. And I know the condition of all your animals, sir. So for your own sake I would most strongly advise against any attempt upon your part to evade doing your patriotic duty . . . Good day to you, sir.'

The vet mounted his dogcart and swept away, chortling with sheer delight as soon as he was out of sight of the other man.

Ernest Barton exploded, ranting and raving ferociously as he stamped up and down the stable yard. He was still furious when he returned to the house, where he found that his wife and sons had already sat down to dinner.

In curt, clipped sentences he told them what Goldman had said, and then went on for several minutes about this terrible sacrifice he was being forced to make, and how tyrannical and unfair the authorities were being.

His family diplomatically refrained from making any comments, and eventually his initial tirade petered out. But still needing to vent his anger, he directed his spleen against his usual target, his elder son.

At first he did so indirectly, by talking to Anthony about the embodiment of the battery.

'When do you expect to get your marching orders, Anthony?'

'I expect we'll be told about them tonight, Father.' The young man was eager and elated. 'We're going to be swearing in the new recruits tonight. Then we shall be at full strength. From what Major Tunbridge told us officers and the NCOs this morning, it appears that we shall be going to the Isle of Wight initially, to relieve one of the regular batteries there. They're off to France. I hope we get to France before it's all over. I'd hate to miss the campaign. Major Tunbridge told us that according to the latest dispatch from the War Office, the French Army is already in position to launch a grand assault through Alsace-Lorraine. He thinks that they'll be across the Rhine within days.' The young man looked very handsome as he laughed gaily. 'Let's just pray that the French don't move too quickly, and that they leave some of the work for us to do. I can't wait to get out there. I asked the Major if there was any chance that I could transfer to a regular battery so that I could go out to the front immediately, but he doesn't think that there's any chance of my being allowed to do that.'

Madeleine kept her head bowed and her eyes fixed on her soup plate, but her distressed agitation betrayed itself as her trembling fingers caused the spoon she was holding to spill its contents.

Ernest beamed proudly at his younger son.

'That's the spirit, my boy. You're a true British bulldog, like myself.' Then, with a spiteful gleam in his eyes, he turned to William.

'And what about you, William? When are you going to join up and do your duty for your King and Country, like your brother is?'

William laid down his soup spoon and regarded his father levelly. 'I've no intention of joining up at all, Father.'

The old man snarled with contempt. 'No, I thought you wouldn't. You're too much of a damned coward to risk your skin, aren't you? God damm and blast you! I'm ashamed that you've got my blood running in your veins!'

'Shut up!' Madeleine hissed with savage fury at her husband. 'How dare you try to shame my son because he refuses to take

339

part in this evil war? I wish to God that Tony was not a part of it. How dare you rant and rave because you're being forced to send your horses to the war, and then attack your own flesh and blood because he does not wish to go and kill other mothers' sons? What sort of man are you? You want to send your own sons to where they can be slaughtered or mutilated, and yet you would not voluntarily send a single one of your precious horses. I'm ashamed to be your wife.'

She pitched the spoon she held on to the table and swept out of the room, leaving the three men sitting in a stunned silence.

William quickly rose and followed his mother out, and Ernest and his younger son stared at each other with shocked eyes.

After some moments the old man blustered, 'Women are no use in times of danger, Anthony. They become hysterical. Even the best of them.'

Anthony made no reply, and a trifle shamefacedly Ernest mumbled, 'Your mother is wrong, you know, Anthony. I don't deliberately want to send you or William into danger. I know that I may appear cruel and hard at times, but I love both of you, even though I may find it hard to tell you that I do. But our country is at war, and it's every man's duty to serve in whatever way he can.'

The young man did something that he had never done before. Leaning towards his father, he took the old man's rope-veined hand in his and pressed it warmly.

'I understand, Father. And I'm proud to be your son. I shall do my best to make you equally proud of me.'

Deeply moved, the old man could only cough gruffly, and blink his suddenly moist eyes.

Outside in the garden Madeleine Barton was standing, staring out over the dusk-shadowed land.

Her elder son came to stand silently by her side, and after a while she turned to him and said quietly, 'I'm not really ashamed to be your father's wife, William. It just that sometimes he makes me so angry that I forget myself and seek to hurt him in any way that I can. He's a good man at heart, and I know he loves both of you, no matter how he might rant and rave at you when he's ill-tempered.'

He forced a smile and took her hand in his, squeezing her fingers gently. 'I've always been a great disappointment to him, Mother. I hope that I'm not such to you.'

She returned both his smile and the pressure of his fingers. 'Never, William. Quite the contrary, in fact. You've always been a tremendous source of pride.'

They stayed standing side by side, and the peace of the evening gradually entered their souls. It was William who broke the long silence.

'I'm truly sorry that I've been behaving so badly these past weeks. It's just that I received a terrible shock, and it has taken me some time to come to terms with it.' He smiled ruefully. 'In fact, I'm not sure that I have properly come to terms with it even now.'

Without looking at him, Madeleine invited, 'If it would help, then you can talk to me about it, my dear. I can assure you that I'm not easily shocked.'

William thought deeply for some time, then hesitantly at first he began to tell his mother about what had occurred between himself and Josie Kitson. As he continued to speak, the words fell more easily from his lips, and the very act of being able to talk to a sympathetic listener gave him thankful release from his bitter burden of thought.

Madeleine listened in silence, only her expressive eyes betraying the sadness she felt at what she was hearing. When her son had finally finished speaking and was waiting expectantly for her reaction, she also was hesitant before replying.

'I fear that I may shock you, William. But nevertheless I shall speak very plainly. Despite what men choose to believe, we women have sexual hungers and needs also. I think that it is to Josie's credit that she was truthful with you. I won't be a hypocrite and condemn the poor girl for having given in to her sexual hunger. In all truth there were times before I married your father when I was sorely tempted myself to experience what a man's loving was like.'

She was aware of her son's shocked stare, and momentary irritation overwhelmed her and she rounded on him angrily.

341

'For God's sake, William. Did you think that you were conceived by the Holy Ghost and the Virgin Mary? I've known joy and pleasure in my husband's arms, and lust and wanting also. You're a man of mature years, not a litle boy. You must learn to accept that women are made out of flesh and blood, not sugar and spice. And if you are lucky enough to find a wife who enjoys your flesh, than that is a blessing, and not a curse. From what I know of Josie, she is a good woman, and would be a good wife to you. I think that you still love her, and that being the case, then you will be a damned fool if you don't marry her.'

She lifted her eyebrows interrogatively. 'Or do you prefer to continue as you are now, miserable and lonely?'

He stared at her with anguish in his dark eyes. 'But she's given herself to another man, and out of wedlock.'

'And she's been honest enough to tell you that she has done so,' Madeleine rejoined. 'She could have kept it a secret, and then you would have had real cause for complaint. You should honour her for being an honest and open woman.'

His troubled thoughts were betrayed on his expressive features, and he kept on shaking his head.

Madeleine gripped his hand hard, jerking it up and down to give emphasis to her words. 'Don't let her mistake ruin both your lives, William. Don't compound her error by making a worse error of your own. I truly believe that if you do not go to her and win her back, then you will be making the worst mistake of your entire life. You will spend the rest of your days grieving for the fact that you let her go.'

'I don't know,' he muttered distractedly. 'I just don't know.'

She released his hand, and turning, he walked away from her until he was just one more dim shadow in the dusk of the evening.

Chapter Thirty-Eight

When Josie Kitson awoke on Tuesday morning Clement Hulme had gone. As on that first occasion when she had made love with the man, she felt that same strange sense that she was divided between two entities, a physical one and a spiritual, and she seemed to inhabit the spiritual entity, able to observe and dispassionately judge her other half.

She lay staring upwards while the dawn lightened outside her window, and she listened to the tuneful whistlings of birds greeting the rising sun.

Slowly she moved her hands over her naked body, remembering how the man's greedy lips had sucked and nibbled, how his hands had cupped and stroked, how his hard thrusting had brought her to orgasmic ecstasies time and time again during the long, dark hours. She tried to recall, but failed, the sequence of events that had brought them to this shared bed.

I drank too much wine, she concluded, and now the shame and remorse began to gnaw at her, forcing her to accept that what she had done was sinful, squalid, totally shameless.

I am what I am, she told herself miserably. And I can't help being like I am.

She spoke to God directly, as if challenging him.

You've given me a body which craves the sexual loving of men. Which torments me unbearably with its sexual hungers. You've given me only loneliness and heartache, instead of a husband's loving company. Is it any wonder that there are times when I am driven to do what is shameful and wrong and wicked?

The slurred shouting of her mother broke Josie's train of thought, and she quickly rose, pulled on a dressing gown to cover her nakedness, and hurried into the adjoining bedroom.

Dorothy Kitson was practically unintelligible as she shouted and gestured with her mobile arm, but the vile stench that rose from her bed was evidence enough of what was distressing her. She was lying in her own excrement.

Josie sighed with bitter resignation, and again in her mind fiercely challenged God.

Can you blame me for what I've done, when you have given me this load to bear? . . . 'All right, Mother. All right! Don't upset yourself so. I'll clean you up straight away.'

Wearily she prepared yet again to begin this sickeningly familiar task.

The day wore slowly on as Josie completed other tedious chores. Washing, ironing, cleaning, preparing food, feeding her mother, Josie toiled through the long hours, working mechanically as her mind wrestled with the knowledge that now that she had once again given herself to Clement Hulme, he would undoubtedly expect their resumed affair to continue.

She did not blame him in any way for what had happened. She blamed herself, but now found that she was becoming somewhat fatalistic about the situation.

I'm trapped, she thought sadly. I can't leave this town to get away from him, because I can't leave Mother. William doesn't want me, because he regards me as little better than a prostitute. I have to face the fact that I'm never going to find a man to love me and take me as I am. She grimaced ironically. Except for Clem Hulme. He accepts me as I am, doesn't he? And he tells me that he loves and wants me. She was forced to give credit to the man. He's been a good friend to me, that's the truth. In all this town he's the only person who has sacrificed his own time and comfort to help me when I most needed it. I truly don't know how I would have managed to get through these past weeks without him. But it cannot be allowed to happen again. Her resolve was steely. It's wrong, and it shan't happen again. I shall tell him so and send him away when he comes here. No matter what he says, or threatens to do, it's finished now. It's over!

She knew with absolute certainty that nothing would alter her decision. She would spend the rest of her life alone rather than surrender to her own weakness again.

Early in the evening she was interrupted at her work by the

sound of her name being called by her neighbour, and when she went outside to the back garden Mrs Harold told her excitedly, 'We 'em at war, Josie. I'se just come back from the town, and theer's all sorts of goings-on up theer. It's like Mafeking night all over again, with people shouting and cheering. We 'em at war with the Germans.'

As she heard the news, hope came instantly into Josie's mind. Perhaps this war will change my life. Perhaps it will set me free.

Far off to the east, thunder echoed faintly through the darkening skies. A thunder that already had its human counterpart along the frontiers of Europe, where the great guns were thundering and hordes of screaming men were charging into savage, bloody battle.

'Everybody's saying that it 'ull all be over by Christmas,' Mrs Harold informed her, then clucked her tongue in disparagement of that opinion. 'Mind you, they said the selfsame thing about the South African war, and that went on for years. And there's a sight more Germans than there was of them Boers. I reckon there'll be a deal of heartbreak before this lot is done with. The ones who are doing all the shouting and cheering now 'ull be weeping before it's over.'

Josie thought of her own brother and briefly imagined the carnage of mighty battle fleets clashing in savage conflict. She felt the clutch of sudden anxiety, and silently prayed, Dear God, keep him safe, Please keep him safe.

Mrs Harold went back into her own house, and Josie stayed where she was, her mind now filled with foreboding for what this war might bring.

The shadows lengthened and a cool breeze sprang up to shiver the leaves of the old tree. Josie turned to go back indoors, and cried out in shock as she saw the dark figure standing watching her from the side of the house.

'I'm so sorry, I didn't mean to alarm you.' William Barton stepped towards her, his long, lantern-jawed face displaying his concern.

She stared at him as if she could not believe the evidence of her own eyes, and he halted a couple of yards away from her, and asked quietly, 'Will you let me speak with you, Josie? Please?'

Bemused by his totally unexpected appearance, she nodded wordlessly, her eyes apprehensive.

'I've come to beg you to forgive me,' he told her huskily. 'I know that I have no right to be forgiven, and that what I said to you was unforgivable, but please, I beg you, forgive me.'

Still she could not speak. The memory of the previous night spent with Clem Hulme now struck through her, and her shame was such that it choked any words she might have uttered.

A tangible aura of misery emanated from William as he pleaded, 'Give me another chance, Josie. I love you more than my life. I can't go on without you. Give me the chance to make amends for the wrong I did you. Forgive me, and marry me. I'll spend all the rest of my days trying to make you happy. Please, Josie, forgive me, and say that you'll marry me. Please.'

Tears stung Josie's eyes, and she held up her hands as if to shield herself from his words.

'Tell me what I must do to gain your forgiveness,' he pleaded desperately. 'I'll do anything. Anything!'

Racked by despair, she shook her head and muttered brokenly, 'It's too late, William.'

'Don't say that,' he begged. 'Give me another chance.'

With both hands she wiped the tears from her eyes, and struggling to control her voice she told him, 'I've always been truthful with you, and even though you'll hate me for this, I'll be truthful now.' She was forced to break off and draw long breaths while she rallied her courage to go on. Then, in a voice that shook with strain, she continued, 'I told you before that I'd given myself to a man. I didn't love him, but my loneliness and need were such that I gave in to my hungers. I don't say this to excuse what I did, because I know to my own bitter shame that it was wicked and wrong to do it. The man is married, which only makes my shame the greater. You called me a prostitute . . .'

'No, wait, I didn't mean . . .' he protested violently, but she waved him to silence and went inexorably on, her voice dropping almost to a whisper.

'Hear me out. You called me a prostitute, and in one sense that word was justified. Because last night I gave myself to that same man again. Oh, I can use the same excuses as I did before. I can tell myself how lonely I was, how sad, how full of despair, how I needed comfort. But they are all merely excuses. I did it because I wanted to do it. I don't love the man. But he has been very good to me, and in his own way I think that he loves and needs me.' Again she paused, her eyes intent upon William's features. Then her voice rose and strengthened. 'I'll tell you truly that I love you, but it is too late for us now. You are a good man, and you deserve a woman who is nearer to your ideal than I can ever be. If you married me then you would be wronging yourself. You deserve a pure and innocent girl, not a woman who has acted as I've done. Who has degraded herself as I have done. I want you to leave now. I am truly grateful that you've come to me in this way, and I thank you for it. But it's too late.'

His head was downcast, his eyes fixed upon the ground before him. The seconds passed and lengthened into minutes, and she could hear the rasping of his breath. Then he slowly lifted his head, and his dark eyes were fiery.

'Oh no,' he told her firmly. 'It's not too late, and I'm not leaving. I love you, Josie, and you've just admitted that you love me. Of course I'm unhappy that you've given yourself to another man. But I'm even more unhappy at the thought of losing you. I cannot bear to think of spending the rest of my life without you. I don't doubt but that there'll be occasions when I shall be angry and jealous, and perhaps speak cruelly to you about what you have done, because I'm a very stupid man, and I'm not experienced in the ways of the world. I've always been privileged and sheltered in my life, so I've little conception of the strains and agonies other people have to endure. I haven't the understanding of what forces people to act in the ways that they do. But I do know and understand one thing for certain. Without you, my life is unendurable to me. With you, I can perhaps find happiness.'

He stepped close to her and took her unresisting hands in his own.

'Please, Josie, will you marry me? Will you give me the chance to find happiness? Will you give a selfish, stupid man the opportunity to know joy in his life?'

She looked deep into his eyes, and saw the love that shone from them, and smiled, and told him simply, 'Yes, I will.'

☐	Tildy	Sara Fraser	£4.99
☐	Tildy 2: Poorhouse Woman	Sara Fraser	£4.99
☐	Tildy 3: Nursing Woman	Sara Fraser	£4.99
☐	Tildy 4: Pointing Woman	Sara Fraser	£4.99
☐	Tildy 5: Radical Woman	Sara Fraser	£4.99
☐	Tildy 6: Gang Woman	Sara Fraser	£4.99
☐	Tildy 7: Widow Woman	Sara Fraser	£4.99
☐	Tildy 8: Invincible Woman	Sara Fraser	£4.99
☐	The Sisterhood	Sara Fraser	£4.99
☐	The Summer of the Fancy Man	Sara Fraser	£4.99

Warner Books now offers an exciting range of quality titles by
both established and new authors. All of the books in this
series are available from:

Little, Brown and Company (UK),
P.O. Box 11,
Falmouth,
Cornwall TR10 9EN.
Telephone No: 01326 372400
Fax No: 01326 317444
E-mail: books@barni.avel.co.uk

Payments can be made as follows: cheque, postal order
(payable to Little, Brown and Company) or by credit cards,
Visa/Access. Do not send cash or currency. UK customers and
B.F.P.O. please allow £1.00 for postage and packing for the
first book, plus 50p for the second book, plus 30p for each
additional book up to a maximum charge of £3.00 (7 books
plus).

Overseas customers including Ireland, please allow £2.00 for
the first book plus £1.00 for the second book, plus 50p for each
additional book.

NAME (Block Letters) ....

....

ADDRESS ....

....

....

☐ I enclose my remittance for ....
☐ I wish to pay by Access/Visa Card

Number ☐☐☐☐☐☐☐☐☐☐☐☐☐☐☐☐

Card Expiry Date ☐☐☐☐